AMERICANS IN ANTARCTICA
1775–1948

AMERICAN GEOGRAPHICAL SOCIETY
Special Publication No. 39

AMERICANS IN ANTARCTICA
1775-1948

KENNETH J. BERTRAND

Professor of Geography

The Catholic University of America

Published under the support of the

NATIONAL SCIENCE FOUNDATION

AMERICAN GEOGRAPHICAL SOCIETY

BROADWAY AT 156TH STREET · NEW YORK

1971

COPYRIGHT © 1971

BY THE AMERICAN GEOGRAPHICAL SOCIETY

LIBRARY OF CONGRESS CATALOG CARD NUMBER 77–155051

PRINTED IN THE UNITED STATES OF AMERICA

THE LANE PRESS, BURLINGTON, VERMONT

Dedicated to the memory of my grandfather,
JOHN C. LANGLAND
*to whom I owe an early and abiding interest
in Lands Beyond the Sea*

CONTENTS

vii

LIST OF ILLUSTRATIONS

MAPS

PLATES   *facing page*

PREFACE

This book is intended to be an objective account of activity by Americans in the Antarctic. It is hoped that Chapter 1 and the references in other chapters to the work of citizens of other countries have provided an adequate perspective for viewing the work of Americans.

This account begins in 1775 in the Falkland Islands, well north of the Antarctic Convergence, and seventeen years before Americans actually reached that line now recognized as the physical boundary of the Antarctic realm. Elephant seals and fur seals were the principal American interests in the Antarctic until the 20th century, and there was a direct connection between the Nantucket whalers who established a wartime base at the Falkland Islands in 1775 and the subsequent development of the sealing business which put Americans just north of the Convergence at Kerguelen Island and well south of the line at South Georgia in the austral summer of 1792-93.

Emphasis has been placed on discovery and scientific investigation. With two exceptions the scientific results of American activity have been published in a wide variety of journals instead of in volumes devoted exclusively to an expedition. In the case of the United States Exploring Expedition, led by Wilkes, the results were contained in 22 volumes and 12 atlases, but except for the narrative, only 100 copies of each were published. A single number of the *Proceedings of the American Philosophical Society* barely serves as a preliminary account of the work of the U. S. Antarctic Service Expedition, much of which is still not reported. For these reasons an attempt has been made to incorporate into the narrative for the period up to 1948 a summary of all scientific activity of every American expedition with a citation to the published or unpublished source.

It will be apparent that the treatment of the various expeditions is unequal. Some aspects of activities discussed in detail for early, little-known expeditions are not treated as extensively in the case of more recent expeditions for which adequate narratives have been published. The longest chapter by far is devoted to the U. S. Antarctic Service Expedition; this was a very big undertaking and no extensive narrative of it has ever been published. To some extent the same may be said for "Operation Highjump."

Geographic names become a problem for anyone dealing with the history of exploration in Antarctica. During the last quarter century there has been a concerted effort to standardize geographic nomenclature. In the process, many name changes have occurred, so that in writing about an earlier time, one must choose between the name in use at that time, or the presently approved name. For the most part, in this book the names approved by the U. S. Board on Geographic Names have been used. In some cases, for the sake of the narrative, the name current at that time is used with the approved name in brackets. In other cases the older name is placed in brackets or an explanatory phrase is introduced. Where complex name problems are involved a citation has been made to an explanatory note at the end of the chapter. Geographic names used in quotations have been left inviolate, although when clarity required it, the approved name has been inserted in brackets. Where official statements have been paraphrased, as in the objectives of the United States Antarctic Service Expedition, names then in use have been used for the sake of historical accuracy, but a citation has been made to an explanatory note. A number of names, such as Discovery Inlet, Lindbergh Inlet, Floyd Bennett Bay, Chamberlain Harbor, and Eleanor Bolling Bight, refer to ephemeral ice features in the front of the Ross Ice Shelf. Although they no longer exist, they had significance to the expeditions which operated in the area in the 1930s, and they have been used in the accounts of those operations. Some of the names appear on Figure 16, page 332.

Throughout the book, distances have been given in nautical miles unless otherwise stated.

In a book of this kind one may choose to illustrate the work of an expedition with maps of its day or by superimposing ship tracks, flight lines, and sledge tracks on a modern map. At the risk of seeming to credit an expedition with discovering more than was actually the case, the latter method has been followed. Anyone who tries to reconstruct from the logbook a ship's track on an older and imperfect map of the South Shetlands and then tries to do the same on a modern map based on aerial photography will soon be convinced of the wisdom of this choice. One must interpret what past explorers saw in terms of what was there for them to see.

The research on which this book is based has extended over a quarter century, beginning in 1946 with an invitation from Dr. Meredith F. Burrill to engage in research on the history of geographic names for the Advisory Committee on Antarctic Names of the U. S. Board on Geographic Names. Membership on the Advisory Committee since 1948 has afforded the author an opportunity to participate in the rational ordering of Antarctic nomenclature for which continued delving in the history of exploration has been necessary. Over the years there has been involvement in other Antarctic projects as well. In each of these undertakings different co-workers have participated, and each of them has made a contribution to this book in one way or another. The book itself began to take form fifteen years ago. Progress since then has been intermittent. Some chapters were completed in this early period, others were finished in 1970, and some have been revised several times.

A sincere debt of gratitude is owed to many people who have contributed in a variety of ways to the production of this book. First, there are those who supplied source material or assisted in locating it. Thanks is offered here to Mrs. Theodore Krueger of Stratford, Connecticut, for permission to photograph the logbook kept by Elof Benson on the voyages of the *Hersilia* and the *Catharina*. Similarly, gratitude to Mr. David B. Heard of Waban, Massachusetts, is expressed for permission to examine and photograph Captain John J. Heard's correspondence and the logbook of the bark *Oriental*. Mr. Edouard A. Stackpole of Nantucket, Massachusetts, then Curator of Mystic Seaport, Mystic, Connecticut, kindly permitted Captain Christopher Burdick's logbook of the *Huntress* to be examined and quoted. Mr. Alexander O. Vietor, Map Curator of Yale Univerity Library, kindly made available a microfilm copy of Captain John Davis' logbook of the

Huron and has consented to having quotations made from it. To both sincere gratitude is expressed.

Thanks are also offered to Dr. Brian Roberts for making available from the Public Record Office in London a microfilm copy of Captain Robert Fildes' journal of a voyage in the brig *Cora* and of Fildes' "Sailing Directions" for the South Shetlands. He also supplied photographic copies of a typescript copy of the latter from the Bruce Collection in the Scott Polar Research Institute at Cambridge. Permission from Mr. Alan Cooke, Curator of Manuscripts at Scott Polar Research Institute, and from the Controller of Her Majesty's Stationery Office, London, to quote from this material is gratefully acknowledged. Appreciation is expressed to the Belknap Press of the Harvard University Press for permission to quote from Matthew Fontaine Maury's *Physical Geography of the Sea and its Meteorology,* edited by Dr. John Leighly. Thanks are offered also to Dr. Phillip G. Law and Mr. B. P. Lambert for permission to quote from their paper, "A New Map of the Coastline of Oates Land and Eastern King George V Land," read at the Buenos Aires Antarctic Symposium, November 18, 1959. Permission from the publishers of the *New York Times* to publish quotations from Lincoln Ellsworth's dispatches is gratefully acknowledged.

Captain Finn Ronne (USNR Ret.) very graciously supplied several photographs for the book. He read Chapter 23 in manuscript, and his helpful suggestions have been incorporated in the final version. For these favors, and for information he supplied on other expeditions in which he participated, sincere thanks are offered. To the late Captain Harold E. Saunders (USN Ret.) and to Captain John W. McElroy (USNR Ret.) who independently reviewed Nathaniel B. Palmer's navigation for the November 1820 cruise as shown by the logbook of the *Hero,* gratitude is due. Thanks are offered also to Dr. G. D. Knapp of the Geophysics Division of the U. S. Coast and Geodetic Survey for calculating the probable magnetic declination in the South Shetlands in 1820.

Richard D. Kane as a co-worker carried out research on New England sealers at the South Shetlands, which has proven extremely valuable, and for which sincere thanks are offered. Appreciation is due also to Fred G. Alberts of the Geographic Names Division of Department of Technical Services of the U. S. Army Topographic Command for assistance rendered on many occasions.

Gratitude is expressed to many others for their assistance. Rear Admiral Richard B. Black (USNR Ret.) turned over notes and some rough drafts of some material pertaining to East Base of the U. S. Antarctic Service Expedition. He also lent the author a copy of his unpublished narrative of activities at East Base. He later read most of the chapters in manuscript, and his comments are deeply appreciated. Dr. Thomas C. Poulter kindly consented to the reprinting in Chapter 18 (Fig. 16) of his map of "Ice Movement in the Bay of Whales," Fig. 31, *Geophysical Studies in the Antarctic,* Stanford, n.d. The late Dr. James E. Mooney, then Deputy to the U. S. Navy Antarctic Projects Officer, read many of the chapters in an early stage and from his long association with Admiral Richard E. Byrd was able to contribute valuable information unknown to the author.

Others who have read various chapters in the initial stage include the late

Colonel Ashley C. McKinley and the late Dr. Paul A. Siple, Captain Lewis O. Smith (USN Ret.), Commander Frederick G. Dustin (USNR Ret.), Dr. Arthur R. Hall, Dr. Henry M. Dater, Dr. Robert D. Hodgson, Dr. Meredith F. Burrill, and Messrs. J. Glenn Dyer, Leonard H. Dykes, Herman R. Friis, Gerald A. Pagano, and Robert H. Simpson. To all of them is felt a sincere sense of gratitude. McKinley, Siple, Smith, Dustin and Dyer, who had been members of expeditions, added valuable firsthand information and insights which have enhanced the accounts of recent expeditions. Mr. Friis was particularly helpful in bibliographic work, in discovering old reports and manuscripts and in suggesting leads to additional information, and his encouragement was most welcome. Dr. Burrill, Dr. Dater and Mr. Pagano have been helpful in many ways.

The author is grateful to scores of people in various historical societies and libraries who have been most gracious in their assistance in locating a wide variety of source material. Among them are Mr. Dwight C. Lyman, President of the New London County Historical Society, Mr. John L. Lochead, Librarian of the Mariners Museum, Newport News, Virginia, Miss Nordis Felland, Librarian, and the late William A. Briesemeister, Cartographer, at the American Geographical Society. Special thanks are due to Mr. Thomas J. Coleman, Jr., of the Naval Records Section, to Mr. Forrest R. Holdcamper of the Industrial Records Branch of the Labor and Transportation Section, and to Mrs. Hope K. Holdcamper of the Diplomatic, Legal, and Fiscal Branch of the Office of Civil Archives of the National Archives for their continued interest and long and patient efforts in locating records relating to this study. Librarians in many other places have been helpful. Special mention should be made to those at the Connecticut State Library, Hartford, the New London, Connecticut, Public Library, the Marine Historical Association Library, Mystic, Connecticut, and the various divisions of the Library of Congress.

A sincere debt of gratitude is owed to the editors, Mr. Wilfrid Webster who did the major part of editing the manuscript and arranging for printing up to the page proofs and to Miss Vivian C. Bushnell who saw the book through its final stages at the American Geographical Society. Their work and that of their assistants has greatly enhanced whatever value the book may have. To Mr. Miklos Pinther, Chief Cartographer, and his staff at the American Geographical Society, appreciation is expressed for their cooperation and for the excellent maps with which the book is illustrated. As author I thank all who have helped in any way, and I take full responsibility for any errors or shortcomings in the book.

Lastly, I am most grateful to the several Directors of the American Geographical Society who have made favorable decisions concerning the publication of the book, and to the National Science Foundation. Their combined support has made this book a reality.

KENNETH J. BERTRAND

Washington, D. C.
June 1971

1

INTRODUCTION

PERSPECTIVE

The Antarctic consists of the continent of Antarctica and its off-lying islands and surrounding seas. Roughly centered on the South Pole, the Antarctic land masses — the continental shield of East Antarctica and the mountainous archipelago of West Antarctica — are buried by thousands of feet of glacial ice which effectively welds them into a continental unit with an area of about 5½ million square miles, almost all within the Antarctic Circle. Various limits can be used for the Antarctic, but in this book the Antarctic Convergence is accepted as the boundary. Today, the Convergence is the boundary most widely accepted by geographers and polar specialists among the other sciences. This line along which the colder, fresher, and denser northward-moving Antarctic surface waters sink beneath the warmer, saltier, less dense waters of the southern Atlantic, Indian, and Pacific Oceans encircles the earth between 50° and 60° south latitude. Shifting only slightly in position from season to season, the Convergence forms a remarkable physical boundary, reflected on its two sides by differences in water temperatures, weather conditions, and marine life (Figs. 8 and 26).*

Antarctica is the most remote, the most inaccessible, and the most inhospitable land area on earth. Consequently, it was the last continent to be discovered, and knowledge of the south polar region was at first accumulated very slowly. Until early in the 20th century the interior was entirely unknown, and even the continental margins had been seen in only a few places. Most of what is known about Antarctica has been discovered in this century, and since 1957 as much has been learned about the area as in all previous history. But the success of recent operations in unveiling Antarctica with the aid of modern technology does not negate the importance of earlier efforts. Present accomplishments have been built on the past, developed step by step since 1674, sometimes haltingly and sometimes failing.

Discoveries in Antarctica, as in other parts of the world, have been made under varied circumstances, and explorations have been conducted for a variety of motives. Discoveries have been made by commercial vessels accidentally blown off course, as was the case of the first discovery south of the Antarctic Convergence: of South Georgia in 1675. Exploration has been conducted and discoveries made by design under the auspices of commercial interests, national governments, scientific societies, and private individuals. In the Antarctic commercial interests have been represented by the seal hunter and the whaler. Governments have sent out naval expeditions for reasons of national strategy or

---

* Although each map in this book was designed for a particular chapter, many of the maps help to illustrate other chapters. For their page locations, see the list of maps in the front matter.

prestige, and they have sent out exploring expeditions in the interests of science and navigation. Some government expeditions have been a combination of these. Geographical and other scientific societies have promoted and sponsored exploring expeditions which have been privately organized and financed. During the International Geophysical Year (1957-58) and in the scientific investigations which have followed, international scientific cooperation in planning and execution has been an outstanding feature. Throughout the history of the Antarctic, individuals have been motivated by financial gain, a desire for personal glory, for adventure, or because of scientific curiosity. The specially organized scientific exploring expedition has made the major contribution, but the whaler and the sealer have made their marks as well. Exploring expeditions, scientific investigations, or commercial operations from fourteen different nations have contributed to our knowledge of the Antarctic.

The true nature of the Antarctic as a frigid region of ice and snow was convincingly proven for the first time by the second voyage of the great English navigator, Captain James Cook, between 1772 and 1775. Earlier penetrations into sub-Antarctic and even Antarctic waters had resulted in the discovery of South Georgia (1675), Bouvet Island (1739), and Kerguelen Island (1772). Widely separated in time and space, these earlier discoveries contributed so little to the over-all knowledge of the far south that in 1772 there was general belief in a large, still-undiscovered continent in the southern hemisphere suitable for European settlement.

On his second voyage Cook circumnavigated Antarctica. Much of his course was south of 60° S. First to cross the Antarctic Circle, his track was south of that line in three places. Although Cook failed to sight any part of the Antarctic continent, he conclusively disproved the existence of the mythical continent of "Terra Australis Incognita" in latitudes north of 60° S. Mariners who followed Cook into high southern latitudes knew what the region was like, but they were attracted to this harsh environment by his reports of great numbers of whales and seals, particularly the latter.

British and American whalers apparently began taking oil from the blubber of elephant seals at the Falkland Islands some time in the early 1770s. The British were the first to cross the Antarctic Convergence when they reportedly began operations in South Georgia in 1778. Americans did not begin sealing at South Georgia until 1792 or 1793. In December, 1792, the first Americans visited Kerguelen which a half century later was an important center for their operations. Although French, Dutch, and Scandinavian sealers were active in the Arctic, they appear to have left the southern hemisphere to the Americans and the British until late in the 19th century. At first only the elephant seal was slain, but after the Chinese market was opened to Americans in 1785 they were much more interested in the fur seal, whose skin brought fabulous prices at Canton. As indiscriminate slaughter reduced fur seal numbers at one locality after another in sub-Antarctic waters, sealers cruised across all of the southern oceans in search of new rookeries. Macquarie Island was a major discovery resulting from a sealing voyage, from Sydney in 1810 (Fig. 8).

The last big boom in the fur seal business occurred at the South Shetland

Islands, discovered by William Smith in the British brig *Williams*, in February 1819 when he was blown off course on a commercial voyage from Montevideo to Valparaiso. In 1820-21 there were at least 30 American, 24 British, and 1 Australian vessels hunting seals in the South Shetlands. The next year the number was at least as great and perhaps doubled. During this time landings were made on the Antarctic Peninsula, the South Orkney Islands were discovered, and at least one and perhaps three Americans made voyages as far as 66° S on the west side of the Antarctic Peninsula as the sealers made competitive cruises in search of beaches on which to place their men. Fairly accurate sketch maps by British sealers James Weddell and George Powell were published. The former discovered the Weddell Sea and was the author of an excellent account of his sealing voyages between 1820 and 1824.[1] Powell and Nathaniel B. Palmer of Stonington, Connecticut, were co-discoverers of the South Orkneys while on a joint cruise in December 1821. An Antarctic winter was also experienced for the first time, involuntarily, in 1821 by an officer and ten crew members from the British sealer *Lord Melville* (Figs. 2, 4 and 5).

Although the number of vessels in the fur seal business dropped sharply after 1821-22, a few sealing captains continued to make regular voyages so that there was probably no year in the second quarter of the 19th century without at least one vessel at sea somewhere in high southern latitudes in search of fur seals, and in most years there were more. Many of these voyages were combined voyages in which oil from the elephant seal made up part of the cargo, and the less valuable pelt of the hair seal was also often included in the take.

Enderby Brothers, the largest English whaling firm, allowed their ship captains wide latitude in making exploratory cruises while on sealing voyages. The result was a number of important discoveries. One of their captains, John Biscoe, made a circumnavigation of Antarctica in which he sighted land in what is now Enderby Land (February 28, 1831) and Adelaide Island and the Biscoe Islands in February 1832. Another Enderby skipper, John Balleny, discovered the Balleny Islands in February 9, 1839, and later reported the appearance of land near what is now known as the Sabrina Coast. Illustrative of how the various threads of the Antarctic tapestry are interwoven, Charles Enderby was an original fellow of the Royal Geographical Society, founded in 1830.

James Eights, a geologist, was the first American scientist to visit Antarctica, where he did excellent work in the South Shetlands on a combined sealing and exploring voyage in 1829-30. A British sealer, Peter Kemp, sighted land on what is now Kemp Coast in December 1833. It is possible that he may also have sighted Heard Island.

As the fur seals were reduced almost to extinction, attention shifted to the elephant seal. During the middle of the 19th century this activity was centered in the Indian Ocean, and it was mainly an American operation. Most of the vessels were from New London, Connecticut, and combined sealing with whaling. First the Crozets and then Kerguelen were visited in large numbers. After the discovery of Heard Island, Americans occupied it continuously for more than 20 years.

A revival of the fur seal industry occurred in the South Shetlands and South

Georgia in the 1870s. This too was mainly an American operation.[2] The seals had recovered only slightly from the earlier slaughter, and it was not long before they were again reduced to almost extinction. When Chile prohibited sealing on its shores the sealers discovered that it was not profitable to work at the South Shetlands if they could not also visit the shores of Tierra del Fuego. One of the sealers of this latter period was Eduard Dallmann. Under the sponsorship of Albert Rosenthal and the German Society for Polar Navigation, he combined sealing with exploration in the South Shetlands, the Palmer Archipelago, and the northern part of the Antarctic Peninsula in 1873-74. Dallmann's ship, the *Grönland,* was the first auxiliary steam vessel to visit this part of Antarctica. While Antarctica was pretty much the domain of the sealers in the 19th century, it was not exclusively so.

NAVAL EXPLORING EXPEDITIONS

Under the stimulus of the rapid development of the natural sciences in the first half of the 19th century and somewhat in the tradition of the great naval expeditions of the 18th century, so fully exemplified by Cook, four great national expeditions explored Antarctica between 1819 and 1843. The first was the Russian naval expedition consisting of the sloops *Vostok* and *Mirnyy* commanded by Captain Thaddeus Bellingshausen. Between December 1819 and February 1821 Bellingshausen made an eastward circumnavigation of Antarctica, mostly south of 60° S. Six times he was south of the Antarctic Circle. New evidence (See note 69, page 193) indicates that he was the first to see the continent, off Princess Martha Coast on January 16, 1820. Later he discovered Peter I Island and Alexander Island. He made a reconnaissance map of the South Shetlands, the South Sandwich Islands, and the south coast of South Georgia.

In September 1837 a French naval expedition, commanded by Admiral J. S. C. Dumont d'Urville, in the corvettes *Astrolabe* and *Zélée,* began a three-year voyage of exploration, primarily among the islands of the Pacific. Survey work was done in the South Orkneys, the South Shetlands, and along the northern extremity of the Antarctic Peninsula in January and February 1838. After more than a year in Oceania, Dumont d'Urville returned to the Antarctic south of Australia in January 1840. While cruising south of 60° S, between 125° E and 145° E, he discovered the Adélie Coast and the Clarie Coast, landing on some small islets of the former.

The United States Exploring Expedition, 1838-1842, commanded by Lieutenant Charles Wilkes, spent most of its time in surveying and scientific investigation in the Pacific, including the west coast of what is now the United States from Puget Sound to San Francisco Bay. Two visits, however, were made to the Antarctic. In February 1839, the *Porpoise* and the *Sea Gull* sailed southeast from Tierra del Fuego to visit the South Shetlands and the extremity of the Antarctic Peninsula. Meanwhile the *Peacock* and the *Flying Fish* sailed southwestward to a point north of Thurston Island, but no land was sighted.

Wilkes sailed south from Sydney with four ships in 1839. The *Flying Fish* and the *Peacock* were soon disabled and had to retreat, but the *Vincennes* and the *Porpoise*, during January and February, sailed westward for 1500 miles along the coast of East Antarctica from the Balleny Islands to Shackleton Ice Shelf. After charting a series of landfalls between 160° E and 98° E, Wilkes reported the existence of an Antarctic continent (Fig. 7).

The fourth national expedition to Antarctica in the first half of the 19th century was the British Admiralty's expedition in the *Erebus* and *Terror*, commanded by Sir James Clark Ross. This was strictly a polar expedition, and unlike Dumont d'Urville and Wilkes, Ross had ships specially strengthened for cruising in loose pack ice. Ross, the discoverer of the north magnetic pole, had had wide experience in the Arctic, and one of his objectives was the discovery of the south magnetic pole. Learning of Wilkes' and Dumont d'Urville's cruises at Hobart, Ross in December 1841 sailed southeastward. In January 1841, he pushed southward into the pack ice to discover open water and the Ross Sea. Shortly after, Victoria Land was discovered and landings were made on Possession and Franklin Islands. After skirting the front of the Ross Ice Shelf, which he called the "Great Icy Barrier," to 167° W, the ships returned to Cape Adare and thence via the Balleny Islands to Hobart. In December 1841, the *Erebus* and *Terror* returned to the Ross Sea and later sailed north and east to the Falkland Islands. The season of 1842-43 was spent exploring Erebus and Terror Gulf and attempting a penetration of the Weddell Sea.

EYES NORTH

From Ross's departure in 1843 until the last decade of the 19th century, Antarctica was almost solely the domain of the sealer. There were a few exceptions. In 1844-45 the Admiralty sent out Lieutenant T. E. L. Moore in the barque *Pagoda* to carry out magnetic work in the south Atlantic and southern Indian Oceans to complement the work of Ross. No land was seen. The *Challenger* Expedition of the British Admiralty (1872-75), although devoted to oceanography, cruised through the south Indian Ocean in January and February 1874, mapping Prince Edward Island, Îles Crozet, Îles de Kerguelen, and Heard Island. Bottom samples revealed fragments of continental rock types, suggesting the existence of a continental land mass to the south.

The lack of Antarctic exploration for so many decades in the 19th century can be attributed to a number of causes. The United States was involved in a great Civil War and reconstruction, and many Americans were interested in development of the West. More important, perhaps, was the fact that any interest in polar matters was directed to the Arctic. Both in Europe and in the United States great sympathy was felt for Sir John Franklin and his expedition, and several expeditions were sent to find him. Also, several attempts at high-latitude records and even to reach the North Pole aroused much public interest. Preoccupation with the Arctic is illustrated by the first International Polar Year, 1882-83, organized as an international cooperative effort emphasizing meteorology and earth magnetism. Eleven stations were planned for the Arctic and four for the Antarctic. Of the latter, only the German station at South Georgia materialized. The United States was responsible for two stations, both in the Arctic.

While there was little official interest in Antarctic exploration in Europe and America in the last quarter of the 19th century, there were many individual scientists and naval officers in Europe who strongly advocated it in speeches and in writing. Committees were formed, but nothing much came of it until the end of the century.

ANTARCTIC WHALING

Meanwhile, whaling firms in Scotland and Norway, concerned by the scarcity of whales in Greenland waters and in the North Atlantic, decided to investigate possibilities in the Antarctic. The four reconnaissance voyages that resulted served to stimulate public interest, and from these voyages three leading figures in later Antarctic affairs emerged.

One of these, C. A. Larsen, was master of the Norwegian whaler *Jason*. He explored Erebus and Terror Gulf at the southeastern side of the tip of the Antarctic Peninsula in 1892-93, and in the following year penetrated farther into the Weddell Sea, discovering Oscar II Coast and Foyn Coast. Meanwhile, the *Hertha* and the *Castor,* consorts of the *Jason,* explored the west side of the Antarctic Peninsula to within sight of Alexander Island.

W. S. Bruce was surgeon and naturalist on the *Balaena,* one of the four Dundee whalers that also visited the outer reaches of the Weddell Sea in 1892-93, where Captain Robertson in the *Active* discovered Dundee Island.

Carsten E. Borchgrevink was a seaman on the Norwegian whaler *Antarctic* during a preliminary whaling reconnaissance and sealing voyage led by Captain Leonard Kristensen and H. J. Bull in 1894-95. The *Antarctic* visited the Ross Sea, and a landing was made on Cape Adare. Little being known of the early British and American sealers' activities, this landing was long thought to be the first on the Antarctic continent. Similarly, for lack of knowledge of James Eights' work in 1829-30, C. A. Larsen is often, to this day, credited with being first to collect fossils in Antarctica. There is evidence, however, that possibly both were anticipated in this respect by Captain Jonathan Winship of the ship *O'Cain* of Boston in 1821. If so, Winship's collection has been lost and its contents unidentified.

Whaling in the southern Indian Ocean had been carried on, mainly by Americans, for several decades in the mid-19th century, but like other whalers of the time they were not catching Rorquals, but the smaller and slower Sperm, Black right, and Humpback whales. The Rorquals, the Blue, the Fin, and the Sei whales are much faster swimmers, and the Blue and Fin whales are much larger. Rorquals also sink when dead, and the carcasses must be inflated with air to be kept afloat. Old historic whaling methods in an open boat with a hand-thrown harpoon were inadequate for the Rorquals. In the 1860s the Norwegians introduced the harpoon gun, invented by Svend Foyn, and the whale catcher, a small and fast stream-driven boat with a harpoon gun in its bow. After the harpoon strikes its mark an explosive charge kills the whale. The catchers tow the whales to plants on shore, for processing.

Antarctic whaling was re-established, based on the Rorquals, in 1904-05 when

Captain C. A. Larsen, with Argentine capital, established the first shore station at Grytviken in South Georgia. Christen Christensen introduced the first factory ship, in the South Shetlands, in 1906. The following year whaling was re-established in the Indian Ocean sector at Îles Crozet. However, most Antarctic whaling in the first quarter of the 20th century was in the area of the Scotia Arc, i.e., the South Georgia, South Sandwich, South Orkney, and South Shetland Islands and the northern shores of the Antarctic Peninsula. This area proved productive, and it provided an abundance of harbors which were necessary for the location of the shore stations and for mooring the early-type factory ships which were also used to process the whales. The industry grew steadily, and by the 1912-13 season there were six shore stations, 21 factory ships, and 62 catchers in Antarctica, mostly Norwegian. They produced 420,000 barrels of oil from 10,760 whales.[3] As part of their operations the whalers explored for suitable harbors for their factory ships, and they charted the more frequented coasts and harbors to insure safer navigation.

THE HEROIC ERA

A resolution passed by the Sixth International Geographical Congress in London in 1895, urging the promotion of Antarctic exploration, apparently was the stimulus for setting in motion forces which had been developing for some decades, and which resulted in a whole series of expeditions and a new era in Antarctic exploration. Before World War I halted such activity, 16 exploring expeditions from Australia, Belgium, England, France, Germany, Japan, Norway, Scotland, and Sweden had visited Antarctica. This is exclusive of exploration by whalers, previously mentioned. The magnitude of this activity was unprecedented for Antarctica, and considering the state of technology and the world's population and wealth, it was probably greater than that of the mechanical age which followed and not incomparable to the operations which were initiated with the International Geophysical Year, 1957-58.

As L.P. Kirwan has pointed out, social and economic changes had taken place in the 19th century which had their effects on polar exploration.[4] There had been a general intellectual ferment which, among other things, had stimulated and accelerated the development of the natural sciences. The general public was being more widely and better educated, and many had developed a layman's appreciation for science. Even more people read with interest popular narratives and newspaper accounts of exploration. The new scientific spirit and expanding commerce fostered the establishment of geographical societies in many cities in Europe and America. These societies encouraged and even sponsored exploring expeditions. The industrial revolution had created an industrial and commercial class among whom were persons of wealth willing to support learned societies and contribute to exploring expeditions. Expanding circulations had made publishers of metropolitan newspapers both influential and wealthy. Thus the scientific community and the general public, for quite different reasons, had a common interest in encouraging exploration. These various factors had influenced Arctic exploration since the middle of the 19th century. Now, in the closing decade of the century, they were beginning to bear on the Antarctic.

Except for the German Navy's oceanographic expedition in the *Valdivia* which briefly penetrated Antarctic waters in 1898, the expeditions of this new era were different in several respects from the great naval expeditions of the Age of Exploration. Private individuals or scientific societies either shared with governments or entirely replaced them in organizing and financing these undertakings. Support was in some instances rather broadly based on private donations. The navy was absent or played a minor role although expedition leaders, ships officers, and men in several instances were naval personnel on leave. The earlier expeditions were ship-based and landings were few in polar regions. In most cases, the earlier expeditions stayed outside of the pack ice. On the other hand, 11 of these latest expeditions proposed to establish bases on land from which journeys could be made to the interior. All ships had auxiliary steam power so that even those expeditions which were ship-based could push through loose pack ice to keep near to land or take advantage of open-water pools. Commensurate with the development of the natural sciences and the proposed land operations, the scientific programs were much expanded.

J. Gordon Hayes has called this period, beginning in 1895, the Heroic Era, and the aptness of the designation is indicated by its wide acceptance.[5] There are no more stirring epics in human history than the stories of Captain Robert Falcon Scott's tragic march back from the South Pole and Sir Ernest Shackleton's voyage in an open boat over 800 miles of storm-tossed sea to South Georgia to get help for his men marooned on Elephant Island. But there are so many instances of heroic deeds under conditions of unbelievable hardship that to single out these, great as they were, is an injustice to others. These were man's first attempts at navigating in Antarctic pack ice, and five ships were beset and two were crushed. These were also man's first attempts at overland journeys for which he was not well prepared. It was through dearly bought experience against the hostile Antarctic environment by these pioneers of the Heroic Era that suitable methods eventually evolved.

Anyone drawing a map of Antarctica in 1895 could have shown the coast as no more than a tentative line, and that only in three areas: part of the coast of Victoria Land, the northern end of the Antarctic Peninsula, and the islands of the Scotia Arc. Except for a few places where landings had been made, all these had been mapped from ships in running surveys, and different maps of the same area did not agree in details. The entire coast of East Antarctica was represented by 14 small segments representing landfalls from Biscoe's Cape Ann (Enderby Land) to the Balleny Islands. Of these, Wilkes was responsible for seven and jointly responsible for two more, but some of these were then questioned.

The first expedition of the Heroic Era to visit Antarctica was organized by Lieutenant Adrien de Gerlache of the Belgian Navy with the aid of the Brussels Geographical Society, government grants, and private contributions. Its personnel was international, with representatives from five different countries. First mate on the expedition ship *Belgica* was Roald Amundsen of Norway.

In 1898 surveying and scientific work was done in the Scotia Arc and along the west side of the Antarctic Peninsula where, within sight of Alexander Island, the *Belgica* was beset on March 3. She drifted in the pack ice across Bellingshausen sea for a year before being released. It thus became, although unintentionally, the first scientific exploring expedition to winter in Antarctica.

Dr. Otto Nordenskjöld led a privately sponsored Swedish expedition which set up winter quarters in 1902 on Snow Hill Island, off the eastern tip of the Antarctic Peninsula, from which base surveying and other scientific work was carried on in Erebus and Terror Gulf and southward. The ship, returning from wintering in South Georgia, was crushed in the pack ice, and the crew was forced to winter on Paulet Island. Three other men were also marooned for the winter of 1903 at Hope Bay. The entire expedition was finally rescued in November 1903 by Captain Julián Irízar in the *Uruguay*, sent out for the purpose by the government of Argentina.

Meanwhile Dr. William S. Bruce organized the Scottish National Antarctic Expedition with privately contributed funds, mostly from the Coats family. It spent most of the 1902-03 season in the Scotia Arc. The winter of 1903 was spent on Laurie Island in the South Orkneys. A weather station established by Bruce has since been operated by Argentina. The second season a deep penetration was made into the Weddell Sea, and Coats Land was discovered on its eastern margin on March 6, 1904.

Dr. Jean-B. Charcot organized and led two French expeditions to the Antarctic with the aid of government grants, private contributions, and support from learned societies. For each expedition a ship was designed and built to his specifications. On his first expedition in the *Français* (1903-05) he originally planned to search for Nordenskjöld's expedition, but when it was rescued he directed his attention to the South Shetlands and the Palmer Archipelago, wintering in 1904 in Port Charcot at Booth Island. A comprehensive scientific program was continued in 1904-05. Charcot returned in the *Pourquoi Pas?* for another two-year stint in 1908, continuing a comprehensive mapping and scientific program on the west side of the Antarctic Peninsula and in the South Shetlands. The winter of 1909 was spent at Petermann Island. During the summer of 1909-10 work was continued southward where Marguerite Bay was discovered before Charcot concluded the expedition with a cruise westward across Bellingshausen Sea south of the Antarctic Circle to beyond 120° W, sighting land on what is now Charcot Island. The quality of the scientific work and of Charcot's maps was excellent, and no explorer has been more conscientious in crediting the discoveries of his predecessors.

At the close of the Heroic Era the major elements of the coast were fairly well located, and a reasonably accurate reconnaissance map, subject to later refinements, could be made for the islands of the Scotia Arc and the coast of the Antarctic Peninsula as far south as Robertson Island on the east coast and Marguerite Bay on the west coast. The northern tip of Alexander Island could be put on the map with some degree of accuracy as to its location.

It was in the Ross Sea area during the Heroic Era that the first great treks inland were made, a feature which distinguished the expeditions of this area from those of the Antarctic Peninsula where only Nordenskjöld made any appreciable surface journeys. The Ross Sea area also was the major area of British operations at this time. Four years after he had left the Ross Sea on H. J. Bull's *Antarctic,* Carsten E. Borchgrevink was back with his own expedition in the *Southern Cross,* under the patronage of Sir George Newnes. Borchgrevink's was the first scientific expedition intentionally to winter in the Antarctic, spending the winter of 1899 in a hut erected for the purpose on Cape Adare. The following spring, when the ship returned, the coast of Victoria Land was examined, and three landings were made. The front of the Ross Ice Shelf was skirted from Ross Island to the Bay of Whales, where a landing was also made.

The British National Antarctic Expedition, led by Captain Robert F. Scott, R.N., was sponsored by the Royal Geographical Society and other organizations, and financed by private donations and government grants. In its organization Sir Clements Markham was the driving force. The *Discovery* was designed and built for the purpose. Landings were made on the coast of Victoria land, and the Ross Ice Shelf was skirted eastward as far as Edward VII Peninsula. Winter quarters were established at Hut Point on McMurdo Sound, from which long sledge journeys were made westward over the mountains onto the ice plateau of Victoria Land and southward on the Ross Ice shelf to 77°59′ S, a new record southing. A comprehensive scientific program was carried out by a very competent staff. The *Discovery,* purposely frozen in at McMurdo Sound, was finally freed in 1904. In the meantime the *Morning,* under Lieutenant William Colbeck, had been sent out in relief in 1902-03 and again, along with the *Terra Nova,* in 1903-04.

Lieutenant Ernest H. Shackleton, R.N.R., who had been with Scott, returned to McMurdo Sound with his own expedition in the *Nimrod* in 1908. He had organized his expedition under the patronage of Sir William Beardmore, the Misses Dawson-Lambton, and other private and public donors. From his winter base at Cape Royds on Ross Island, Shackleton sledged over the Ross Ice Shelf and up Beardmore Glacier in December and January to a point within 97 miles of the South Pole, where he was forced to retreat because of a shortage of food. Professor T. W. Edgeworth David sledged northwestward up onto the Victoria Land plateau where he discovered the south magnetic pole in about 72°25′ S, 155°16′ E.

No period in the history of exploration has been packed with more drama than the Antarctic summer of 1911-12, when the South Pole was reached by parties from two different expeditions. Roald Amundsen, veteran Norwegian Arctic explorer, had organized a private expedition to attempt to reach the North Pole. In 1909, after Robert E. Peary reached that goal, Amundsen turned his attention to the attainment of the South Pole. Setting up winter quarters at the Bay of Whales in January 1911, Amundsen laid depots for the next season's journey southward. On October 19, 1911, he and four companions, with 52 dogs and 4 sledges set out over the Ross Ice Shelf. Ascending the polar plateau via Axel Heiberg Glacier, they reached the Pole on December 14. Remaining there for sufficient sun sights to fix their position, on December 17 they began the return to the Bay of Whales which was reached on January 25, 1912. Meanwhile Lieutenant K. Prestrud sledged to the Scott Nunataks by way of a wide circuit south and east of the Bay of Whales.

Also in 1909, Captain Robert F. Scott had begun organizing his second Antarctic expedition as a privately sponsored British venture. He planned a broad program of scientific observation and exploration, but an important objective was also to be an attempt to reach the South Pole. Again winter quarters were set up at McMurdo Sound, and depots were laid for the polar journey. Scott's polar party and two supporting parties set out on November 3, 1911, along the route pioneered by Shackleton. Scott used 10 Siberian ponies and two dog teams across the Ross Ice Shelf on the outward journey, but from there the men hauled the sledges. Such exhausting labor on an inadequate trail diet wore the men down. They reached the Pole on January 17, 1912, but their weakened condition, many storms, and bad surfaces so prolonged the return march that fuel and food were exhausted and the polar party perished. The following November, the bodies of Scott, Dr. Edward A. Wilson, and Lieutenant Henry R. Bowers were found in their tent only 11 miles south of One Ton Depot and 176 statute miles from the base. Notebooks, sketches, and films were recovered as well as 35 pounds of geological specimens found on the sledges. Two others of the party had perished earlier.

The Northern Party of the expedition was marooned for the winter of 1912 at Terra Nova Bay when the ship was unable to relieve them. In spite of these difficulties, most of the planned scientific program was completed.

A Japanese expedition, led by Lieutenant Choku Shirase in the *Kainan Maru,* also visited the Ross Sea area in 1911 and 1912. The ship did not reach the Ross Sea until March in 1911 and she was forced by pack ice to retreat. In 1912 the *Kainan Maru* visited the Bay of Whales, Kainan Bay, and Okuma Bay and cruised off the Edward VII Peninsula. Two sledge journeys were made, one to the edge of the Alexandra Mountains and another for 160 miles southeastward from the Bay of Whales.

By 1916 the outline of the coast in the Ross Sea sector, insofar as major features were concerned, was firmly fixed from Robertson Bay, north of Cape Adare, to Beardmore Glacier at the head of the Ross Ice Shelf. Some localities along this stretch had been mapped at scales of 1:250,000 and larger. The geographic and the magnetic poles had been reached, Axel Heiberg Glacier and adjacent mountains at the head of the Ross Sea had been discovered, and some idea had been gained of the persistence of the position of the front of the Ross Ice Shelf.

A German expedition was organized at the turn of the century by a committee representing various interests, including the science associations. Its program was coordinated with that of the British National Antarctic Expedition, and a ship was built for the expedition, which was supported by government funds and private contributions. It was under the leadership of Dr. Erich von Drygalski, who had had experience in Greenland, and was well staffed with scientists. Unfortunately, exploration was cut short when the expedition ship, *Gauss*, was frozen in off what is now known as Wilhelm II Coast, on the coast of East Antarctica. However, a great deal of scientific observation was concluded before the ship departed in 1903.

The Indian Ocean sector of East Antarctica was not visited again until the Australasian Antarctic Expedition of 1911-14 under Sir Douglas Mawson established a main base at Cape Denison on Commonwealth Bay in January, 1912. A second base was established on the Shackleton Ice Shelf. Five major surveys were carried out by trail parties from the main base. The Magnetic Pole Party sledged to 70°36' S, 148°10' E, 301 miles south-southeast of the base. The Far Eastern Party sledged with dog teams to a point more than 300 miles from Cape Denison. Two of the men perished, but Mawson through great exertion and much suffering managed to survive. Two sledge journeys were made from West Base.

The eastern margin of the Weddell Sea had first been seen by William S. Bruce in 1904. While Scott was suffering disaster, a German expedition under Dr. Wilhelm Filchner was having difficulties in its attempt to set up a base on the Weddell Sea. After work in South Georgia and the South Sandwich Islands, Filchner's ship *Deutschland* was stopped by the Filchner Ice Shelf at the head of Weddell Sea. Attempts to erect a base failed when a large floe broke off and floated away. Finally, on March 6, 1912, the ship was beset and drifted in the pack for nine months before she was freed November 26, 1912, some 600 miles away.

The next expedition to the Weddell Sea, and the last for several decades fared even worse than Filchner's. The British Imperial Trans-Antarctic Expedition was organized by Sir Ernest Shackleton with contributions from Sir James Caird and other private donors and aid from the Royal Geographical Society and the British government. He planned to trek across Antarctica from the Weddell Sea to the Ross Sea, via the South Pole. In support, Captain A. Mackintosh sailed in the *Aurora* to establish a base at McMurdo Sound from which depots were subsequently laid across the Ross Ice Shelf to the Beardmore Glacier. Shackleton sailed into the Weddell Sea on the *Endurance*, discovering the Caird Coast on January 12, 1915. Seven days later, on January 19, the *Endurance* was beset and drifted northwestward for 573 miles until she was crushed. The men took to the ice, drifting northward on the floe until they finally took to the boats to reach Elephant Island, October 27, 1915. It was from here that Shackleton made his famous boat journey to South Georgia. The men were finally rescued by Shackleton in the Chilean ship *Yelcho*. The *Aurora* was also beset and drifted away before all supplies had been unloaded, which added to the hardships of the men under Mackintosh. Mackintosh and two other men perished.

The Heroic Era ended with Shackleton's death at South Georgia, January 5, 1922, on his last expedition, financed by John Q. Rowett. For all practical purposes, however, the Era ended in 1916. By that time, the coast of East Antarctica from Cape Adare to Coats Land, except for the parts explored by Mawson, was no better known than it had been in 1895. The least known area of all was West Antarctica from the Ross Sea to Marguerite Bay.

Unlike all other periods in Antarctic history, American citizens played only a minor role from 1895 to 1916. During that time American attention was focused on the Arctic and the attempts of Robert E. Peary to reach the North Pole, a goal which he attained on April 6, 1909. Peary's adversary, Dr. Frederick A. Cook, served as physician on the *Belgica* under de Gerlache in 1897-99, and it is unfortunate that subsequent controversies so damaged Cook's reputation that few now recall his excellent work in Antarctica. Dr. Cook not only labored to keep the men fit, psychologically as well as physically, during the 12 months that the *Belgica* was beset in the drifting pack ice, but he also participated in the scientific observation. The excellent though single-handed work of another American in Antarctica is reported in Chapter 15.

Another American activity during the Heroic Era that is rarely mentioned in accounts of Antarctic exploration was the sub-Antarctic circumnavigation of the *Carnegie* in 1915-16. This cruise was part of a world-wide magnetic investigation begun by the Department of Terrestrial Magnetism of the Carnegie Institution of Washington, D.C.

THE BEGINNING OF THE MECHANICAL AGE

Urgent military requirements of World War I accelerated the development of the airplane, the aerial camera, radio, and motorized transport, and the training of military personnel in their use. It was only natural that the more adventurous of those men should apply these new devices to polar exploration, first in the Arctic and then in the Antarctic. It is worthy of note that the leaders or flying personnel of all expeditions using aircraft in those first years were men with previous military experience.

An Australian, Sir Hubert Wilkins, leader of the American-financed Wilkins-Hearst Expedition, made the first airplane flight in Antarctic history on November 26, 1928, a reconnaissance flight about Deception Island, and on December 20 he made a 10-hour exploratory flight with Carl B. Eielsen south over the Antarctic Peninsula to Stefansson Strait. By the end of 1929 three other expeditions had begun aerial exploration. After establishing the base for his first Antarctic expedition at the Bay of Whales, Commander Richard E. Byrd made his first Antarctic flight January 15, 1929. On November 29 and 30, Byrd made his first flight to the South Pole. Other flights by the expedition are detailed in Chapter 17. Captain Hjalmar Riiser-Larsen, on December 7, 1929, flew from his ship, the *Norvegia*, over the coast of Enderby Land in a seaplane. This was the first of a series of such flights along the coast from Enderby Land to Coats Land during 1929-30 and 1930-31. On the last day of 1929 a flight was made in a seaplane over Mac.Robertson Land from the British-Australian-New Zealand Antarctic Research Expedition's ship *Discovery*. During 1929-30 and 1930-31 Sir Douglas Mawson cruised along the coast from George V Coast to Enderby Land, landing at Proclamation Island, Enderby Land, during the first season and at Cape Denison, Scullin Monolith, Murray Monolith, and Cape Bruce during the second. A number of flights were made over Mac.Robertson Land. Sir Hubert Wilkins also returned to the Antarctic Peninsula area in 1929-30 and made a number of flights, most of them from the water beside the *William Scoresby*.

Three different forms of aerial operations had thus been introduced at the very beginning of the Mechanical Age of Antarctic exploration. In his first expedition, Wilkins confined his activity to aerial exploration, flying from a land base. This was essentially the system followed by Lincoln Ellsworth in the three expeditions leading to the first successful transantarctic flight, from Dundee Island to the Bay of Whales, in 1935. Riiser-Larsen and Mawson took off from the water beside the expedition ship which was cruising along the coast, and made short flights inland. Their flight range was limited by the small size of the planes that the ships could carry. Byrd introduced a form of operation integrating long flights by land-based planes with long overland journeys with dog teams, both in touch with the base camp by radio. The trail parties supplied weather information for the flights and obtained ground control for the aerial photographs. The trail parties received supplies by plane and were available for rescue if planes were forced down. Trail parties were also directed through or around crevassed areas by flight personnel.

The Second Byrd Antarctic Expedition, 1933-35, marked a further development of mechanical aids to exploration. A much more extensive flight program was carried out, first with a plane equipped with pontoons in flights from the expedition ship *Jacob Ruppert* in the Amundsen Sea and later with land-based planes from the Bay of Whales. As a result Marie Byrd Land was more fully explored from the air than had been possible in 1929. This expedition was also the first on which automotive land transport proved practical. With tractors they laid depots and gasoline dumps, built and supplied the Advance Base, and made a long, unsupported exploratory trip over the Rockefeller Plateau.

The British Graham Land Expedition of 1934-37, sponsored by the Colonial Office, the Royal Geographical Society, and several other public and private organizations and individuals, was led by John Rymill and operated on much the same plan as the Byrd expedition. The 16 men and one small plane had a limited range of operations, but they accomplished an outstanding amount of work, including the first land crossing of the Antarctic Peninsula and a long trek down George VI Sound, which they discovered. Because of the rough terrain, automotive transport was not extensively used by this expedition except for work about the base, nor by subsequent expeditions in the Antarctic Peninsula area.

The United States Antarctic Service Expedition, 1939-41, led by Admiral Richard E. Byrd, was the first government-sponsored Antarctic expedition from the United States since 1842. The largest Antarctic expedition up to this time, its methods were similar to those of the Second Byrd Antarctic Expedition. The operations are described in Chapter 22 and will not be summarized here. The expedition was intended to establish two bases which would be permanently occupied by personnel which would be changed each year. However, the entry of the United States in World War II prevented the fulfillment of that plan.

The Ronne Antarctic Research Expedition, 1947-48, privately organized by Commander Finn Ronne, reoccupied East Base of the U.S. Antarctic Service Expedition. Except for the use of a second plane to accompany the main plane part of the way to support and extend the main flight, Ronne's operations were similar to those of the U.S. Antarctic Service Expedition. His ground surveys were carried out partly in conjunction with a surface party from the Falkland Islands Dependencies Survey, also based on Stonington Island. Like the British Graham Land Expedition, Ronne's was a relatively small one, but both accomplished a great deal of work. Ronne finally closed the gap at the head of the Weddell Sea.

The Norwegian-British-Swedish Antarctic Expedition, 1949-52, sponsored by the respective governments and national geographical and scientific societies, operated from a base, Maudheim, established on the ice shelf on the Princess Martha Coast at about 71°02' S, 10°55' W. A subsidiary base was set up 185 miles inland at an elevation of about 5000 feet. Field surveys provided control for aerial photography covering an area of 38,000 square miles. A geophysical profile of the thickness of the ice cap was made along the Greenwich meridian from the coast inland to about 70°20' S.

Not all of the expeditions during the development of the Mechanical Age were land based. Ship-based operations were of three kinds: the hydrographic and marine biological investigations of the Discovery Committee, the explorations of the Norwegian whalers, and the exploring expeditions of the German and the United States governments. These latter expeditions included the German New Schwabenland Expedition, 1938-39, the United States Navy's "Operation Highjump," 1946-47, and the Navy's "Operation Windmill," 1947-48.

In 1923 the British Colonial Office established the Discovery Committee to carry out investigations with a view to conserving the dwindling stock of Antarctic whales. Oceanographic investigations begun in 1925 were at first carried out from Scott's old ship, the *Discovery*, which in 1929 was replaced by the *Discovery II*, an all-steel motor vessel specially built for oceanographic research. In 1926 a small fast vessel of the whale-catcher type, the *William Scoresby*, was commissioned for marking whales to obtain migration data. Until World War II these two ships engaged continuously in investigations of physical and biological conditions of Antarctic waters. On occasion they also explored and mapped portions of the coast or island groups. The results of the investigations of the Discovery Committee, published to date, total 35 volumes. Perhaps the most significant geographic discovery of the Discovery Committee investigations was the existence of the Antarctic Convergence. In 1949 the newly founded National Institute of Oceanography took over the staff and equipment of the Discovery Committee. The first assignment of the *Discovery II* under the Institute was a two-year commission to complete investigations in the southern Indian Ocean, but the scope of the research program of the Institute is otherwise much broader.

An important aspect of Antarctic exploration during the second quarter of the 20th century was the mapping and exploration by Norwegian whalers, sometimes as a special assignment but often incidental to regular operations. Whalers also often assisted other investigators and explorers by providing transportation. Especially important was the work sponsored and financed by Lars Christensen, head of a large whaling firm of Sandefjord, Norway. Between 1927 and 1931 he sent out first the *Odd I* and then the *Norvegia* on five separate expeditions. Most of the work was centered in the South Atlantic from Bouvet Island to the South Shetlands. In 1929-30 and 1930-31 special emphasis was placed on exploration of the coast of what is now Queen Maud Land. Also in 1930-31, the Lars Christensen Coast was discovered by Norwegian whalers who also saw land at several points along the Mac.Robertson Land coast. Similarly the Ingrid Christensen Coast was discovered in 1935, a landing being made on the coast on February 20. In the party was Caroline Mikkelsen, wife of Klarius Mikkelsen, captain of the tanker *Thorshavn*. She thus became the first woman to set foot on Antarctica. During four seasons, 1931-32, 1932-33, 1933-34, and 1936-37, Christensen, aboard the *Thorshavn,* personally directed exploration by whale catchers and a seaplane. The result was a set of maps at a scale of 1:500,000 from 52°30′ E to 81° E and two other sheets at the same scale farther west in Queen Maud Land.[6]

A calculatedly spectacular ship-based operation was carried out by the German expedition under Captain Alfred Ritscher in 1938-39. The *Schwabenland,* equipped with a catapult and two flying boats, spent three weeks off the coast of Queen Maud Land during which a sufficient number of photographic flights were made to permit the Germans to map the mountains inland from the Princess Martha and Princess Astrid Coasts. No landings were made to obtain ground control, and as a result the map has been found in error both as to longitude and elevation.

The ship-based operations of the United States Navy's "Operation Highjump" and "Operation Windmill" are described in detail in Chapters 22 and 24. They represent the first use of icebreakers and helicopters in Antarctica.

ANTARCTIC BASES

The concept of a continuously manned base with annually rotated personnel was initiated with the U.S. Antarctic Service Expedition of 1939-41, but only one winter was spent in Antarctica and the concept was never carried further because of World War II. The idea, however, was later implemented by the United Kingdom, Argentina, and Chile in the Antarctic Peninsula area, where their territorial claims overlap. The first base was established by "Operation Tabarin," a joint venture of the Colonial Office and the Admiralty in February 1944 on Deception Island, ostensibly to deny access to this harbor to German naval raiders. A second base was established by the British in the same year at Port Lockroy on Wiencke Island in the Palmer Archipelago, and a third at Hope Bay on the tip of the Antarctic Peninsula in 1945. At the close of World War II these bases were taken over by the Falkland Islands Dependencies Survey of the Colonial Office, which continued the operation of these bases with rotated personnel. In 1962 it was renamed the British Antarctic Survey.

On January 31, 1947, Argentina established a base on Gamma Island in the Melchior Islands of the Palmer Archipelago, and in February 1947 a Chilean naval expedition established a base at Discovery Bay, Greenwich Island, in the South Shetlands. All three nations subsequently established other bases, either as additional stations or as replacements for those discontinued. In 1956 there were eight British stations, eight Argentine stations, and four Chilean stations in the area, each nation maintaining one on Deception Island. The maintenance and relief of these bases has required annual expeditions, and the establishment of the bases has involved much diplomatic activity. While the men occupying the stations have engaged in meteorological observations, surveying and mapping, and a variety of scientific investigations, their presence also had political significance in supporting territorial claims until the signing of the Antarctic Treaty of 1959, which placed in abeyance such claims for 30 years. Several long sledge journeys have been made by members of the Falkland Islands Dependencies Survey. Argentina has been particularly active in setting up and maintaining navigational aids.

In 1947 Australia established an Antarctic Division in the Department of External Affairs to administer the Australian National Antarctic Research Expedition, in order to put scientific research on a more permanent and better financial basis in the Australian Antarctic Territories. The first operation under the new organization was the establishment in 1947-48 of permanent stations on Macquarie Island and on Heard Island. After eight years of scientific investigations, the Heard Island base was evacuated early in 1955. In the meantime Mawson Station had been established in February, 1954, near Murray Monolith on the coast of Mac.Robertson Land, and a similar extensive scientific program has been maintained there. A number of tractor journeys have been made from Mawson Station for the purpose of surveying and geological investigation.

French polar exploration is under the direction of Expéditions Polaires Françaises. After being thwarted by ice the previous season, a base was established on the Adélie Coast in January 1950. A wide range of scientific investigations and a surveying program were carried out before the base was evacuated in January 1953. It was later re-established as part of the French program for the International Geophysical Year.

THE INTERNATIONAL GEOPHYSICAL YEAR

From July 1, 1957, to December 31, 1958, scientists from 56 nations cooperated in a vast scientific investigation of atmospheric and other geophysical phenomena at nearly 2000 stations in 5 meridianal belts from pole to pole. Some of the many fields of investigation in this International Geophysical Year were aurora, airglow, cosmic rays, geomagnetism, glaciology, gravity, ionosphere, meteorology, oceanography, seismology, and solar activity. To obtain some of the data, rockets and earth satellites were used. An important part of the IGY investigations was centered in Antarctica, where 12 nations maintained 65 stations and operational facilities on the mainland and islands. The United States established six stations, including one at the South Pole. The establishment and support of these bases was the responsibility of U.S. Naval Task Force 43. The base at Cape Hallet, established by the United States, was jointly maintained with New Zealand. The United States also operated the McMurdo Sound Air Operation Facility. Sites for bases had been investigated during the voyage of the U. S. S. *Atka* in 1954-55. Scientific personnel began occupying the bases in January 1957.

They were relieved by a second group a year later. Aerial exploration and long tractor journeys incidental to establishing and maintaining the bases and as part of the scientific program revealed to man, for the first time, vast areas of Antarctica. Almost routine flights by cargo planes from New Zealand to McMurdo Sound and from Tierra del Fuego to the head of the Weddell Sea, regular air support for the South Pole Station, tractor journeys of hundreds of miles, including a transcontinental trek under the joint auspices of Great Britain and New Zealand, were ample proof that mechanical exploration had come of age in Antarctica.

Data collected in the IGY investigations were freely exchanged among the cooperating nations to be eventually assembled, coordinated and published. In this way the contributions of each nation have benefitted all.

The preliminary findings from IGY investigations in Antarctica were so successful and so challenging that at the urging of scientists the participating nations decided to continue the work much on the same basis. Consequently, many of the old bases have been replaced and enlarged. Some have been closed and others have been opened in new locations. All of the original 12 nations have carried out scientific investigations as part of the post-IGY program. Some have done so continuously, others intermittently. Each nation is represented through its national academy of science on the Scientific Committee on Antarctic Research (SCAR) established in 1957 by the International Council of Scientific Unions to coordinate the plans and their execution so that the very important international scientific cooperation can continue.

AMERICAN INTERESTS IN THE ANTARCTIC

From the foregoing sketch of the history of Antarctic exploration, it is apparent that Americans have played a major role. American interest in the Antarctic is as old as the nation itself. While interest has waxed and waned there has been no decade when at least some Americans have not been in the Antarctic as seal hunters, whalers, or explorers.

This book is concerned with American activity in the Antarctic up to 1948, and the brief sketch of the history of Antarctic exploration in this introductory chapter is intended to be a frame of reference. The chapters which follow are straightforward and detailed accounts of American activities beginning with the first sealing in the Falkland Islands in 1775. Except for this initial activity, the account is limited to activity within the Antarctic Convergence. No attempt has been made even to list all of the early sealing voyages, but all of those known to have had a part in the unveiling of the Antarctic region are described. The detailed account, however, does not include operations associated with American participation in IGY activity. The scope and nature of this activity is entirely different from that related here, and its magnitude is such that it cannot be included in a single volume with the earlier work and do justice to either.

NOTES

1. James Weddell, *A Voyage Towards the South Pole,* etc. (London, 1825).
2. Edwin Swift Balch, "Antarctica Addenda," *Journal of the Franklin Institute,* vol. 156, No. 2, February, 1904, pp. 81-84.
3. S. G. Brown, "A Review of Antarctic Whaling," *Polar Record,* vol. 11, No. 74, May, 1963, p. 558.
4. L. P. Kirwan, *A History of Polar Exploration* (New York, 1959), pp. 178-179.
5. J. Gordon Hayes, *The Conquest of the South Pole* (London, 1932), pp. 29-33.
6. H. E. Hansen, *Atlas of Parts of the Antarctic Coastal Lands* (Oslo, 1946), 12 sheets at 1:500,000, 9 pages of text in Norwegian and English. Map legend also in Norwegian and English.

BIBLIOGRAPHY

Ault, J. P., "Sailing the Seven Seas in the Interest of Science," *National Geographic Magazine,* vol. 42, No. 6, December, 1922, pp. 631-690.
Balch, Edwin Swift, *Antarctica* (Philadelphia, Allen, Lane and Scott, 1902), 230 pp., map.
——, "Antarctic Addenda," *Journal of the Franklin Institute,* vol. 156, No. 2, February, 1904, pp. 81-84.
Brown, S. G. "Review of Antarctic Whaling," *Polar Record,* vol. 11, No. 74, May, 1963, pp. 555-566.
Christie, E. W. Hunter, *The Antarctic Problem* (London, George Allen & Unwin Ltd., 1951), 336 pp., maps, endpapers.
Crary, A. P., "The Antarctic," *Scientific American,* vol. 207, No. 3, September, 1962, pp. 60-73.
[Dater, Henry M.] *Introduction to Antarctica* (Washington, U.S. Naval Support Force, 1969) 4th revision. U.S. Government Printing Office, 54 pp.
Debenham, Frank, *Antarctica, the Story of a Continent* (London, Herbert Jenkins, 1959), 264 pp., endpaper maps, illus.
Geographical Names of Antarctica, Gazetteer No. 14 (Washington, U. S. Government Printing Office, 1956), U. S. Board on Geographical Names, ii and 332 pp.
Gould, Laurence M., "Antarctic Prospect," *Geographical Review,* vol. 47, No. 1, January, 1957, pp. 1-28.
——, *The Polar Regions in Their Relations to Human Affairs* (New York, American Geographical Society, 1958), Bowman Memorial Lectures, Series 4, iv and 54 pp., map.
Hayes, J. Gordon, *The Conquest of the South Pole* (London, Thornton Butterworth, Ltd., 1936), 318 pp.
Kirwan, L. P., *A History of Polar Exploration* (New York, W. W. Norton & Co., Inc., 1960), x and 374 pp. maps, illus.
Mill, Hugh Robert, *The Siege of the South Pole* (New York, Frederick A. Stokes Co., 1905) xvi and 455 pp., map, illus.
Mountevans, Admiral Lord, *The Desolate Antarctic* (London, Lutterworth Press, 1950), xvi and 172 pp., endpaper maps, illus.
Roberts, Brian, "Chronological List of Antarctic Expeditions," *Polar Record,* vol. 9, No. 59, May, 1958, pp. 97-134, No. 60, September, 1958, pp. 191-239.
Sullivan, Walter, *Quest for a Continent* (New York, McGraw-Hill, 1957), xiv and 372 pp., endpapers.
Victor, Paul-Émile, *Man and the Conquest of the Poles* (New York, Simon and Schuster, 1963), translated by Scott Sullivan, 320 pp., endpaper maps, illus.

2

EARLY AMERICAN SEALERS IN THE ANTARCTIC

INCEPTION OF THE AMERICAN SEALING INDUSTRY

EFFECTS OF THE AMERICAN REVOLUTION

The early American sealing industry, which ultimately was centered in the Antarctic, was initiated by American whalers, in part as an outgrowth of a sequence of events related to the American Revolution. The war closed London, the principal market for American oil, to American merchants and subjected American whaleships and their crews to seizure by British naval vessels. This state of affairs was particularly distressing to the island of Nantucket, which at that time was by far the most important center for American whaling. Without the income from whaling, the relatively infertile and limited area of the island could not support the population. To alleviate this situation, attempts were made to send out whaleships under permits granted by either the American authorities or by the commanding officers of British forces of occupation. Financial returns from successful voyages, however, were outweighed by losses sustained due to seizures of vessels by opposing naval forces.[1]

THE FALKLAND FLEET

At the outset a bold plan to save at least part of the whaling fleet was conceived by four oil merchants — Francis Rotch of Nantucket and New Bedford, Richard B. Smith of Boston, Aaron Lopez of Newport, and Leonard Jarvis of Dartmouth — who established in exile the so-called "Falkland Fleet." The economic plight of the whalers and the fact that most of the people of Nantucket were members of the Society of Friends, who objected to war on religious principles, made this neutralist action a logical and, in their eyes, an entirely ethical undertaking.

Rotch and Lopez succeeded on August 30, 1775, in obtaining from the General Court of Massachusetts permits to dispatch vessels from that Commonwealth. A bond of £2000 was required of each ship, which was ordered to land all bone and oil taken on the voyage at a Massachusetts port other than Boston or Nantucket.[2] The four oil merchants, however, did not intend that the whaleships should return to Massachusetts. The captains of the fleet of 16 vessels outfitted at Martha's Vineyard were instructed to cruise off the coast of Brazil until they had obtained a cargo or were forced by accident or bad weather to seek a haven. They were then to proceed to a rendezvous at Port Egmont in the Falkland Islands, where they were to spend the winter and where they would be met by Francis Rotch. The instructions also encouraged the captains to further their voyage by engaging in the "seal fishery" while at the Falklands. Hair, fur, and elephant seals occupied the beaches in great numbers in the breeding season. The blubber of the elephant seal produced an oil almost equal to whale oil.

20

That conditions at the Falkland Islands were favorable for his purpose was known to Rotch, for Nantucket whalers had penetrated as far south as the Falklands for some years prior to 1775. In these objectives and instructions Francis Rotch was the first American merchant, according to Stackpole, to recognize the value of the southern hemisphere sealing industry.[3]

When the Falkland Fleet sailed from Martha's Vineyard, Rotch hurried to London where he sought protection for his fleet from seizure by the British Navy. He argued that he and his associates intended to reside in England, that the oil would be sold in England, that the ships would strengthen the British whaling fleet, and that there was no other way of successfully transplanting the American whaling industry to England.[4] He presented his case successfully, and five vessels of the Falkland Fleet which already had been captured off the Azores before his arrival in London were released. Thus by playing both ends against the middle, Rotch established an American fleet in exile at the Falklands, where he himself remained for a great part of the war (Fig. 6).

SEA OTTERS, FUR SEALS, AND THE TRADE WITH CHINA

The first vessels reaching London after the close of the American Revolution were able to dispose of their oil at favorable prices, and hopes were high for a prosperous renewal of whaling as ships returned from successful whaling voyages with reports that the respite given the whales during the war had caused them to return to their old haunts in increased numbers. This cheerful prospect was soon ended by the British Parliament's placing an import duty of £18 per ton on alien oil, which effectively closed the London market to the American product. The small American market was soon glutted, and the price of oil was depressed to disastrous levels as more and more ships arrived with full casks from the whaling grounds. Under these circumstances, the American merchants had to seek new markets or divert their vessels to some other business.

While Francis Rotch had exiled himself to the Falkland Islands during the war, his brother William, who was sympathetic to the cause of the Colonists, remained at Nantucket managing the family business. During the war he was one of those Nantucket leaders who worked unstintingly to gain concessions from both British and American authorities to alleviate the plight of his fellow islanders and to save at least some part of the whaling industry. With the glutted oil market affording him little hope of regaining the $60,000 he had lost during the Revolution, William Rotch sailed for Europe in 1785 to see what concessions he might gain from the British and/or the French by moving his business to one or the other country. In London, in the newly published account of Captain James Cook's third voyage, in 1776-80, Rotch read of Lieutenant King's having sold 20 sea otter skins in China for $800. The skins had been obtained for nails, buttons, and pieces of iron from the Indians on the northwest coast of North America.[5] In a letter home he reported that the British East India Company was permitting two private vessels to be fitted out for the Pacific northwest coast of America, from whence they would take sea otter skins to China where they could expect a high price for them.[6] Here was an activity to which the American whalers might turn with anticipation of profit. Competition from the British in the China market was limited by the fact that the British trade in that area was controlled by the British East India Company.

In the meantime, Americans were also learning of the profitable China fur trade from John Ledyard of Groton, Connecticut, who had served as Corporal of Marines on Cook's third voyage. Not only was his journal published and widely circulated after his return to America, but he also traveled from New London to Philadelphia and back to Boston trying to interest ship owners and merchants in fitting out a vessel for the northwest fur trade.[7] Although no one then accepted Ledyard's proposition, his ideas were soon responsible for the establishment of an important trade with China. But it was the Antarctic rather than the Pacific northwest that was to be the principal source of furs.

After considering Ledyard's proposal, Robert Morris, noted Philadelphia financier, decided on a less daring plan. He and Daniel Parker of New York, on February 22, 1784, sent out the 360-ton *Empress of China,* via the Cape of Good Hope, with a small cargo of ginseng and furs, the latter from eastern North American trading posts.[8] In May of 1785 the *Empress* returned to New York with a variety of goods from the Orient and news of the importance of the Siberian fur trade in China. As the first American ship to that port, the *Empress* had been well received at Canton. The China trade was thus launched. Lacking gold or silver specie, the American merchants had to have an acceptable commodity to exchange for Chinese goods, and furs were that commodity.

THE VOYAGE OF THE *UNITED STATES*

While his fellow Americans were hesitating to enter the northwest Pacific coast fur trade, Francis Rotch, on the basis of his experience with the Falkland Fleet during the war, decided on a different course. He did so in spite of letters from his brother William, then in England, advising him to enter the northwest fur trade. Francis Rotch was apparently a close friend of George Hayley, a wealthy London oil merchant who had had extensive dealings with American whaling firms. After Hayley's death early in 1784, Francis Rotch, who was then in England, assumed the management of much of the firm's affairs for Hayley's widow. Later in the year she and Rotch sailed on the ship *United States* for Boston. From Boston the vessel was dispatched to Nantucket, where she was fitted out for a sealing voyage to the Falkland Islands under command of Captain Benjamin Hussey. The crew was added to by signing on Nantucket whalemen. The *United States* was apparently registered in Mrs. Hayley's name, but Stackpole has found evidence which indicates that it was actually the property of Francis Rotch.[9] Apparently both were financially involved in the undertaking.

The *United States* sailed for the Falkland Islands late in 1784, where she joined other vessels belonging to the Rotches. Ninety tons of sperm oil were transshipped aboard the *Mary,* which reached London on September 1, 1785, with 130 tons of oil. Contemporary accounts of other mariners shed light on the activities of the *United States,* whose crew took both fur seals and elephant seals, the latter for their oil. One of these contemporary accounts is the narrative of Captain Nathaniel Portlock, who with Captain George Dixon commanded the *King George* and the *Queen Charlotte,* the first British merchant vessels to sail from London to the northwest coast of North America.

En route from England to round Cape Horn, the two vessels visited the Falkland Islands. While at anchor at Port Egmont in January 1786, Captain Portlock encountered the sloop *Speedwell* which was serving as a tender to the *United States.* From Captain Coffin of the *Speedwell,* Portlock learned that the *United States,* then moored at Swan Island, had on board 300 tons of oil, mostly from elephant seals, and six or seven thousand fur sealskins. If they could be purchased at a moderate price, Portlock was particularly interested in the latter, for he was sure there would be a good market for sealskins in China. Portlock's partner, Captain Dixon, concurred in this view, and it was agreed that they would pay a visit to Captain Hussey on the *United States.*[10]

At noon on January 20 the *King George* and the *Queen Charlotte* approached Swan Island. Their arrival at States Bay (or States Harbor) and the subsequently unsuccessful bargaining session with Captain Hussey is described by Captain Portlock as follows:

... At one o'clock we passed Loop's Head, and stood into States Bay, so named by Captain Benjamin Hussey, who discovered it when on a whaling voyage to these islands some years ago.

Within the bay are several fine harbours, the principal of which I shall distinguish by the name of Hussey's Harbour, in honor of the discoverer. Here we found riding at anchor the United States, the Canton, and the Speedwell and Maria, sloops, tenders to the United States.

As soon as the ship was secured I went in my whaleboat, accompanied by Captain Dixon, on board the United States, to have some conversation with Captain Hussey, regarding the purchase of his fur seals, but we found he was not disposed to part with them; and I am inclined to think he meant them for an Eastern market, as he mentioned to me his intention of going to China immediately on his return home.[11]

Ebenezer Townsend of New Haven, supercargo on a sealing voyage from New York in the ship *Neptune* which took him to Canton and around the world, wrote as follows from "States Harbour" at Swan Island (Townsend called it Swain Island) in the Falklands in 1797:

This harbor derives its name from the ship States [sic] which lay here two years ago to obtain sea-elephant oil and hair-seal skins. She was a very large ship, about 1,000 tons, and from Boston. She was fitted out from there soon after the Revolutionary War, and the first ship that we know of that took any fur-seal skins. She was owned by Lady Haley [sic], living in Boston. They took about 13,000 fur-seal skins as an experiment, which sold in New York without their value being known and were thought to be sea-otter skins. They were afterward shipped to Calcutta and thence to Canton by Capt. Metcalf of New York, who started from New York about the same time Capt. Kendrick started from Boston.[12]

When the *United States* reached New York in 1786 the skins were sold and put aboard the brig *Eleanora,* commanded by Captain Metcalf, and as reported by Townsend, taken to Calcutta and Canton, where they were sold for $65,000. Thus began the Antarctic fur seal trade with China.

To what extent Rotch and Mrs. Hayley were influenced by reports of the northwest coast and the China fur trade cannot be determined. Considering Rotch's previous experience at the Falkland Islands and the reported conversation between Captains Portlock and Hussey, it would seem that all the principals in the business were well aware of the potentials.

The timing is also worthy of note. The *Eleanora* sailed from New York in 1786, but it was September 1787 before the Boston merchants finally inaugurated the American fur trade on the northwest coast by sending out around Cape Horn the ship *Columbia* and the sloop *Lady Washington*.

DEVELOPMENTS DURING THE EARLY YEARS OF THE SEALING TRADE

THE BEGINNING OF SEPARATE SEALING VOYAGES

The first sealing was done in conjunction with whaling, and some whalers continued for many years to combine the taking of elephant seals and "trying out" the elephant oil with their whaling operations. Typical examples of this early association are given by Stackpole.[13] In May 1786 the Nantucket vessel *Canton,* belonging to William Rotch and commanded by Captain James Whippey, arrived at Falmouth, England, from the Falklands with oil and "three to four thousand" sealskins. The British duty on alien oil being in effect, William Rotch, who was in England at the time, ordered the vessel to Dunkirk where he disposed of the cargo. On July 24, 1794, Captain Latham Gardner of the schooner *Swallow* returned to Nantucket from a voyage of slightly more than a year with 16,000 sealskins, as well as quantities of sperm oil, whale oil, and elephant oil.

As the word spread of the fabulous profits realized by some sealing captains and their associates, vessels were fitted out from American ports specifically for the purpose of taking fur seals. The first voyages were to the Falkland Islands, but soon vessels were ranging along the coast of Patagonia, rounding the Horn, working up the coast of Chile, and cruising along the coast of South Africa.

From August 1790 to April 1791 Captain Patten and part of the crew of the ship *Industry* of Philadelphia obtained 5000 fur sealskins for the China market from one of the islands of Tristan da Cunha.[14] Boston vessels were mostly engaged in the northwest coast fur trade, but one of these also engaged in southern fur sealing in 1791. The 250-ton brigantine *Hancock,* commanded by Captain Samuel Crowell, sailed from Boston in November 1790, for Cape Horn and the Pacific coast of North America. En route, Captain Crowell took a large number of seals at Staten Island (Isla de los Estados), the small island just off the eastern tip of Tierra del Fuego. Proceeding into the Pacific, the *Hancock* next stopped at the island of Más Afuera, of the Juan Fernandez Islands, which in a few years became the main source of sealskins in the southern hemisphere. Amasa Delano believed that the ship *Eliza* of New York, in 1793, was the first vessel to take seals from this island for the China market, but as Edward Raymond has pointed out, it is not likely that Captain Crowell stopped here without obtaining sealskins.[15] The *Hancock* spent the summer of 1791 on the northwest coast of America and then sailed for Canton.

The year 1790 also marked the development of American sealing in another direction when a Nantucket vessel was sent out to the Atlantic coast of South Africa. The *Asia* and the *Alliance,* commanded by Elijah Coffin and Bartlett Coffin, respectively, left Nantucket on October 6, 1791, on a whaling voyage to the Indian Ocean. From December 17, 1792, to March 11, 1793, the vessels remained at Kerguelen Island, whaling and taking elephant seals.[16] Thus by the time the new nation was ten years old, American sealers were cruising over the South Atlantic, the Pacific, and even the Indian Ocean, establishing "a new maritime industry spasmodic in its phases, erratic in its yields, and not negligible in either its geographical or international aspects."[17]

AMERICAN VESSELS AT SOUTH GEORGIA

The earliest American sealing voyages were limited to sub-Antarctic waters and islands, or to places even farther equatorward. The northern boundary of the Antarctic is the Antarctic Convergence (see Chapter 1). The first American vessels to cross this line, so far as we know, did so en route to South Georgia, which lies well south of the Convergence (Fig. 8).

Among the papers of Ebenezer Townsend was a sheet, published as a prelude to his diary, which contains among others the following statement:

. . . In the year 1790, Elijah Austin, an enterprising merchant of New Haven, Conn., fitted out two vessels on sealing voyages for Falkland [sic] in consequence of the information derived from Lady Haley's [sic] ship. These were the first vessels that undertook the fur seal-skin voyages for the China market. One was commanded by Capt. Daniel Greene and the other by Capt. Roswell Woodward, both men of uncommon enterprise. They were very successful and obtained part of their skins at South Georgia. Capt. Greene only proceeded on to Canton; Capt. Woodward returned to the United States. In this voyage Capt. Greene circumnavigated the globe and was absent three years.[18]

Townsend was supercargo on the *Neptune,* commanded by Captain Greene, on the sealing voyage to Canton and around the world in 1796-99. He was therefore in a position to learn from Greene himself of his earlier voyage to South Georgia. It appears, however, that Townsend recorded this information separate from his diary and at a time sufficiently long after to have erred as to the date. The Custom House records for the port of New Haven show both Captains Greene and Woodward engaged in trading voyages to the West Indies in 1790.

The first of the two vessels to sail for South Georgia, the brig *Nancy,* was a 143-ton vessel built in New Haven in 1783 and rebuilt in 1791. The brig, 71 feet 10 inches long, was wholly owned by Elijah Austin of New Haven. When the *Nancy* cleared the port of New Haven, May 15, 1792, for the reported destination of the Falkland Islands, she carried a company of 23 men under the command of Captain Daniel Greene.

Privateers and pirates were at that time a very real menace to merchant shipping. The ordinary merchant vessel could do little against the privateers except to try to avoid them. A sealing vessel with a cargo of skins, especially one returning to the United States, was relatively safe, for its cargo was of very limited value to either privateer or pirate. Those vessels which had delivered a cargo of skins to Canton and were laden with goods from China were, however, especially vulnerable. The return voyage to the United States via the Cape of Good Hope passed through the Sunda Straits, where pirates were particularly troublesome. For this reason the brig *Nancy* was armed with four guns.

The departure of the brigantine *Polly,* commanded by Captain Roswell Woodward, was reported in the "Marine List" of the weekly New Haven *Connecticut Journal* for June 20, 1792. The destination of the vessel was vaguely noted as "fishing." The *Polly* was built in Massachusetts in 1784 and rebuilt at New Haven in 1792. Prior to the latter date, the 95-ton brigantine had been commanded by Captain Greene on several voyages to the West Indies. In 1792 her owners were listed as Elijah Austin, Peleg Sandford of Hartford, and Daniel Cotton of New York. The *Polly* was unarmed, apparently because she was destined to return directly to the United States.

Except for Custom House documents and the statement by Townsend, little is now known about the voyage to South Georgia of the *Nancy* and the *Polly.* The arrival of the *Polly* and Captain Woodward from South Georgia is recorded as of May 19, 1794. The arrival is also noted in the *Connecticut Journal* for May 21, 1794, and although the *Polly* is reported as arriving from South Georgia, it is surprising that no special comment is made of that fact in the "Marine List" of the paper. Captain Woodward was either unimpressed with the far south or he was purposely reticent.

The arrival of the brig *Nancy* at New York on May 6, 1795, was reported next day in *The Daily Advertiser.* Captain Greene's remarks on his five months' voyage from Canton, including troubles that Captain Magee and the ship *Pennsylvania* had with first French and then Dutch privateers, were reported, but not a word appeared concerning the first part of the voyage. This is not surprising, for sealers kept secret from their competitors as long as possible the existence of new rookeries.

The inward manifest for the *Nancy,* dated May 6, 1795, at the New York Custom House, showed the cargo to consist of tea, sugar, nankeens, chinaware, silk, lacquer, and wine on which a duty of $10,324.60 was levied. This is an example of the wealth that a successful sealing voyage brought to the United States. The next year Captain Greene sailed on a second three-year voyage, this time as master of the ship *Neptune* of which Ebenezer Townsend was supercargo. This second voyage was even more successful. The goods brought in from Canton were sold for $280,000 and paid a duty of $74,000.[19] Captain Greene did not return again to South Georgia in the *Neptune,* but visited Más Afuera and the coast of Chile.

SEALING DURING THE FIRST PART OF THE 19TH CENTURY

IN SUB-ANTARCTIC WATERS

The principal area of activity of American sealers during the first part of the 19th century continued to be the Falkland Islands, Patagonia, Staten Island, the Cape Horn region, the coast of Chile, the island of Mocha and the Juan Fernandez group, especially Más Afuera. Even islands as far north as San Felix and San Ambrosia and the Galápagos Islands, off the Pacific coast of South America, were visited by sealers. Continued slaughter soon greatly reduced the number of seals at the Falkland Islands, but as long as the business continued, sealers called at these islands because they provided many good harbors for refreshing the crews, and for obtaining supplies of fresh water, ducks, geese, eggs, wild bullocks, and wood. Vessels were often repaired there, and it was common practice for a small sloop or shallop that had been brought down in pieces in the hold of a larger vessel to be assembled there. The Falklands also served as a wintering place for vessels that remained for more than one season. Isla Santa Maria (Saint Mary's Island of the sealers), southwest of Concepción, Chile, in the Golfo Arauco was also widely used by the sealers as a place of refreshment. One stretch of beach on the coast of Patagonia was used to such an extent by sealers for drying sealskins that it became known among them as "New Haven Green." The Cape Horn region with its stormy weather and treacherous waters was at first avoided until the seals of the less inhospitable regions were depleted.

There was probably no greater source of sealskins, certainly in terms of area, than the island of Más Afuera (now Isla Alejandro Selkirk) of the Juan Fernandez group. Neighboring Más a Tierra (now Isla Robinson Crusoe) had already been made famous by Defoe's *Robinson Crusoe* based on Alexander Selkirk's experience there. From Más Afuera Clark has estimated that "between the years 1793 and 1807, upwards of 3,500,000 fur-seal skins were obtained, and most of them taken to China."[20] Speaking of the height of sealing activity on Más Afuera, Amasa Delano wrote, "When the Americans came to Mas-a-Fuera about the year 1797, and began to make a business of killing seals, there is no doubt but there were two or three million of them on the island. I have made an estimate of more than three million that have been carried to Canton from thence in the space of seven years. I have carried more than 100,000 myself, and have been at the place when there were the people of 14 ships or vessels on the island at one time, killing seals."[21]

ACTIVITY AT SOUTH GEORGIA

Although statements made in 1820 indicate that it is possible that American sealers visited the South Shetlands at an early date, South Georgia is the only land area within the Antarctic Convergence for which we have positive proof of sealing activity before the close of the 18th century. British and American sealers were attracted to South Georgia by the narrative of Captain James Cook's second voyage around the world (1772-75), published in 1777 and in many subsequent editions. Cook, who landed here and made a rough survey of the island, reported large numbers of "sea lions and sea dogs" both at South Georgia and at Staten Island. As previously noted, the first Americans to visit South Georgia probably reached there in the austral summer of 1792-93 (Fig. 10).

Captain Edmund Fanning, commanding the corvette *Aspasia*, sailed from New York on May 11, 1800. After stops at Pernambuco, Brazil, and the island of Tristan da Cunha, the *Aspasia* proceeded to South Georgia where Fanning expected to find the crew of the *Regulator*, a vessel belonging to the owners of the *Aspasia* and which had been wrecked there. Fanning called at what he referred to as "Sparrow Bay," which must have been on the northwestern end of the island, to the west of the Bay of Isles. Here he found an abandoned shelter of the crew of the *Regulator*. Cruising eastward along the north shore of South Georgia, past the Bay of Isles, the *Aspasia* came to anchor in what Fanning called "Woodward Harbor," apparently named by the Americans for Roswell Woodward, captain of the brigantine *Polly*. Here Fanning found the British vessel *Morse*, and from a former crew member of the *Regulator* now aboard the *Morse*, he learned that the crew of the former had sold their cargo of approximately 14,000 fur sealskins and salvage from the vessel to the captain of a British ship on which they had taken passage.

It was now September and Fanning prepared for the advent of the fur seals on the beaches by converting the launch into a shallop, buying a second shallop that belonged to a British vessel hunting elephant seals, and building a third from materials brought from home and from parts salvaged from the wreck of the *Regulator*. Thus prepared, and with men all at advantageous locations when the sealing season opened, the crew of the *Aspasia* succeeded in taking 57,000 seals. At the same time, Fanning reported the arrival of 17 sealing vessels, mostly ships and shallops, who took a total of 55,000 skins.[22] On February 9, 1801, the *Aspasia* sailed from South Georgia en route for Canton via Cape Horn.

The following is a statement of the early sealing on South Georgia by the famous British sealer-explorer, Captain James Weddell:

. . . since the year in which seals were known to be so abundant not less than 20,000 tons of the sea-elephant oil has been procured for the London market. A quantity of fur-seal skins were usually brought along with a cargo of oil, but formerly the furriers in England had not the method of dressing them, on which account they were of so little value as to be almost neglected. At the same time, however, the Americans were carrying from Georgia cargoes of these skins to China, where they frequently obtained a price of from $5 to $6 apiece. It is generally known that the English did not enjoy the same privilege, by which means the Americans took entirely out of our hands this valuable article of trade. The number of skins brought from off Georgia cannot be estimated at fewer than 1,200,000.[23]

ATTEMPTS AT EXPLORATION

The magnitude of the slaughter described for Más Afuera and South Georgia was typical of all the sealing grounds. Indiscriminate killing, regardless of sex or age, soon decimated the seals, and losing ventures succeeded fabulously suc-

cessful voyages. Under the circumstances, sealers were ever on the lookout for
new seal rookeries and ship owners at home pored over marine columns of
American newspapers for any hint of new discoveries. Narratives and charts of
voyages of exploration were carefully examined for clues. In this way Captain
Henry Fanning of the ship *Catharine* of New York, by using Crozet's narrative,
found and landed on the Crozet Islands in 1805. Captain Jonathan Paddock
with the *Favourite* and Captain Peter Chase of the *Criterion,* both of Nantucket,
also were at the Crozets about the same time.[24] All obtained valuable cargoes
of fur sealskins. One of these ships appears to have been the first vessel to have
visited the islands since their discovery in 1772. Edmund Fanning credits Henry
Fanning with naming several geographical features, names which were used by
sealers who frequented the islands for the next 40 years.

Captain Isaac Pendleton sailed from New York in 1803 in the brig *Union* on
a wide-ranging voyage to the Pacific via the Cape of Good Hope. Guided by Captain George Vancouver's narrative, he sailed along the south coast of Australia,
landing on an island which he called Borders Island where he took 14,000 sealskins and built a 40-ton schooner. Later he sailed to New Zealand and landed
a crew on the Antipodes Islands. These men had to be rescued by Captain Paddock in the *Favourite* after the *Union* was wrecked and its crew murdered at the
Fiji Islands.

It is impossible to say how many captains were instructed by their ship owners to carry out exploration for new sealing grounds. There is a record of operations of at least one such undertaking and the curtailment of another. Board-
man and Pope, Boston merchants, sent out the ship *Topaz* in 1807, under the
command of Captain Mayhew Folger of Nantucket, on a combined sealing and
exploring voyage.[25] Sailing from Boston on April 5, 1807, the *Topaz* touched at
the Cape Verde Islands and then proceeded to the island of Trinidade in the
south Atlantic. Captain Folger set a course southward from Trinidade in a vain
search first for Grande Island (reported to be in 47°40′ S, 38°43′ W) and then
for Pepys Island. Next a course was set to the eastward at a latitude sufficiently
high to remain in unfrequented waters. During this voyage of July, August, and
September the *Topaz* was severely buffeted by many storms, one of which drove
the vessel away from the coast of Kerguelen Island, where Captain Folger had
planned to refresh his crew and repair his leaking vessel. Finally, in the middle
of October the *Topaz* arrived in Adventure Bay, Tasmania. Leaving Hobart,
November 3, 1807, the *Topaz* sailed eastward and southeastward to round
Stewart Island at the southern end of New Zealand, from where a course was set
for Chatham Islands. Leaving Chatham Islands, November 26, 1807, the *Topaz*
next sailed southwestward for the Antipodes Islands. Finding no seals here,
Captain Folger pushed southeastward on a cruise of discovery. Finding icebergs
as far north as 53° S, 179°49′ W but no seal islands, Folger was in January 1808
at last forced to turn northward for want of drinking water.

Weary of sub-polar conditions, Captain Folger decided to look for Pitcairn
Island, which had been discovered in the South Pacific in 1767. He sighted the
island on February 6, 1808, about 3.5° west of its reported position, and, much

to his surprise, was hailed by sons of the mutineers from H.M.S. *Bounty*. Thus, through Captain Folger, the world eventually learned for the first time the fate of Fletcher Christian and his associates.

After a two-day stay on Pitcairn Island, Captain Folger continued eastward across the Pacific, arriving at Más Afuera on March 20, 1808. A few days later, on suspicion of carrying contraband, the *Topaz* and her company were seized by Chilean authorities and taken to Valparaiso. Finally cleared on July 22, 1808, Captain Folger eventually succeeded in getting provisions for the final stage of the voyage, which ended at Boston in December 1808. As Stackpole has pointed out, the success or failure of Captain Folger's voyage of discovery depended on the course he took after failing to find Grande Island and Pepys Island in the South Atlantic. Had he sailed westward beyond South Georgia instead of toward Kerguelen, it is possible that he would have discovered the South Shetland Islands.[26]

It is interesting to speculate what might have been the results if another plan for exploration of far southern waters and the Pacific had materialized four years later. In this instance the ships *Volunteer* and *Hope* were being fitted out by private interests for an expedition to be headed by the veteran sealer Edmund Fanning. Fanning visited Washington, where he obtained government approval and support as expressed in the following document.[27]

THE UNITED STATES OF AMERICA
To all to whom these shall come greeting:

Whereas, the American vessel, the Volunteer, whereof Edmund Fanning is master, is now fully equipped for, and ready to proceed to sea, at private expense, from the port of New York, on a voyage of discovery and in pursuit of physical science, particularly in natural history:

And as it is not the design of those concerned in it, to enter into any trade or commerce with any civilized nations further than may be necessary to procure refreshments or repairs; or with any uncivilized nation further than may be necessary to accomplish the great objects of the voyage, and obtain for the crew a fair remuneration for their labors: These are, therefore, to command all armed and public vessels of the United States, and all persons holding commissions, or having authority under them, to suffer the said vessel to prosecute her said voyage without hindrance, and in case of need, to afford to the persons embarked therein, and to the said vessel, all necessary aid and succor, towards the prosecution of the said voyage, and in consideration also of the importance of useful science, and of the respect due to those engaged in the promotion of it, the vessel aforesaid, and the persons on board are, in a special manner recommended to the favorable attention of others, the officers, citizens, and subjects, of all friendly nations and powers whatever.

In testimony thereof, I have caused the seal of the United States to be hereunto affixed, and signed the same with my hand, at the City of Washington, the 17th day of March, A. D. 1812, and in the thirty-sixth year of the Independence of the United States of America.

James Madison

By the President

James Monroe
Secretary of State

Just as the vessels were about to sail, however, the whole project was ended very suddenly in June by the declaration of war against Great Britain.

AMERICAN SEALERS AFTER 1812

The continued slaughter of fur seals through the first decade of the 19th century in all their known haunts in the southern hemisphere resulted in three gradual changes in the nature of the American sealing industry: a decrease in the number of vessels engaged, an increased interest in the elephant seal, and a gradual decline in the Chinese fur market.

Some losing voyages were expected in this normally hazardous business, but as an increasing percentage of vessels returned with incomplete cargoes of furs, losses increased and profits declined. As a result, fewer ships sailed for the sealing grounds. Of those vessels continuing in the sealing trade, an increasing percentage came home with supplementary cargoes of elephant oil or with elephant oil only. Oil voyages were not unprofitable, but their returns were not comparable to the fabulous profits realized from a cargo of sealskins.

Until the end of the 18th century, Canton was the market at which the vast majority of skins were sold by American sealers. Very few were sold at home or in Europe. After the turn of the century, more and more American sealing vessels returned home with their cargoes, which were sold at auction. In less than 20 years all cargoes came to be disposed of in this manner. The sealers thus passed to the merchants the responsibility for disposal of the furs at home or for their shipment to foreign markets. A sealing voyage which involved taking a cargo of skins to Canton required three years and meant long unproductive months at sea for a crew considerably larger than necessary to work the vessel. Only in boom times was it practical to leave part of the crew on a seal island to procure the next cargo. Moreover, the European market was greatly expanded by the discovery in 1796 by Thomas Chapman of London of a process similar to that previously known only to the Chinese by which the coarse outer hair could be removed from a sealskin, exposing the soft fur beneath.

Clark's list of American sealing voyages from 1783 to 1839, obviously incomplete for the earlier years, shows the last three voyages by American sealers to China were made in 1804-07, 1807-09, and 1815-18.[28] The last two were made by Captain Caleb Brintnall of New Haven in the ships *Triumph* and *Zephyr,* respectively. The last was an unsuccessful voyage. By contrast, six of the eight ships which sailed from American ports in 1799 sailed for Canton, returning in 1802. Two of the six vessels sailing from United States ports in 1800 continued on to China, and the next year half of the six vessels which sailed from America went to Canton.

Although the reported destination of sealing voyages in Custom House papers is often so vague as to render any calculation of them subject to omissions, it would appear that not a single sealer left port in 1808, 1809, and 1810. Only one vessel sailed in 1811 and another in 1812. The low ebb of the business is indicated by the lone voyage for 1812, that of the brig *Nanina* of New York, of which Captain Charles H. Barnard was master. In the ship's company were at least four unemployed former sealing masters.

Thomas A. Stevens, from a careful examination of Custom House records and marine columns of newspapers, has compiled a list of sealing voyages originating from the United States ports from 1812 to 1819.[29] This information is summarized in the following table:

SEALING VOYAGES FROM AMERICAN PORTS, 1812-1819

Year	Number of Sailings	No. Taking Oil Only	No. Taking Skins Only	Remarks
1812	1			Seized by Britishers at the Falklands.
1813	0			
1814	0			
1815	6	4	1	
1816	2	1		
1817	4	2		
1818	5	1		One vessel wrecked.
1819	5	1		Two remained for 1820-21 at So. Shetlands.

In this list Stevens reveals a close relationship among the leading personalities in the business. One of the leading merchants at this time and later in the sealing business was James Byers of New York, with whom Captain Edmund Fanning was associated and for whom he commanded several ships. One of these was the ship *Volunteer* on a voyage from 1815 to 1817. The ship's company comprised many of the leading figures in the period from 1819-22 at the South Shetlands. First mate on the *Volunteer* was Benjamin Pendleton, the second mate was James P. Sheffield, and the third mate was Daniel W. Clark. William A. Fanning was purser and Edmund Fanning of Nantucket was sailing master. Crew members included Robert Johnson, Abraham Blauvelt, Benjamin Cutler, and William Atkins. On Fanning's last voyage, in the *Sea Fox*, 1817-18, his first mate was Donald MacKay. The brig *Jane Maria*, which accompanied the *Sea Fox*, was commanded by Benjamin Pendleton, and his first mate was James P. Sheffield.

THE SOUTH SHETLANDS

THEIR DISCOVERY BY WILLIAM SMITH

The discovery of the South Shetland Islands, a volcanic chain lying off the Antarctic Peninsula about 400 miles southeast of Cape Horn, is generally credited to William Smith in the British brig *Williams,* in 1819.[30] Facing strong head winds while rounding Cape Horn in February 1819 on a merchant voyage from Montevideo to Valparaiso, he steered to the southward of the usual track of ships making this passage. On February 19 he twice sighted land to the south. Smith's report was not given much credence by British naval authorities in Valparaiso. On his return to Montevideo in June, Smith retraced his route to the southward, but failed to sight land. Consequently, British naval authorities at Montevideo paid little heed to his report, but American sealers then at Montevideo showed great interest. They are reported to have tried unsuccessfully to charter Smith's vessel for a return voyage to the new land. Smith left Montevideo in September 1819 on another voyage to Valparaiso. Now somewhat piqued, he steered south for the new land, which he sighted on October 14. After exploring the coast for two days he landed on October 16 and took possession in the name of King George III. Smith named the new land New South Britain, but it soon became generally known as the South Shetland Islands.

ANNOUNCEMENT OF THE DISCOVERY IN THE UNITED STATES

The most immediate result of the discovery of the South Shetlands, so far as the United States was concerned, was that the brig *Hersilia,* which had sailed on a sealing voyage from Stonington, Connecticut, July 22, 1819, went in search of the new land after second mate Nathaniel B. Palmer learned of their discovery while at the Falkland Islands. A full account of this voyage is contained in the next chapter.

Stevens claims that the first report of the discovery of the South Shetlands to reach the United States appeared in the marine columns of several papers late in March 1820.[31] This report originated from a Mr. Strong, who sailed from Buenos Aires on January 7, 1820. Upon Strong's arrival in New York, the *New-York Mercantile Advertiser* carried the following report of his account:

A new land has been discovered off Cape Horn lat. 61 long. 55 by the ship *William* [sic] on a voyage from Montevideo to Valparaiso. The fact is susceptable of no doubt — the same ship was again dispatched there by Capt. Sherriff, of the *Andromache* frigate, to survey the coast, which the W. explored for 200 miles: the Captain landed, found it covered with snow, an abundance of seals and whales — no inhabitants.

This also appeared in the *Independent Chronicle and Boston Patriot* for April 1, 1820. Such information was enough to excite into immediate action any sealing master or ship owner. The *Hersilia,* too, arrived at Stonington on May 21, 1820, with confirming information for anyone privileged to learn of it. The effects of this information on American sealers and their subsequent exploration of the shores of Antarctica are reported in the chapters which follow.

OFFICIAL REACTION TO THE DISCOVERY

These were troublous times in Latin America, where wars of independence were being fought. To keep a careful check on these affairs and to look out for the commercial interests of United States citizens, the Department of State had commissioned special agents in the key cities of South America. One of these men was Jeremy Robinson, although for some indiscretion he seems, temporarily at least, to have lost his position in 1820. Robinson wrote a letter, dated Valparaiso, November 15, 1819, to Secretary of State John Quincy Adams in which he described in some detail Smith's first sighting and subsequent exploration of the South Shetlands. Significant excerpts of the letter are given below:

November 15, 1819

Sir:

I avail myself of an opportunity to write by way of England, to notify you of a recent important discovery of land in the South Seas.

. . . .

Captain Sherriff, the commander of the Andromache and other British naval forces in these seas, will dispatch a vessel in a few days to survey this land and report upon it.

Thinking this discovery and information may be interesting to you, Sir, inasmuch as it may be ultimately the means of throwing new light upon navigation, geography and the theory of the earth, I take the liberty to communicate it, in the hopes that the facts will be gratifying to the government and useful to society in general.

Permit me to suggest that it is probable many great discoveries are to be made in this hemisphere, and that much has escaped the vigilance and search of the most scrutinizing observations in the Pacific Ocean — Should the Govt. of the United States think fit to equip and commission a vessel, and suitable persons upon a voyage of discovery in this quarter of the world, it is perhaps fair to infer that it and the nation would be amply repaid, in an acquisition of knowledge in addition to the conscious satisfaction arising from having patronized and promoted laudable intelligence, adventure and enterprise. Not merely these results might be realized but perhaps new sources of wealth, power and happiness, would be disclosed and revenues and science itself be benefited thereby —

> With the greatest respect,
> I have the honor to be, Sir
> Your most obedient, humble servant
>
> J. Robinson

An impression has been made upon my mind that Captain Fanning of New York discovered the land alluded to above several years ago — or perhaps it is *Drakes Land*.

The vessel employed by Captain Sheriff, will return with —?— in a few weeks when with permission, I will communicate the result of his observations to you as they can be obtained.

> Valparaiso — Jany. 22, 1820
>
> J. R.

Robinson's letter was apparently not sent until January 22, which would account for the postscript.[32]

J. B. Prevost, special agent at Buenos Aires, in a letter dated January 10, 1820, also reported the discovery of the South Shetlands by Captain Smith. Due to the reportedly harsh environment, he deprecated the value of the land, but added "It offers, however, a new field to the adventures of our countrymen in the numbers of seals and whales that abound on its coast."[33]

The Secretary of State also received information about the discovery of the South Shetlands from another source. James Byers of New York learned from Captain James P. Sheffield of the visit of the *Hersilia* to the South Shetlands in 1820. Byers in turn wrote three letters to Brigadier General Daniel Parker, Adjutant and Inspector General of the United States Army. In the second, dated August 24, 1820, he told of the discovery and added, "it would afford great satisfaction to every American if our Government was the first to survey and name the new islands."[34] In the third letter, dated September 4, 1820, he urged that the United States send an armed ship to protect American sealers, for as he said, "There is not the least doubt in my mind that but the British will attempt to drive our vessels from the islands. Not by open hostility but by blustering & threats."

General Parker forwarded the first letter from Byers to Secretary of State Adams, who in turn sent it along with the two letters of Jeremy Robinson to

President James Monroe with a covering letter dated August 26, 1820. The following are significant excerpts:

Washington, 26, August, 1820

Dear Sir:

The enclosed letter from J. Byers of New York to General Parker was delivered to me by that officer, and relates to a subject of very considerable importance. To give you a more perfect understanding of its contents, I enclose with it a letter of 15 November, 1819, from Jeremy Robinson at Valparaiso. General Parker says that more than twenty vessels have been fitted out from New York, and have sailed or are about to sail upon sealing and whaling voyages to this newly discovered island or continent. Byers says they will be on the spot before the English, but whether they can reach latitude 61°40' south in October, which answers to our April, is to be seen. I much doubt it. If they do, and the English adventurers come there afterwards, we shall hear more of it. Nootka Sound[35] and Falkland Island questions may be expected. I beg leave to recommend the affair to your particular consideration. . . .

I desired General Parker to advise Mr. Byers to see the Secretary of the Navy and confer with him about this project of a settlement and sending a frigate *to take possession.* I hope this plan will meet your approbation. There can be no doubt of the right, and the settlement is a very good expedient for protecting the real objects — to catch seals and whales. . . .[36]

The President replied to Adams in a letter of September 1, 1820:

The discovery of land in the Pacific, of great extent, is an important event, and there are strong reasons in favor of your suggestion to aim at its occupancy on our part. Communicate the documents to the Secretary of the Navy and suggest the motive, asking how far it would be practicable to send a frigate there, and thence to strengthen our force along the American coast. I shall also write him on the subject.[37]

PUBLIC REACTION TO THE NEWS OF THE DISCOVERY

Widespread public interest and general editorial comment regarding the announcement of the discovery of the South Shetland Islands awaited the publication of a letter from Jeremy Robinson to Dr. Samuel L. Mitchill, president of the Lyceum of Natural History of New York. This letter, dated January 23, 1820, was essentially the same as that sent to John Quincy Adams. Merely a few words were changed to fit the circumstances. The letter was published in the *New York Evening Post* of September 16, 1820, and in many other American papers during the same month. In October other accounts were printed, based on notices of Smith's discovery appearing in British newspapers. The general tenor of American newspaper editorial comment regarding the news of Smith's discovery was that the islands had previously been discovered by Americans but that the fact had been kept secret for commercial reasons. The following examples are typical.

Following Robinson's letter to Dr. Mitchill in the *New York Evening Post* for September 16, 1820, was this editorial comment: "It is said by Mr. Land that one of our late enterprising merchants, formerly made voyages to the above place; but the discovery of it was kept secret."

The *Boston Patriot and Daily Mercantile Advertiser* for September 25, 1820, and the *Independent Chronicle and Boston Patriot* for September 30, 1820, carried the following article credited to the New York *Mercantile Advertiser:*

"The Discovery"

It is a singular fact that the newly discovered land in the Pacific Ocean, south of Cape Horn, has been known to *Brother Jonathan,*[38] at least as long that a voyage to and from the Island has actually been completed out of the port of Stonington, Conn. But less ambitious about the honor than the profit he was content from the experience of the first voyage to move on quietly in the purchase of ships, which he has done to the extent of seven or eight within a few months — all of which have ostensibly gone *a whaling,* but they have been more probably gone *a sealing.*

About two years ago, a ship was fitted out of this port (New York) on shares for 'an island unknown to anyone except the Captain, where seals which have never been disturbed by man were as tame as kittens, and more plenty than at any other place upon earth.' This was the language used to induce others to take an interest, the possessor of the secret being rich in knowledge but poor in purse. The ship, however, proceeded, but was unfortunately cast away before she reached her destination.

When our brethern at Stonington have made as much as they wish by keeping the secret, we hope they will favor the world with some account of their discovery. It is probable that the people of New Haven have been making some guess of the existence of this island, as they too, have been looking out for whale ships.

Several versions of comments such as these appeared in many American newspapers in September and October 1820. *Niles' Weekly Register,* the national news magazine published in Baltimore, faithfully published all of them, sometimes with comments of its own. It was perhaps these reports that were responsible for an article published in the *Annales Maritimes et Coloniales,* 1821, *Deuxième Partie.* Translation of an excerpt from page 1034 is as follows:

I have before me several reports proving that United States' vessels have been calling at southern New Shetland, which the British claim to have discovered last year, for the past ten years, or even longer, and that they take cargo there similar to the cargo they obtain from the Crozet Islands, using such cargo to maintain their trade with China.

In his *Siege of the South Pole,* Hugh Robert Mill reported in a similar vein, perhaps inspired by the same sources. He wrote:

According to a communication which was made by Captain J. Horsburgh, Hydrographer to the East India Company, to Professor Heinrich Berghaus, the distinguished author of the "Physical Atlas," American sealers had been at work in the South Shetlands since 1812, and had kept their field operations a profound secret in order to exclude competition. . . .[39]

If an American sealer actually did sight the South Shetlands before 1819, no logbook of such a voyage has ever come to light, and none of the sealers who authored narratives ever directly made such an assertion. It would be difficult to prove from Custom House records that such a voyage did take place or that such a discovery was made, because — as has been remarked — sealers were purposely vague in reporting their destinations and the places from which they sailed.

If such a discovery was made and kept secret for commercial reasons, it was an extremely well-kept secret. It is significant that James Byers, a man as experienced in the sealing business as any American of his time, said in his letter of August 25, 1820, to Brigadier General Daniel Parker, "The first information I ever received respecting the new discovery was from a Captain Sheffield who arrived at Stonington last spring from the new Islands."[40] Once the discovery of the South Shetlands was well advertised, it did not take long for American sealers to set out for them. In 1820-21, thirty American vessels were at work there. The following chapters record their operations.

NOTES

1. Edouard A. Stackpole, *The Sea-Hunters* (Philadelphia, 1953), pp. 88-93.

2. *Ibid.*, pp. 71-72. Although some Nantucketers actively supported the revolution, the conditions set by the Court reflected the suspicion with which many of their countrymen regarded the pacifistic convictions of the islanders. Some Nantucket people were, of course, Tories.

3. *Ibid.*, p. 75.

4. *Ibid.*, pp. 76-77. The practical aspects of this move outweighed any objections on the basis of ethics. The Nantucket whaling captains and crews were, after all, residents of the vast oceans of the world and their principal loyalty was to their native island, whose economy was being ruined by the acts of both belligerents.

5. James Cook, *A Voyage to the Pacific Ocean*, etc. (London, 1784), vol. 2, pp. 270-271, 295, 357-358; vol. 3, p. 429.

6. Stackpole, *op. cit.*, p. 182.

7. John Ledyard, *A Journal of Captain Cook's Last Voyage to the Pacific Ocean*, etc. (Hartford, Conn., 1783), see pp. 166-167, 200; Helen Augur, *Passage to Glory, John Ledyard's America* (Garden City, N.Y. 1946), pp. 132-139.

8. Augur, *op. cit.*, pp. 139-140.

9. Stackpole, *op. cit.*, p. 188.

10. Capt. Nathaniel Portlock, *"A Voyage Round the World; but More Particularly to the North-West Coast of America*, etc. (London, 1809), pp. 34, 37-38.

11. *Ibid.*, pp. 41-42.

12. Ebenezer Townsend, "The Diary of Mr. Ebenezer Townsend, Jr., the Supercargo of the Sealing Ship 'Neptune,' on her Voyage to the South Pacific and Canton," *New Haven Colony Historical Society Papers*, vol. 4 (1888), p. 3.

13. Stackpole, *op. cit.*, pp. 189-190.

14. Alonzo Howard Clark, "The Antarctic Fur-Seal and Sea-elephant Industries," *The Fisheries and Fishery Industries of the United States*, U. S. Bureau of Fish and Fisheries, 77th Congr., 1st Sess., Sen. Misc. Doc. 124, Sec. V, vol. 2, p. 441, Washington, 1887.

15. Edward H. Raymond, "The Fur-Seal Fishery and Salem," *Essex Institute Historical Collections*, vol. 72, No. 3, July 6, 1936, p. 187.

16. Stackpole, *op. cit.*, pp. 194-205.

17. Raymond, *op cit.*, p. 186.

18. Townsend, *op cit.*, p. 3. The same information was also reported by Clark, who had access to Townsend's manuscripts. See Clark, *op. cit.*, p. 441.

19. Townsend, *op. cit.*, p. 1.

20. Clark, *op. cit.*, p. 407.

21. Amasa Delano, *Narrative of Voyages and Travels in the Northern and Southern Hemispheres* (Boston, 1817), p. 306.

22. Edmund Fanning, *Voyages Round the World*, etc. (New York, 1833), p. 299.

23. James Weddell, *A Voyage Towards the South Pole*, etc. (London, 1825), p. 53.

24. Clark, *op. cit.*, p. 417; Fanning, *op. cit.*, chap. xvii; and Stackpole, *op. cit.*, pp. 233-236. The Crozet Islands were discovered by a French expedition under Capt. Marion-Dufresne on January 23, 1772. Crozet assumed command after Marion-Dufresne was murdered in New Zealand.

25. Stackpole, *op cit.*, pp. 238-247. Stackpole's account is based on the logbook of the *Topaz*, property of the Nantucket Whaling Museum.

26. *Ibid.*, p. 247.

27. Edmund Fanning, "Memorial of Edmund Fanning, Exploration — South Seas., etc.," January 1840, 26th Congr., 1st Sess., House Doc. 57, p. 9. A brief account of the proposed expedition is given by Fanning on p. 3 of the memorial and also in his *Voyages Round the World*, *op. cit.*, pp. 492-494.

28. Clark, *op. cit.*, pp. 440-453.

29. Thomas A. Stevens, "The First American Sealers in the Antarctic, 1812-1819, and the First Voyage of the Brig *Hersilia*, of Stonington, Connecticut, 1819-1820." (Mimeographed report, May 1, 1954), pp. 17-29.

30. A concise account of the discovery is given by E. W. Hunter Christie in *The Antarctic Problem* (London, Allen & Unwin, 1951), pp. 70-76.

31. Stevens, *op. cit.*, p. 9.

32. This and another letter of Robinson to John Quincy Adams, January 17, 1820, are in the Records of the Department of State, Special Agent File, vol. 5, 1817, Record Group 59, U. S. National Archives. These letters have been microfilmed by the National Archives as part of microcopy M-37, roll 5.

33. J. B. Prevost, letter, January 10, 1820, to Secretary of State John Quincy Adams, Records of the Department of State, Special Agent File, vol. 5, 1817, Record Group 59, U. S. National Archives.

34. The three letters of Byers to General Parker are filed in the records of the Department of State, Miscellaneous Letters File, August-October, 1820, Record Group 59, U. S. National Archives. These letters have been microfilmed by the National Archives as part of microcopy M-179, roll 49.

35. Nootka Sound is on the west side of Vancouver Island, on the west coast of North America.

36. John Quincy Adams, "Letter of, to President James Monroe, August 26, 1820," *Writings of John Quincy Adams*, W. C. Ford, ed. (New York, 1917), vol. 7, pp. 66-68.

37. *Ibid.*, see footnote, p. 67.

38. For several decades after the American Revolution "Brother Jonathan" was commonly applied as a collective sobriquet to the people of the United States. The term is of uncertain origin, although it is believed by many to have developed from General George Washington's reference to Jonathan Trumbull, the elder, as "Brother Jonathan." Trumbull, then governor of Connecticut, was a key figure in supplying Washington's troops.

39. Hugh Robert Mill, *The Siege of the South Pole* (New York, 1905), p. 92.

40. James Byers, letter, August 25, 1820, to Brig. Gen. Daniel Parker, *op. cit.*

BIBLIOGRAPHY

PUBLISHED MATERIAL

Adams, John Quincy, "Letter to President James Monroe, August 26, 1820," *The Writings of John Quincy Adams*, W. C. Ford, ed. (New York, Macmillan, 1917), vol. 7, pp. 66-68.

Annales Maritimes et Coloniales, 1821, *Deuxième Partie* (Paris, 1821), p. 1034.

Augur, Helen, *Passage to Glory, John Ledyard's America* (Garden City, N. Y., Doubleday & Co., 1946), 310 pp.

Barnard, Charles H., *A Narrative of the Suffering and Adventures of Captain Charles H. Barnard, in a Voyage Round the World, during the years, 1812, 1813, 1814, 1815 and 1816* (printed for the author by J. Lindon, New York, 1829), vii, 266 pp., 6 plates, map.

Boston Patriot and Daily Mercantile Advertiser, September 25, 1820.

Christie, E. W. Hunter, *The Antarctic Problem* (London, Allen & Unwin, 1951), 336 pp., maps, end papers.

Clark, Alonzo Howard, "The Antarctic Fur-seal and Sea-elephant Industries," *The Fisheries and Fishery Industries of the United States*, U. S. Bureau of Fish and Fisheries, 77th Congr., 1st Sess., Sen. Misc. Doc. 124, Sec. V, vol. 2, Washington, 1887, pp. 400-467.

The Connecticut Journal, New Haven, June 20, 1792, May 21, 1794, "Port of New Haven."

Cook, James, *A Voyage to the Pacific Ocean. Undertaken, by the command of His Majesty, for making discoveries in the Northern Hemisphere. Performed under the direction of Captains Cook, Clerke, and Gore, in his Majesty's ships the Resolution and Discovery; in the years 1776, 1777, 1778, 1779, and 1780.* vols. I and II written by Capt. James Cook; vol. III by Capt. James King. Published by order of the Lords Commissioners of the Admiralty (London, G. Nicol and T. Cadell, 1784).

The Daily Advertiser, New York, May 7, 1795.

Delano, Amasa, *Narrative of Voyages and Travels in the Northern and Southern Hemispheres,* etc. (Boston, E. G. House, 1817), 589 pp.

Fanning, Edmund, *Voyages Round the World,* etc. (New York, Collins and Hannay, 1833), 499 pp., 5 plates.

"Memorial of Edmund Fanning, Exploration — South Seas. Respectfully Soliciting a loan from Congress to the Support and Advancement of Commerce, the Fisheries, etc., by exploration in the South Seas," January 1840. Referred to Committee on Naval Affairs, February 5, 1840. 26th Congr. 1st Sess., House Doc. 57, 11 pp. Serial 364.

Independent Chronicle and Boston Patriot, April 1, September 30, 1820.

Ledyard, John, *A Journal of Captain Cook's Last Voyage to the Pacific Ocean,* etc. (Hartford, Conn., Nathaniel Patten, 1783), 208 pp., map.

Mill, Hugh R., *The Siege of the South Pole* (New York, Frederick A. Stokes, 1905), xvi and 455 pp., maps, plates.

New York Evening Post, September 16, 1820.

Portlock, Capt. Nathaniel, *A Voyage Round the World; But More Particularly to the North-West Coast of America,* etc. (London, J. Stockdale and G. Goulding, 1789), xii and 384 pp.

Raymond, Edward H., "The Fur-Seal Fishery and Salem," *Essex Institute Historical Collections,* vol. 72, No. 3, July, 1936, pp. 181-207.

"Report Communicated to 1st Sess. 9th Congress, March 12, 1804, to the House of Representatives from a Committee considering memorials of sundry Merchants of the Cities of New York and Hudson, in the State of New York, to the House on the 17th of February and 9th of March, 1804. Praying the vessels owned by Americans, but built in foreign ports and ⅔ rebuilt in United States, and employed in Whale & Seal fisheries may pay no higher duty than vessels built in the United States," *American State Papers, Commerce and Navigation,* vol. I, 1789-1815, pp. 1573-1574.

Root, Joel, "Narrative of a Sealing and Trading Voyage in the Ship Huron, from New Haven around the World, September 1802 to October 1806, by the Supercargo," *New Haven Colony Historical Society Papers,* vol. 5, 1894, pp. 149-171.

Sparks, Jared, *Memoirs of the Life and Travels of John Ledyard* (London, H. Colburn, 1828), xii and 428 pp.

Stackpole, Edouard A., *The Sea-Hunters* (Philadelphia, Lippincott, 1953), 510 pp.

Townsend, Ebenezer, "The Diary of Mr. Ebenezer Townsend, Jr., the Supercargo of the Sealing Ship 'Neptune,' on her Voyage to the South Pacific and Canton," *New Haven Colony Historical Society Papers,* vol. 4, 1888, pp. 1-115.

Trowbridge, Henry, *Grandfather's Voyage Around the World in the Ship Betsey,* 1799-1801, Thomas R. Trowbridge, ed. (New Haven, Dibble & Brink, 1895), 54 pp., plates.

Weddell James, *A Voyage Towards the South Pole Performed in the Years 1822-24* (London, Longman, Hurst, Rees, Orme, Brown and Green, 1825), iv and 276 pp., map.

MANUSCRIPT MATERIAL

Byers, James, Letters of James Byers of New York, August 17 and 24, and September 4, 1820, to Brig. Gen. Daniel Parker, Adjutant and Insp. Gen. of the United States Army, Records of the Department of State, Misc. Letters File, August-October, 1820. Record Group 59, U. S. National Archives. These letters have been microfilmed by the National Archives as part of microcopy M-179, roll 49.

Custom Records, District of New Haven, List of Foreign Outwards, September 17, 1762-June 24, 1801. Records of the Bureau of Customs, French Spoliation Claims, Record Group 36, U. S. National Archives.

Custom Records, District of New Haven, List of Foreign Inwards, September 17, 1762-July 20, 1801. Records of the Bureau of Customs, French Spoliation Claims, Record Group 36, U. S. National Archives.

Custom Records, Register of Vessels, Port of New Haven, Book I, November 7, 1789-October 13, 1792. Register of the Brig Nancy, Reg. No. 4, April 16, 1791; Register of the brigantine Polly, Reg. No. 8, June 4, 1792. Records of the Bureau of Customs, French Spoliation Claims, Record Group 36, U. S. National Archives.

Custom Records, District of New York, Foreign Inward Coastal Manifests, "Nabby to Narcissa," 1795. Inward cargo manifest of the brig *Nancy,* May 9, 1795. Records of the Bureau of Customs, French Spoliation Claims, Record Group 36, U. S. National Archives.

Prevost, J. B., Letter of J. B. Prevost, January 10, 1820, to Secretary of State John Quincy Adams. Records of the Department of State, Special Agent File, 1817, Record Group 59, U. S. National Archives.

Robinson, Jeremy, Letters of Jeremy Robinson, November 15, 1819, and January 17, 1820, to Secretary of State John Quincy Adams. Records of the Department of State, Special Agent File, 1817, vol. 5, Record Group 59, U. S. National Archives. This letter has been micro-filmed by the National Archives as part of microcopy M-37, roll 5.

Stevens, Thomas A., "The First American Sealers in the Antarctic, 1812-1819, and the First Voyage of the Brig *Hersilia,* of Stonington, Connecticut, 1819-1820." Mimeographed report, May 1, 1954, pp. 17-29.

3

THE VOYAGE OF THE *HERSILIA*, 1819–1820

ORGANIZATION AND ACCOMPLISHMENTS

SIGNIFICANCE OF THE VOYAGE

The incomplete records of the early American sealing industry reveal the voyage of the *Hersilia* in 1819-1820 to have been planned as a voyage of exploration for new sealing grounds and to have resulted in the *Hersilia* being the first American vessel, so far as we now know, to arrive at the South Shetland Islands. The news of its successful voyage served to revive the declining fur seal industry. Reports of the discovery of the South Shetland Islands by William Smith in 1819 aroused the interest of ship owners and captains engaged in the sealing business. The return of the *Hersilia* in 1820 confirmed the existence of the islands, and the news of the abundance of fur seals also justified hopes for a revival of the industry. The electrifying effect of this news is indicated by the fact that 30 American vessels visited the South Shetlands in 1820-21, one year later and only two years after their discovery.

BACKGROUND FOR THE VOYAGE

For a number of years Captain Edmund Fanning, veteran commander of many sealing voyages, had been associated in the sealing business with James Byers & Co., of New York. The junior member of this firm was his son William A. Fanning. Captain Fanning made his last voyage, in the ship *Sea Fox*, in 1817-18 after which he retired to his home town of Stonington, Connecticut. His son apparently left the firm of Byers & Co. at approximately the same time, and, as Stevens has shown, subsequent events indicate that the Fannings planned to promote sealing voyages of their own.[1]

William A. Fanning purchased the brig *Frederick* in New Haven, brought it to Stonington, and fitted it for a sealing voyage. On September 30, 1818, the vessel was registered at the New London Custom House with William A. Fanning of New York, merchant, as managing owner and Captain Benjamin Pendleton as master and part owner. Letters from William A. Fanning to his father indicate that the elder man provided considerable guidance, although he is never on record as being financially involved.[2] In the fall of 1818 William also contracted with Christopher Leeds, master shipbuilder of Stonington and Mystic, Connecticut, to build a new brig, the *Hersilia*.

Captain Fanning believed that new sealing grounds would be found if the mythical Aurora Islands could be located.[3] In 1833 he stated the evidence for his earlier belief that land existed to the southwest of South Georgia:

[In 1819 Fanning was] in possession of the corrected survey of the Spanish corvette, Atrevida's position of the Aurora Islands, also of the manuscript of Captain Dirck Gherritz's discovery of land to the south of Cape Horn, in the Dutch ship Good News [Blijde

Bootschap], in the year 1599. The author had previously been in the spring of the year, at South Georgia at the breaking up of winter ice, a few days after a gale had set in from the W. S. W.; fleets of ice islands came from that quarter, and in passing to the eastward, brought up against the south-western coast of South Georgia, giving decisive evidence that extensive land did exist in that direction, for as numerous ice islands had formed at South Georgia, and drifted away to the eastward in these gales, it was certain that the ice islands first spoken of, must have had land to form at, or they could never have been in existence. The author was therefore convinced that the land was to be found, some-where between the latitudes of 60° and 65° south, and between 50° and 60° west; be-sides this, the correctness of the manuscript of Gherritz's discovery was beyond doubt.[4]

Thomas A. Stevens has shown that Fanning actually held these views at the time of the *Hersilia*'s voyage and that they were not something that he had learned by the time he wrote his book, which was published 14 years after the event.[5] Writing on November 20, 1820, to correct errors he had seen in a news-paper article, Fanning said,

The fact is, I do not consider this land [the South Shetlands] as a new discovery. It was first seen by a Dutch Captain in the latter part of the 15th Century, and Frazier saw it in 1712, and called it South Iceland. This came to my knowledge in the year 1799, and I now have before me a manuscript chart of this *New South Iceland* as we call it to an extent between 11 and 12 degrees of longitude and of between 5 and 6 degrees of lati-tude.[6]

One of the two sealing vessels sent out in 1818 by James Byers of New York was the *Jane Maria* under the command of Captain James P. Sheffield of Ston-ington. Sailing from New York in July, 1818, and returning in the spring of 1819, Captain Sheffield had cruised in and about the Falkland Islands and Cape Horn, hunting fur seals. There is no particular significance to the fact that he left the employment of James Byers at the conclusion of the voyage to take com-mand of the *Hersilia,* for Sheffield was a Stonington man and had served under Captain Edmund Fanning. There is no evidence that Captain Sheffield had learned anything of William Smith's first sighting of the South Shetlands in Feb-ruary 1819. It is not at all probable that he did, since Smith was then en route to Valparaiso. Neither is there any evidence that Sheffield made any discoveries of his own of new land. If he had, there is no reason to believe he would have been less willing to continue in the employ of Byers than to join the Fannings, as his letter to Byers following the *Hersilia*'s voyage would indicate. It would seem that he accepted command of the *Hersilia* because the prospects for a successful voyage in her appeared better than going out again in the *Jane Maria.*

The *Hersilia* was registered at the Custom House at New London on July 20, 1819. She was a 131-ton brig, 68 feet in length with a square stern. She had a breadth of 22 feet 8 inches and a depth of 10 feet 1 inch. Records show William A. Fanning as managing owner and James P. Sheffield as master. The owners listed were William A. Fanning of New York, merchant; James P. Sheffield, mar-iner, Stonington; and Ephraim Williams, Elisha Faxon, Elisha Faxon, Jr., Sam-uel F. Denison, Henry Smith, and Jedediah Randall, all of the County of New London. While William A. Fanning was away on the *Hersilia,* his father took over his business interests even to the extent of purchasing a vessel in his name.

OBJECTIVES AND ACCOMPLISHMENTS

The *Hersilia* was "bound for the South Seas and Pacific Ocean," according to the original crew list filed at the New London Custom House, July 20, 1819. Fanning has recorded that the brig was going in search of new islands which it was hoped would contain seal rookeries. His convictions regarding the existence of land to the south of Cape Horn have been cited. Consequently, he dispatched the *Hersilia* to find that land and explore for seals. His instructions to his son and to Captain Sheffield have been recorded in his book:

The master and supercargo of the *Hersilia,* both possessing nautical talents, and both able lunarians, were therefore directed, in their instructions, to touch first at the Falk- land Islands, there to fill up their water and refresh the crew, thence to proceed in

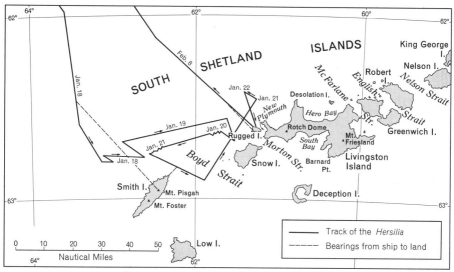

FIGURE 1. Track of the Brig *Hersilia,* 1820.

search of the Aurora Islands, and should seals be there found, to procure their cargo, if not, to return westward to Staten Land [Staten Island, immediately east of the tip of Tierra del Fuego], and after wooding and watering, to stand to the southward, keeping as nearly in the latitude [sic] of Cape Horn as the wind would admit, until they arrived in the latitude of about 63° south, then to bear up and steer east, when it was confident- ly expected they would meet with land; but after all, should they be still unfortunate in the search, and find no seals, then to enter the Pacific, or return to the Falklands, or is- lands about Cape Horn, and endeavor to procure a cargo.[7]

To avoid a complete financial loss in the event that few seals were found, the brig had on board a half cargo of general merchandise to be used in trade at South American ports.

Geographically, the accomplishments of the voyage of the *Hersilia* reportedly included the rediscovery of what were considered to be the illusive Aurora Is- lands, 115 miles west-northwest of South Georgia and now called Shag Rocks.[8] Considering the instructions given by Captain Edmund Fanning, it is possible that Captain Sheffield would have independently rediscovered the South Shet-land Islands or, as Fanning called them, New South Iceland. As it turned out, however, he made a successful search for them after learning, somewhere en route, of their existence. No doubt Fanning's instructions were of assistance in this search. Smith Island was the first island of the South Shetlands, according to Fanning, to be seen from the *Hersilia*, which was later anchored off Rugged Island after a brief exploration of waters bordering the islands (Fig. 1). From this anchorage sealing operations were conducted on the beaches of the adjacent islands. It is possible that the crew of the *Hersilia* sighted not only the western islands of the South Shetlands but some of the eastern islands as well. There is also a possibility that the shores of the Antarctic Peninsula were sighted at this time although there is no direct supporting evidence. From a height of several hundred feet on the west end of Livingston Island, which was accessible to the men from the *Hersilia*, the peaks behind Trinity Island can be seen on a clear day.

The voyage was a commercial success, with approximately 9000 seals being taken in 15 days. Any number more could have been taken, but there was not enough salt for more skins because of the half cargo of merchandise that had been brought out for trade in South America as insurance against a losing voyage.

DETAILED RECORD OF OPERATIONS

LOGBOOK OF THE *HERSILIA*

Until 1956, other than contemporary accounts of the voyage of the *Hersilia* were based on Captain Edmund Fanning's report and on other fragmentary evidence. Twentieth century writers concerned with the voyage of 1819-20 assumed that the logbook of the *Hersilia* was lost when the brig was seized off the coast of Chile on its second voyage.[9] It was thought logical for Captain Sheffield to have taken the logbook of the voyage of 1819-20 on the second voyage of the *Hersilia*. The nature of the fragmentary and incomplete evidence of the voyage was such that it invited speculation of various kinds. It was felt that the logbook, if it were available, would have cleared up several important questions.

In actual fact the logbook, as was customary, had been kept by the mate, Elof Benson, and he retained possession of it after the voyage. It has since been the property of his descendants. Late in 1956, Mrs. Theodore Krueger of Stratford, Connecticut, great-granddaughter of Benson, having read an article in a newspaper which referred to the missing logbook, revealed its existence to Alexander O. Vietor of Yale University.[10]

The logbook supplies a number of facts, confirms some previous assumptions regarding the voyage, and disproves others. However, it leaves most of the big questions still unanswered. Like many logbooks kept by whalers and sealers, it was begun in the middle of a voyage, presumably after another volume had been filled. It begins on January 11, 1820, as the *Hersilia* departs from Staten Island to sail south across Drake Passage. The remarks relating to each day's entry are mostly confined to working the vessel. Once the brig is close in to the land, no positions are given in terms of latitude and longitude, and from January 29 until February 8 there are no entries at all.

The entries are not easily read, for Benson, who had come to the United States from Sweden early in the 19th century, wrote English in his own phonetic spelling. He occasionally but not consistently used a Swedish word such as "med," meaning "with," or "af," meaning "by" or "from."

FIRST PART OF THE VOYAGE

The *Hersilia*, under command of James P. Sheffield, sailed from Stonington with a company of 19 men, including the captain and William A. Fanning, supercargo.[11] Benson was first mate, and Nathaniel B. Palmer was second mate. From interpolation of the various dates and lengths of service shown for the men on the crew lists filed at the New London Custom House before sailing and after returning, the brig got under way sometime during the three days July 21-23, 1819.

Since the logbook in possession of Mrs. Krueger was begun on January 11, 1820, it is necessary to piece together an account of the first part of the voyage from the few bits of information that are available. In his *Voyages Round the World*, Fanning states that the *Hersilia* first touched at the Falkland Islands and from there went in search of the Aurora Islands, which were "found to be three in number, each in the form of a sugar-loaf."[12] The central island was reported to lie in 52°58′ south latitude and 47°51′ west longitude. From this is would appear that the "Aurora Islands" must be Shag Rocks, lying in 53°33′ S, 42°02′ W. In Fanning's letter of November 20, 1820, we find additional information on the "Aurora Islands":

... they are three peaked mountains, lying in a triangular position from each other--a short reef runs out S. W. from the southernmost island, the latitude of them as laid down in Patten's chart is sufficiently correct but they are about 4 degrees to the Eastward from their situation on this chart. In nearly a direct line between the Aurora Islands and the Northeast Cape of New South Iceland, lies Shag Rock Reef, a most extensive and dangerous reef of rocks, some of which are above water and the size of a ship's hull, in about 54°45′ S.[13]

From Fanning's statement, just quoted, we have proof that the sealers were aware of Shag Rocks. His confusion between Shag Rocks and the "Aurora Islands" must result from errors in geographical positions, especially in longitude. It is possible that Black Rock, about 10 feet high and 10 miles south-southeast of Shag Rocks, was identified as "Shag Rock" by the *Hersilia*, but its position does not fit the location given by Fanning. However, there is no known island or reef that fits even approximately the position he gives. If Shag Rocks are not the "Aurora Islands," it is difficult to imagine any now-undiscovered islands in the general vicinity of the positions given by Fanning.

If the instructions which Captain Edmund Fanning reportedly gave to his son and Captain Sheffield and which have been previously quoted were followed by them, the *Hersilia* would have independently rediscovered the South Shetlands.

Fanning says, "Leaving the Auroras, the brig's course was shaped westward for Staten Land; . . ." from where the logbook begins. However, there are separate accounts that Sheffield heard about the discovery of the South Shetlands before he left Staten Island, or Staten Land, as the sealers called the island off the tip of Tierra del Fuego.

In a letter dated September 4, 1820, to Brigadier General Daniel Parker, James Byers wrote, "The Capt. had heard a report of the new islands and went to look for them."[14] More will be said later of Byers' correspondence with General Parker. From the letter, however, we do not know where Captain Sheffield heard of the South Shetlands. It could have been at Buenos Aires if he stopped there on his way south. There he could have heard of William Smith's February landfall, but not of his landing on King George Island, October 16, 1819. If as reported, the *Hersilia* carried a partial cargo for the South American market as a hedge against failure in the sealing venture, it would have been logical for Captain Sheffield to have called at Buenos Aires.

Two latter-day accounts of the voyage indicate that Captain Sheffield heard of the discovery of the South Shetlands at the Falkland Islands. Nathaniel B. Palmer's niece, Mrs. Richard Fanning Loper, said in a biographical sketch of her uncle that "young Nat" and a sailor had been left at the Falklands to kill bullocks for fresh meat while the brig was searching for the Aurora Islands. While they were so employed, the *Espírito Santo* of Buenos Aires hove to, and Palmer piloted her into an anchorage in the bay. Apparently in return for a supply of fresh meat, the captain told Palmer that he was bound for islands where seals were plentiful, but he would not give the location.[15] Because some of her statements verge on the incredible, critics have tended to discount Mrs. Loper's story.

The second latter-day account is by Captain Thomas Davidson as reported by Clark.

In 1819, according to Captain Davidson, of Stonington, a brig was fitted at Buenos Ayres for sealing in the New Land. At this season the brig Hersilia, of Stonington, was cruising about in search of seals, and had left Capt. Nath. Palmer and others of her crew at the Falklands while the vessel went on a short trip about Cape Horn, to return to the Falklands for those left behind.

In the meantime the Buenos Ayres brig put into the Falklands, and Captain Palmer, always on the watch for information about new sealing grounds, was not slow in obtaining from the mate of the brig definite knowledge of a new land where fur-seals could be captured by the thousands. The brig went on her course, and Captain Palmer waited impatiently for the Hersilia, which at last made her appearance, and very quickly prepared for the four day's sail to South Shetlands.[16]

Davidson had been a member of the crew of the schooner *Express,* one of the vessels of the Fanning-Pendleton fleet of 1820-21.

At the South Shetland Islands

Some of the difficulties in dealing with the logbook have been mentioned. Because no features in the South Shetlands are mentioned by name in the logbook and because from the logbook entries it is impossible to trace with certainty the track of the brig among the South Shetlands, it is still necessary to rely on collateral evidence to piece together a plausible account of the voyage of the *Hersilia*. The most important contemporary collateral evidence is given below.

In 1820 James Byers of New York wrote three letters containing information regarding the voyage of the *Hersilia* which he had received from Captain Sheffield. They were addressed to Brigadier General Daniel Parker, Adjutant and Inspector General of the United States Army, to be forwarded to John Quincy Adams, then Secretary of State.[17] Pertinent parts of the second letter, dated August 25, 1820, are as follows:

The first information I ever received respecting the new discovery was from a Capt. Sheffield who arrived at Stonington last spring from the new islands. As soon as he reached this country he wrote me a letter informing me of his success & offering to [go] out again in my employ. He had formerly been in my service and I knew him to be worthy of all confidence. In order to obtain correct information, I authorized Mr. Walter Nexsen, a respectable Mercht. and also a partner in my sealing enterprises to go to Stonington and have an interview with Capt. S. Mr. Nexsen obtained from [him] the following particulars from his Log Book.

The great new Island or Continent is in Lat. 61:10 St — Long. 57 = 15 Wt. Coasted about 50 miles. saw no end South Wt. Returned to what he thought the St. Wt end & came to anchor between a number of islands, a short distance from the Mainland. He found pretty good Anchorage in 15 Fathams Water. On one of these Islands he took 9,000 fur Seal [sic] in 15 days. He had no more salt or could killed any number. He says he saw at one View 300,000 Seal. He thinks the country is uninhabited & destitute of wood. Water plenty & good. The land runs about No. East & St. West. In additional [sic] to the above I have learned from other sources of the existence of these Islands, and all nearly agree in Lt. & Long. Capt. Fanning [of Nantucket] late of the Spartan mentions the subject in the letter enclosed. . . .

From James Byers' letter, dated September 4, 1820, to General Parker, the following is pertinent:

My dear Sir:
I have just received your favr of 31st ult. The Stonington vessel reached the new Islands in Decr. last. The Capt. had heard a report of new islands and went to look for them. He was out on a sealing voyage, but to guard against a bad voyage in not finding seal he had on board about half a cargo calculated for the Spanish Market— In consequence of this he could carry but a small quantity of salt and therefore able to cure but about 9000 skins. He stated on his return that at the place he lay, he could have loaded 10 vessels like his. Other accounts fully establish the fact of seal being in immense quantities. . . .

Edmund Fanning, in a letter dated November 20, 1820, to the editor of the *New England Palladium and Commercial Advertiser* of Boston, which has been previously cited, communicated the following pertinent information:

Where the writer got the information that he communicated to the Boston editor, I know not--but this much I know to be fact, that the *Hersilia* did not speak with the English brig *William* while on her voyage, nor did her super-cargo during his voyage, previous to his being at those new islands (as they are called) know that there was such a vessel in existence as the English brig *William*, Capt. Smith.
. . . Strait Despair, the mouth of which is on the South-western coast of it, is a piece of the most dangerous navigation that seamen ever traversed, from the stupendous height, and large and dismal appearance of the coast, and water too deep for anchorage. It is

also filled with single spiral rocks and sunken reefs of the most dangerous kind, and there is no kelp or sea weed on the coast to mark out those dangerous reefs to the mariner. Whoever visits this land, will not want for gales, ice or snow.

The *Hersilia* procured her cargo of skins at "Fanning's Islands", a cluster of islands to the N.W. from this coast. From the knowledge which I possess respecting New South Iceland I have no doubt that Cook's Southern Thule and this land belong to one and the same continent, and that the Island of South Georgia lies off the mouth of a very large bay, into which you cannot sail far I think without being obstructed by the solid and fast ice.[18]

In his book, *Voyages Round the World,* published in 1833, Fanning gave the following account:

Leaving the Auroras, the brig's course was shaped westward for Staten Land; from this, after taking on board wood and water, they steered to the south; on arriving in about the latitude of 63° south, at 1 P. M. they bore away east, under a good breeze from the westward, attended with clear weather; hove to when night closed in, during which many seals came swiming about the vessel; this gave them strong hopes of being in the vicinity of land. In the morning, they bore away again to the eastward, and at 10 A. M. to their great joy, a high and round mountain was discovered, covered with snow, although in the month of February, and the last summer month in the region. From its singular form they named this Mount Pisgah Island [Smith Island at the southwest end of the South Shetlands in 63°00′ S, 62°30′ W]; upon approaching nearer, more land, or rather mountains, of craggy rocks, to the eastward were discovered.

After passing Mount Pisgah Island, they arrived at the group last seen, and called them Fanning's Islands; after sailing into a passage between the first two, they came to a harbor at the starboard island which was then named Ragged Island [Rugged Island in 62°38′ S, 61°15′ W], and there anchored, calling it "Hersilia cove." From elevated positions they had discovered more land to the eastward, but as the season was drawing to a close, and they were anxious to hasten home and report such vast numbers of seals to their friends in time for the next season, they had no leisure to visit or make a survey of it. After procuring several thousand skins of the choisest and richest furs, as the weather or climate would not admit of their drying them at this place, they were therefore not prepared with a sufficiency of salt for a full cargo, but calculated to dry a part of the skins where they should take them; thus with as many as they had salt to save, they left Ragged Island, leaving, according to their estimation, 50,000 fur seals.[19]

According to the logbook, the *Hersilia* got underway from East Harbor on Staten Island at 6:00 a. m., January 11, 1820. At noon, Cape St. John was four leagues to the west of them as a course was set to the ESE. The next day, 24 hours later, the brig's position was recorded as 55°08′ S, 62°12′ W, approximately 70 miles ESE of Cape St. John. From this position a southwesterly and then a south-southwesterly course was followed with fine weather and mostly light to fresh breezes from the southeast. The good weather was interrupted briefly by rain squalls at 4:00 a. m., January 15. At noon the recorded position was 58°22′ S, 63°34′ W.

Up to this point the course sailed was essentially that suggested by Captain Edmund Fanning in his instructions to his son and to Captain Sheffield. Although the logbook indicates that a course of south by east was sailed from noon, January 15 until 6:00 a. m., and then south until noon, January 16, the latter position, 59°20′ S, 61°20′ W, shows the brig was heading toward Elephant Island instead of toward the western end of the South Shetlands. The weather was still good, except for some rain at 10 p. m. on the 15th. An allowance of two degrees was made for the current. Either there was an error in longitude or the easterly drift through Drake Passage was greater than Captain Sheffield thought. Successive positions on the next three days show that the *Hersilia* was continuing to the southeast, passing between King George and Elephant Islands; that is, if the longitudes recorded in the logbook were correct.

Land was discovered on January 18. January 17 was a repetition of the preceding days, and at noon on the 17th the brig's position was recorded as 60° 50′ S, 58° 38′ W, about 65 nautical miles north of King George Island. From this position the course was southeast by south. Under remarks, on the 18th Benson recorded the following:

> Commense leit windes from WNW with studding sat before
> the wind at 10 dagk [dark] and faggi [foggy] wether
> at 4 A m deskoward [discovered] the Land berring be [by]
> the compas ESE disten [distance] 16 leegs [leagues]
> at 6 Lieit [light] wind from n wast
>   No opservation the Day

The latitude by dead reckoning was 61° 59′ S, the longitude 56° 20′ W.

In the first half of the 19th century it was customary on merchant vessels for the day at sea to begin and close at noon. Thus the sea day was 12 hours ahead of civil time. Therefore, the dark and foggy weather reported at 10:00 p. m. on January 18, since it was before midnight, was actually at 10:00 p. m. on January 17 on the civil calendar. However, at 4:00 a. m., when land was discovered, it was January 18 at sea and on the civil calendar.

The sea day was divided into three parts: first, middle, and latter, each of eight hours duration. Each noon, as the day changed, if the weather was clear, a celestial observation was made to determine the latitude. If the sun was hidden, latitude was determined by deduced reckoning, commonly referred to as dead reckoning. It was deduced from the speed of the ship and the distance sailed on each tack. Longitude was determined by the difference between local sun time and the time of a chronometer set at some standard meridian time. On clear nights longitude can be calculated from the position of the moon, but at the best this method gives only approximate positions. Star sights are more reliable.

Referring again to Elof Benson's entry in the *Hersilia*'s logbook for January 18, we find that the position at the end of the day was by dead reckoning. Therefore, it is not reliable. If it is assumed to be reasonably accurate, however, what was the land that was sighted at 4:00 a. m.? The logbook indicates that the course was southeast by east at every hour. The distance sailed was recorded as 82 miles, most of it before midnight, since the speed was greatly reduced after that hour. Calculating from either the observation of January 17 or the dead reckoning of the 18th places the *Hersilia* approximately midway between North Foreland on the eastern tip of King George Island and Gibbs Island to the east-northeast (Fig. 5). On a bearing of east-southeast from this point there is no land at 16 leagues distant. If consideration is given to the magnetic declination of 24° E for this area in 1821,[20] the bearing would be an azimuth of 136° or roughly southeast. There is no land to be viewed in this direction. It would appear, therefore, that the longitude is in error. Considering the means that the sealers had for determining longitude, errors of considerable magnitude should be expected.

The first position recorded after the *Hersilia* left its anchorage on the return voyage is 61°22′ S, 52°51′ W. If the anchorage was adjacent to Rugged Island, as it is generally regarded to have been, the above position is about 9° too far east. This would indicate the direction of error, but 9° west of the assumed position at 4:00 a. m., January 18, or of the recorded dead reckoning at noon of that day would be unrealistic. A shift westward of somewhat less magnitude, however, would make plausible Fanning's statement that the first land sighted was Mount Pisgah on Smith Island (Fig. 1).

As Wednesday January 19 began at sea (actually the afternoon of January 18 by the civil calendar), the wind was from the north and the *Hersilia* was on a course east-northeast at two knots. Under remarks, Benson recorded the following:

> Commences light winds Dark foggy weather and rain
> Wind from North Bent the cables at 2 p m tacked
> ship to westward 6 tacked to Nor'wards at 2 A m
> tacked to westward 6 tacked to No'ward
> Latter part clear and pleasant and light winds
> Latt Op 62 - 31 South

In the above quotation the spelling has been altered to make it more intelligible, but no words have been added. However, there is an apparent inconsistency between the remarks and the columns on the left-hand side of the page where the knots, the course the vessel is sailing, and the direction of the wind are recorded at two-hour intervals. At 2 p. m. the course was east-northeast at 2 knots with the wind from the north. At 4 p. m. the brig was on a westerly course at 2 knots, and at 6 p. m. the course was east-northeast at 2 knots. At 2 a. m. (January 19) the course was changed to the west. There is no indication of a change to the northward at 6 a. m. to conform with the remarks. The sea day closed at noon on January 19 with a recorded latitude of 62°31′ S by observation. This is the last record of latitude by observation until noon, February 8, 18 hours after the *Hersilia* had set sail for home.

From January 20 to 29 entries in the logbook are limited to remarks. The columns on the left half of the page, where the hour, the knots, the course, and the wind are recorded, are blank. The remarks are quoted below, with altered spelling.

> Remarks on Thursday January 20
> Commences with calm at 4 p m was close on shore on account
> swell running towards the shore got out the whale boat and
> towed her off at 10 light breeze from East hoist in boat
> set all sail to best advantage course WNW Latter part
> foggy and calm

> Friday January the 21 --
> Commences with foggy weather and light winds from East
> No'East at 8 p m Calm at 10 fresh breezes from West At

4 A M Bore away for the Islands at half past 12 the East
End Bore SSW Distance 3 miles and saw 2 more [This is a three-
letter word which may be mor or man, meaning more or main.]
Island Those Island are all covered with snow.

Remarks on Saturday the 22
Commences with light winds from No'west and pleasant weather
with all sail set before the wind at 8 p m hauled on the
wind to the north East at 12 tacked ship to westward at
2 A m dark and foggy weather and some rain at 6 reefed fore
top sail Latter part more pleasant

Sunday Jan. 23 Commences with fresh breezes from SW and steering
S East Course towards the Island at 8 A [M] came to anchor
in one of the harber (sic) in 8 fathoms sandie bottom in company
with a [illegible word, perhaps "belake" (sic) or "pelake"] Brig from
Buenos Aires The boats went on shore 470 S [skins]

Monday January 24 1820 Commences with pleasant weather
all hands employed in skinning got on board
400 skins

The remarks for the remaining days refer to the weather and to the number of
sealskins taken on board.

Whatever names the Stonington sealers may have tentatively applied to the
geographic features they discovered in January 1820, no record of them appears
in the logbook to help in identifying them now. However, it is generally acknowledged that Hersilia Cove, where the brig anchored on Sunday, January
23, is on the east side of Rugged Island. This was apparently the agreed meeting
place for the Fanning Fleet in 1820-21, for the various vessels of the fleet, either
singly or in company, arrived at this point from Stonington in late October and
early November 1820.

This supports the account given by Edmund Fanning in his *Voyages Round
the World*. Moreover, two geographical names used by Fanning, Mount Pisgah
and Ragged Island, appear in the logbook kept by Nathaniel B. Palmer on the
sloop *Hero* in November 1820. Since his approach to Hersilia Cove was probably similar to that of the *Hersilia* in January 1820, when he was Second Mate,
it is worth recording here the entries from his logbook.

REMARKS

Friday   November 10, 1820
Commences with fair weather Light airs from WNW course ESE
Took in the mainsail & square sail for the Express to come
up --- Middle part Light winds at 4 A M made the Land
Bearing East and Northerly about 10 Leagues Distant stood
in for it made it to be Mount Pisga [sic] at 11 tacked ship
to the Northard & Westward wind N East Clear and cold
the Express off our Lee 7 miles Distant -----
62.50 S. 63.4 W.

Saturday   November 11, 1820
These 24 hours commences with fine weather fresh Breeses
from N. East at 2 P. M. high Reef[d] the mainsail Tacked

to Northward & Eastward Toward the Land at 8 Tacked off
shore heading up N. West off to E by N & ENE in ----
Middle part fresh Breese & cloudy -----
Latter part moderate Breese from NNE & Cloudy close hauled
by the wind heading up ENE at 12 saw the Land Bearing South
½ East.

[No position given]

Sunday   November 12, 1820

Commences with Thick weather fresh breeses from N by E
at 4 P M saw Castle Rock stood in for Ragged Iland [sic]
at 8 being in the mouth of the harbor we were boarded by
a boat from the Hersilia Capt Sheffield he informed us
that he had been in 12 days and that the Frederick &
Free Gift Capt Pendleton & Dunbar were in a harbor on the
opposite side of the strait at 10 came Too alongside the
Hersilia Let go the short anchor in 4 fathoms middle
part thick snow storm the Express outside at 8 A M the
Express came in got out the Boat went over to President
Harbor at 10 went along side the Frederick & Freegift
Ends with Pleasant weather no seals up[21]

Several facts suggest that the *Hersilia* in January 1820 did not sail along a track indicated by the positions recorded in the logbook. There is an apparent error in longitude which seems to have begun in the middle of Drake Passage and to have increased as the brig sailed southward. An error of as much as nine degrees too far east can be demonstrated for the first position recorded after departure from Hersilia Cove on February 8. However, errors may not have been as great on the approach to the islands on January 18 and 19. From the reported position from which land was seen from the *Hersilia* on January 18, there is no land to be seen in the reported direction. According to the position determined by observation at noon on January 19, the *Hersilia* was about 30 miles north of Joinville Island, hardly close enough during calm weather to have to be towed off four hours later because of the swell. The names given by the Americans to geographic features in the South Shetlands indicate that they first visited and operated chiefly in the western islands. Nathaniel B. Palmer's identification of these features as he approached the islands in November 1820 suggests that he knew them from the previous voyage.

Referring again to Captain Fanning's letter of November 20, 1820 to the *New England Palladium and Commercial Advertiser,* which was quoted earlier, we find a description of Strait Despair, the first known in print. The location of the strait adjacent to Rugged Island (Ragged Island of the sealers) and the hazards it presents to the navigator are confirmed by Captain Robert Fildes who commanded the brig *Cora* of Liverpool at the South Shetlands the following year. After the *Cora* was wrecked off Desolation Island on the north side of Livingston Island, January 6, 1821, Fildes sailed about the islands as a passenger in the shallops of other sealers. His "journal," including sailing directions which he wrote for the South Shetlands, has been preserved. Concluding a description of the northern part of the straits between Rugged Island and Livingston Island, which the British called New Plymouth Harbour and which the Americans called President Harbor, he wrote:

On the southern part of this harbour there is a boat passage called *Hell Gates* where many boats and lives have been lost, it runs into the Strait of Despair which strait lies between Snow I. Livingstons (sic) Island and Ragged Island. In these straits the tide runs like a sluice which creates an overwhelming sea with dreadful whirls, no vessel should in my opinion attempt these straits, though I have come through them in a shallop, but was nearly lost by striking a sunken rock, we were obliged to run on shore on Snow Island to save our lives.[22]

This strait was named Morton's Strait by Captain James Weddell on his "Chart of South Shetland," and that name (without the possessive) permanently replaced Straits of Despair.[23]

The evidence is conclusive that after January 15, in the middle of Drake Passage, the longitudes recorded in the logbook for positions of the *Hersilia* are too far east, for the brig was actually approaching the western end of the South Shetland Islands on January 18.

Using the information in the logbook of the *Hersilia,* beginning 4 a. m., January 18, when land was reported as bearing ESE, 16 leagues distant, the track of the brig was plotted on a piece of clear acetate placed over British Admiralty Chart 2305, *South Shetland Islands and Bransfield Strait,* scale 1:500,000 at latitude 67° S, 1967 edition. Reference was also made to the maps of *British Antarctic Territory, South Shetland Islands,* Sheets W 62 62, W 62 60, and W 62 58, 1:200,000, published by Directorate of Overseas Surveys, 1968. The following is a table of elevations of landmarks in the western part of the South Shetlands that might have been sighted from the *Hersilia* at 4 a. m., January 18, and the maximum distance that they are visible from the deck of a small vessel at sea.[24] In plotting the track of the brig for January 20, 21, 22, and 23, one can only guess at the distances sailed on each tack.

TABLE OF VISIBILITY AT SEA OF FEATURES LOCATED IN THE SOUTH SHETLAND ISLANDS

Feature	Elevation		Visible Up To	
	Meters	Feet	Nautical Miles	Statute Miles
Rugged Island	200+	650	29	33
Livingston Island				
Start Point	268	880	34	39
Snow Peak	428	1416	43	49
Rotch Dome	360	1170	39	44
Mount Friesland	1600	5200	82	95
Snow Island	300	975	35	40
Smith Island				
Mount Pisgah	1880	6100	89	102
Mount Foster	2120	6900	95	109

After the track was plotted up to noon, January 19, it was possible to move the acetate sheet about the map, looking for a fit. It can be laid on the map, using the bearings reported in the logbook, or the whole plot can be rotated 24° to the east on the assumption that Captain Sheffield and First Mate Benson did not correct for the magnetic declination. The latter makes a somewhat better fit, but it is not impractical to use the bearings as given. It is necessary to accept Benson's estimate of 16 leagues (48 miles) as the distance from land when it was discovered at 4 a. m., January 18. Considering conditions of visibility on a clear day in Antarctica, he was more likely to err by underestimating the distance than by overestimating it, but at 10 p. m. on January 17, he had reported "dark and foggy weather." At noon on January 18 he made no observation, presumably because of poor visibility. However, by sliding the acetate sheet over the map parallel to the bearing to the landfall it is possible to use varying distances in obtaining a fit. By this means, it appears that Benson may have overestimated the distance by as much as five miles.

The evidence supports Fanning's statement in his *Voyages Round the World*, previously quoted, that the *Hersilia*'s landfall was Mount Pisgah.[25] As the table shows, the two peaks on Smith Island are higher and visible from a greater distance than any on Livingston Island. If Benson's estimate of 16 leagues is fairly accurate, he would have been as close or closer to Mount Pisgah than he was to any landmark that would have been visible on Rugged, Livingston, or Snow Island. An exception would be Snow Peak viewed on a bearing corrected for magnetic declination. Mount Friesland must be rejected as the probable landfall, because this would place the track of the brig over the land in some places.

Reconciling the latitude observed at noon January 19, 62°31', is difficult in any case if, as recorded, the brig "tacked to No'ward" at 6 a. m. and remained on that course until noon at a reported speed of 2 to 3 knots. This eliminates Rugged and Livingston Island. The reported data fit Smith Island, but a noon position of 62°51' S is too far away from Smith Island for the swell during a calm to have carried the brig so close to shore by 4 p. m. that it was necessary to get out the whaleboat to tow her off.

If we accept Benson's "tacked to No'ward," as meaning northward and not due north, if we add a further easting of 24° to correct for the magnetic declination, and if we accept something less than 16 leagues as the distance from which land (Mount Pisgah) was originally sighted, we can place the brig somewhere north of Snow Island and near 62°31' S at noon on January 19. No other landfall and no other combination of adjustments fits the map anywhere nearly as well, while accepting all the remaining data in the logbook as they were recorded (Fig. 1).

On January 20 (January 19 by the civil calendar) the *Hersilia* remained in danger of going ashore due to the swell from 4 to 10 p. m. when a light breeze from the east sprang up and they were able to hoist the whaleboat aboard and "set all sail to best advantage course WNW." The latter part (from 4 a. m. until noon, January 20 by the calendar) was "foggy and calm" so the brig could not have sailed many miles to the WNW with light breezes from 10 p. m. until 4 a. m., but sailing across Boyd Strait to somewhere north of Smith Island is probable.

This rules out the possibility suggested by James Byers in his letter of August

25 to General Parker (quoted on page 47), that the *Hersilia* might have made a landfall on Livingston or Rugged Island and then sailed southwestward to Smith Island before returning to Rugged Island and anchoring. Byers wrote, "Coasted about 50 miles. Saw no end South Wt. Returned to what he thought the St. Wt. end & came to anchor between a number of islands a short distance from the Mainland."

Referring to Benson's remarks for Friday, January 21 (beginning at noon January 20 by the civil calendar), we find that they had foggy weather with light winds from the east-northeast followed by calm. At 4 a. m. the next morning they "Bore away for the Islands" on a fresh breeze from the west that had sprung up during the night. "At half past 12 the East End Bore SSW Distance 3 miles and Saw 2 more Island. Those Island are all covered with Snow." These remarks by Benson indicate that they were sailing back toward the islands they had seen on January 19. At half past twelve they were three miles off the east cape of Smith Island, for this falls logically into the whole pattern of the track of the *Hersilia,* and no other point in the entire western half of the South Shetlands fits at all.

When they were off the east cape of Smith Island, in Boyd Strait, they saw two more islands which were all covered with snow. The description fits Snow Island and Low Island, but they already must have seen Snow Island. Smith Island, Snow Island, and Livingston Island logically would have been the islands to which they "Bore away" at 4 a. m. Therefore, the two islands all covered with snow could well have been Low Island and Deception Island. Low Island is snow covered and it is visible from Boyd Strait.[26] Deception Island, compared with others in the South Shetlands, has relatively little snow cover. The lower western rim of this breached volcanic caldera normally has no snow on it, but its maximum elevation of 300 meters (640 feet) is not visible from Boyd Strait. However, the higher southern rim (Mt. Kirkwood, el. 464 m, 1500′) and the eastern rim (Mt. Pond, el. 584 m, 1900′) are permanently snow covered and visible from Boyd Strait.

If Deception Island was one of the two islands seen from Boyd Strait, that fact adds nothing to support a conclusion as to the position of the *Hersilia* when the swell was carrying her onshore on January 19. She could just as well have been off Smith Island as off Snow Island. The former position would not have afforded a view of Deception on January 19. The distance from any point north of Smith Island is too great for any part of Deception Island to be visible.

During the afternoon of January 21 the *Hersilia* was crossing Boyd Strait with all sail set before a light wind from the northwest. At 8:00 p. m. they hauled on the wind to the northeast. At midnight, Saturday, January 22, they tacked to the westward. Twenty-four hours later the *Hersilia* was still tacking back and forth or lying to northwest of Snow Island. Finally, on Sunday morning, January 23, the *Hersilia* came to anchor in Hersilia Cove on the northeast side of Rugged Island.

In Hersilia Cove the Stonington sealers discovered a "black brig from Buenos Aires." Captain Thomas Davidson reported to A. Howard Clark that this was the brig that Nathaniel B. Palmer had encountered at the Falkland Islands, and that the crew welcomed the Americans, saying that there were enough seals for all.[27] Two sealing vessels other than the *Hersilia* were in the South Shetlands in 1819-20, the *Espírito Santo* and the *San Juan Nepomuceno,* both of Buenos Aires.

THE RETURN VOYAGE

Sixteen days after arriving at Hersilia Cove, the *Hersilia* made her departure for Stonington. The logbook contains brief notations relative to sealing operations and the weather for each day from January 24 to 29. After that the record is blank until the day of departure.

The entry recording the departure is dated February 8, but since the brig got underway at 6:00 p. m., this would be February 7 on the civil calendar. Under remarks, Elof Benson recorded (corrected spelling):

> Commences with fresh breeze from SW at 6 p m got under way
> from the new Island and stood out from the bay at 12
> westward most part of the island bore by the compass East SE
> distance 6 leagues
> Latter part pleasant with all sail set at 8 a m fore topmast
> studding sail -- (sic)

The position at noon, February 8, closing out the day, was 61°22' S, 52°51' W, apparently by dead reckoning.

If the *Hersilia* was departing from Hersilia Cove, it is obvious that the longitude recorded at the close of February 8 is in error. It is not too difficult to determine the magnitude of the error, for the brig covered a recorded 79 miles on that first day on a course WNW and NW. Assuming the reported latitude and distance sailed to be approximately correct, the longitude should have been 62°20' W. Considering the magnetic declination, this position is compatible with the course sailed. The reported longitude is, therefore, roughly nine degrees (9°29') too far east.

Correcting for longitude, the logbook shows that the *Hersilia* sailed northwestward to about 59°37' S, 64°30' W and then northward to a point east of Staten Island. No land was sighted in the vicinity on February 11. The daily positions across Drake Passage were all obtained by dead reckoning. Winds from a northerly quarter brought overcast weather which precluded observations. This situation continued as the *Hersilia* sailed a course northeasterly from Staten Island to pass around on the east side of the Falkland Islands. The first observation was obtained on February 16, by which time the *Hersilia* was already north of the Falklands. The islands were not sighted.

From east of the Falkland Islands the *Hersilia*'s course was northward toward Buenos Aires. During this part of the cruise the weather was much improved, and on only two days, February 18 and 19, were no observations obtained. The *Hersilia* entered the mouth of the Rio de la Plata on February 25. Elof Benson recorded the event as follows:

> Remarks on Saturday February 25
> Commences pleasant and fair weather at 12 Cape Anthony

bore by the compass west by north -?- Leagues. The
soundings 7 fathoms at 2 Am Squals and rain and
standing up the river of Platte Latter part pleasant

Sunday February 26
Commences with pleasant weather at 8 p m came to anchor
in 3 fathoms water in the boat went on board the English
Brig at 5 Am get under way at 12 come to anchor in the
outer roads the boat went to the city.

On March 20, 1820, Captain Sheffield filed a revised crew list with Juan Zim-
merman, United States Vice Consul at Buenos Aires. The *Hersilia* sailed for
Stonington on the morning of March 23, for according to remarks in the logbooks for Friday, March 24 (sea day), "at noon the land Bore by the Compass
WSW ½ W distance 2 leagues. The soundings 3 fathoms." This is the first date
of entry after the arrival on February 26.

The voyage north was uneventful. As they passed close to the "hump" of Brazil, land was sighted on April 20, 21 and 22. Two ships were spoken en route.
The last entry in the logbook closes on May 20, about 110 miles south-southeast
of Stonington. The next day, Sunday, May 21, 1820, the *Hersilia* arrived in
Stonington. The *Connecticut Gazette* of New London, May 24 and 31, 1820, reported the arrival of the brig with a cargo of 8868 sealskins, which were sold for
$22,146.49.

NOTES

1. Thomas A. Stevens, "The First American Sealers in the Antarctic, 1812-1819 and the First
Voyage of the *Hersilia* of Stonington, Conn., 1819-1820," Deep River, Conn., 1954. Mimeographed, iv and 61 pp., pp. 31-32.

2. Papers of Edmund Fanning in the American Geographical Society of New York.

3. The Aurora Islands were reported to have been discovered in 1762 by the ship *Aurora*.
The *Atrevida*, which was ordered to search for them in 1794, reported three rocks in approximately 53° S, 48° W. These have since been considered to have been Shag Rocks, 53°33′ S,
42°02′ W.

4. Edmund Fanning, *Voyages Round the World*, etc. (New York, 1833), pp. 427-428.

5. Stevens, *op. cit.*, p. 36.

6. *New England Palladium and Commercial Advertiser*, Boston, December 5, 1820.

7. Fanning, *op. cit.*, p. 429.

8. Although the Shag Rocks became well known to American and British sealers, it is thought
that they were the features seen by the *Aurora* in 1762, which would account for the doubtful
existence of the Aurora Islands.

9. The *Hersilia*'s bond, filed among the papers of the New London Custom House, bears an
endorsement signed by James P. Sheffield on February 27, 1822, in which he testifies that the
brig with all her papers was seized by armed forces under Spanish General Veicente Benavides
at the Island of St. Marys [Isla Santa Maria], off the coast of Chile, on May 13, 1821. The captain and his crew were made prisoners, he and part of his crew making good their escape on
September 2, 1821. The brig subsequently was destroyed by fire when the nearby mainland port
of Arauco was burned.

10. Microfilm copies of the logbook of the *Hersilia* are on file in the Yale University Library
and in the library of the Marine Historical Association, Mystic, Connecticut. Mrs. Krueger also
very graciously permitted the author to examine and make photographic copies of the logbook
in July, 1957. According to Mrs. Krueger, Benson is an anglicization of Berndtson. Elof Berndtson was born in Göteborg, Sweden, and came to this country as a young man. He married Lucy
Starr Bevins of Stonington, and they had two children, Charles and Jane Maria. The daughter
was named after the brig which made several sealing voyages to the Antarctic. Berndtson was
lost at sea in the 1820s, supposedly on board the *Jane Maria*, but documentary proof is lacking.

Benson or Berndtson was first mate on the brig *Catharina* on a voyage to the South Shetlands in 1820-21. The log of this voyage is in the same book as that of the *Hersilia* of 1819-20. The voyage of the *Catharina* is related in Chap. 6.

11. The crew lists filed at the New London Custom House show that two men left the vessel during the voyage and one was signed on at Buenos Aires.

12. Fanning, *op. cit.*, pp. 429-430.

13. *New England Palladium and Commercial Advertiser*, Boston, December 5, 1820.

14. On file with Miscellaneous Letters, August-October, 1820, Records of the Department of State, Record Group 59, United States National Archives. These letters have been microfilmed by the National Archives as part of Microcopy M-179, roll 149.

15. New London *Daily Globe*, January 28, 1907. Republished in William Herbert Hobbs, "The Discoveries of Antarctica Within the American Sector, as Revealed by Maps and Documents," *Transactions of the American Philosophical Society*, New Series, vol. 33, pt. 1, January, 1939, pp. 12-13. Another substantially similar account by Mrs. Loper appears in John R. Spears, *Captain Nathaniel Brown Palmer, an Old-Time Sailor of the Sea* (New York, 1922), pp. 23-32.

16. A. Howard Clark, "The Antarctic Fur-seal and Sea-elephant Industries," *The Fisheries and Fishery Industries of the United States*, George Brown Goode, ed. U. S. Bureau of Fish and Fisheries, Sen. Misc. Doc. 124, 47th Congr., 1st Sess., Washington, 1887, Sec. V, vol. 2, p. 406.

17. Letters dated August 17, August 25, and September 4, 1820, on file with Miscellaneous Letters, August-October, 1820, Records of the Department of State, Record Group 59, United States National Archives. Also on microfilm as Microcopy M-179, roll 49.

18. *New England Palladium and Commercial Advertiser*, Boston, December 5, 1820.

19. Fanning, *op. cit.*, pp. 430-431.

20. At the request of the author, Dr. D. G. Knapp of the Geophysics Division of the U. S. Coast and Geodetic Survey calculated that the magnetic declination (magnetic variation on hydrographic charts) was 24° E in the area of the South Shetlands in 1821, with a probable error of plus or minus 3°.

21. Logbook of the sloop *Hero*, 1820-1821, Marine Misc. Acc. 3680, Manuscript Division, Library of Congress.

22. Capt. Robert Fildes, "Remarks made during a Voyage to New South Shetland," Typescript copy in Scott Polar Research Institute, Cambridge, England, Ref. MS 393, p. 6. Original in Public Record Office, London, No. 753 Adm. 55/143.

23. Published in James Weddell, *A Voyage Towards the South Pole Performed in the Years 1822-24* (London, 1825).

24. Distances are based on "Distance of Visibility of Objects at Sea," Table 8, Part 2, [Bowditch's] *American Practical Navigator*, U. S. Navy Hydrographic Office, Publ. No. 9, Washington, 1943.

25. This name was applied to the island by the American sealers because the peaks resembled the double-topped Mount Pisgah in the town of Durham, Connecticut. The name Smith Island, however, has been in general usage for well over 100 years, and it is now accepted officially by at least all English-speaking countries. The name honors Captain William Smith, discoverer of the South Shetlands. The name Mount Pisgah is now applied to the northern peak on the island.

26. See the view facing p. 166 in *Antarctic Pilot*, Hydrographic Department of the Admiralty, 2nd ed. (London, 1948).

27. Clark, *op. cit.*, p. 406.

BIBLIOGRAPHY

PUBLISHED MATERIAL

Boston Daily Advertiser, Wednesday, September 27, 1820.

Clark, A. Howard, "The Antarctic Fur-seal and Sea-elephant Industries," *The Fisheries and Fishery Industries of the United States*, George Brown Goode, ed., U. S. Bureau of Fish and Fisheries, Sen. Misc. Doc. 124, 47th Congr. 1st Sess., Washington, 1887, Sec. V, vol. 2, pp. 400-467.

Connecticut Gazette, New London, May 24 and 31, 1820.

Daily Globe, New London, January 28, 1907.

Fanning, Edmund, *Voyages Round the World* (New York, Collins and Hannay, 1833), 499 pp.

Hobbs, William Herbert, "The Discoveries of Antarctica Within the American Sector, as Revealed by Maps and Documents," *Transactions of the American Philosophical Society*, new series, vol. 33, Part 1, January, 1939.

Spears, John R., *Captain Nathaniel Brown Palmer, An Old-Time Sailor of the Sea*, (New York, Macmillan, 1922), 252 pp. Pages 23-32 give an account embellished with the Palmer family tradition similar to the one of Mrs. Loper (in Hobbs, above).

Vietor, Alexander O., "New Light on the Activities of American Sealing Vessels in the South Shetland Islands and Antarctica, 1819-1822," *Geography and Map Division, Special Libraries Association*, Bull. No. 26, December, 1956, pp. 5-9.

MANUSCRIPT MATERIAL

Byers, James, Letters to Brig. Gen. Daniel Parker, Adjutant and Insp. Gen., U. S. Army, Washington, August 17, August 25, and September 4, 1820. U. S. National Archives, Records of the Department of State, Misc. Letters, August-October, 1820, Record Group 59. These letters have been microfilmed by the National Archives as part of Microcopy M-179, roll 49.

Fanning, Edmund, Papers of, American Geographical Society, New York.

Fildes, Capt. Robert, "Remarks made during a Voyage to New South Shetland," Typescript copy in Scott Polar Research Institute, Cambridge, England, Ref. MS 393, p. 6. Original in Public Record Office, London, No. 753 Adm. 55/143.

Logbook of the *Hero*, Marine Misc., Acc. 3680, Library of Congress, Manuscript Division.

Logbook of the Brig *Hersilia*, 1820, "Journal of a Voyage from Falkland Iland to the Pacific Ocean Kep on Bord the Breg Hersilia af [by] Elof Benson First officer on bord." Actually begins at Staten Island, January 11, 1820 and ends May 20, 1820, one day out of Stonington. Property of Mrs. Theodore H. Krueger, Stratford, Conn. Microfilm copies in Yale University Library and in the Library of the Marine Historical Association, Mystic, Conn.

Stevens, Thomas A. "The First American Sealers in the Antarctic, 1812-1819 and the First Voyage of the *Hersilia* of Stonington, Conn., 1819-1820," Deep River, Conn., 1954. Mimeographed, iv and 61 pp.

United States Custom House Records, Port of Stonington and Port of New London, Federal Records Center, Waltham, Mass.

4

THE FANNING-PENDLETON SEALING FLEET, 1820-1821

ORGANIZATION AND ACCOMPLISHMENTS

Significance of the Fleet's Activities

News of the discovery of the South Shetland Islands, and of the thousands of fur seals to be had there, spread rapidly. In 1819-20 the *Hersilia,* so far as we know, was the only American vessel at the South Shetlands. The following year there were 30 American sealing vessels operating there. The five vessels comprising the fleet sent out from Stonington by the Fannings and their associates, in command of Benjamin Pendleton, have become the best known of these. The most publicized of all has been the sloop *Hero,* commanded by the youthful Nathaniel B. Palmer.

Palmer's exploratory cruise to the shores of the Antarctic Peninsula at the northeastern end of the Orléans Strait in November 1820 and another cruise by Palmer or some other member of the fleet to the southwestward along the peninsula and the off-lying islands in January 1821 have been cited by geographers as the basis for American rights in this area. Some have claimed that Palmer — by virtue of the November cruise — was the discoverer of Antarctica, but this has been challenged by other geographers.[1]

As a result of these cruises, Palmer's name has been applied in some form to the land south of the South Shetlands on many maps since the early 1820s.[2] Palmer's acclaim is deserved, but he has also benefited from the fact that his activities were reported widely at an early date. The chapters which immediately follow will show that at least three other American sealers also explored this part of Antarctica during the same season, but their story has been largely neglected until recently for lack of data concerning them. On the other hand, an account of the activities of the Fanning-Pendleton fleet was given by Fanning in his *Voyages Round the World* as early as 1833.[3] Fanning's book, which enjoyed wide popularity, has long been regarded as the chief contemporary account of early American sealing. Palmer's later fame as a pioneer clipper ship master and designer also helped to draw attention to his earlier feats in the Antarctic.

Establishment and Composition of the Fleet

At least 32 persons were financially involved in the sealing venture headed by William A. Fanning in 1820-21. In addition to Fanning, the principal partners were Elisha Faxon, Ephraim Williams, Benjamin Pendleton, Samuel Denison, and James P. Sheffield, all of Stonington. Nathaniel B. Palmer also was a part owner of the *Express* and the *Hero,* and Thomas Dunbar, Jr., was part owner of the *Free Gift.* Edmund Fanning may also have been involved financially, but he was not listed as one of the ship owners in the ship registrations at the New London Custom House. He certainly acted as an advisor to his son, and as agent while the fleet was away from Stonington.

The organization and dispatch of the Fanning-Pendleton sealing fleet of 1820-21 was spread over a period of three months in the spring and summer of 1820. Captain Benjamin Pendleton, who had returned on November 13, 1819, from a successful sealing voyage in the brig *Frederick* along the west coast of South America, was the first to leave. He sailed from Stonington, again in the *Frederick*, on May 14, 1820. By the time he left, the news of Smith's discovery of the South Shetlands had reached the United States, and Pendleton may have sailed with the intention of looking for them. However, he reportedly was headed for the "Northwest Coast." Perhaps a rendezvous with other vessels of the Fanning organization was planned at the Falkland Islands or at Staten Island.

The tempo increased with the return of the *Hersilia* on May 21, 1820, with the very good news of the great number of seals at the South Shetlands. The schooner *Free Gift* sailed shortly after the return of the *Hersilia*. Her skipper, Thomas Dunbar, must have been thoroughly briefed by Captain Sheffield and William A. Fanning, for the information they supplied surely resulted in the alteration of earlier plans. At least two more vessels, the schooner *Express* and the sloop *Hero*, were added to the fleet. Profits from the *Hersilia*'s voyage were apparently re-invested, for the owners of the *Hersilia* were also the principal owners of the *Express*. Moreover, Nathaniel B. Palmer, who owned no part of the *Hersilia* but who had received a second mate's share of her $22,000 cargo, was listed in 1820 as part owner of both the *Express* and the *Hero*. The *Hersilia, Express,* and *Hero* sailed from Stonington on July 31, 1820.

The flagship of the Fanning-Pendleton fleet was the brig *Frederick,* a 147-ton vessel built at Guilford, Connecticut, in 1815. The 131-ton brig *Hersilia* had just returned from her maiden voyage when she was sent out again in the summer of 1820 as part of this fleet. The *Express* was a 138-ton schooner built at Hudson, New York, in 1816. The *Free Gift,* like the *Express,* was a two-masted schooner, but a much smaller vessel. Built at Pawcatuck, Rhode Island, in 1807, she was registered at 52 tons with a length of 56 feet 7 inches. Since she was ready for sea when the *Hersilia* arrived home, and sailed soon after the *Frederick,* it is quite probable that the small schooner was meant to serve as a tender to the *Frederick*. The sloop *Hero* was smallest of all. Built at Groton, Connecticut, in 1800, she was registered as a sloop of 44 tons with a length of 47 feet 3 inches. That such a small vessel could survive an Antarctic voyage speaks much for the seamanship of her crew, yet they were not exceptional. Three other American fleets had tenders or, as they called them, "shallops," of comparable size. In fact, those who lacked such a vessel were at a distinct disadvantage.

Edmund Fanning has reported that because of his seniority as a captain, Benjamin Pendleton, master of the brig *Frederick,* was chosen as leader of the fleet.[4] It is quite probable that this responsibility was given him at the Falklands in a message carried by Captain Dunbar of the *Free Gift,* because it is doubtful, at the time Pendleton left Stonington on May 14, that a fleet of five vessels was contemplated. Since William A. Fanning, a principal owner and managing agent of the enterprise, was aboard the *Express,* he could well have conferred the responsibility on Pendleton at the South Shetlands. None of the other people involved,

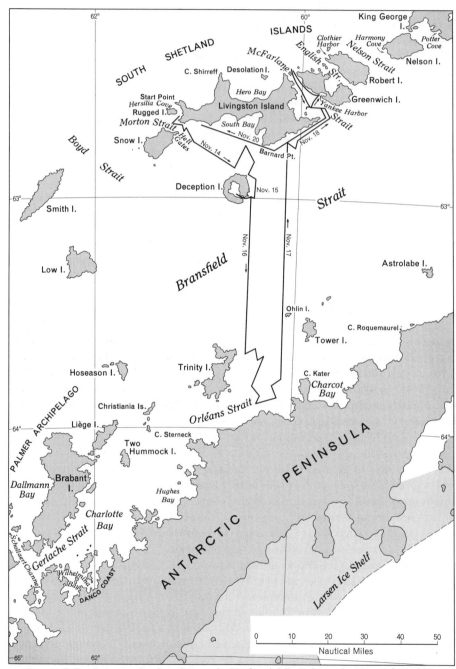

FIGURE 2. Exploratory Cruise of Captain Nathaniel B. Palmer, in November 1820.

including William A. Fanning, had Pendleton's practical experience.

The *Hersilia* was again in command of James P. Sheffield. Ephraim Williams, one of the principal associates in the venture, was captain of the *Express.* Thomas Dunbar of Westerly, Rhode Island, was master of the *Free Gift.* Nathaniel B. Palmer, who was to make a name for himself as an Antarctic explorer on this voyage, was only 20 years old when he was given his first command as master of the sloop *Hero.* A short time later, August 8, was his 21st birthday.

Of the five vessels of the fleet only the crew list of the *Hero* is now present among the Custom House records. There were only five men, including Palmer, aboard the sloop. Sheffield reported that there were 15 men aboard the *Hersilia* when she was captured on the coast of Chile, May 13, 1821, but on her first voyage she had a crew of 19. From other indirect evidence the crews of the several vessels can be estimated to have been 17 for the *Hersilia,* 21 for the *Frederick,* 17 for the *Express,* and 11 for the *Free Gift,* or approximately 70 men for the fleet.

OBJECTIVES AND ACCOMPLISHMENTS

The primary objective of the sealing fleet sent to the South Shetlands in 1820 by the Fannings was to procure full cargoes of fur sealskins. That the *Hero* and perhaps the *Free Gift* might be used for exploratory cruises was merely incidental to the main objective, for such exploration was for beaches with seal rookeries on them. The two ships were also necessary to carry men and supplies to the beaches from the larger ships which would be moored in a safe harbor and to collect the skins from these crews on the beaches. Any geographical information which they might gather would certainly not be published until its disclosure could be of no great value to a competitor.

The Fanning-Pendleton fleet during the austral summer of 1820-21 spent almost four months at the South Shetlands. Most of this time at least three of the vessels spent moored in Yankee Harbor, a small bay on the northeast side of McFarlane Strait, where the larger vessels of two other American sealing fleets also lay at anchor.

The *Hero* made one and very likely two exploratory cruises. On the first of these, Captain Palmer explored inside Deception Island, probably the first man to do so. From Deception Island he sailed southward to Trinity Island and the mainland shore of the Antarctic Peninsula. On November 17, 1820, he found himself at the northeast portal of Orléans Strait, then filled with ice (Fig. 2). Palmer was possibly the discoverer of the strait. Returning northward, Palmer next explored the full length of McFarlane Strait and discovered Yankee Harbor, to which the fleet moved a few days later. Two sketch maps on rough brown paper, one of McFarlane Strait and the other of the southern portion of the strait and the offshore waters, including Deception Island, are among the papers of Edmund Fanning at the American Geographical Society.[5]

There is strong evidence that another exploratory voyage was made in the *Hero* along the west side of the Antarctic Peninsula to as far south as perhaps 68° S. Some credit this voyage to Palmer, others to Pendleton, and some suggest it was made by an unknown third person in a vessel other than the *Hero.* It could very likely have been made in the *Hero* by both Pendleton and Palmer, for the latter was master of the sloop and Pendleton was senior commander of the fleet.

As a result of the experience gained by the skippers of the Fanning-Pendleton Sealing Fleet of 1820-21 and perhaps by skippers of other American vessels as well, the tenth edition of *The American Coast Pilot, 1822,* carried the following sailing directions as part of an appendix.

After obtaining sight of Statten Land, bring Cape St. John's to bear W. 5 or 6 leagues distant; then on account of the N. E. set off Cape Horn, endeavour to make a course good S. by compass, until you arrive in the latitude 62°50′ S. Then steer E. keeping between the latitude of 62° S. and 63°5′ S. until you make the land, which will be Mount Pisgo Island; when you have got sight of this island, bring the center of it to bear S. W. by compass, 5 leagues distant. If, when in this situation, the weather should set in thick or foggy, keep this situation by lying by, or on short tacks, until the weather lights up, then steer N. E. ½ E. by compass until you make Castle Rock broad on your starboard bow, and keep steering north and eastward past the mouth of the strait, when you will make Ragged Island, which keep off your starboard bow and beam until you open the pass between the N. W. end of Ragged Island and the Main Island; then steer into the pass E.S.E. keeping Ragged Island shore nearest on board, and anchor in the harbor, around the second point of Ragged Island, in 6 or 8 fathoms. Double this second point well on board, to avoid the reefs that lie off on the pass abreast of the harbour of Port Sheffield in Ragged Island.

There are some reefs in the offing off the mouth of Ragged Island pass, and in it, but with care, and a good look out they are easily avoided, as the breakers, or ripples, will show where they are.

N.B. Mount Pisgo is a very round island, with a bold shore all around it, and may be seen in clear weather at least 30 leagues.[6]

The accumulation of such information was surely an accomplishment of 1820-21, for the preface to the tenth edition is dated March 1822. Whether it should be credited to a particular fleet or to a particular man cannot be determined, but both from the place names and from the date it could not have come from other than American sources.

DETAILED ACCOUNT OF OPERATIONS

The Outbound Voyages

The brig *Frederick* sailed from Stonington in command of Captain Benjamin Pendleton on May 14, 1820. From New London Custom House records it appears that the schooner *Free Gift,* commanded by Captain Thomas Dunbar, Jr., sailed on or shortly after May 22. Very little is known of the voyages of the *Frederick* and the *Free Gift,* but a rendezvous must have been arranged for some place at the Falkland Islands or at Staten Island. Only in this way could Pendleton have learned from Dunbar the news of the South Shetlands and that the fleet would gather at President Harbor, an anchorage in the strait between Rugged Island and Livingston Island.

On July 31, 1820, according to the logbook of the *Hero,* the little sloop sailed out of Stonington harbor. An illegible part of the day's entry may well indicate that the *Express* and the *Hersilia* also departed at that time, for on August 2

Palmer recorded that he was sailing in company with those two vessels. During an uneventful outbound voyage the *Hero* and the *Express* remained almost always in sight of one another, and on several occasions Palmer went on board the *Express*. After August 13 the *Hersilia* was lost sight of until August 21, when Palmer and Sheffield both boarded the *Express,* apparently to confer with Captain Ephraim Williams and William A. Fanning. The *Hersilia* was again lost sight of on August 23, and no further mention is made of her in the logbook of the *Hero* until the sloop reached the South Shetlands.

The Falkland Islands were sighted on the afternoon of October 16, and at 10:00 the next morning the *Hero* and the *Express* anchored in Berkeley Sound. The two vessels remained at the Falklands until October 27, during which time they sailed in and out of various straits and harbors in the islands, collecting wood and provisions, the latter consisting mostly of eggs and fowl. During the stay here Palmer, Fanning, and Williams met several other sealers with whom they conferred and exchanged invitations. These included the subsequently famous British sealer James Weddell in the brig *Jane,* with his tender, the cutter *Beaufoy*. They also met Captain William B. Orne in the ship *General Knox* from Salem, Massachusetts, and Nicholas Withem of the schooner *Governor Brooks,* tender to the *General Knox*. As Palmer and Williams were about to leave the Falklands, they encountered their fellow townsmen Captain Jeremiah Holmes in the brig *Emeline,* Captain Joseph Henfield in the brig *Catharina,* and Elof Benson, his first mate.

Late on October 27 the *Hero* and the *Express* sailed from the Falklands toward Staten Island. At noon on October 29, while Palmer wore the *Hero* to speak the *Express,* the two vessels accidentally collided, resulting in minor damage. At 3:30 a. m., October 31, Staten Island was sighted, and the two vessels came to anchor in what Palmer called "Woodward's Harbor" at 7:00. Several days were spent at Staten Island gathering wood, eggs, and other provisions and making needed repairs to the ships. From 2 p. m., October 31, until noon, November 2, Palmer and a boat crew were away on a westward cruise along the north side of Staten Island. On November 4 the *Hero* and the *Express* were ready for sea.

On the morning of November 5 the two vessels hove anchor and moved out to sea. At noon they rounded Cape St. John (C. San Juan), at the eastern end of Staten Island, and sailed southward. With one exception the weather remained reasonably good as they continued southward, favored by light winds from a northerly quarter. November 7, however, brought thick weather and snow squalls, and ice formed on the deck that night. On the morning of November 9 Palmer recorded, "We are anxiously Looking for Land. Plenty Penguins Whales and Gulls about us."

AT PRESIDENT HARBOR

The South Shetlands were at last sighted on the morning of November 10, 1820, and the following entry in the logbook of the *Hero* describes the landfall:

> at 4 AM made the Land Bearing East & Northerly About 10 Leagues
> Distant stood in for it made it to be Mount Pisga [Mount Pisgah
> Island of the Yankee sealers but now and also then known as Smith
> Island -- 63°00' S, 62°30' W.]

The sloop's position at noon was 62°50′ S, 63°04′ W, and Palmer wrote that the *Express* was then about seven miles to leeward. The wind continued as a moderate to fresh breeze from a northeasterly direction, and it was necessary to tack to the north and west to beat up to the land, passing to the north of Smith Island. At 4 p. m. on November 11 they sighted Castle Rock and stood in for Ragged Island [Rugged Island]. At 8 p. m. the *Hero* was at the entrance to the strait between Rugged Island and Livingston Island when she was met by a boat from the *Hersilia*. Captain Sheffield informed Palmer that he had been there 12 days and that the *Frederick* and the *Free Gift* were anchored across the strait over against Friesland [Livingston Island] in what the Yankees called President Harbor. At 10 p. m. the *Hero* came to anchor beside the *Hersilia* in Hersilia Cove on the northeast side of Rugged Island. Meanwhile a thick snow storm came up which kept the *Express* outside until 8 a. m., November 12.

As the *Express* came to anchor, Palmer got out the whaleboat and crossed the strait to President Harbor to visit the *Frederick* and the *Free Gift*. Here it was concluded that all five vessels should be moored at President Harbor and on that evening the move was begun. At midnight the *Hero* anchored at President Harbor, but the weather having become thick and rainy, the *Hersilia* put back into her old anchorage and the *Express* went out to sea for the night. The next morning, November 13, the *Hersilia* and the *Express* anchored at President Harbor. British sealers later renamed this roadstead New Plymouth, which is its name today. The weather was still thick, and later a heavy snow storm set in. It did not, however, prevent the men from unloading spars, casks, and wood on the beach.

November 1820 Exploratory Cruise of the *Hero*

Subsequent events would indicate that Captain Pendleton was not entirely satisfied with the situation at President Harbor. He must have felt that the vessels were not entirely secure there, and it must also have been apparent to him, after hearing Palmer's report, that other sealing vessels, both British and American, were arriving in increasing numbers. It was important, therefore, that they find additional beaches where seal were hauling up and, if possible, locate a better mooring place. To this end Nathaniel B. Palmer was sent out on an exploratory cruise in the *Hero*. The account of the cruise is best related in Palmer's own words, recorded in the logbook of the *Hero* beginning on November 15.[7]

Wednesday November 15th [1820]

These 24 hours commences with Thick weather
Light Breese from N W - at 2 P M clearing off
Got underweigh on a cruise stood over for Deception
Course East for the North head wind Light at
N by W at 8 Being close in with the Land Tacked
to the Northward middle part Thick snow
storm at 12 Two Reefd the mainsail Tacked
to the Ewd at 5 made the Land stood along
to the sd & Ed saw what we thought to Be a harbor

Launched Down the Boat and Examined it but
were Disappointed stood along to the Southwd saw
an opening Stood in found it to be a spacious harbor
with very deep water 50 or 60 fathoms got out the Boat
to sound found Anchorage about a mile & half from
the mouth at 11 we came too in 18 fathoms off the mouth
of a lagoon went on shore and got some Eggs
Ends with thick weather & calm --

Thursday November 16th

Commences with fresh Breeses from N West
and cloudy at 2 P M got underweigh to
Beat up the Harbor stood over to the south
Shore sounded along and found no anchorage.
at 6 P M got up to the head in very suddenly
shoalend [?] our water to 2½ fathoms and came
Too middle part thick snow storm at
5 A M went into a Lagoon with the Boat
sounded it out found plenty of water from
5 to 3 & 2 fathoms went to another farther down
sounded in 15 fathoms at the Entrance and
10 7-6-5 within found it to be an Excellent
Harbor secure from all winds Returned
on Board Got underweigh at 10 we were clear
from the Harbor stood over for the Land Course S by E ½ E
Ends with fresh Breeses from S W and Pleasant

Friday November 17th

These 24 hours commences with fresh Breeses
from S West and pleasant at 8 P M got over under
the Land found the sea filled with imense [sic]
Ice Bergs -- at 12 hove too under the Jib Laid
off & on until morning at 4 A M made sail
in shore and Discovered - a strait- Tending
S SW & N NE -- it was Literally filled with Ice
and the shore inaccessible we thought it not Prudent
to venture in we Bore away to the Northward
& saw 2 small Islands and the shore every where
Perpendicular we stood across towards freeseland
course N NW. The Latitude of the mouth of the
strait was 63-45 s. Ends with fine weather wind
at S SW --

Saturday November 18 1820

Commences with fine weather Light winds
from W SW -- saw a Plenty of whales & Ice ---
Middle part Pleasant -- at 2 A M hauled Down
the mainsail Laid off and on under Freeseland
at 4 made sail Running along shore course by
compass N NE at 6 discovered the mouth of a
harbor stood in got out the Boat went on shore
got one seal - at 10 came too in a fine harbor
in an Iland about 2 miles from the straits mouth
in 10 fathoms fine holding ground. went on shore

Sunday November 19th

Commences with fine weather
Got 6 skins & a Quantity of Eggs -- found a fine Beaches [sic]
for seal at 4 P M got underweigh got out the harbor
wind Dying away Towed her in again middle
part fresh Breese from S W at 4 a m got underweigh got
out the harbor wind Dying away got out the Boat found
a fine harbor fine Beaches for seal Ends with calm

Monday November 20th

Commences with calm pleasant weather
at 2 P M got up to the head found a Passage
out to the westward on the Larboard shore
the starboard side being filled with Islands
Dunbars - &c. found a fine Plain 2 miles in length
& 1 in Breadth -- and fine harbors -- Navigation
appearing Dangerous on the North side several
Reefs lying off 5 & 6 miles at 3 m started got
on Board at 5 -- the sloop having been becalmed
all the time we were about -- stood out to sea
Middle part Calm with Light airs ---
Latter part Light Breeses from S W to N West
at Meridian Freeseland Point Bore N by E-
4 miles Distant

Tuesday November 21th

These 24 hours commences with Light &
variable winds from S W & N W at 4 P M shut
in thick with a fresh Breese from S. W.
at 9 anchored in President Bay with
the Fleet -- Latter part Fresh gales from
S West with hail squalls

It seems clear from the logbook that Palmer sailed from President Harbor at 2:00 p. m., November 14 [civil calendar], and, after getting clear of the eastern portal of Morton Strait between Snow Island and Livingston Island, set an easterly course toward the north cape of Deception Island[8] (Fig. 2). Since the compass variation in 1820 in the vicinity of Deception Island was about 25° easterly, Palmer's course was a direct line for the north cape.[9] By 8:00 that evening he was close in to Deception Island and with the wind from north by west was forced to tack to the north. During the next eight hours a thick snow storm forced him, for reasons of safety, to tack about under double reefed mainsail between Livingston and Deception islands. At 5:00 a. m., November 15, he sighted Deception Island again, not too far away, and then sailed southward and eastward along the east side of the island.

Deception Island (62°57' S, 60°38' W), about ten miles south of Livingston Island, is one of the more remarkable topographic features in Antarctica. From eight to nine miles wide, it is the remnant of a former volcanic cone now forming a great crater or, more precisely, a caldera whose walls are breached in four places. One of these breaks, Neptunes Bellows, on the southeast side, is sufficiently deep to permit the sea to enter the crater, forming an almost completely land-locked harbor from three and one half to five and one half miles wide. On the southwest side there is another break in the wall dropping to a col which is about 300 feet above sea level. The inner end of this breach is a low plain occupied by a sea-level lagoon. The two other breaches are merely notches in the encircling walls of the crater, which rise to crests ranging from 750 to 1778 feet above sea level.

Sailing along the east side of Deception Island, the first and most likely place that Palmer could have mistaken for a harbor is the cove between South East Point and Rancho Point (Baily Head). Upon closer examination he was disappointed. It is sufficiently large and sheltered from the north and west, but not from the northward-moving ice floes nor from southerly gales. There is another cove southwest of South East Point, but when Palmer was in a position to view it, he could easily have seen the opening, Neptunes Bellows, through which he entered and discovered the great enclosed bay inside the crater of the old volcano (Fig. 3). Since 1829, when it was visited by the British expedition ship *Chanticleer*, the bay has been known as Port Foster. At 11:00 a. m., November 15, the *Hero* came to anchor in 18 fathoms in Whalers Bay, just inside and to the north of Fildes Point on the north side of Neptunes Bellows.[10]

According to Palmer's entry for November 16, the first half of which applies to the p. m. hours of November 15 of the civil calendar, at 2:00 p. m. he began his exploration of the inside of Deception Island by coasting along the south shore. By 6:00 p. m. the *Hero* had reached the head of Port Foster and entered Telefon Bay, where Palmer found the water quite shallow. After riding out a snow storm here, he continued the next morning to explore the shoreline of Port Foster and discovered Pendulum Cove, which he sounded with a boat and found to be "an Excellent Harbor secure from all winds." Palmer completed his circuit of the shoreline of Port Foster, and at 10:00 a. m., November 16, having cleared Neptunes Bellows, he was again outside of Deception Island in the open sea.

An important point concerning Palmer's visit to Deception Island is worthy of further comment. Does "stood over for Deception," which he wrote in the logbook for November 15, indicate that he already knew about the island and that it already had been named? What are the probabilities? First, this statement may give a clue as to the manner in which Palmer kept his logbook in which case he may have been writing after the fact and not actually have known the name or nature of the island when he cleared Morton Strait on the afternoon of November 14. The second possibility is that Pendleton had learned of the island from another sealer before he sent Palmer to investigate it.

Critics have questioned the authenticity of the logbook of the *Hero* because it has the appearance of having been written after the fact and lacks the appearance of a first draft. While at the South Shetlands Palmer did not record at two-hour intervals the speed in knots, the course sailed, and the wind direction in the columns on the left, and the remarks are written completely across the page. Martin has suggested that Palmer kept a rough log in a small pocket notebook or on a slate and transferred the pertinent information, minus calculations, to the official logbook when time permitted.[11] This was not an unusual practice, and it is a reasonable explanation. It also must be remembered that when the *Hero* was sailing among the South Shetlands in clear weather she was always in sight of land. At any rate there can no longer be any question of the logbook's authenticity, for the logbooks of the ship *Huron,* the brig *Catharina,* and the schooner *Huntress* during the austral summer of 1820-21 provide means for cross checking the activities of several of the sealers at the South Shetlands.

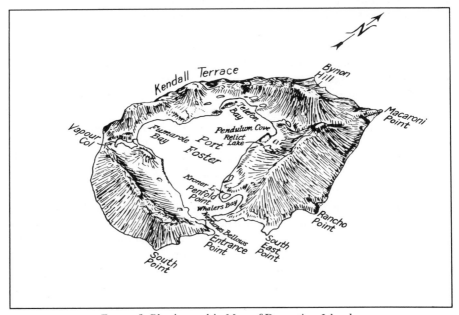

FIGURE 3. Physiographic Map of Deception Island.

There are too many times when Palmer mentions another vessel or when he or the *Hero* are reported in the logbook of another sealer, all of which can be authenticated, for the logbook to have been faked years later by a Palmer supporter to prove a priority of discovery.

What are the probabilities that Captain Pendleton had heard of Deception Island before he sent Palmer to investigate it? In that case Palmer already knew the island by its name when he cleared Morton Strait.

Edward Bransfield, sailing master of H.M.S. *Andromache* of the English squadron at Valparaiso, with William Smith in the latter's brig *Williams* which had been chartered for the occasion, explored and roughly mapped the South Shetlands in January and February 1820. Bransfield is acknowledged as the first mariner known to have sailed through Bransfield Strait, the body of water between the South Shetlands and the Antarctic Peninsula. His map, now in the files of the British Admiralty, shows the south shore of Livingston Island trending as a solid line southward beyond the latitude of Deception Island.[12] On the coastline is the notation, "Here the Land was lost in a Hazy fog." If Bransfield saw Deception Island, he did not recognize it. Gould also published a copy of a crude map which William Smith submitted to the Admiralty with a memorial in December 1821, which shows an island (without a hollow center) in the general vicinity of Deception Island. He named it Edwards Island.[13] How much was based on personal observation is not clear, but he was at the South Shetlands again in the austral summer of 1820-21.

From the entries in the logbook of the *Hersilia* for January and February 1820 (Chapter 3) and from other information concerning that voyage, it does not seem likely that anyone from that vessel sailed in Bransfield Strait or visited Deception Island at that time. Unless the *Free Gift* had visited Deception Island in November 1820 before Palmer's arrival, the *Hero* is the first American vessel to have visited there. It is not likely that Palmer was preceded by someone from the Fanning-Pendleton fleet, for in that case there would be no point in sending the *Hero*.

Reference was made in Chapter 3 to Captain Robert Fildes of the brig *Cora* of Liverpool and of his "Journal" and "Sailing Directions."[14] In his logbook or journal for December 16, 1820, Fildes reported coming to anchor off Desolation Island at 6 p. m. and sending the boats in search of seals. Then he wrote, "soon after a Whale boat belonging to the Brig Dragon of Liverpool, last from Valparaiso came alongside, had been seven weeks on the Coast and had obtained Five thousand Fur Seals. . . ."

This means that Captain McFarlane arrived at the South Shetlands during the first few days of November. The *Hersilia* had arrived at Rugged Island on October 31, and the *Frederick* and *Free Gift* may have arrived at the same time or earlier. It is not known whether McFarlane had a shallop, but he appears to have gotten about a great deal during the one season he was at the South Shetlands. It is not known, for instance, when he landed on the shores of the Antarctic Peninsula. Since he was hunting seals, it would seem more likely for him to have gone exploring after the seals became scarce. However, it is possible that he could have visited Deception Island in search of a harbor during his first two weeks at the South Shetlands and to have reported this to Pendleton.

Referring again to Fildes, in describing Deception Island in his "Sailing Directions" he says, "The entrance is by the Americans called Neptune's Bellow's [sic] owing to the gusts that blow in and out as if they came through a trumpet or funnell, . . ."[15]

There is no contemporary statement regarding the acknowledged discoverer of the true nature of Deception Island nor of its very appropriate naming in the published works or other material on the sealers now available in the United States or England. Until evidence to the contrary comes to light, it would seem that only McFarlane possibly could have preceded Palmer, and this is uncertain.

From Deception Island, Palmer then set a course S by E½E (163°07′30″ of azimuth) toward the mountainous shores of Trinity Island and the Antarctic Peninsula. He had pleasant weather with a southwest breeze, which also meant clear weather and good visibility. Trinity Island rises to a summit height of 3600 feet and is only 40 miles south of Deception Island. The Antarctic Peninsula is about 55 miles south of Deception Island. Cliffs, some over 1000 feet high, rise from the shoreline, and an ice-covered, plateau-like upland back from the coast rises to elevations as high as 6000 feet. As others under similar circumstances have since discovered, there can be no doubt that Palmer was able to see from his position, off the southeast coast of Deception Island, the Antarctic mainland toward which he was setting his course.[16]

The *Hero* sailed an average of four knots an hour on a course of 163° of azimuth. If correction is made for the compass variation of 24° or 25° east, which was the case in the vicinity of Deception Island in 1820, and for the drift caused by the currents and by the southwest wind on the little sloop, that course would take the *Hero* to the northeast coast of Trinity Island. At 8:00 p. m., November 16, eight hours after clearing Neptunes Bellows, Palmer reported that he was "over under the Land" or across Bransfield Strait and under the brow of Trinity Island. He found the sea full of immense icebergs and prudently hove to under the lee of Trinity Island, where he tacked back and forth with only the jib to the wind during the short period of darkness that prevailed at that season.

At 4:00 a. m., November 17, Palmer made sail again. Working south and a little easterly, he discovered the northeast portal of a strait trending SSW and NNE and "literally filled with ice." Palmer determined the latitude of its mouth to be 63°45′ S. This description can fit one place only, Orléans Strait. Referring again to Edward Bransfield's map, it is clear that he was also in this vicinity, for he mapped, but did not name, Kendall Rocks and Tower Island. What appears to be either a small island or an ink blot occupies the approximate position of Trinity Island. It is labeled "Towers Ld." Between it and the mainland of the Antarctic Peninsula is the notation "Breakers." It appears, therefore, that Bransfield saw the eastern portal of Orléans Strait. His logbook is lost, consequently we do not have a more detailed description of what he saw, nor do we know whether or not he recognized a strait. Bransfield is probably the discoverer of Orléans Strait; if not, the credit belongs to Palmer.[17]

The shores of the ice-filled strait being inaccessible, Palmer decided it would not be prudent to enter, especially since he apparently saw no sign of fur seals. He therefore bore away to the northward.[18] As he did so he saw two small islands, one of which must have been Ohlin Island (63°30′ S, 60°07′ W). Unless Palmer was referring to some rocks southwest of Ohlin Island, the other one must have been Tower Island (63°33′ S, 59°51′ W), although it is about four miles long and much larger than Ohlin Island. The statement that the shores were everywhere perpendicular may have referred to the shores of the two islands, but it would have been equally appropriate if applied to the Antarctic Peninsula. From a position near Ohlin Island a broad sweep of the precipitous shores of the mainland would have been visible on a clear day, and the logbook indicates it was clear.

The weather remained good as the *Hero* sailed northward toward "Freeseland" (Livingston Island). At 2 a. m., November 18, the sloop was close in to Livingston Island, and the mainsail was furled while the vessel tacked back and forth offshore until it became light enough to run along an unfamiliar coast. Palmer's course, NNE along shore, when corrected for the compass variation, makes it apparent that he was sailing somewhere along the shore of Livingston Island northeast of Barnard Point.

At 6:00 a. m. he discovered "the mouth of a harbor," actually the southeastern entrance to McFarlane Strait, which separates Livingston and Greenwich Islands. The *Hero* entered McFarlane Strait, which in 1820-21 the Americans called Yankee Sound, and Palmer got out the boat and went on shore. Returning on board, he got under way again and at 10:00 a. m. discovered a fine harbor in an island about two miles from the mouth of McFarlane Strait. This was undoubtedly Half Moon Island and the cove enclosed within its crescent shape. Palmer sounded in 10 fathoms of water and found a good holding ground for the anchor. He went on shore and apparently reconnoitered the island on foot, for he returned with six sealskins, a quantity of eggs, and the knowledge that the island possessed a fine beach for seals.

At 4:00 p. m. on November 18 Palmer tried to sail out of the harbor of Half Moon Island, but, the wind dying away, it was necessary to get out the boat and tow the *Hero* back in again. The next morning at 4:00 a. m. another attempt to get out of the harbor also failed for lack of a breeze. Apparently Palmer then left the *Hero* moored in the harbor of Half Moon Island and set out in the whaleboat to explore McFarlane Strait. The morning of November 19 he discovered "fine harbor with fine beaches for seal." Since it is the only fine harbor in the vicinity, besides Half Moon Island, this notation probably records Palmer's discovery of Yankee Harbor, to which the fleet moved after the *Hero* returned to President Harbor. By 2:00 p. m. Palmer and his whaleboat crew appear to have reached the northern end of McFarlane Strait. He discovered a passage to the westward, but considered the northern entrance to the strait a dangerous place to navigate a ship because of small islets, reefs, and dunbars.[19] At 3:00 p. m. they started back toward the *Hero* which they reached two hours later. Palmer reported that the sloop was becalmed all the while they were away, but it seems probable that on his exploratory cruise in the whaleboat he had a sail which he rigged to take advantage of whatever breeze might have arisen.

Sometime later the *Hero* stood out to sea, but calm and light airs allowed for little progress. By noon on November 20 they were roughly four miles southwest of "Freeseland Point" (probably Barnard Point). At 9:00 p. m. that evening, the *Hero* anchored beside the fleet in President Harbor. Palmer had thus completed his first exploratory cruise of the 1820-21 season. It had lasted seven days, and during that time Palmer had discovered the crater harbor of Deception Island, rediscovered Orléans Strait and Trinity Island and two small islands to the northeast of it, and explored McFarlane Strait.[20]

THE FLEET MOVES TO YANKEE HARBOR

The need for a safer mooring for the fleet was demonstrated immediately after the *Hero*'s return to President Harbor. On his exploratory cruise Palmer had been favored by generally fine weather, but as he approached the fleet the weather became thick. The next day a fresh gale brought hail squalls, and as it increased in intensity on the afternoon of November 21 the *Frederick* began to drag her anchors. It was decided to move to the newly discovered harbor in McFarlane Strait or, as the Stonington sealers then called it, Yankee Sound. The gale continued through November 22, and Palmer recorded, "all anxiously waiting for a time to get underweigh as the holding ground is very bad."

On November 23 the weather began to moderate, and all were busy preparing to leave. At 11:00 a. m. the *Free Gift* started, and at 2:00 p. m. all the vessels were under way, the *Hero* astern. At 11:00 a. m., November 24, after having a period of calm during the night, the *Hero* and the *Hersilia* led the fleet into McFarlane Strait. Later Palmer recorded, "at 2 P M came to Anchor in Port Williams in 15 Fathoms Water Muddy Bottom --- at 4 the Fleet were all moored."

It is not clear whether "Port Williams" applied to the almost circular bay on the west side of Greenwich Island, set off from McFarlane Strait by a spit, or to only a particular mooring within that bay. A short time later other American vessels moored here and, as did the Stonington vessels, remained for the entire 1820-21 season. Some returned again in 1821-22. Soon the term "Yankee Harbor" came into general usage by the Americans for this protected body of water, and that name has come down to modern times. It is conceivable that the Fanning-Pendleton group first named it for Ephraim Williams, master of the *Express,* but that his name was supplanted in general usage by Yankee Harbor. It is also possible that from the first the Stonington group restricted the name to only a portion of the entire bay, the part in which they moored. In 1820-21 Palmer used "Port Williams" exclusively. The letter sent to the editor of th *New Haven Journal* by Daniel W. Clark, first mate of the *Hersilia,* about which more will be said later, was dated at "Port William, New S. Shetland."[21]

CRUISES ABOUT LIVINGSTON ISLAND

After mooring at "Port Williams," or Yankee Harbor, little time was wasted getting down to the business of sealing. At 11:00 p. m. the *Hero* got under way on a cruise to visit the various camps established by the fleet on the beaches of Livingston Island, and for the next several weeks Palmer and his crew were engaged in a series of such cruises, supplying the camps with provisions and collecting sealskins which were stowed in one or another of the vessels moored at Yankee Harbor. During this time the logbook of the *Hero* records three circumnavigations of Livingston Island, and more may have been made in the latter part represented by incomplete entries. The following entries record the first of these cruises:

Tuesday November 28th
commences with Thick snow fresh Gales from
W N W. middle part Pleasant - at 6 P M
all hands started ashore after Ballast - got on
Board hauled alongside the vessels Took on
Board Provisions Boards & sails - at 10 Got underweigh
for the Camp Midnight were abreast of Dread Point[22]

Wednesday November 29th

commences with fine weather and calm - Got
the Boat ahead at 6 P M Breese springing up
Took the starboard in and the other wind
Astern Middle part Light Breese with snow
squalls - Latter part fresh Gales from W S W
at 6 A M two Reefed the mainsail Ends
with heavy gales and Pleasant

Thursday November 30th

These 24 hours commences with fresh Gales
at 11 P M Anchored Abreast the camp -- the
Boats came off with skins Turned Too
Got the Things Landed at 2 A M got under
weigh for P Williams at 8 were Abreast
of Ragged [Rugged] Island Run along the North
side of Freeseland [Livingston] saw plenty seal and
three vessels Took them to be English at meridian were
abreast of Sherriff Cape

Friday December 1th [sic]

commences with Pleasant weather wind
W S W -- at 5 Thick fog running into
the mouth of Yankey sound got on to
a Shoal but soon got off without
much Injury went into elephant Bay
anchored went on shore Took 25 seal
Returned middle part Thick fog - at
5 P M [?] Got underweigh at 9 Anchored
in Port Williams - got the skins out
Ends with Thick fog wind W S W

The logbook entry for December 5 reports that the *Hero* anchored at "Port Williams" where Palmer learned that the *Cecilia,* tender to the ship *Huron* of New Haven, had been in port for a few hours before going in search of the *Huron,* which along with the schooner *Huntress* would moor in the harbor. On December 8, Palmer returned from another cruise to find them in the harbor. On this latter cruise, as the *Hero* rounded "the Point of Freeseland" (probably Barnard Point) at noon on December 6, Palmer discovered a current running NNE at three miles per hour.

The second circumnavigation of Livingston Island was begun as the *Hero* got under way from "Port Williams" at 11:00 p. m., December 11. In spite of stormy weather, two camps were visited on the south shore of Livingston Island. By noon, December 14, Palmer reported the *Hero* "clear of the straits," presumably Morton Strait between Livingston and Snow Islands. The next 24 hours are covered by the following entry in the logbook:

Thursday 15th December

Commences Pleasant with a fine Breese at
11 P. M. came Too abreast the camp - sent the
Boat on shore - soon Returned with Mr. Pendleton
Put the Provisions Bedding &c into the Boat

and she Returned - Got underweigh for the
Fleet - at 10 were abreast of sherriff's Cape
saw a Brig Beating in among the Islands
showed English colours - Got an Observation
which puts the Mouth of Yankey sound
in 62-24 South Latitude

The *Hero* had fortunately arrived at the northern entrance to McFarlane Strait at noon, permitting Palmer to take an observation. Modern maps place the northern entrance to the strait at 62°27′ S, giving Palmer a very small error of only three miles, and he might well have been that far out from the treacherous mouth of the strait when he took his observation. At any rate, the near accuracy of this position helps to support the position which Palmer gave for the northeast entrance to Orléans Strait a few weeks earlier. The entry for December 16 indicated that he started through the passage at the northern end of McFarlane Strait at 1:00 p. m. Three hours later Palmer arrived at Yankee Harbor, where he learned of the wreck, on December 8, of the ship *Clothier,* one of the vessels of a second Stonington fleet.

At 8:00 p. m. on December 16, while cruising westward along the south side of Livingston Island on the third circumnavigation, the *Hero* met four sealing vessels from New York: the brigs *Jane Maria* and *Charity,* the schooner *Henry,* and a shallop. On December 17, after calling at the camps on the south shore of Livingston Island, Palmer reported getting under way "for the camp on the north side." By now the matter of cruising between the sealing camps and the fleet must have become routine, for Palmer's daily entries hereafter were very brief, being merely a mention of the weather each day. Later no entries were made at all until the *Hero* sailed for home. Moreover, the brief notations concerning the weather appear to have been entered all at one time as though abstracted from a rough log kept perhaps, as Martin suggested, on a pocket notebook.[23]

JANUARY 1821 CRUISE OF THE *HERO*

Much has been written about another exploratory cruise made by the *Hero* in January 1821. Contemporary confirmation of the cruise is given by Captain Christopher Burdick in the logbook of the schooner *Huntress* of Nantucket. On January 28 he recorded: ". . . the Stonington shallop came in from a Cruise to the northward and Eastward of 14 days and Reported they had found no seal . . ."[24] It is significant that he does not mention who was in command and that he gives the length of the cruise as 14 days. It explains why Palmer and the *Hero* and it perhaps explains why Pendleton are not mentioned as having taken part in the abortive excursion that the Americans at Yankee Harbor mounted against English sealers who had driven them off the beaches at Cape Shirreff, which is discussed in Chapter 5.

Other evidence suggests that a cruise was made to the southwest along the west side of the Antarctic Peninsula. On the basis of this evidence Martin projected a cruise by Palmer in January 1821 as far south as Marguerite Bay.[25] Unfortunately the evidence is of a secondary nature, for the logbook of the *Hero*, as stated above, contains only five entries, January 14 to 18, for the period when the cruise is supposed to have taken place. These describe only the winds and the weather.

Arthur R. Hinks has discounted Martin's interpretation and has suggested that Palmer's cruise was limited to a circumnavigation of the South Shetlands.[26] Burdick's entry for January 28 in the logbook of the *Huntress* would seem to support Hinks, who also implied that if a cruise was made to the south it was not necessarily made by Palmer.

One bit of evidence suggesting that Palmer made an exploratory cruise in January is a manuscript sheet among the Palmer papers in the Manuscript Division of the Library of Congress. It contains the following excerpts from the logbook of the brig *Frederick*, flagship of the fleet.

> In the Brig Frederick log book Jany 14th 1821 Says
> "the Sloop Hero Capt. N. B. Palmer Sailed to Eastward
> to look for more seal Ids." Same log book Says on
> Jany 28th/21. "6 Am the Sloop came in after
> Examining North East and South West to their
> Satisfaction for Seal found None. - -
> Stopped at Camp took in about 4000 skins put on board
> Frederick 1200 -- Employed getting shallop ready for a
> cruise. So Ends this day.

A second manuscript sheet, apparently in the same hand as the first, lists the number of skins brought to the fleet by the *Hero* at the close of ten different cruises to the sealing camps on the beaches. The first date is November 17, following the close of the first cruise after the fleet moved to Yankee Harbor. The last date is January 12, and since there was more room on the sheet for additional notations, it probably indicates a change in assignment for the *Hero*, after January 12. This is consistent with and confirms the excerpts from the logbook of the *Frederick*. From this we merely know that the *Hero* cruised in search of seal rookeries. It is necessary to look for other evidence as to where the cruise was made if indeed it was southward along the west coast of the Antarctic Peninsula.

Edmund Fanning's *Voyages Round the World*, published in 1833, contained a brief account of a cruise by Palmer in the *Hero* to the ice-covered, mountainous lands south of the South Shetlands "in the midsummer of this hemisphere."[27] Fanning described how the *Hero* became fogbound as it neared the South Shetlands on the return from the south and how, when the fog lifted, Palmer found himself close to two Russian naval vessels. These proved to be the *Vostok* and the *Mirnyy* under the command of Captain Thaddeus Bellingshausen, nearing the completion of a circumnavigation of Antarctica, mostly south of the 60th parallel, begun in 1819. According to Bellingshausen's account, this meeting took place about 10:00 a. m., February 6 (Gregorian calendar), in the strait between Deception and Livingston Islands.[28] The meeting, therefore, took place after Palmer's January cruise in the *Hero*. The significance of the meeting of Palmer and Bellingshausen is that it serves as a convenient reference from which to date Palmer's activities. Years later, when time had dulled his memory of the details, it must have served to distinguish in Palmer's mind the events of 1820-21 from those of 1821-22. Moreover, Palmer's recollection of the meeting served in later years as an occasion for him to recount events pertaining to his explorations in 1820-21.

On March 13, 1876, in a letter to Mr. Frank T. Bush, apparently in answer to an inquiry, Palmer gave an account of the meeting with Bellingshausen which throws some light on Palmer's activities in 1820-21 insofar as he then recalled them. The essential part of this letter, a copy of which is now among the Palmer papers in the Manuscript Division of the Library of Congress, is contained in the following excerpt.[29]

My first command was the Sloop "Hero" in 1820. - it was on this Voyage that Palmers Land was discovered & subsequently we fell in with the Russian Squadron under Admiral Krustenstern [Bellingshausen] consisting of Frigate "Rostok" [Vostok] & a Sloop of the name I have forgotten. - it was with great difficulty that I could make the old Admiral believe I had come from U states in so small a vessel. he treated me with great Kindness. for the Services I rendered him in extricating his ships from a dilemma he found himself when the Fog lit up Surrounded by land & other obstacles - and as we was the first vessel that had circumnavigated the Shetland Group & had to make our own Charts - from which he took a copy on Tissue paper was the means of taking his Ships from all the dangers & proceed on his way to Rio Janiero among other Things I informed him of our Trip to the South in Latt 68° & the discovery of a Land (never before seen) and it was him that Named it Palmers Land.

There are obvious discrepancies between Palmer's and Bellingshausen's accounts of the meeting, but nevertheless, if Palmer's memory was not completely faulty, his account does throw some light on what he had accomplished up to February 6, 1821. It is not known whether Bellingshausen spoke English or whether the interview was carried on through an interpreter. In either case, some of the differences in the two accounts can be attributed to language difficulties. The fact that Palmer in 1876 confused Bellingshausen with Ivan F. Kruzenshtern, who circumnavigated the world in 1803-06, may possibly be credited to a faulty memory, but it is more likely an indication of the lack of comprehension that characterized the conversation between Palmer and Bellingshausen. It is probable that Bellingshausen's identity was confused in the minds of Palmer and his associates from the beginning. An announcement of the arrival of the schooner *Express* at Stonington, April 29, 1821, appearing in the *Connecticut Gazette,* New London, April 30, 1821, and reprinted in the *New York American,* May 4, 1821, contained the following: "The Russian frigate Wostok, Capt. Hellershausen, and a sloop of war, were at New South Iceland in February last on a survey. . . ." Other contemporary accounts and even Fanning did not mention Bellingshausen by name. An account of the arrival of the *Express* which appeared in the *Boston Patriot & Daily Mercantile Advertiser,* May 3, 1821, contained this final statement: "Two Russian ships of war surveying the coast."

If Palmer had originally been uncertain regarding Bellingshausen's identity, it is understandable that he later associated Kruzenshtern's name with the Russian leader he met at the South Shetlands, for the land to the south was named "Terre de Palmer" on map No. 1, "Carte générale de l'océan Pacifique, Hémisphère Australe," in the 1838 revised edition of Kruzenshtern's *Atlas de l'océan Pacifique,* published in St. Petersburg in 1838.[30] It would seem that the naming was based on the Powell map of the South Shetlands. Bellingshausen's voyage was never well known in the United States. An English translation of his narrative, which was originally printed in Russian, did not appear until 1945. On the other hand, Kruzenshtern's circumnavigation of the world received much wider publicity and was known as one of the great voyages of the time. An English translation of Kruzenshtern's narrative, originally published in German, was published in London in 1813.[31] It might be expected that Palmer and some of his associates read this book, for many New England mariners of the time were well acquainted with books on voyages of exploration.

Bellingshausen's account gives no indication of his having been in any difficulty, but Palmer, thinking the Russian ships in jeopardy in uncharted waters, may well have offered his services. Bellingshausen reported in his narrative information received from Palmer concerning the sealing business at the South Shetlands, but he made no mention of having seen or copied any charts made by Palmer. Neither did he mention any discoveries claimed by Palmer. It is conceivable that Bellingshausen, if he understood all that Palmer was trying to convey to him, thought Palmer's story not entirely credible and therefore discounted part of it when making his report and writing his narrative. Bellingshausen assiduously strove for accuracy in his navigation and surveying. Therefore, even if he courteously examined rough sketches which Palmer showed him, it is not likely that he would rely on the work of a young, unknown sealer in making his own charts.

An analysis of the two accounts of the meeting, when considered in terms of the circumstances then and later, makes it reasonable to assume that although Palmer's account of 1876 does not agree with Bellingshausen's narrative, both are honest reports. Bellingshausen's account, being based in all probability on a journal entry and having been published only ten years after the meeting, must be considered the more reliable insofar as the element of memory is involved.

Balch, Spears, Hobbs, and Martin have called attention to other items which provide details of the cruise by Palmer to the southwestward, along the west side of the Antarctic Peninsula in 1821.[32] In some the incident of the meeting between Palmer and Bellingshausen has been considerably embellished. Obviously these are secondary sources, originating many years after the cruise of 1821, and therefore are not of unquestioned reliability. They do, however, tend to confirm the fact that Palmer did make such a cruise to the southwest of the South Shetlands in 1821, although not necessarily in the manner they describe.

One of these latter-day sources is an article written by Mr. Frank T. Bush and published in the *New London Daily Globe,* September 10, 1881. While Bush had been American Consul at Hong Kong in the 1840s he had entertained Palmer, then master of the China clipper *Houqua,* and Admiral Sir Francis W. Austen of the British Navy. From his recollection of the after-dinner conversation, Bush quoted Palmer as saying:

"I pointed the bow of the little craft to the Southward . . . until she brought us in sight of land not laid down on my chart. I cruised for several days in order to satisfy myself that it was not an island. I ran into several bays without meeting with seals, and headed northward, drifting along under easy canvas, laying-to at night. . . ."

If, as Palmer says, he cruised for several days to make sure that the land was not an island, he was referring to something other than his November cruise when he spent only one day in the vicinity of Trinity Island.

Contemporary evidence that some vessel of the Fanning-Pendleton fleet made an exploratory cruise as far south as 66° S during the 1820-21 season is contained in a letter by Daniel W. Clark, first mate aboard the *Hersilia,* to the editor of the *Connecticut Journal* of New Haven. Since only the last two sentences have previously been quoted in articles dealing with Antarctic exploration and since a question has been raised concerning the meaning of the pronoun "we," the letter as it appeared in *The Gazette* of Providence, Rhode Island, for May 9, 1821, is reproduced in full.

NEW-SHETLAND

The following letter from Mr. Daniel W. Clark, to the editor of the New Haven Journal, provides many interesting particulars of this newly discovered land:

Port William, New S. Shetland
Islands, February 18, 1821

We arrived at these Islands on the 31st of Oct. after a pleasant passage of 85 days. We are now loaded with fur skins, having taken upwards of 18,000 of superior quality, but being anxious to obtain a second voyage before returning to the United States, we have agreed to send our cargo home, then to proceed around Cape Horn into the Pacific Ocean in search of a second cargo, which, I doubt not will be obtained soon. As for getting another cargo in these islands, it is utterly impossible--for there is scarcely a seal left alive. The country is full of vessels from most quarters of the globe, and I am certain that one half of them will not obtain half a cargo. Our being the first vessel in the country, and getting possession of the best ground, is the reason why we succeeded in a valuable cargo.

There are now lying in this port 12 sail of American vessels; among the number is the ship Huron, Davis, of New-Haven, which made out rather indifferently. Where they are next bound I am not able to ascertain; but they, as well as ourselves, must push off soon, on account of the severity of the approaching season. There is scarcely a day passes without snow, hail, or rain, although midsummer with us -- and ice makes every night. In truth it is a climate I am glad to leave.

The brig Aurora, of N. York, has lately arrived here--I understand she has been looking for these islands nearly two months.

Perhaps the American dealers in fur skins have an idea that this country will be overstocked with skins, and that they will be bought for little or nothing; but I can assure them they will be mistaken; for I am certain at least 6 sail of American vessels will be obliged to seek for a cargo in some other parts.

This harbour lies in about 62½ deg. S. lat. and 63 deg. 5 min. W. long. We have been as far S. as 66 deg. and found land. How much farther the land extends I know not. -- It is entirely covered (except the low land and beaches where the seals come up) with snow and ice at this season of the year, which is the middle of summer.

Even from the full context of his letter it is difficult to determine what Clark meant by his use of the pronoun "we." The first paragraph seems to apply exclusively to the *Hersilia*. It is not known whether the *Hersilia* arrived in company with the *Frederick* and the *Free Gift,* but it is quite likely that she did. The "upwards of 18,000" skins taken, however, applies only to the *Hersilia,* for between November 27 and January 12 a total of 50,895 skins had been discharged at the fleet. Since he twice referred specifically to other American vessels, it is reasonable to assume that he would have done so again in the last paragraph if the voyage to 66° S had been made by a vessel other than one with which he was associated. Yet, it is not likely that the *Hersilia* made such a voyage. It is quite clear from the full entries in the logbook of the *Hero* that the *Hersilia* did not make such a voyage between November 12 and December 18. Before that, ice conditions would not have been conducive to a penetration so far south, and the men were then also busy establishing their positions on the beaches. After December 18 it would not have been practical to risk so large a vessel with a partial cargo of skins on such a venture when the *Hero* or the *Free Gift* would have been more suitable.

Entries for November 26, December 10, and December 13 in the logbook of the *Hero* specifically refer to "Mr. Clark" as head of one of the sealing camps on the south shore of Livingston Island. It is conceivable, however, that Clark was relieved of this duty as the number of seals declined and that he was transferred to a vessel, perhaps the *Hero,* bound on a cruise to the south. If no more seals were arriving on his beach on Livingston Island, he and his whole crew might well have been put aboard to be transferred to a new beach inhabited with seals, if one were found.

Another bit of contemporary evidence is found in the report of Mr. J. N. Reynolds submitted to the Secretary of the Navy under date of September 24, 1828.[33] Reynolds had been commissioned by the Secretary to interview New England whalers and sealers regarding islands and shoals which they had discovered and which were not accurately located. This was done as a preliminary to the preparations for the proposed government expedition of 1829. The following excerpts are from pages 26 and 27 of the published report.

... Captain Pendleton, of Stonington, Connecticut, one of the most practical and intelligent sealers I met with, and who has spent many years in the South Sea fur trade, is strongly of the opinion that there are many valuable discoveries to be made in the seas southwest of the Shetlands. The quality of the ice, nature of the currents, &c. make his conjecture highly probable.

... On the northern part of Palmer's land, and in latitude 66° S. and in about 63° W. longitude, Captain Pendleton discovered a bay, clear of ice, into which he run for a great distance, but could not ascertain its full extent south. In these seas the prevailing winds are from W. N. W. to W. S. W., and all gales from northeast. A gale seldom continues more than six hours. Clear weather from S. S. W. and S. S. E., which is not many days in a month.

Whether Pendleton's discovery of a bay in about 66° S was made in 1821 or the following season, when he was also at the South Shetlands, cannot be determined from evidence now available.[34] Neither has evidence been found to justify Martin's assertion that the discovery was actually Palmer's.[35] It is possible that Pendleton, as leader of the fleet, accompanied Palmer on an exploratory cruise in the *Hero,* but he might also have made an independent cruise. Chapters 5 and 6 will show that other American sealers, while their ships were moored at Yankee Harbor in charge of a small band of "ship keepers," sailed on exploratory cruises in their tenders or shallops. Captain John Davis and Captain Christopher Burdick, who were associated in a joint enterprise, more than once left their vessels to go on cruises in the shallop *Cecilia.* Captain Robert Johnson, leader of the New York fleet of James Byers and master of the brig *Jane Maria,* also made an exploratory cruise to the southwest in his shallop *Sarah.* Therefore, it is possible that Pendleton, like them, left the *Frederick* and the rest of his fleet for a time while he led an exploratory cruise in the *Hero.*

The noted French explorer, Dr. Jean-B. Charcot, led two expeditions to the west side of the Antarctic Peninsula early in the 20th century. In the narrative of his second expedition, under date of January 13, 1909, in his journal, he makes the following statement:

The great inlet at whose entrance we are is situated in 66°15′ South latitude. Although it does not appear on the English Admiralty charts, it seems to me very probable that it was seen and perhaps even visited by the sealing captain B. Pendleton, of whom we have already spoken in connexion with Deception Island and who commanded the flotilla on which was N. Palmer.

After quoting the Reynolds report, Charcot goes on to say:

These last statements prove that Pendleton at least sailed in these regions, although our experience is that even in the good season the north-easterly gales often last more than six hours.

It seems to me only just to give this bay, whose entrance we have definitely marked on the map, the name of Pendleton, which will at all events recall a brave American captain who visited these regions and deserves to have his name commemorated here.[36]

Charcot later read a paper before the Royal Geographical Society of London on December 19, 1910, in which he said:

Almost exactly in the latitude indicated by the American whaler Pendleton we succeeded, by passing between some of the more widely spaced of the Biscoe islands, in making our way into a vast bay encumbered by ice. The details given by Pendleton prove without question that he did cruise in this region, and I do not doubt for a moment that the bay indicated by him is really that rediscovered by us.[37]

The evidence at hand indicates the possibility of three separate exploratory cruises southwestward along the western side of Antarctic Peninsula by vessels of the Fanning-Pendleton fleet in 1820-21. It is possible, however, as explained above, that all of the statements refer to the same voyage. If such is the case, it would most likely be that of the *Hero,* for no vessel is specifically named by Clark or Pendleton.

With such strong evidence that at least one and possibly three exploratory cruises were made to the southwest, the big mystery is Palmer's failure to make any record of such in the logbook of the *Hero.* Martin has speculated on this.[38] The official crew list shows the *Hero* carried a total of five men, including Palmer. The logbook entries from November 25 to December 18 show that the little craft and her crew were kept on a continual round of activities servicing the men on the beaches. This was very hard work, in which the officers took part, yet the record shows there was never a break for a rest. What rest they had was on watches when they were off duty, but on the short cruises from camp to camp, watches were often interrupted and all hands turned to. Under such conditions, keeping the logbook was an added responsibility that seems to have been dispensed with as soon as the cruises about Livingston Island became routine. William A. Fanning, Pendleton, Sheffield, Williams, and Palmer himself were financially involved in the enterprise. They needed no logbook as a record of Palmer's activities at the South Shetlands. This explanation, however, cannot apply to a cruise of exploration.

If Pendleton accompanied Palmer on the exploratory cruise to the southwest, perhaps he kept the logbook. Captain Davis kept the record of his cruises in the *Cecilia* in the logbook of the *Huron*.

It has been suggested that Palmer made rough entries in a small pocket notebook with the intention of later transcribing them in the logbook. He is known to have done this on a later voyage in the *Southerner*. This would also have been consistent with the practice of others who calculated positions and jotted remarks on a slate from which they were copied in the logbook at the end of the day. On the assumption that Palmer kept such a rough log and on a clue gained from a letter, dated in 1938, in the papers of Colonel Lawrence Martin, Lieutenant Richard D. Kane (U.S.N.R.) interviewed Mr. Charles H. Cushman of Westerly, Rhode Island, on March 24, 1954. Mr. Cushman said that he had seen the logbook of the "whaling ship," as he called it, many times. In it, he said, was a reference to meeting the Russian warships and to the discovery of land which was of little use because it was "too frigid." Mr. Cushman stated that he was under the impression that the owner of the logbook, Mr. Donald P. Stanton, had destroyed the logbook many years ago. Consistent with this statement was one by Mr. A. P. Loper, Nathaniel B. Palmer's grand-nephew, who told Lieutenant Kane that Mr. Stanton had destroyed many old papers which he had inherited from his father, and that among these papers were a lot of Palmer material. The destroyed papers apparently contained information concerning his family, which Mr. Stanton considered personal and private. Miss Lillian Palmer, who inherited the remaining papers from Mr. Stanton in 1933, was unable to give any clues as to the missing material.

THE HOMEWARD VOYAGE

The logbook of the *Huntress,* the Nantucket schooner which also moored at Yankee Harbor in 1820-21, records the departure of the *Free Gift* for the United States on February 4, 1821. New England newspaper items, however, indicate that the *Free Gift* arrived home on May 2, 1821, in company with the brig *Frederick* and that the two vessels had left the South Shetlands at the same time. Palmer recorded in the logbook of the *Hero* that he "Got underweigh for Sea in Company with the Express Frederick & Hersilia" on the morning of February

22, 1821. It would appear, therefore, that the *Free Gift* did leave at an earlier date and that the schooner had a rendezvous with the *Frederick* at some point on the homeward voyage, perhaps at Staten Island or at the Falklands. Three of the vessels which departed from Yankee Harbor on February 22, 1821, sailed for home, but the *Hersilia*, as related by Daniel W. Clark, was bound for the Pacific. On the morning of March 1, as the *Hero* sailed past the Falkland Islands on the homeward voyage, land was sighted to the westward at a distance of 14 leagues. By then the *Express* and the *Frederick* were no longer in company with the *Hero*.

The *Express* arrived at Stonington on April 29, 1821. The *Frederick* and the *Free Gift* arrived on May 2, and the *Hero* reached home on May 8. The *Hersilia* never returned from the Pacific. On May 13, 1821, she was captured by Chilean patriots off the coast of Chile and converted into a warship, which later burned at Arauco. The crew was imprisoned, but most of the men returned to the United States later after escaping from their captors.

NOTES

1. The purpose of this chapter is to give a fresh and straightforward account of the activities of the Fanning-Pendleton fleet as a result of the author's reexamination of available data. No purpose can be served by detailing the long and often heated controversy over whether Bransfield or Palmer first saw the Antarctic mainland. It would take more space than is available here. Readers who wish to pursue the matter are referred to the bibliography below for three papers by Lawrence Martin, and to the paper by William H. Hobbs, for arguments in favor of Palmer. The position of Martin and Hobbs has been challenged in papers by R. N. Rudmose Brown, by R. T. Gould, and by Arthur R. Hinks. A still different approach has been taken by Edouard A. Stackpole in his book *The Voyage of the Huron and the Huntress* (see the bibliography). There is now evidence (See note 69, page 193) that Bellingshausen reported seeing ice-covered land on January 16, 1820, two weeks before Bransfield's landfall on January 30, 1820.

2. William Channing Woodbridge included a map of the world in two hemispheres in his *Modern Atlas on a New Plan to Accompany the System of Universal Geography by William Channing Woodbridge*, published by Oliver D. Cooke, Hartford, Conn., and copyrighted September 28, 1821. The South Shetland Islands were shown on the western hemisphere map, and south of them is an indication of land which is labeled "Palmer's Land." See William H. Hobbs, "The Discoveries of Antarctica within the American Sector, as revealed by Maps and Documents," *Transactions of the American Philosophical Society*, new series, vol. 31, Part I, January 1939, frontispiece and pp. 23-24. "Palmer's Land" also appeared on *Chart of South Shetland including Coronation Island, &c. from the Exploration of the Sloop Dove in the Years 1821 and 1822* by George Powell, published by R. H. Laurie, London, 1822. Through the years, usage has changed with more complete exploration by expeditions of various kinds from 10 different countries. In the United States, first Palmer Land and then Palmer Peninsula was applied to the mountainous peninsula that extends in a great arc toward South America. Several countries have used Graham Land, which was applied by John Biscoe after his discovery of Adelaide Island and the Biscoe Islands in 1832 and which became the official British name. Chile has named the peninsula Tierra O'Higgins, and Argentina has used the name Tierra de San Martin for it. Since 1958, scientists have increasingly used the name Antarctic Peninsula. In 1964 the name Antarctic Peninsula was officially adopted for use in the United States, the United Kingdom, Australia, and New Zealand. The peninsula can be conveniently divided into a narrower northern part, north of 69° S, and a broader southern part. In 1964 these same English-speaking countries adopted the name Graham Land for the northern part and Palmer Land for the southern part. For many decades there has been almost universal acceptance of the name Palmer Archipelago applied to Brabant, Anvers, and adjacent smaller islands.

3. Edmund Fanning, *Voyages Round the World* (New York, 1833), pp. 434-438. Palmer's activities also have gained the attention of scholars due to the fact that his logbooks, including the logbook of the *Hero*, and his papers were made available by his niece, Mrs. Richard Fan-

ning Loper, and were later deposited in the Manuscript Division of the Library of Congress, where they have been available for many years. Since November 23, 1932, the papers of Edmund Fanning have been available to scholars at the American Geographical Society of New York.

4. Fanning, op. cit., p. 434.

5. These maps have been reproduced by Lawrence Martin in "Antarctica Discovered by a Connecticut Yankee, Captain Nathaniel Brown Palmer," Geographical Review, vol. 30, No. 4, October, 1940, Fig. 5, p. 533.

6. Edmund M. Blunt, The American Coast Pilot (New York, 1822), 10th ed., p. 497.

7. Palmer's first entry is dated November 15, but the cruise actually began at 2 p. m., November 14. It must be understood that Palmer, following the accepted procedure of his time, was using what he called a "sea day" or what was often referred to as a "sea account." (See Chap. 3, p. 49.) Throughout this account, except when the logbook is being quoted directly, nautical days have been converted where necessary to calendar days.

8. In view of the controversies regarding the interpretation of the logbook of the Hero, Capt. Harold E. Saunders (USN Ret.) and Capt. John W. McElroy (USNR) were asked to review independently the entries pertaining to Palmer's cruise in November 1820. They independently reached the same conclusions, and the present account is in accord with their interpretation. Capt. Saunders was cartographer for the First and Second Byrd Antarctic Expeditions and had a wide range of experience in Antarctic matters as well as experience in sailing small craft. Capt. McElroy assisted Dr. Samuel Eliot Morison on problems of navigation involved in the latter's biography of Columbus, Admiral of the Ocean Sea. He also served as navigator on Morison's yawl when Morison tried to retrace Columbus' route.

9. For data on magnetic declination see Martin, op. cit., footnote 3, p. 534. See also note 20, Chap. 3.

10. In his interpretation of Palmer's logbook, Lawrence Martin felt that the Hero sailed down the west side of Deception Island to reach Neptunes Bellows; that the apparent harbor which Palmer found disappointing was the great breach in the crater wall on the southwest side of the island. See Martin, op. cit., pp. 530-531 and Fig. 2.

11. Martin, op. cit., p. 545.

12. For a published photographic copy of this map see Lt. Comdr. R. T. Gould, R. N. (Ret.), "The Charting of the South Shetlands, 1819-28," Mariner's Mirror, vol. 94, No. 4, October 1939, Plate 3. Also, E. W. Hunter Christie, The Antarctic Problem (London, 1951), Plate VII, opposite p. 225.

13. Gould, op. cit., p. 226.

14. Robert Fildes, "A Journal of a voyage kept on board Brig Cora of Liverpool bound to New South Shetland." Public Record Office, London, 753 Adm. 55/143. The sailing directions follow the journal in the bound volume, and a typescript of them is available at the Scott Polar Research Institute, Cambridge, England, Reference Ms. 393.

15. Fildes, "Journal," op. cit., p. 51. Typescript copy of "Sailing Directions," op. cit., p. 7.

16. Assuming the level of a man's eye on the deck of the Hero to have been 9 feet above sea level, any elevation over 1000 feet above sea level would have been visible 40 miles away in clear weather. The axial line of the peninsula behind Trinity Island is about 70 miles south of Deception Island. At this distance anything over 3400 feet high should have been visible to a man on the deck of the Hero. From the masthead the range of visibility would have been still greater. See [Nathaniel Bowditch] American Practical Navigator, U. S. Navy, Hydrographic Office, No. 9, Washington, 1943, Part 2, p. 130.

17. The strait was named by the French explorer Dumont D'Urville, who saw it at the end of February 1838 and mapped it as a bay.

18. Edouard A. Stackpole does not agree with this interpretation up to this point. See his The Voyage of the Huron and the Huntress (Marine Historical Association, Mystic, Conn., 1955), pp. 28-32. He feels that after tacking about in the snow storm between Deception and Livingston Islands on the night of November 14, Palmer did not return to Deception Island but instead explored the south coast of Livingston Island. He contends that on November 15 and 16 Palmer was exploring South Bay and False Bay on the south shore of Livingston Island instead of Deception Island. In support for his contention he points out that Weddell named False Bay "Palmer's Bay." (James Weddell, A Voyage Towards the South Pole Performed in the Years 1822-1824 [London, 1825], Chart of South Shetland, etc., facing p. 132.) He further insists that Palmer did not sail south to the Antarctic Peninsula on November 16, that there is no supporting evidence for Palmer's stated latitude of 63°45′ S, and that he was actually at the southern entrance to McFarlane Strait instead of at the northeastern portal of Orléans Strait. In rebuttal it must be stated that it is hard to conceive of Palmer spending so much time beat-

ing about the strait between Deception Island and Livingston Island after he cleared the harbor at 10:00 a. m., November 16, especially since he continually reported pleasant or fine weather with southwest breezes. Moreover, there is no justification for discounting Palmer's recorded latitude.

19. The name "dunbar" as a geographical term must have had special significance for the Stonington sealers, perhaps even in a facetious reference to their fellow mariner, Thomas Dunbar, Jr. In the logbook of the *Hero* for 1821-22, kept by Harris Pendleton, there is a notation that the sloop got "through the Dunbars." Whatever its meaning, the term never entered the professional vocabularies of the geographer, the geologist, or the hydrographer. Palmer's caution is supported by Captain Fildes who in his "Sailing Directions" (see note 14, above) wrote, "The North entrance into McFarlane's Straits should not be attempted by a vessel of 9 feet unless well acquainted. . . ."

20. McFarlane Strait is so named on Powell's map of the South Shetlands, published in 1822, *op. cit.* It apparently commemorated Captain McFarlane of the British brig *Dragon,* who arrived at the South Shetlands about November 1, 1820. His connection with the strait is not known. Weddell on his map of 1825, *op. cit.,* named it Duff's Straits.

21. No evidence has been found to support Martin's parenthetical application of Port Williams to Deception Island. ("Antarctica Discovered . . .," *op. cit.,* p. 529). Logbooks for eight American sealing voyages to the South Shetlands in the 1820s have now been located. Those which contain any reference to Deception Island refer to Deception Bay or Deception Harbor or to the harbor in Deception. Exceptions are two instances in 1821-22: on November 6 the *Alabama Packet* "Came a Anchor in Deception Harbour now called Port Dunbar." There is one reference in the logbook of the *Hero* for the same season to "Dunbar's Harbor."

22. From the context of this and other entries where Palmer mentions "Dread Point," it would appear to apply to the tip of the long narrow peninsula on Livingston Island forming the southwest portal of McFarlane Strait in about 62°37'S, 59°48'W, Renier Point.

23. Martin, *op. cit.,* p. 545.

24. Captain Christopher Burdick, Logbook of the schooner *Huntress,* property of Edouard A. Stackpole, and quoted by Stackpole in *The Voyage . . ., op. cit.,* p. 58.

25. Martin, *op. cit.,* pp. 541-551.

26. Arthur R. Hinks, "The Log of the Hero," *Geographical Journal,* vol. 96, No. 6, 1940, pp. 428-430.

27. Fanning, *op. cit.,* pp. 434-436. Although he was closely connected with the enterprise, the elder Fanning did not participate in the voyage of 1820-21 and never visited the South Shetlands. Writing more than a decade later, he confused events of the 1820-21 season with those of 1821-22. For instance, he said the fleet in 1820-21 was moored at Deception Island, which he mistakenly refers to as Yankee Harbor. Deception Island was used as the fleet headquarters in 1821-22. Fanning described only one exploratory cruise to the south, presumably that in January 1821, and does not mention the November 1820 cruise. He could not have had the logbooks in his possession and was obviously writing from memory.

28. Frank Debenham (editor), *The Voyage of Captain Bellingshausen to the Antarctic Seas 1819-1821* (translated from the Russian), Hakluyt Society, 2nd ser. No. 91, 1945, London, vol. 2, pp. 425-426. Bellingshausen gave the date of the meeting as January 25, according to the Julian calendar. To convert this to the Gregorian calendar it is necessary to add 12 days. For Debenham's comments about the meeting, see pages xxiii-xxvii.

29. A photograph of this part of the copy of Palmer's letter, apparently not in Palmer's handwriting, is included in Fig. 7, p. 537, in Martin's article in the *Geographical Review, op. cit.*

30. For a reproduction of a portion of this map see William H. Hobbs, "The Discoveries of Antarctica within the American Sector, as Revealed by Maps and Documents," *Transactions, American Philosophical Society,* new series, vol. 31, Part 1, January, 1939, Plate 7, lower part.

31. A. J. von Kruzenstern, *Voyage Round the World, in the years 1803, 1804, 1805 and 1806* (translated by Hoppner), 2 vols. in one (London, 1813).

32. Edwin S. Balch, "Stonington Antarctic Explorers," *Bulletin of the American Geographical Society,* vol. 41, No. 8, August, 1909, p. 478; John R. Spears, *Captain Nathaniel Brown Palmer, An Old-Time Sailor of the Sea* (New York, 1922), pp. 70-75; Hobbs, *op. cit.,* pp. 18-21; Martin, *op. cit.,* pp. 545-546, 548.

33. "Report of J. N. Reynolds of facts obtained at Nantucket of South Sea and Pacific Ocean," filed in Record Group 45, Naval Records Section, U. S. National Archives. Published as "Letter from the Secretary of the Navy, transmitting a report of J. N. Reynolds, in relation to islands, reefs, and shoals in the Pacific Ocean, etc." Referred to the Committee on Commerce, January 27, 1835, House Doc. 105, 23rd Congr., 2nd Sess., 1835.

34. The longitude given by Pendleton is about 3°30′ too far east, but such errors in longitude were common in that day.

35. Martin, *op. cit.*, p. 549.

36. Dr. Jean-B. Charcot, *The Voyage of the 'Why Not?' in the Antarctic*, translated by Philip Walsh (London, 1911), p. 85. Subsequent exploration has shown the bay to be actually a strait, and the name of this feature has accordingly been changed to Pendleton Strait.

37. Dr. Jean-B. Charcot, "The Second French Antarctic Expedition," *Geographical Journal*, vol. 37, No. 3, March, 1911, pp. 250-252.

38. Martin, *op. cit.*, pp. 544-545.

BIBLIOGRAPHY

PUBLISHED MATERIAL

Balch, Edwin Swift, *Antarctica* (Philadelphia, Allen, Lane & Scott, 1902), 230 pp., map.

——, "Stonington Antarctic Explorers," *Bulletin American Geographical Society*, vol. 41, No. 8, August, 1909, pp. 473-492.

Bellingshausen, Thaddeus, *The Voyage of Captain Bellingshausen to the Antarctic Seas 1819-1821*, 2 vols., Hakluyt Society, 2nd series, Nos. 91-92; edited by Frank Debenham (London, Hakluyt Society, 1945), 474 pp., maps.

Blunt, Edmund M., *The American Coast Pilot* (New York, Edmund M. Blunt, 10 ed., 1822), xviii and 497 pp.

Boston Patriot & Daily Mercantile Advertiser, May 3, 5 and 12, 1821.

Brown, R. N. Rudmose, "Antarctic History: a Reply to Professor W. H. Hobbs," *Scottish Geographical Magazine*, vol. 55, No. 3, May 1939, pp. 170-173.

Bush, Frank T., "History of the Discovery of Palmer's Land," *Daily Globe*, New London, Conn., September 10, 1881.

Charcot, Dr. Jean-B., "The Second French Antarctic Expedition," *Geographical Journal*, vol. 37, No. 3, March, 1911, pp. 241-260.

——, *The Voyage of the 'Why Not?' in the Antarctic*, translated by Philip Walsh (London, Hodder and Stoughton, 1911), viii and 315 pp., illus.

Christie, E. W. Hunter, *The Antarctic Problem* (London, Allen & Unwin, 1951), 336 pp., maps, illus.

Connecticut Gazette, New London, May 17, 24, 1820; August 2, 16, 1820; May 2, 9, 1821.

Connecticut Journal, New Haven, May 2, 1821.

Fanning, Edmund, *Voyages Round the World* (New York, Collins and Hannay, 1833), 499 pp.

The Gazette, Providence, R. I., May 9, 1821.

Gould, Lt.-Comdr. R. T., R. N. (Ret.), "The First Sighting of the Antarctic Continent," *Geographical Journal*, vol. 65, No. 3, March, 1925, pp. 220-225.

——, "The Charting of the South Shetlands, 1819-28," *Mariner's Mirror*, vol. 27, No. 3, July, 1941, pp. 206-242.

A. R. H. [Hinks, A. R.], "On Some Misrepresentations of Antarctic History," *Geographical Journal*, vol. 94, No. 4, October, 1939, pp. 309-330.

Hinks, Arthur R., "The Log of the Hero," *Geographical Journal*, vol. 96, No. 6, December, 1940, pp. 419-430.

——, "Antarctica Discovered: A Reply," *Geographical Review*, vol. 31, No. 3, July, 1941, pp. 491-498.

Hobbs, William Herbert, "The Discoveries of Antarctica within the American Sector, as Revealed by Maps and Documents," *Transactions of the American Philosophical Society*, new series, vol. 31, Part I, January, 1939, pp. 1-70, 31 plates.

Loper, Mrs. Richard Fanning [article on N. B. Palmer], *Daily Globe*, New London, Conn., January 28, 1907.

Martin, Lawrence, "The Log of Palmer's Discovery of Antarctica," *Science*, vol. 87, new series No. 2251, February 18, 1938, pp. 165-166.

——, "Palmer's Instrumental Observations in Connection with the Discovery of Antarctica," *Science*, vol. 87, new series No. 2264, May 20, 1938, pp. 465-466.

——, "Antarctica Discovered by a Connecticut Yankee, Captain Nathaniel Brown Palmer," *Geographical Review*, vol. 30, No. 4, October, 1940, pp. 529-552.

Mill, Hugh R., *The Siege of the South Pole* (London, Alston Rivers Ltd., 1905), xvi and 455 pp., maps.

Niles Weekly Register, vols. 19-23, September, 1820-March, 1823. Various articles copied from New England newspapers. See index for each volume.

Republican Advocate, New London, Conn., July 26, 1820; August 2, 1820; May 2, 1821.

Reynolds, J. N., "Report of in relation to islands, reefs, and shoals in the Pacific Ocean, Etc.," transmitted as a letter from the Secretary of the Navy and referred to the Committee on Commerce, January 27, 1835, House Doc. 105, 23rd Congr., 2nd Sess., 1835.

Spears, John R., *Captain Nathaniel Brown Palmer, An Old-Time Sailor of the Sea* (New York, Macmillan, 1922), 252 pp.

Stackpole, Edouard A., *The Sea-Hunters* (Philadelphia, J. B. Lippincott, 1953), 510 pp. (See Chap. 25.)

———, *The Voyage of the Huron and the Huntress* (Mystic, Conn.: Marine Historical Association, Publ. No. 29, 1955), 86 pp., map.

Woodbridge, William Channing, *Modern Atlas on a New Plan to Accompany the System of Universal Geography by William Channing Woodbridge,* (Hartford, Conn., Oliver D. Cooke, 1821).

MANUSCRIPT MATERIAL

Crew List of the *Hero,* 1820, New London, Conn., Custom House Records, Federal Records Center, Waltham, Mass.

The Papers of Edmund Fanning, American Geographical Society, New York, N. Y.

Fildes, Capt. Robert, "Remarks made during a Voyage to New South Shetland," typescript copy in Scott Polar Research Institute, Ref. Ms 393, 16 pp. Original titled, "A Journal of a Voyage kept on board Brig Cora of Liverpool bound to New South Shetland." Public Record Office, 753 Adm. 55/143.

Logbook of the sloop *Hero,* 1820-1821, Marine Misc., Acc. 3680, Manuscript Division, Library of Congress.

Logbook of the schooner *Huntress,* 1820-1821, personal property of Edouard A. Stackpole, Nantucket, Mass., formerly Curator of the Marine Historical Association, Mystic, Conn.

The papers of Alexander S. and Nathaniel B. Palmer, Acc. 3807, Manuscript Division, Library of Congress. (18 boxes.)

Ship Registrations, Port of New London. Brig *Hersilia,* No. 9, July 20, 1819; brig *Frederick,* Nos. 3-4, May 2, 1820; schooner *Free Gift,* No. 5, May 15, 1820; schooner *Express,* No. 10, July 25, 1820; sloop *Hero,* No. 11, July 25, 1820. Vessel Documentation Series, Records of the Bureau of Marine Inspection and Navigation, Record Group 41, U. S. National Archives. The brig *Hersilia* was registered again (due to partial change in ownership) on July 28, 1820, but the certificate was never surrendered because of the ship's capture and destruction in Chile.

5

THE SEALING EXPEDITION OF THE *HURON* AND THE *HUNTRESS*, 1820-1821

ORGANIZATION AND ACCOMPLISHMENTS

SIGNIFICANCE OF THE EXPEDITION

Two logbooks were discovered in the early 1950s which record the operations of the ship *Huron* of New Haven, Connecticut, and of the schooner *Huntress* of Nantucket Island, Massachusetts, on a joint sealing voyage in the South Shetlands in the austral summer of 1820-21.[1] Nothing about the operations of these vessels at the South Shetlands was known in modern times until the discovery of these logbooks. The logbook of the *Huron* bears witness to what may be the first landing on the Antarctic continent, in the vicinity of Hughes Bay, February 7, 1821. At least, it is the first landing supported by documentary evidence.[2]

ESTABLISHMENT AND COMPOSITION OF THE EXPEDITION

The joint operation of Captains Davis and Burdick during the austral summer of 1820-21 began as separate sealing voyages. Their agreement to join forces and operate as a unit was made at the Falkland Islands. It would seem to have been mutually advantageous, for Captain Burdick supplied information and Captain Davis supplied the shallop. Since Captain Davis was supplying the shallop and approximately twice as many men, it was agreed that he would receive roughly three-fourths of the sealskins taken by the combined crews.

The *Huron,* according to its register at the New Haven Custom House, was a square-rigged ship of 250 tons and 89 feet, 8 inches long, built at Guilford, Connecticut, in 1819. She was owned by Elias Shipman, Solomon Collis, Asa Bradley, and 16 other men. The *Huntress* was an 80-ton two-masted schooner, 68 feet long, built at Barnstable, Massachusetts, in 1817. Captain Burdick was listed as one of four owners, all of Nantucket. The *Cecilia* was a small schooner, probably assembled by Captain Davis' crew at the Falkland Islands from precut framing and planking brought in the hold of the *Huron.* Her dimensions are unknown as her register has not been found. According to an item in the *Connecticut Journal* of July 16, 1822, the "Young Huron" was sold for $500. This would indicate that she was a small vessel which would be consistent with her role as a tender or shallop. It is not known whether the term "Young Huron" was a nickname or whether it indicated a name change.

The combined crews of the three vessels probably totaled somewhat more than 40 men. Captain Davis headed a company of 31 men when the *Huron* sailed from New Haven. Samuel H. Goddard was first mate and Charles Philips was second mate. The crew list of the *Huntress* cannot be found, and there is no secondary evidence which reveals the size of the crew. Comparable vessels, how-

89

ever, carried a crew of something like 15 men on a sealing voyage. Men from either or both larger vessels were used to man the *Cecilia* on its several cruises at the South Shetlands.

OBJECTIVES AND ACCOMPLISHMENTS

Like all sealers, Captains Davis and Burdick were primarily intent on obtaining a cargo of sealskins. If necessary, they were prepared to take elephant seals for their oil to fill out a cargo. Exploration was merely incidental and carried on to find seal rookeries.

Today, 150 years later, perhaps the most important result of the joint operation of Captains Davis and Burdick are their logbooks. The careful and detailed entries of these two men provide the best firsthand documentary evidence, now available, of the activities of the American sealers at the South Shetlands during 1820-21.

In his exploration for seal rookeries, Captain Davis circumnavigated the South Shetlands in the *Cecilia* at least once. He sailed the little schooner south from Low Island to the Antarctic Peninsula were a boat crew landed in the vicinity of Hughes Bay, February 7, 1821. This is one of the first landings on the Antarctic continent and the first for which the time and place is supported by documentary evidence.

DETAILED RECORD OF OPERATIONS

THE OUTBOUND VOYAGES

Captain John Davis and the ship *Huron* sailed from New Haven, Connecticut, March 20, 1820, bound for the Pacific Ocean, for so he reported when he stopped at "Bonavista" [Boa Vista] of the Cape Verde Islands on April 19. At the time he sailed, he probably was unaware of the discovery of the South Shetlands by Captain William Smith in 1819. Information about this discovery was not published in American newspapers until late March and early April.

The *Huron* was next reported in the Falkland Islands, where Captain Burdick found her on November 11, 1820, lying at anchor in Hope Harbor with the *Cecilia,* Captain Davis' shallop, and with another vessel and its shallop from Salem. Captain Davis was apparently not yet aware of the South Shetlands for Captain Burdick reported her, "Bound to the East'd."[3] The Salem vessel had been at the Falklands for two years but had only a partial cargo of oil and skins.

Captain Christopher Burdick had heard the news of the South Shetlands, and they were his destination when he sailed the schooner *Huntress* from his home port of Nantucket, August 4, 1820. He stopped en route first at the Azores and then at the Cape Verde Islands to take on salt for curing the sealskins he hoped to get.

Land was sighted at the Falkland Islands on October 31, and the *Huntress* was anchored in Bense Harbor off King George Bay in West Falkland. Here the salt in the hold was shifted to get at the mainmast which was hoisted out of its step and the lower five feet cut off. Finally, with the schooner's mast reset and the rigging replaced, the water casks filled, and the stores replenished, the *Huntress* got under way on November 11. Sailing through West Point Pass, the schooner finally entered Hope Harbor on the north side of West Point Island. Burdick was looking for a small schooner that had sailed by Bense Harbor on November 4, while the *Huntress* was being repaired. Its skipper had spoke the *Huntress* but failed to stop.[4] At Hope Harbor, as noted above, Burdick found Captain Davis and the *Huron*. There is no further reference in Burdick's logbook to the schooner he was seeking, nor is there any indication that the *Cecilia* or the Salem shallop was it. It was apparently at Hope Harbor that Davis and Burdick agreed to work together at the South Shetlands.

The *Huron*, the *Huntress*, and the *Cecilia* sailed in company from Hope Harbor on November 22. Staten Island, on the eastern tip of Tierra del Fuego, was sighted at 8 a.m., November 25, and the course was set for the South Shetlands, to the south-southeast. After experiencing thick, rainy weather, and a snow storm in crossing Drake Passage, land was sighted on November 30, bearing southeast. The weather did not improve, and the three vessels lay to or sailed off and on along the north coast of the South Shetlands. On December 3 the two larger vessels were forced to move offshore as a dense fog enveloped them, and while they tacked off and on for the next several days, the *Cecilia* went in search of a safe harbor. A day later the shallop had located Yankee Harbor, where four vessels of the Fanning-Pendleton fleet lay at anchor, but because of thick weather it was not until December 7 that the *Cecilia* was again in company with the *Huron* and the *Huntress*. Early on that day the *Cecilia* began leading the two larger vessels into McFarlane Strait to Yankee Harbor. In the logbook of the *Huntress* for December 8, Burdick wrote:

. . . At 4 p. m. hauled our wind to Beat up the harbor in Co with ship Huron of New Haven and her shallop. Middle and Latter part brisk winds. Stood in the Yanky Sound and went into harbor came two at 6 a. m. in 16 fathoms. Landlocked found four Stonington vessels here. So ends sea account.

Since Burdick was following nautical practice, his day began at noon, 12 hours in advance of the civil calendar. Therefore, he began beating up McFarlane Strait on the afternoon of December 7 and came to anchor at 6 a. m., December 8.

Captain Burdick's logbook shows that no time was wasted in securing the schooner and the ship, and getting on with the business of sealing. On December 9, the *Cecilia* set out to look for seal rookeries. Burdick sent William Coleman, first mate of the *Huntress*, with eight men and a whaleboat aboard the shallop. Davis sent out 22 men and two whaleboats on the *Cecilia*. By December 28 the *Cecilia* had made three cruises along the south shore of Livingston Island. The second had been made with Burdick in command of the shallop, and the third was made by Davis. In 20 days the combined crews of the *Huron* and the *Huntress* had collected only 2527 sealskins. This must have been a discouragingly small number compared to the some 21,000 skins that the crews of the Fanning-Pendleton fleet had collected in the same time, and it could have provided the motive for a 12-day cruise by Davis in the *Cecilia* in search of seal

rookeries to the eastward. It is succinctly summed up by Captain Burdick who
recorded Davis' return to Yankee Harbor on December 28.

... at 4 p. m. Capt. Davis returned with the shallop he had crused as far to the NE as
the Land Extended but found now Seal to speak of. He fell in with an English Ship
and Brig that wher Castaway; took part of ther Crews and put them on Board of English Vessels Lying at Reged Island. Returned by where the men were Stationed Brought
in 2470 Skins--took 969 on Board being my part.

Davis had apparently circumnavigated the South Shetlands from the eastern
end of King George Island to the western end of Livingston Island. Since the
pages of this part of Captain Davis' logbook are missing, his account of the
cruise and the probable identity of the British vessels is unavailable. Captain
Fildes reported, "On the north side of King George's Island was found a mast
step, and part of the keels and floor of two vessels, one supposed to be about 80,
and the other about 200 tons," but he did not identify them further.[5] He did
mention the brig *Lady Trowbridge,* commanded by Richard Sherratt, of Liverpool, which was wrecked on December 25, 1820, off Cape Melville, the southeastern point of King George Island. The *Hannah,* also of Liverpool, was
wrecked on the same day, but the position is not known.[6] It is probable that
these vessels were wrecked too late for Captain Davis to have rescued the crew,
taken them to Rugged Island, and returned to Yankee Harbor by December 28.
The *Lord Melville* was another British vessel reported to have been wrecked
off King George Island about this time.[7]

Meanwhile a fleet of four vessels from New York, including the shallop *Sarah,*
had joined the other Americans at Yankee Harbor. Captain Burdick had encountered these vessels on December 18 as he was heading for the sealing camps
on the south shore of Livingston Island in the *Cecilia,* and he found them in
Yankee Harbor when he returned on December 20. There were then anchored
at Yankee Harbor nine vessels, and in addition, three shallops operated from
there. The operations of the five vessels of the Fanning-Pendleton fleet of Stonington have been reported in Chapter 4; the activities of the New York fleet will
be described in Chapter 6.

With 30 American and at least 24 British vessels at the South Shetlands in
1820-21, things were becoming crowded, and as the wholesale slaughter of the
fur seals progressed competition at times became intense. James Byers, in his
letters to General Parker in August and September, quoted in Chapters 3 and
6, predicted friction between British and American sealers, but the sealers generally got along very well with one another. Perhaps their common struggle
against a hostile environment developed a sense of fellowship, regardless of na-
tionality. Captain Fildes reveals some of the competitive though not necessarily
unfriendly feeling that existed. Anchored at Desolation Island, off the north
shore of Livingston Island, on December 20 he made a long entry in his journal
of which the following excerpt is relevant:

Fresh Gales and cloudy at ½ past 2 A M the launch returned from the island with 128
fur seal skins could discover nothing like a place for shelter or holding better than
where in the Cora lay. had spoken the Boat of the American Ship Clothier which Ship
had been lost in endeavoring to find an Harbor [sic] ... The launch crew likewise got

the information of no less than eight vessels laying in a place scarely deserving the name of a harbor [sic] This news determined me to stop for the season where the Cora is I hope safely fast in Port Wood as we are now getting at the rate of 100 skins a day off the ——— of Coast facing Cora's Island Port Wood && at 11 p m dispatched the launch to the Westward. the wind blowing from the East . . . The launches crew had orders to seal first outside the range of the whale boats, and to continue then onto [?] to the westward as long the [sic] had good success, and as our present situation Port Wood not appearing to have been discovered before, and me wanting no body here but myselfe [sic] I likewise gave them orders to conceal our present situation and our success also but above all to endeavor to find good holding ground and a harbour safer than (if any here about exists) our own. . . .

Two incidents are reported, one by Fildes and the other by Davis and Burdick, which show that if hostility did arise from the competition in a business where the stakes were high it was not necessarily motivated by anti-British or anti-American feeling. On December 23 Fildes reported the following:

. . . at 4 No 1 and 2 whale boats returned with eighty skins each being as much as the boat would hold had been threatened by the united crews of 4 vessells to be knocked down if they killed a seal on what they pleased to call their premises the beach in a manner being alive with Seals their numbers being Incredible.[8]

Fildes was not willing to be intimidated and when his first mate returned without any skins on December 27, sought the captains of the four vessels who agreed to allot a portion of the beach to his men. However, his victory was a costly one, for in his absence a gale from the east northeast arose which prevented him from returning to the brig. Meanwhile, on January 6 the *Cora* dragged her anchor, struck a submerged rock, and then went ashore where she quickly broke up.

One of the New York vessels anchored at Yankee Harbor was the brig *Charity*, commanded by Captain Charles H. Barnard. Apparently a crew in one of his whaleboats had a brush with the same British sealers that Captain Fildes' men had encountered. Burdick reports this incident and a similar one by his own men on January 24:

. . . a boat came in belonging to Captain Barnard brig Charity having ben robed of Eighty Skins by the English at Sheriff's Cape and Drove off the Beach 4 P. M. our Boat came in from a Cruse with 52 having Likewise ben Drove from the beach at Sheriffs Cape by the English wher he said there was plenty of Seal.

Burdick and Davis report in their logbooks the ensuing attempts at retaliation taken by the captains at Yankee Harbor. The story is well told by Stackpole, who also reports a third encounter, this apparently in November or December, 1820, between men on the beaches on the north shore of Livingston Island and a landing party from the British sealer *Hetty* of London, commanded by Captain Ralph Bond. Several of Bond's men were injured in the fracas.[9] Although the British and American sealers generally got on well together, such treatment must have rankled Captain Barnard who, as Stackpole points out, had his vessel seized by the British in the wartime year of 1813 after he had rescued the crew, including marines, of a British vessel at the Falkland Islands.

The nine masters of sealing vessels then at Yankee Harbor held a conference

aboard the *Huron* in which it was agreed to ". . . muster all our men from our
Several Camps and as one body to go on to said beach at Sheriff's Cape and to
take Seal by fair means if we Could but at all Events to take them. So Ends."[10]
At 6 a. m., January 26, Captain Benjamin J. Brunow of the New York schooner

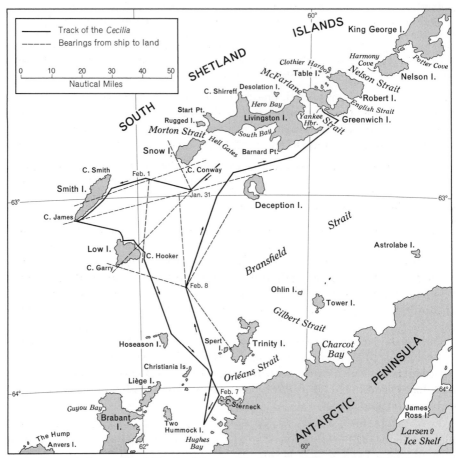

FIGURE 4. Generalized Track of the *Cecilia*, January 31 to February 10, 1821.

Henry set out in a whaleboat with the first officer from the *Express* of the Fanning-Pendleton fleet to gather all but one man from each of the camps on the
various beaches. By this means it was hoped to muster a total of 120 men. At
8 p. m. that evening Davis and Barnard with five boats and 33 men set out in
the *Cecilia* to meet Captain Brunow and the men he was to have mustered, apparently at Blythe Bay, off Desolation Island. The shallop had to be towed out
of McFarlane Strait when the winds died down and finally came to anchor at
Blythe Bay at 7 p. m. January 27. Later they were joined by Captain Robert
Johnson in the shallop *Sarah*.

    Leaving Blythe Bay, they sailed south and westward toward Cape Shirreff. At
11 p. m. they met Captain Brunow. In his logbook Davis recorded, ". . . Capt

Bruno came alongside in his boat and reported he had examined the Beaches round Sheriffs Cape and Saw but a very few Seal nothing to make an object to stop for. . . ."[11]

It would appear that Brunow had not mustered the men as planned, and as a result of his report the American sealers dispersed. Most returned to Yankee Harbor, but Davis in the *Cecilia* and Johnson in the *Sarah* proceeded westward. Davis sent a crew in a whaleboat to land at Cape Shirreff. Samuel H. Goddard, first mate, returned to the shallop and reported that they had not been permitted to land, the beaches being held by 60 to 75 well-armed men. It is likely that Captain Brunow had also discovered this fact and that it had influenced his report to his compatriots. From Cape Shirreff, Captain Davis proceeded westward; Captain Johnson bore away to the north and eastward.

Captain Davis was on his way around the west end of Livingston Island to visit his and Burdick's men on the south shore. A day earlier he had recorded his plan in his logbook ". . . Concluded to make the best of our way for our People that is stationed on the South Beach and then to go on a cruise to find new Lands as the Seal is done here. . . ."

Having visited his crews on the beaches on the south side of Livingston Island by January 30, Davis began his cruise to find new lands, the cruise which resulted in a boat crew from the *Cecilia* landing on the shores of the Antarctic Peninsula in the vicinity of Hughes Bay (Fig. 4). He first steered for Smith Island. The logbook entry for January 31 fixes his position in terms of bearings to the surrounding islands.

. . . Middle part clear and Pleasant at Meridian our Latt was 63°-06' South at same time Mount Pisgo bore S W ½ W per compass, President Island NW by W, Deception Island NE and a new discovered Island S by W ½ W At P M discovered Land bearing from East by N to W by S. Ends with moderate breeze and clear weather.

The mariner's compass of that day was divided into 32 divisions, called points, of 11½ degrees each. The following table gives Davis' bearings as he recorded them in points and the equivalent degrees azimuth (reading clockwise from north for a total of 360°):

	Bearings in Points	Azimuths
Mount Pisgo [Smith Island]	SW ½ W	230°37'30"
President Island [Snow Island]	NW by W	303°45'00"
Deception Island	NE	45°00'00"
A new discovered Island [Low Island]	S by W ½ W	196°52'30"

He recorded his latitude as 63° 06' S, but gave no longitude.

To determine Davis' position a clear sheet of acetate on which lines were drawn to each of the azimuths from a point representing the *Cecilia* was placed over British Admiralty Chart 3205, *South Shetland Islands and Bransfield Strait*, January, 1967 (scale 1:500,000 at Lat. 67° S, Mercator projection). The acetate sheet was then moved about until a fit was found for the landmarks to which Davis made his bearings. In trying for such a fit it was assumed that Davis would take a bearing to either a prominent peak or to a bold headland or cape silhouetted against the sky rather than to the indeterminate center of an island.

Using Davis' uncorrected bearings gives very poor results, with only two of the four landmarks making any kind of a fit. It is possible to get a bearing on the north end (Cape Smith) of Smith Island and the east end (Cape Hooker) of Low Island from 63°17' S, 62°09' W, or to get a bearing on the southwest shore of Snow Island and the northwest headland of Deception Island from 62°57' S, 60°38' W. Neither of these is considered acceptable. By rotating the acetate sheet 24° clockwise to account for the magnetic declination calculated to exist in the South Shetlands in 1820 (see note 20, Chapter 3), three of the four landmarks, Cape James, Cape Hooker, and the southwest side of Snow Island, fit roughly from 62°54' S, 61°09' W. The bearing to the northeast, however, strikes Barnard Point on Livingston Island, considerably north of the north side of Deception Island.

It is interesting that the British sealing captain, James Weddell, gave the magnetic declination as 28° E. When this figure is used, and the acetate rotated an additional four degrees clockwise, a better fit is obtained to Cape James, the southwest side of Snow Island, and the north side of Deception Island. However, the bearing to Low Island is somewhat west of Cape Hooker at the east end of Low Island. This position (62°58'30" S, 61°18' W) for the *Cecilia* is accepted as the best possible (although not perfect) fit for the bearings given by Davis. His recorded latitude is thus 7½ minutes too far south. His recorded latitude is considered the least reliable because no fit is possible from any point on the parallel of 63°06'. This is not a serious discrepancy, and part of it can be explained by the fact that Davis probably had difficulty taking accurate bearings and sighting the sun from the pitching deck of a small vessel. In any case it is a close approximation of his actual position, and it is consistent with his immediate destination, Smith Island.

From his position midway between Smith and Deception Islands, Davis, with good visibility, had within sight a broad sweep of the Antarctic Peninsula and, to the southwest, Brabant and Anvers Islands. In his logbook he wrote, "At P M [sic] discovered Land bearing from East by N to W by S. Ends with moderate breeze and clear weather."[12]

There is no difficulty in determining rather precisely the position of the *Cecilia* on February 1, for which Davis wrote:

first and middle part fresh breeze from SBW with clear weather at noon our Latitude was 62° . . 56' South the middle of mount Pisgo bore SW dist 10 to 12 miles President Island NW 16 to 18 miles and anew Low Island discovered yesterday [Low Island] bore SSE 25 miles distance. . . .

Following the method used for January 31 and accepting Weddell's figure of 28° E for magnetic declination, Davis' bearings make an excellent fit to the north side of Mount Foster on Smith Island, to the east cape of Low Island (Cape Hooker) and to the south point of Snow Island (Cape Conway). It should be remembered that the Americans called Smith Island Mount Pisgah because its two peaks, Mount Foster and Mount Pisgah, reminded them of double-topped Mount Pisgah in the town of Durham, Connecticut. Therefore, sighting either one of the peaks or the saddle between them would have been a logical procedure for Davis. His estimated distance to Cape Hooker is correct, slightly overestimated to Cape Conway, and underestimated to Mount Foster. These bearings converge at 62°54′ S, 61°50′ W, two minutes or two nautical miles north of his recorded latitude.

If a magnetic declination of 24° E is accepted, the bearings do not fit quite as well, the bearing to Mount Foster being south instead of north of that peak and somewhat farther removed. Distances are approximately the same as above, and the position of the *Cecilia* would be 62°56′ S, 61°52′ E. Since using a compass declination of 28° E fits better for January 31 and almost exactly for February 1, it is considered to be more acceptable.

Clearly, the *Cecilia* was in the middle of Boyd Strait, midway between Smith and Snow Islands at noon February 1. Sailing around to the south side of Smith Island, Davis put a boat crew ashore to hunt seals. Since 17 British sealers were already encamped there, the *Cecilia* did not remain at Smith Island.

On the following day the *Cecilia* sailed toward Low Island, which Davis correctly reported as "bearing from mount Pisgo SE." Davis came to anchor on the north side of Low Island, where the *Cecilia* remained until February 6 while men were ashore hunting seals. On February 5, Davis recorded his latitude as being 63°25′ S, which was about 10 minutes too far south for a position on the north side of Low Island.

The anchor was weighed on February 6, and the *Cecilia* "Stood Round Low Island." At 7 p. m. that evening Davis, "hoisted in the boats and stood for an Island bearing SE pr Compass." This was apparently Hoseason Island, for it is the nearest island to Low Island from which it bears SE if a magnetic declination of from 24° E to 28° E is accepted.

The entry for the next day is quoted in full, for it has historic significance as the earliest documentary evidence of a landing on the continent of Antarctica.

Wednesday 7th February 1821
Commences with open cloudy Weather and light winds a Standing for a Large Body of Land in that Direction SE at 10 a. m. close in with it out Boat and Sent her on Shore to looke for Seal at 11 a. m. the Boat returned but found no signs of Seal at noon our Latitude was 64° . .01′ South Stood up a Large Bay the Land high and covered entirely with snow the wind coming Round to the North[d] & Eastward with Thick weather Tacked ship and headed off shore at 4 p. m. fresh Gale and Thick weather with Snow Reefed the main Sail and tooke the Bonnet off the fore sail Ends with Strong Gales at ENE with cloudy unpleasant weather attended with Snow and a heavy Sea Concluded to make the Best of our way for the ship I think this Southern Land to be a Continent.

From the logbook it would appear that Davis sailed by Hoseason Island and the Christiania Islands and headed for the mainland. He was close enough to the mainland at 10 a. m. to send a crew on shore in a boat. Davis' reported latitude can be accepted as only approximately accurate, and it may be farther south than his actual position. As shown on January 31, his reported latitude was apparently 7½ minutes too far south, and on February 5 it was apparently 10 minutes too far south. However, on February 1 it was correct if a magnetic declination of 24° E is accepted, or 2 minutes too far south if a magnetic declination of 28° E is allowed. It is probable then that the land which was made two hours before meridian was somewhere in the vicinity of Cape Sterneck on the northeast portal of Hughes Bay. Immediately after meridian the *Cecilia* "Stood up a Large Bay the Land high and covered entirely with snow." This was most probably Hughes Bay, for if Davis had headed northeastward into Orléans Strait he would not have called it a bay. Nor is he likely to have confused Liège Island or Brabant Island with the mainland. The coast of the Antarctic Peninsula and the adjacent islands as they most probably appeared to Davis as he sailed toward them from Low Island are well shown in Maurice Bongrain's panoramic sketch entitled "Archipel De Palmer (Vue prise de L'Ile Low)," made during the Second French Antarctic Expedition, 1908-10, commanded by Dr. Jean-B. Charcot.[13]

From this sketch it is clear that Davis should have been able to distinguish between the mainland and the off-lying islands as he approached the Antarctic Peninsula from Low Island. Consequently, the large body of land toward which he was standing and on which his boat crew landed at 10:00 a. m. was what he thought to be a continent.

The weather was becoming ominous and Captain Davis decided to return to the *Huron* in Yankee Harbor. During the night the schooner was under double-reefed sails in a strong northeast gale with snow and a heavy sea. Early in the morning the gale moderated, and at 8 a. m. Davis was able to take bearings to determine his position which he recorded as: ". . . we saw Castle Rock [lying two miles off the west side of Snow Island] bearing NNW and the middle of President Island [Snow Island] north. . . ." Shortly after the wind backed to the ENE, and the gale commenced again. Heavy seas, a strong gale, and thick snow prevailed at noon. The weather cleared again later in the day, and at 8 p. m. he recorded the following:

. . . Deception Island bore north, Land bearing from SSW to E by N, Low Island W by S, President Island NW [by] N and Bluff Point SE by E, off of which lays a number of Single rocks at the distance of 8 to 10 miles. Ends with light winds from the north and westward. On Bonnets and out reefs, making the best of our way for the Ship.

Using a piece of transparent acetate on which lines were drawn to correspond to the angles of Davis' recorded bearings, and rotating the acetate to correspond to a magnetic declination of 28° E, results in an excellent fit to Cape Garry at the southwest corner of Low Island, to the west side of Snow Island, and to the northwest cape of Deception Island. Davis' Bluff Point is a high bluff which rises to an inland height of over 2000 feet on the west side of and near the south end of Trinity Island. Immediately west of this bluff is Spert Island which rises to a height of 525 feet. Spert Island is triangular, with the apex of the triangle pointing toward Trinity Island. Lines of rocky islets project northwest and southwest from each of the other corners. One is tempted to suggest that Davis' bearing to Bluff Point may be somewhat too far east, and that he was actually sighting Spert Island. At 8 p. m., however, he was approximately 28 miles from Spert Island, and it would be barely visible from his deck. Therefore, in referring to "a number of Single rocks at the distance of 8 to 10 miles," Davis was referring to Spert Island and to the rocks which extend from it to the southwest and to the northwest as he remembered seeing them when closer aboard. Because of its bold height, his Bluff Point was no doubt a conspicuous landmark for him on his return northward.

The excellent fit of Davis' bearings to landmarks which he probably would sight places the *Cecilia* at 8 p. m. on February 8 at approximately 63°27'30" S, 61°22' W, about 7 miles west of Austin Rocks. Thanks to aerial photography and modern surveys, accurate maps now available portray what the sealers were viewing. For the first time their navigation can be checked, and it is interesting to see how good it was. Scholars such as Edouard A. Stackpole, working as late as 10 or 15 years ago, sometimes had difficulty reconciling the data given in logbooks with the less-than-accurate maps that were then available. Because the sealers were not always accurate, some of these difficulties will never be resolved, but the modern maps do solve many of the problems.

The *Cecilia* worked northward against a northeast breeze, sometimes moderate, sometimes fresh. On the afternoon of February 9 she was in the lee of Deception Island. The next morning the wind shifted to the south and westward, and with a favoring wind Davis was able to bring the shallop into Yankee Harbor at 9 a. m., February 10. He had 1670 sealskins aboard.

Davis and Burdick were probably pleased with the number of seals obtained at Low Island, for on February 12 the *Cecilia* again sailed out of Yankee Harbor at 3 a. m., this time in command of Captain Burdick. He was apparently headed for the crews on the south shore of Livingston Island, but due to light airs from the west he did not reach them until the next morning. Then snow and a strong wind from the northeast, which prevented a boat from landing, held him off until 2 p. m.

At 8 p. m. February 14 Burdick left Livingston Island, heading south for Low Island. On February 15 he made the following entry in the logbook:

Begins with Light airs and variable with Calm pleasant wether [sic] at meridian Lat by obs 63.17S. President Island Bearing North 3 Leagues mount Pisco SW b W dist 7 Leagues the peak of Frezeland NE½ E 11 Leagues Deception Island NE b N 8 Leagues and a small low Iisland [sic] SSW 6 Leagues to which I am bound and Land from South to ESE which I suppose to be a Continent Later part fresh brezes at North at 6 P M Came to anchor under Low Island among a parcel of rocks Sent the Boat on Shore she returned with 22 [??] Seal So ends this 24 hours

In checking Burdick's navigation, it is impossible to reconcile all his bearings with the latitude he gives for February 15. His latitude is undoubtedly in error, for if his position is moved northward to about 62°57' S, 61°28' W all of his bearings, on one condition, and most of his distances, can be reconciled. That condition is that, in recording his data, Burdick transposed the bearings for Deception Island with that for his "Peak of Frezeland." Something of this sort must have been the case, for it would have been impossible for him to have seen a peak on Livingston Island to the southeast of Deception Island. Regardless of the error in latitude, the sum total of the evidence definitely points to his sailing to Low Island, where Captain Davis had been before him and from where Captain Burdick viewed the Antarctic Continent.

Burdick first put crews on the west shore of Low Island, but on February 16 a westerly gale forced him away from his anchorage "among a parcel of rocks." He then moved around to the northeast side of the island, but on February 17 a hard gale from the northeast blew right into the harbor in which the *Cecilia* was anchored. Again he called in his men, and worked away from his anchorage. This time he headed northward toward Yankee Harbor in a snowstorm under double reefed sails. Early the next morning he sighted Snow Island to the northeast, and tacked away to the south. Later, with a south wind, he headed northeastward and made Deception Island at 8 p. m. However, it was 1 p. m., February 19, before he entered Yankee Harbor. By then the wind had died down, and it was necessary for the men to use the whaleboat to tow the *Cecilia* into the harbor.

This ended the exploratory cruises of Captains Davis and Burdick. The *Cecilia* made a short two-day cruise to the north and east, beginning on February 22. The shallop was in charge of Captain Donald MacKay of New York with a mixed crew from the brig *Aurora,* the *Huron,* and the *Huntress.* On March 10, Captain Burdick sailed for home, the *Huntress* reaching Nantucket on June 10, 1821. Captain Davis remained in Yankee Harbor until March 30, 1821, when the *Huron* and the *Cecilia* sailed in company with the vessels from New York to winter at the Falkland Islands. Captain Davis returned to the South Shetlands in the austral summer of 1821-22, but confined his operations to these islands and made no exploratory cruises. Due to the scarcity of the fur seals he was compelled to spend part of his time killing elephant seals for the oil in their blubber.

On February 17, 1822, Captain Davis left the South Shetlands for the United States. Several of the crew were suffering from scurvy, and Davis remained at the Falkland Islands while the men recuperated. Finally sailing for home, the *Huron* arrived at New Haven on June 17, 1822. The *Cecilia,* or "Young Huron," as she was referred to in the New Haven newspapers, arrived on June 29.

NOTES

1. The logbook of the *Huron,* Capt. John Davis. Formerly the property of Mr. Alexander O. Vietor, Curator of Maps of the Yale University Library, has been presented by him to the Yale University Library. The logbook of the *Huntress,* Capt. Christopher Burdick, is the property of Mr. Edouard A. Stackpole, at Nantucket, Mass.

2. Capt. Robert Fildes, after his brig *Cora* of Liverpool was wrecked at Blythe Bay off Desolation Island off the north side of Livingston Island on January 6, 1821, sailed about the South Shetlands as a passenger in the shallops of other sealers during which time he prepared the first sailing directions for the islands. After describing Port Foster, the interior of Deception Island, he said,

Half a mile outside the entrance you will have on a clear day a fine view of the land to the southward, which appears covered with snow and here and there black patches where the rock shows, it is very high and a counterpart of the land to the Northward. Cap[n] McFarlane of the Brig Dragon a very intelligent man told me he landed on it and found Leopard and Elephants but no seal; The Caraquette of Liverpool also found an harbour and moored there a few days, but not getting seal left it.

Captain Robert Fildes, "Remarks made during a Voyage to New South Shetland," typescript copy in Scott Polar Research Institute, Reference MS 393, pp. 8-9. The original is part of "A Journal of a Voyage kept on board Brig Cora of Liverpool bound to New South Shetland," Public Record Office, London, 753 Adm. 55/143. Captain Fildes gives no dates for these landings.

Captain Fildes returned to the South Shetlands for the austral summer of 1821-22 as captain of the brig *Robert*. Captain McFarlane was at the South Shetlands, so far as is known, only in the austral summer of 1820-21, but we have no specific record nor date of his actual landing on the Antarctic Peninsula. Capt. J. Usher and the *Caraquette* were at the South Shetlands only in 1821-22.

3. Capt. Christopher Burdick, Logbook of the Schooner *Huntress*, entry for November 11, 1820; Edouard A. Stackpole, *The Voyage of the Huron and the Huntress* (Mystic, Conn., The Marine Historical Association, No. 29, 1955), pp. 23-24.

4. Stackpole, *ibid*.

5. Fildes, "Remarks made, . . ." *op. cit.*, p. 10.

6. Brian Roberts, "Chronological List of Antarctic Expeditions," *Polar Record*, vol. 9, No. 59, May, 1958, pp. 104, 105.

7. E. W. Hunter Christie, *The Antarctic Problem* (London, Allen & Unwin, 1951), p. 94.

8. Capt. Robert Fildes, "Journal of a Voyage, etc.," Public Record Office, London, No. 753 Adm. 55/43. His "Remarks made during a Voyage, etc.," typescript copy in Scott Polar Research Institute, Cambridge, Ref. MS 393 (see note 2 above), are copied from the latter part of the "Journal" and do not include the above or any other daily entry.

9. Stackpole, *op. cit.*, pp. 44-46.

10. *Ibid.*, from Capt. Burdick's logbook of the *Huntress*, January 25.

11. Capt. John Davis, Logbook of the *Huron*, January 28, 1821.

12. As this entry and the following one show, now that Davis was no longer on a sea voyage but making what he must have considered local cruises, he was keeping his logbook on the civil calendar and local time with the day beginning and ending at midnight.

13. M. Bongrain, *Description des Cotes et Banquises, Instructions Nautique, Deuxieme Expedition Antarctique Francaise, 1908-10* (Paris, Masson, 1914), Vues de Cotes, Nr. 14. Reprinted in *Sailing Directions for Antarctica*, U. S. Navy Hydrographic Office, No. H.O. 138 (Washington, 1943), p. 120. This is also referred to by Stackpole, *Voyage of the Huron . . ., op. cit.*, p. 52.

BIBLIOGRAPHY

PUBLISHED MATERIAL

Columbian Register, New Haven, June 24, 1820, and June 22, 1822.

Connecticut Journal, New Haven, June 25, July 2 and 16, 1822.

Stackpole, Edouard A., *The Sea-Hunters* (Philadelphia, J. B. Lippincott Co., 1953), Chap. XXV "The First Recognition of Antarctica," pp. 355-368. This chapter is a narrative of Captain Burdick's operations in Antarctica in 1820-21, based on his logbook. It was done before Stackpole knew of the logbook of the *Huron*. With the benefit of the latter he changed his interpretation in his subsequent publication, below.

——, *The Voyage of the Huron and the Huntress*, Marine Historical Society, Mystic, Conn., 1955, 86 pp. This is an excellent summary, the most complete to date, of the activities of American sealers in the South Shetlands in 1820-21. It is based on many sources but mainly on the logbooks of the *Huron*, the *Huntress*, and the *Hero*.

MANUSCRIPT MATERIAL

Logbook of the schooner *Huntress*, 1820-21. Personal property of Edouard A. Stackpole, Nantucket, Mass.

Logbook of the ship *Huron*, Jan. 18, 1821-Apr. 27, 1822. Sterling Memorial Library, Yale University, New Haven, Conn.

Fildes, Captain Robert, "Journal of a Voyage kept on board Brig Cora of Liverpool bound to New South Shetland," Public Record Office, London, 755 Adm./143.

——, "Remarks made during a Voyage to New South Shetland," typescript copy of latter part of his *Journal*, pp. 8-9, Sailing Directions. Scott Polar Research Institute, Ref. MS 393.

United States Custom House Records, ports of Nantucket and New Haven, 1820.

6

OTHER AMERICAN SEALING FLEETS
AT THE SOUTH SHETLANDS, 1820-1821

INTRODUCTION

SIGNIFICANCE OF THESE FLEETS

There were 30 American sealing vessels at the South Shetland Islands during the 1820-21 season. The activities of five of these — the Fanning-Pendleton Fleet of Stonington, especially the exploratory cruises of Captain Nathaniel B. Palmer in the *Hero* — have been related in Chapter 4. The operations of three others, the *Huron* of New Haven, the *Huntress* of Nantucket, and especially the exploratory cruises of Captains Davis and Burdick in the *Cecilia,* have been discussed in Chapter 5. What is known of the other 22 vessels at the islands in 1820-21, including fleets from New York, Boston, and Salem, and a second fleet from Stonington, will be recorded in this chapter.

Incomplete evidence, including notices in marine columns of contemporary New England and New York newspapers, indicates that exploits of several of the captains of these 22 vessels would also justify separate chapters if all of the facts concerning them were known. We do know that Captain Robert Johnson made a major exploratory cruise as far south as 66° S, 70° W in January 1821 and that Harmony Cove on Nelson Island, Clothier Harbor on Robert Island, Potter Cove and Esther Harbor on King George Island were named by American sealers who operated from these particular harbors in 1820-21. Several manuscript maps were drawn and collections of rocks and minerals and plants were brought back from the South Shetlands by American sealers in this season. Unfortunately, American science was then not sufficiently well organized and financed to produce a completely satisfactory record of these efforts.

SOURCE MATERIALS

As previously noted in Chapter 4, latter-day scholars dealing with the activities of early American sealers generally have been concerned with exploits of Captain Nathaniel B. Palmer while neglecting the very important achievements of his contemporaries. To a large extent this neglect has been due to the availability of material on Palmer and the lack of information regarding other American sealers, although Clark at one point in his admirable report on early American sealing lists 18 different American vessels at the South Shetlands in 1820-21 and in another part mentions 15 different vessels.[1] Clark certainly showed that further investigation into the activities of the American sealers was likely to be profitable, yet later writers not only neglected these possibilities but seem to have been unaware of the Clark report. In at least one instance neglect was compounded into ridicule when Karl Fricker, incredulously summarizing Benjamin Morrell's narrative, wrote, "A course towards the northwest is taken, and land is seen the very next day, the east coast of the land already named New South Greenland by an apocryphal Captain Johnson. . . ."[2] Our present fragmentary evidence. shows that Captain Johnson was not only a very real person but one whose accomplishments were notable.

The imbalance regarding the accounts of early sealers has been offset in recent years by Edouard Stackpole in *The Sea Hunters* and in *The Voyage of the Huron and the Huntress*.[3] This was made possible by his uncovering Captain Christopher Burdick's logbook of the *Huntress,* which had been used as a child's scrapbook, and the subsequent discovery by Alexander O. Vietor of Captain John Davis' logbook of the *Huron.* Stackpole also used various newspaper accounts and Custom House records and was the first modern writer to call attention to Clark's report.

In the course of preparing this report of American activity in the Antarctic, the logbooks of the *Hersilia* (1819-20) and of the *Catharina* (1820-21), and a partial logbook of the *Adventure* (1821-22), have been made available by their present owner, Mrs. Theodore H. Krueger of Stratford, Connecticut.[4] Diligent search through contemporary newspapers and Custom House records has added to the present store of information. Although the information is far from complete, a significant account can be developed from it. Moreover, the results of recent research have been so rewarding that it is hoped readers who have seafaring ancestors may be encouraged to re-examine family papers for old letters and storage chests for old logbooks that may contribute to a more complete picture of the period. The fragmentary account here presented may offer clues which will lead to new sources of information that might remain unknown and perhaps be destroyed because their significance would otherwise be unappreciated.

INFORMATION LEADING TO THE ORGANIZATION OF FLEETS

Much has been written concerning the importance that sealers placed in keeping their operations secret, and there is considerable evidence that the locations of profitable sealing grounds were kept secret as long as possible. If that were true and if the *Hersilia* was the only American vessel at the South Shetlands in 1819-20, how was it possible for 30 American vessels to have visited the islands the following year?

Secrecy may well have been an important stock-in-trade among the sealers, but there is also considerable evidence that there was much more cooperation among them than is generally believed. If, upon the return of the *Hersilia* in May, 1820 from her maiden voyage to the South Shetlands, William A. Fanning had wished to keep the new bonanza a secret, he must have realized that news of the discovery of the islands would soon reach England and be transmitted to the United States. He knew how sealing masters would react to such news, and he realized that the *Espírito Santo* had also been at the South Shetlands in 1819-20. Under the circumstances there would not be much point in withholding information from his fellow townsmen who might be able to capitalize on an early voyage before the seals at the South Shetlands suffered the same fate as those at the older sealing grounds.

By their nature, sealers' secrets were difficult to keep. Although ordinary seamen were purposely kept ignorant of positions of latitude and longitude and of the compass directions for a specific course, they did acquire considerable information which was readily exchanged in waterfront taverns. There were also other means by which secrets were divulged. Officers sometimes had divided loyalties, and many vessels were owned by several shareholders, not all of whom were necessarily reticent and many of whom also owned shares in several other vessels. Thus the news of the discovery of the South Shetlands and of the *Hersilia*'s good fortune there spread rapidly among the sealing masters and ship owners from New York to Salem. The nature of their reaction to the news is shown by the 30 ships they immediately dispatched to the islands.

THE NEW YORK FLEET OF JAMES BYERS AND ASSOCIATES

ORGANIZATION OF THE FLEET

James Byers of New York had been engaged in the sealing business for a number of years when the news of the discovery of the South Shetlands reached the United States in 1820. Edmund Fanning and his son William had lately been associated with Byers, and the elder Fanning had served as master of some of Byers' ships. In 1820 Byers' business associates were Benjamin Rogers, William McIntire, and Walter Nexsen. As noted above on page 32, many of the ship masters at the South Shetlands in 1820-21 had previously served on Byers' ships in a variety of capacities. For instance, James P. Sheffield of the *Hersilia* had been second mate to Edmund Fanning on the round-the-world voyage of the *Volunteer* (1815-17), first mate (1817-18) and then master (1818-19) of the *Jane Maria*.

The manner in which James Byers learned from Captain James P. Sheffield in 1820 of the discovery of the South Shetland Islands and of the great number of fur seals to be found there has been related in Chapter 3. Later that same summer he received a letter from Captain Edmund Fanning of Nantucket, also telling of Smith's discovery of the South Shetlands, which was further confirmed by subsequent reports from London in American newspapers. Accordingly, when Byers wrote to General Parker on August 17, 1820, he had already dispatched two vessels to the South Shetlands. He said, "Our vessels were ordered to be on the ground by the first of Oct. Some think that the 1st of Dec. is as early as we ought venture in that high latitude — but I know better." In his letter of September 4, he repeated, "Our vessels are ordered to reach the new islands by the first of October. We are so well prepared with good vessels, Iron cables, etc., etc., that we feel quite confident we can hold on in safety."[5]

COMPOSITION OF THE FLEET

The first of the Byers ships to sail for the South Shetlands was the schooner *Henry*, which departed New York on June 24, 1820, under the command of Captain Benjamin J. Brunow.[6] The 150-ton, three-masted schooner had been built at Saybrook, Connecticut, in 1817. She was 83 feet long and carried a company of 26 officers and men. Brunow undoubtedly carried orders to contact Captain Robert Johnson of the brig *Jane Maria* which had sailed for the Falkland Islands July 1, 1819, for Johnson was subsequently leader of the fleet at the South Shetlands. The *Jane Maria,* built in New York in 1796, was 74 feet long and registered at 170 tons. The brig was accompanied by the *Sarah,* a small schooner which served as tender.[7] The brig *Aurora,* of which Robert R. Macy was master, sailed from New York on July 1, 1820. This 190-ton vessel was 82 feet long and had been built at Saybrook, Connecticut, in 1815. The last of the Byers fleet to depart was the schooner *Venus,* which sailed from New York, under Captain William Napier, on October 9, 1820. The *Venus,* built at Woodbridge, New Jersey, in 1811, was a two-masted schooner of 131 tons and was 68 feet long.

Although she was not a Byers ship, it seems appropriate here to discuss the brig *Charity* and her veteran sealing master, Charles H. Barnard, of New York. Although Barnard had no financial connection with Byers, he operated in company with Byers' vessels throughout the 1820-21 season and to a lesser extent in the following season. Available official records are not clear regarding the origin of this particular voyage of the *Charity.* She was rated as 122 tons, was 72 feet long and was built at St. Michaels, Maryland, in 1817. She had previously been registered at Baltimore, but was purchased by Captain Barnard as sole owner on June 2, 1820, at Pernambuco, Brazil. From there he apparently sailed to the Falkland Islands where he fell in with the Byers fleet. Where and how he learned of the South Shetlands is not known. Six days after he returned to New York he registered the brig at that port on May 27, 1822.

ACCOMPLISHMENTS OF THE BYERS FLEET

From bits of evidence now available, it would seem that the New York fleet did not arrive at the South Shetlands until December, much later than the time Byers intended they would. A notation on the crew list of the schooner *Henry* indicates that vessel was still at the Falkland Islands on November 17, for four crew members are listed as having deserted there on that date. The logbook of the *Hero* shows that Nathaniel B. Palmer, while cruising westward along the south coast of Livingston Island at 8:00 p. m. on December 16, met the brigs *Jane Maria* and *Charity,* and the schooners *Henry* and *Sarah.* On December 18 Captain Christopher Burdick, visiting the beaches of the south coast in the *Cecilia,* ". . . fell in with Captain Johnson's fleet of New York from Ruged Island looking for Yankee Harbor."[8] When Burdick returned to Yankee Harbor on December 20 he found the New York fleet moored there. The fact that the New York fleet was still looking for a safe mooring at such a late date indicates that by the time they arrived at the South Shetlands the more accessible beaches on which the seals hauled up in large numbers already had been occupied by other sealers. This is borne out by the fact that Captain Johnson a short time later made a long exploratory cruise southward in search of sealing grounds. The brig *Aurora* and the schooner *Venus* were still later in arriving, the former reaching Yankee Harbor on February 8 after looking for the South Shetlands for nearly two months.[9] This late arrival is also confirmed by Captain Burdick of the *Huntress*.[10]

Captain Robert Johnson's exploratory cruise in the *Sarah* is recorded in the logbooks of two of his contemporaries. At noon on January 27, as Captain John Davis with Captain Charles H. Barnard and the mates of several of the vessels in Yankee Harbor were about to head up McFarlane Strait in the *Cecilia,* en route to Blythe Bay, they "spoke Capt. Johnson in his shallop bound in having been gone 20 days on a cruise to the South and Westward to look for seal found Plenty of Land in that Direction, but no seal . . ."[11] More details were recorded by Captain Burdick, who spoke with Johnson after the latter moored at Yankee Harbor. The entry in the logbook of the *Huntress* for January 27 includes the following:

> . . . Captain Johnson came in in schallop from a cruce of 22 days, said he had ben to the Lat. 66° South and the Long. of 70° West and still found what [he] took to be Land but appeared to be nothing but Sollid Islands of Ice and Snow Whether he had found any seal he did not inform, nor otherwise Land, than to say ther was none so far south as he had ben.[12]

On January 28, 1821, according to the logbook of the *Huron,* Captain Johnson in the *Sarah* joined Captains Davis and Barnard at Blythe Bay. Some of the American sealers, as reported earlier,[13] planned to raid British sealing parties on the north shore of Livingston Island in retaliation for two boat crews from Yankee Harbor having been driven from these beaches and their sealskins taken from them. After the Americans dispersed, having been dissuaded from their purpose by Captain Brunow, Captains Davis and Johnson continued in company toward Cape Shirreff. Some distance off the cape, being satisfied that few if any seals were present, they separated to go on individual cruises.

Johnson sailed to the northeast. The time of his return to Yankee Harbor is uncertain, but he probably left again before February 22. On that day a mixed crew of men from the *Huron,* the *Huntress,* and the *Aurora* sailed for the northeast in the *Cecilia.* Donald MacKay, who had seen seals on some islands in that direction on a previous cruise, was acting as pilot. MacKay, who belonged to the New York fleet, might well have seen these islands while with Johnson in the *Sarah* on the cruise that began on January 28 off Cape Shirreff. At noon on February 24 the *Cecilia,* having run into very bad weather, was back at the entrance to Yankee Harbor. Finally at 4:00 p. m., February 25, she was able to enter. A short distance out the *Cecilia* had spoken the *Sarah,* and Captain Johnson had reported that he had just come from the islands to which they were bound, and that he had taken all the seals that were there.

The weather continued to deteriorate, and ice began floating in the harbor. On March 3 a strong gale from the east with snow and sleet caused the brigs *Jane Maria* and *Nancy* to run afoul of one another, and the *Aurora* dragged her anchors. On March 6 the *Sarah* was blown on shore, and on March 7 the *Cecilia* was beached to avoid worse damage on submerged rocks.

Captain Johnson had by this time been out for two seasons. Thus at 6:00 p. m. on March 9, 1821, the *Jane Maria* sailed for New York, leaving the *Sarah* with the other vessels of the fleet who proposed to winter at the Falklands because, by their late arrival, they had not obtained a full cargo.

That some members of the New York fleet had been engaged in activities other than sealing was revealed when the *Jane Maria* arrived in New York on May 11. The following article, originally published in the *New-York Gazette & General Advertiser,* May 16, 1821, and subsequently in other American papers and in *Niles Weekly Register,* bears witness to this fact.

Vessels from the lands situate to the south of Cape Horn, have arrived in different ports with cargoes of seal skins. The regions visited by the New-York navigators lie in about the latitude of 62°, where vegetable life is so rare, that a little grass in a few favored places, and some moss on the rocks are all the forms of it that exist. The dreary climate exhibits, during the entire summer perpetual snow and ice; not a tree nor even shrub appears. The minerals brought home by Mr. B. Astor are partly *primitive* and partly *volcanic.* The examples produced to Dr. Mitchell are--1. Quartz in compact and chrystalized forms. 2. Amethysts, in chrystals. 3. Porphyry, in small masses. 4. Rouen onyx, in pebbles. 5. Lumps of coarse flint. 6. Elegant zealite, like that of the Ferro groupe in the North Atlantic ocean. 7. Pumice stone. 8. Pyrites, surcharged with sulphur.

The manuscript chart made by Mr. Hampton Stewart, is an instructive addition to geography, and ought to be incorporated into the charts of the globe.

Geologists will learn with surprise that the high grounds and summit of the rocks in several of the spots that have been visited, are strewed with skeletons of whales, and relics of other marine animals, leading to a belief that the whole of the materials have been hove up by the operation of volcanic fire, from the depths of the ocean.

Further disclosures of the natural constitution of this curious region are expected with impatience from future adventurers. There appears to be a wide field for new and original observation.

It is also hoped we shall soon receive a more full and satisfactory account of the Terra Australis, or continent of the southern hemisphere, occupying the vast space between the tracts already surveyed and the pole.

The same newspaper on May 22, 1821, also published the following extract of a letter from Donald MacKay.[14]

Southern Thule

The following is an extract of a letter from Captain Donald MacKay, dated among the Antarctic islands, lat. 63, south, long. 61, west, "or thereabouts."

This land is but little known yet, except the range of islands at which we now are, extending from E. N. E. to S. S. W. about two hundred miles in length. These are, in general, composed of high and broken land, or rather rocks, clad with an immense body of snow, except here and there a naked peak, or some low rocks near the sea. The snow, consolidated by lapse of time, forms perpendicular cliffs, much higher than those bordering on the river Hudson. These are common along the coast, but more particularly in the bosoms of bays and harbors, where the water is from four to ten fathoms in depth, under the very brink of them. This body of ice, being constantly dissolving underneath, cracks and is precipitated into the sea in great masses, with a report resembling thunder, or heavy ordnance--it may be heard from 15 to 25 miles distant.

No shoal or perpendicular rock would be more fatal to a vessel or lives, than would this ice-bound shore, in case of her being driven against it by violence of wind--this would be the case in the most secure harbor, for should she drive against this impending mass of ice, which is contantly falling, she would be crushed to pieces or instantly carried to the bottom, with hardly a possibility of escape in boats.

Southward of this range of islands, at the distance of from fifty to eighty miles, lies a large body of land, yet but little known, and will probably so remain, by reason of the danger and difficulty of approaching the shore, from the great quantity of floating ice with which it is surrounded. This is of the same description as that of the islands, but it is not yet ascertained whether cut up into islands or not. 'Tis not improbable that it is connected with Sandwich Land. It is said there are several active volcanoes on the first mentioned islands, but I am uncertain as to the truth of the assertion.

I have seen a small but high conical formed island, from the top of which we supposed we perceived smoke to issue; but we were at too great a distance to be positive of the fact. Others say they have seen both fire and smoke emitted from it. From the circumstances of the island being bare of snow there is little doubt of its being a volcano.

There is a small island at no great distance from our present position, which has been described to me, by several who have visited it, as being so hot that, on many parts of it, the foot or hand cannot be held to the sand, and that on the shore of a basin forming a small harbor, (probably the ancient crater of a volcano) the water boils.

My opinion of the land which I have seen here is, that it had a volcanic origin. But this subject I submit to the speculation of such learned gentlemen as our friend (for he is the friend of humanity) Dr. Mitchell.

'Tis impossible for me to convey to you an adequate idea of the dreary yet sublime scenery of this region of frost. I think the land abounds in minerals, but of what kind I am too ignorant of mineralogy to determine. But however valuable the mines may be, they must remain useless to the world, from their being buried under mountains of ice. I have had but little opportunity to collect speciments of stone, &c., but such as I have procured, I forward by the Jane Maria, Capt. Johnson, for which I beg you to call on board this brig, and present them, with my respectful compliments, to Dr. Samuel L. Mitchell, and request he will accept such specimens as he wishes to retain, and present the remainder in my name, to the New-York Lyceum of Natural History. It was my intention to have written to him, and as far as my feeble talents would admit, and describe to him this new world; but time will not now admit of attempting it. I have further to request that you will solicit from him to do me the honor of communicating his ideas, by letter, on these specimens of stone, ore, &c.

Pertinent scientific literature of the period has been examined to determine what became of the mineral and rock specimens presented to Dr. Samuel L. Mitchill. Mitchill, trained as a physician, was a man of parts and was one of the prominent figures in early American science. Sometimes called "the Father of American Chemistry," he played an important role in the early life of the New York Lyceum of Natural History, predecessor of the New York Academy of Sciences. No scientific article has been located dealing with the rock and mineral specimens. Mitchill apparently was more interested in obtaining plant specimens, and Captain Napier of the *Venus* supplied him with several specimens of a lichen he found in the South Shetlands. This plant was examined and described by Dr. John Torrey, a well-known early American botanist.[15]

Mitchill was a frequent contributor to scientific journals of the day. He often submitted brief notes of new discoveries or items of news value to scientists. In only one of these did he mention the specimens from the South Shetlands, and in this case it was the lichen described by Dr. Torrey.[16] A list of materials presented to the New York Lyceum of Natural History in 1826 by Dr. Mitchill contains only one item of interest in the present report, a sample of kelp from the Falkland Islands presented by MacKay.[17]

Mitchill's letter to Torrey, previously cited, and other evidence proves that Mitchill received and valued the mineral and rock specimens. It appears that they eventually found their way to the New York Lyceum of Natural History. Although it cannot be positively stated, evidence indicates that the collection of minerals and rocks from the South Shetlands was lost along with the rest of the collection of the Lyceum when the rented quarters of that organization were destroyed by fire on May 21, 1866.

The fate of the manuscript chart of Hampton Stewart is unknown. There is evidence that Captain Charles H. Barnard of the brig *Charity* also drew manuscript maps as shown by the following quotation:

> I trust it will not be deemed irrelevant, since I am leaving Massafuero, [in 1816] the last place of my solitude to refer to the account which James Weddell, master in the Royal Navy gave of my history, which he heard from my own lips; but which in some parts, owing to forgetfulness, or misunderstanding, he misrepresented. This gentleman was my particular friend, and meeting with him in the Falklands, I furnished him with some sketches for his chart of the South Shetland Islands, and several other places which he has not mentioned in his narrative.[18]

HEAVY LOSSES OF THE NEW YORK FLEET

The 1820-21 season at the South Shetlands could hardly have been a financial success for James Byers and his associates. The late arrival of the fleet at the islands meant that they did not obtain full cargoes of skins, and their consequent late departure from the South Shetlands subjected the fleet to severe weather which resulted in the loss of three vessels. On March 7, 1821, the schooner *Venus* dragged all her anchors in a gale and ran on a reef at the entrance to Esther Harbor on the north side near the east end of King George Island.[19] The schooner's stern was stove in. The crew and what could be salvaged were picked up by the ship *Esther* and the brig *Emerald* of Boston.[20]

A succession of gales continued to plague the vessels remaining in Yankee Harbor. Some of the vessels were unable to leave because their sealing crews were still on outlying beaches, and it was impossible to bring them in because if a gale was not raging, lack of wind kept the shallops from sailing. A violent gale began on March 19 and lasted until 5:00 p. m., March 21. Meanwhile, at 10:00 a. m. on March 21 the *Aurora* dragged all three of her anchors and went on shore. Men from the other vessels assisted the crew in efforts to get her off, but it was not until high tide on the evening of March 24 that she again floated freely. Captain Davis felt that she was in poor condition to go to sea.[21]

Finally, on March 30, 1821, with light northerly winds, the last remaining vessels at Yankee Harbor put to sea. They included the *Huron,* the brigs *Charity* and *Aurora,* the schooner *Henry,* and the shallops *Cecilia* and *Sarah.* They sailed into Bransfield Strait, but had to lay off and on during the night because the weather was thick and it was too dark to go through Nelson Strait. The next morning, having been drifted by the west-southwest wind to the northeast of the entrance of Nelson Strait, the *Huron, Charity,* and *Cecilia,* which had now lost sight of the other vessels, set a course to the north-northeast to round the eastern end of King George Island. Meanwhile the *Aurora, Henry,* and *Sarah* also sailed northeastward in company.

A gale which commenced on the afternoon of April 4 while the *Huron, Cecilia,* and *Charity* were in about 55°50′ S, 61°10′ W, east of Staten Island and south of the Falklands, continued with increasing fury until the morning of April 6.[22] During the storm the three vessels became separated. The mainsail and the main staysail on the *Huron* were split and the larboard quarter boat was smashed. When the vessels began to sight one another after the storm it was found that the foresail, squaresail and boat on the *Cecilia* were lost. The schooner *Henry,* which was with the *Aurora* and the *Sarah* in about latitude 57° S when the storm struck, had most of her bulwarks knocked in, her foregaff carried away, and two of her boats stove in. The brig *Aurora* lost three boats, spare spars, and everything movable on deck. All her bulwarks had been stove in. She was almost capsized, and was so battered from this storm and previous accidents at Yankee Harbor that she was later condemned at the Falklands. The *Sarah* was never seen again and, when she failed to arrive at the Falklands, was presumed lost with nine men aboard. The brig *Charity* was more fortunate, losing only one boat.

WINTER AT THE FALKLAND ISLANDS

On April 10 the *Huron,* the *Cecilia,* and the *Henry* arrived at Ship Harbor in New Island of the Falklands, and the *Aurora* arrived the next day. Some days later Captain Davis moved his two vessels to Hog Island Harbor where, by previous agreement, he wintered in company with Captain Barnard and the brig *Charity.* Nearby, at West Point Harbor, they met Captain Siddons of the brig *Lynx* of Port Jackson, New South Wales, who was wintering there.

At the request of Captain Macy, a survey board was formed to examine the brig *Aurora* and assess the extent of her damage. The survey was conducted on June 17 and 18 by Captain Davis of the *Huron,* Captain Siddons of the *Lynx,* Captain Upton of the brig *Nancy* of Salem, and Captain Brunow of the schooner *Henry.* The result of the survey was recorded in the logbook of the *Huron* as follows:

. . . we found her unseaworthy being very much injured in the Bottom, Keele and upper work, so much that it would be impossible to repair her in this country and have recommended Captn Macy to sell her at auction for the benefit of whom it may concern.

The proposed auction occurred on August 1, the salvage from the ship bringing about $1100. Davis offered to transport Captain Macy with his whaleboat and belongings. Four of the *Aurora*'s crew also signed on to work their passage.

Soon activity increased as the next sealing season approached. Captain Johnson arrived back at the Falklands on September 3, this time as master of the schooner *Wasp,* a new ship belonging to James Byers and his associates. The *Aurora* having been stripped, Captain Brunow moved the *Henry* over from New Island to Hog Island Harbor on September 4, and Captain Macy joined the *Huron* later in the month.

A SECOND SEASON AT THE SOUTH SHETLANDS, 1821-1822

On October 9, 1822, the *Huron, Cecilia,* and *Lynx* sailed from the Falklands for Staten Island and the South Shetlands, and in succeeding days were followed by the other vessels singly or in company. It is interesting to note that after setting a course for the South Shetlands they spoke several vessels arriving from the United States. Apparently everyone wanted to arrive early this season. The *Huron*, in company with several other vessels, sighted Smith Island on October 16, but it was not until the 21st that they were able to enter Yankee Harbor, still half frozen over. Captain Johnson in the *Wasp* arrived later that day. The *Henry* arrived on October 23, Captain Abraham Blauvelt arrived from New York in the *Jane Maria* on the 27th, and the *Charity* arrived on October 31. This year the New York vessels would not be late.

Captain Johnson seems to have taken up his exploratory cruises where he left off the previous season, for the *Wasp* made only brief calls at Yankee Harbor during the season. Blauvelt, lacking a shallop, also did considerable cruising with the *Jane Maria*. Misfortune continued to plague Robert Macy, for on November 3, although it was drawn up on shore in Yankee Harbor and lashed down, his whaleboat was carried away and later found smashed in McFarlane Strait. Later he borrowed a boat from Captain Upton and somehow managed to collect 332 fur sealskins. The fur seals were understandably scarce that year, and many of the sealers were also procuring elephant oil.

On December 22 Captain Davis recorded the brief call at Yankee Harbor of Captain McLeod in the sloop *Beaufoy*. On board were Captains James Weddell and Charles H. Barnard, returning from a cruise to the eastward as far as the Seal Islands. They had found few seals. The *Beaufoy* made at least two other visits to Yankee Harbor during the season, and several other British vessels made occasional calls. In fact, there was a considerable amount of friendly cooperation between British and American crews.

Ice conditions were bad and storms were frequent in 1821-22. Taking heed of the misfortunes of the previous season, the sealers began sailing for home early in 1822. The schooner *George* of Stonington sailed as early as January 20. On January 26 the brig *Charity* sailed for the Falklands, where Captain Barnard remained until the middle of March before sailing for New York. Calling at Pernambuco en route, he arrived home May 21, 1822, the *Charity*'s cargo of sealskins and oil being consigned to J. F. Delaplaine. The *Henry* also left the South Shetlands the latter part of January, visiting Staten Island and the Falklands. Leaving the latter on March 21, Captain Brunow arrived in New York on May 15, 1822. Captain Blauvelt was the last to leave the South Shetlands but, sailing directly to New York, his was the first of the Byers ships to reach home in 1822, arriving at New York on April 25 after a voyage of 70 days.

THE SECOND STONINGTON OR CLARK FLEET

ORGANIZATION OF THE FLEET

So very little has been known regarding the second sealing fleet from Stonington in 1820-21 that, except for Clark's and, more recently, Stackpole's reports, it is not mentioned in accounts of Antarctic exploration.[23] There can be little doubt that the return of the *Hersilia* in May 1820 from her first voyage to the South Shetlands created quite a stir in Stonington. Knowledge of these islands and the millions of fur seals on their beaches could not be kept secret for long.

Three of the eight men who owned shares in the *Hersilia* also owned shares in one or more of the vessels of the second fleet, and 10 of the 32 men who owned shares in one or more of the vessels of the Fanning-Pendleton Fleet of 1820-21 also owned shares in the vessels of the second fleet. Under these circumstances it is not difficult to find motivation for the organization of the second fleet.

The principal owners of the second Stonington fleet were William Williams and Samuel F. Denison of Stonington, Thomas W. Williams of New London, and Alfred Weller of Hartford, all merchants; and Jeremiah Holmes, Stonington mariner. Stackpole has called it the Clark Fleet, after Alexander Clark, who in newspaper articles was referred to as the leader. Clark's position as leader is difficult to explain in view of the fact that he owned no shares in any of the ships and that Jeremiah Holmes, a principal owner, was also master of one of the vessels in the fleet.

COMPOSITION OF THE FLEET

The second Stonington or Clark Fleet of 1820-21 consisted of the ship *Clothier*, the brigs *Emeline* and *Catharina*, and the shallop *Spark*. The *Clothier*, built at Philadelphia in 1810, was 94 feet long and was registered as 285 tons. Commanded by Alexander Clark of Nantucket, she was the flagship of the fleet. The *Emeline*, a 108-ton brig, was built in Lyme, Connecticut, in 1818. She was 67 feet long and was commanded by Jeremiah Holmes. The 71-foot, 160-ton brig *Catharina* was of unknown origin, her registration showing that she had been forfeited in 1818 for breach of the laws of the United States.[24] She was commanded in 1820-21 by Joseph Henfield. Except for being mentioned in the logbook of the *Catharina*, little is known of the *Spark*. Notice of the fleet's sailing in the *Boston Patriot & Daily Mercantile Advertiser* for December 7, 1820, lists her as a schooner, which designation is also sometimes given her in the logbook of the *Catharina*.

THE OUTBOUND VOYAGES

The *Catharina* sailed from Stonington early July 30 and was followed the next day by the brig *Emeline*. The *Clothier* did not sail until August 9, apparently with the *Spark* as consort. The two brigs were in company only during August 11, 12, and 13. The voyage followed the usual course for sailing vessels of the day, southeastward toward the Cape Verde Islands, which were sighted from the *Catharina* on August 23, and then south-southwest toward the coast of Brazil. The *Emeline* called at Rio de Janeiro, but the *Catharina* did not make port from the time she left Stonington until she reached the Falkland Islands on October 25. The *Emeline* must have arrived at about the same time, for on October 26 Nathaniel B. Palmer recorded in the logbook of the sloop *Hero* that he anchored beside the brig and spoke to Captain Holmes.

Captains Holmes and Henfield remained at the Falklands, making preparations for the voyage south, until Captain Clark arrived with the *Clothier* and the *Spark*. On October 27 Mr. Perry, one of the mates of the *Catharina*, and another man were drowned when a whaleboat was upset.

On the morning of November 25, 1820, Captain Clark's four vessels sailed in company from the Falklands for the South Shetlands. Except for the expected rain and snow squalls, the weather was favorable. As they approached the South Shetlands on December 1, a great many fur seals and Cape pigeons were seen. At 10:00 p. m. land was sighted to the south, five leagues distant.

OPERATIONS AT THE SOUTH SHETLANDS

As the four Stonington vessels were approaching the northwestern end of Livingston Island on the morning of December 2, the *Spark* was sent ahead to reconnoiter for a suitable harbor. At 4:00 p. m. the *Spark* returned from an unsuccessful search; an hour later she resumed the quest in the opposite direction while the three larger vessels continued to sail off and on offshore, waiting her return. At 2:00 a. m., December 4, the shallop returned with a favorable report and was sent ahead to sound the intended harbor. The *Clothier* and the two brigs followed, staying some distance offshore while the *Spark* made a reconnaissance sounding of what was later named Clothier Harbor, on the north side of Robert Island. The weather was dark and foggy with some snow. Wind was from the northwest. The two brigs came to anchor safely on December 7, but in spite of the precautions, the *Clothier,* partly due to a sudden deterioration of the weather, ran upon a reef and was lost.[25] All hands were saved, and a considerable part of the gear was salvaged. A large number of American and British sealing masters from various parts of the South Shetlands congregated at Clothier Harbor on February 1, 1821, when salvage from the wreck was sold at auction.[26]

Very little is known of the activities of the Second Stonington or Clark Fleet at the South Shetlands in 1820-21. First Mate Elof Benson made no entries in the logbook of the *Catharina* from December 7, 1820, the date on which the brig entered Clothier Harbor, to March 9, 1821, the day on which she sailed for home. In spite of the loss of the *Clothier,* the fleet seems to have been fairly successful in its sealing operations; The *Catharina* reported a cargo of 10,000 sealskins, and the *Emeline* reported 10,500 fur sealskins.

The *Emeline* and *Catharina* sailed from Clothier Harbor on March 9, 1821. When the *Spark* sailed and what disposal was made of her are not known. Seven of the crew of the *Clothier* returned home in the *O'Cain* of Boston. Beauchêne Island, to the south of East Falkland, was sighted from the *Catharina* on March 13. Meanwhile, the *Emeline* sailed for Staten Island, at the eastern tip of Tierra del Fuego, where Captain Holmes remained until mid-April. Captain Henfield made a brief stop for water at St. Vincent of the Windward Isles of the Lesser Antilles; the *Catharina* reached Stonington on May 13 after a voyage of 65 days from the South Shetlands. The *Emeline* arrived at Stonington on June 9, 57 days from Staten Island.

THE BOSTON FLEET

ORGANIZATION AND COMPOSITION

To designate the three Boston vessels at the South Shetlands in 1820-21 as a fleet is more convenient than appropriate, for only two of them were jointly owned and seem to have worked together. Nevertheless, all three Boston vessels shared the same harbor on occasion, and because their major field of activity was the eastern part of the South Shetlands they had little contact with the other Americans headquartering at Yankee Harbor.

The rather late departure of the vessels from Boston would seem to indicate that their owners did not know or were late in learning of the discovery of the South Shetlands. The 280-ton, 93-foot ship *O'Cain*, built at Scituate, Massachusetts in 1802, was wholly owned by Abiel Winship. With Jonathan Winship as master, she sailed from Boston on August 19, 1820, for a reported destination of "Indian Ocean and Canton." The ship *Esther* and the brig *Emerald* were owned by John Dorr and David W. Child of Boston and Sullivan Dorr of Providence. The two vessels cleared the Boston Custom House "for the South Seas" on September 23, 1820. The *Emerald,* commanded by Captain John G. Scott, was an 81-ton brig built at Providence in 1817. Captain F. G. Low was master of the ship *Esther*.[27]

ACTIVITIES OF THE BOSTON VESSELS

Very little is known of the activities of the three Boston vessels at the South Shetlands. The *O'Cain* was moored at Potter Cove on the southwest end of King George Island. The *Esther* and the *Emerald* appear to have been at both Potter Cove and Esther Harbor. The position of the latter anchorage, named for the Boston ship by the sealers, is southeast of Ridley Island in Venus Bay, on the north side near the eastern end of King George Island. Captain F. G. Low is credited with being the first to visit Esther Harbor, which sealers considered a good anchorage.[28] On December 25, 1820, the *O'Cain* was anchored in Perry Sound, riding out a gale with "two anchors ahead," when one of the cables parted. To avoid being driven ashore the other cable was slipped. One man fell overboard and was drowned.[29] The following excerpt from the notice of the *O'Cain's* arrival in Boston adds further information.

Brig Emerald arr. at Potter's Cove March 10, and informed that sch. Venus, just arr. from New-York dragged all her anchors in a gale, and went on a reef, at the entrance of Esther Harbor, bilged and had her stern stove in. The E. sailed again the 12th, and on the 16th was followed by the ship Esther.[30]

The *Emerald* and the *Esther,* after taking off the crew of the *Venus* and salvaging what they could from the wrecked schooner, sailed round Cape Horn for the Pacific. At the time the two Boston vessels had about 9000 skins between them. Sealing in the Pacific off the coast of South America could not have proven very successful, for the *Emerald* was sold at Valparaiso, Chile, on July 12, 1821.[31]

On March 18, with 12,000 sealskins on board, the *O'Cain* sailed from Potter Cove in company with the ship *King George* of Liverpool, of which Captain Roberts was master. On the homeward voyage Captain Winship put in at Maldonado, a small port on the coast of Uruguay, on April 10. Sailing again on April 28, he brought the *O'Cain* into Boston harbor on June 8, 1821. The arrival of the *O'Cain* from the newly discovered and forbidding land of ice and snow in the far south created a wave of public interest in Boston, and crowds of people came down to the wharf to view the ship.

The following note from the *New England Palladium & Commercial Adver-tiser* for June 19, 1821, indicates that Captain Winship, like several other Ameri-can sealing masters, had an amateur's interest in natural science.

The ship O'Cain brought home from N. S. Shetland, several kinds of curious stones, shells, minerals and fossil coal--some of which have been presented to Mr. Topliff, and may be seen at the bar of Merchants' Hall.

It would gratify many to have the articles from those islands examined by gentlemen skilled in Mineralogy and Chemistry, and the result published.

Samuel Topliff himself described the specimens as follows:

Capt. Winship has brought home several specimens of ore, found on the Coast of New South Shetland, stones, shells, &c; and a sample of coal which he says is not inferior to New Castle, and which was found in great abundance.

Mr. Topliff[32]

THE SALEM FLEET

ORGANIZATION AND COMPOSITION

The Salem, Massachusetts, sailing fleet at the South Shetlands in 1820-21 con-sisted of the ship *General Knox,* the brig *Nancy,* and the schooner *Governor Brooks,* owned by a group of five men. Stephen White of Salem owned a share in all three vessels; William Fettyplace and John Dodd held shares in two. White and Fettyplace also owned shares in the brig *Frederick* of the Fanning-Pendle-ton Fleet of Stonington, and Fettyplace also was a part owner of the *Clothier* of Stonington.

The *General Knox* was a 266-ton ship, 96 feet in length, which was built in 1810 at Thomaston, Maine, then a part of Massachusetts. The 151-ton *Nancy* was a 73-foot brig built at Amesbury, Massachusetts, in 1819. The schooner *Gov-ernor Brooks,* which served as a tender, was a 40-ton vessel built in 1816 at Free-port, Maine.

The *General Knox,* commanded by William B. Orne, sailed from Salem, pre-sumably for the Falklands and other sub-Antarctic sealing grounds, on August 23, 1818. The *Governor Brooks,* tender to the *General Knox,* sailed at the same time under command of Captain Nicholas Withem. If they had not heard the news from other sources, Captains Orne and Withem were apparently informed of the discovery of the South Shetlands by Captain Benjamin Upton, who sailed from Boston in the brig *Nancy* on August 13, 1820.

ACTIVITIES

The first record of the activities of the Salem fleet in 1820 is contained in Na-thaniel B. Palmer's remark of October 17 in the logbook of the *Hero* that he had entered Berkeley Sound where he found two shallops belonging to the *Gen-eral Knox.* Presumably one was the *Governor Brooks.* The second shallop is dif-ficult to explain unless Palmer carelessly used the term also for the brig *Nancy.* On October 20, Palmer anchored in West Point Harbor beside the *General Knox.* The date of departure of the Salem fleet for the South Shetlands is un-

known; they were still at the Falklands on November 6. The next date of record
is January 19, 1821, when Captain John Davis noted in the logbook of the *Huron* that the schooner *Governor Brooks* had arrived in Yankee Harbor. The next
day Captain Withem was one of the several officers and men who helped Davis
get the *Huron* moored safely again after she had dragged her anchors in a sudden gale. On February 16, Davis reported the arrival in Yankee Harbor of Captain Upton in the brig *Nancy*. She had previously been moored at Harmony
Cove on Nelson Island. A violent gale from the east, with snow and sleet, caused
the *Nancy* to run afoul of the *Jane Maria* of New York on March 3. On the
morning of March 10, 1821, Captain Burdick in the schooner *Huntress* and Captain Upton in the brig *Nancy* sailed in company from Yankee Harbor. The
Huntress was bound for Staten Island and home, while Captain Upton intended to winter the *Nancy* at the Falkland Islands. The activities of the ship *General Knox* during all this time are unknown. She arrived home on June 5, 1821,
87 days from the Falkland Islands, with 5000 skins and 600 barrels of oil.[33] En
route, Captain Orne had put in at St. Barthélemy of the Leeward Islands of the
Lesser Antilles.

Having reached the Falkland Islands, Captains Upton and Withem cruised
about and finally moored the *Nancy* and the *Governor Brooks* at Beaver Island
for the winter. Captain Upton was one of the four sealing masters who made a
survey of the damages sustained by the brig *Aurora* of New York, and on June
18 had condemned the vessel as unseaworthy.

The *Nancy* and the *Governor Brooks* anchored at Clothier Harbor at the beginning of the 1821-22 season at the South Shetlands. The exact time of their
arrival is not known, but they were there early in November. On January 20,
1822, the schooner visited Yankee Harbor, where Captain Upton purchased five
puncheons of bread, four barrels of mess pork, and eight barrels of beef from
Captain Davis. On January 25 the *Governor Brooks* was back at Yankee Harbor,
where she remained for two days before beginning a cruise to the westward.

On March 6, 1822, the *Nancy* and her tender sailed from Clothier Harbor for
the Falkland Islands. On May 25, 82 days later, the *Nancy* arrived at Salem with
1800 skins and 100 barrels of oil, not a very profitable return.[34] The small cargo
would seem to indicate that at least part of the sealskins obtained by the *Nancy*'s
crew in 1820-21 had been sent home on the *General Knox*.

VESSELS FROM NANTUCKET

Nantucket sent five vessels to the South Shetlands in 1820-21. The activities of
Captain Christopher Burdick and the schooner *Huntress* have been related in
Chapter 5. The other four vessels were the ship *Samuel,* the brig *Diana,* and the
schooners *Harmony* and *William and Nancy.* There was no attempt at fleet organization, each vessel operating separately. At least three of them were whalers
temporarily diverted from their regular occupation to capitalize on the reported
new bonanza at the South Shetlands.

The ship *Samuel,* the property of Ariel Coffin, Samuel Carey, Jethro Mitchell,
and James Athea of Nantucket, was a whaler built at Scituate, Massachusetts, in

1804. She was 92 feet long and was registered as of 287 tons. The *Samuel,* in command of Captain Robert Inott, sailed on a whaling voyage on October 25, 1820. Having taken 90 barrels of sperm oil, Captain Inott put into "Port Praya" where the oil was put aboard the brig *Hazard* bound for Boston.[35] On November 19, 1820, the *Samuel* sailed for the South Shetlands on a sealing venture which, because of her late arrival, was unsuccessful. Starbuck reports that the *Samuel* was condemned at Rio de Janeiro in 1822 and that her cargo of 1800 barrels of oil was shipped home.[36]

The schooner *Harmony,* although registered at Nantucket, was the property of Josiah and William Sampson of Barnstable, Massachusetts, where the vessel was built in 1818.[37] The 71-foot, 111-ton schooner was commanded by Captain Nathaniel Ray. Very little is known of Captain Ray's activities on this voyage. The *Harmony* sailed for the South Shetlands in the latter part of August. She gave her name to Harmony Cove on the west side of Nelson Island, where the schooner was moored during the 1820-21 season. The *Harmony,* with a cargo of 4500 sealskins, arrived home in company with the schooner *Huntress* on June 6, 1821. On the homeward voyage in about 18° N, 54° W Captain Ray spoke the ship *Triton* and learned from Captain Wood of the loss of the whaleship *Essex.* This was one of the great disasters of the period, and any report Captain Ray may have made of his own voyage was ignored by the newspapers in favor of the account he gave of the fate of the *Essex.* On August 1, 1821, Captain Isaac Hodges succeeded Captain Ray as commander of the schooner on a second voyage to the South Shetlands in 1821-22.

The schooner *William and Nancy* was registered on June 1, 1819, under the sole ownership of Thomas V. McClure of Nantucket. She was a whaler built at Bath in 1810 and for a time was rigged as a brig, but had been reconverted to a two-masted schooner, 64 feet long and of 100 tons burden. Tristan Folger assumed command of the vessel on May 2, 1820, and sailed on a whaling voyage from which the ship returned "clean" November 27, 1820.[38] Folger then sailed for the South Shetlands, but arriving there late in the season had little success as a sealer. It has not been determined when the schooner returned home, but her register shows that Captain Folger was succeeded by Ferdinand Gardiner on April 21, 1821.

Calvin Bunker of Nantucket was both master and managing owner of the *Diana,* a 60-foot, 86-ton whaling brig built at New Bedford in 1794. The *Diana* arrived at Nantucket on May 10, 1821, from the South Shetlands with 2000 sealskins. It would appear that Captain Bunker had been forced to return before he had wished because of the loss of two boats and eight men.[39]

NEW BEDFORD AND FAIRHAVEN VESSELS

Two vessels sailed for the South Shetlands late in 1820 from New Bedford and Fairhaven, Massachusetts, twin ports lying on opposite banks at the mouth of the Acushnet River. New Bedford was then the leading whaling center in the country, and it is not surprising that both vessels were normally engaged in that occupation.

The brig *Gleaner,* a 166-ton vessel built in 1818 at Troy, Maine, then a part of Massachusetts, was the property of John A. Parker and David Leslie of New Bedford. The latter was also master of the brig when she sailed for the South Shetlands at the end of October, 1820. Captain Leslie apparently found that he had arrived too late for a successful season. On April 12, 1821, a British brig reported at Buenos Aires that she had spoken the *Gleaner,* then en route to the Pacific with very few skins, having sailed from the South Shetlands on March 24.[40] At Valparaiso, July 5, 1821, Thomas A. Boyd succeeded Captain Leslie as master of the *Gleaner.*

The brig *Stranger* was registered at Boston, but on this voyage of 1820 sailed from Fairhaven in command of Captain Joseph Adams. She was spoken on February 16, 1821 by Captain Bunker of the whaling ship *John Jay* of Nantucket in 57°10' S, 65°30' W.[41] Captain Jonathan Winship of the ship *O'Cain,* when he reached Boston on June 8, 1821, reported that the *Stranger* had arrived "in Yankee Streights" (probably Yankee Sound of McFarlane Strait) and had obtained 1000 or 1500 skins.[42] Further information on the voyage is lacking.

NOTES

1. Alonzo Howard Clark, "The Antarctic Fur-seal and Sea-elephant Industries," *The Fisheries and Fishery Industries of the United States,* U. S. Bureau of Fish and Fisheries, Sen. Misc. Doc. 124, 77th Congr., 1st Sess., 1887, Sec. V, vol. 2, pp. 402, 448.

2. Dr. Karl Fricker, *The Antarctic Regions* (London and New York, 1900), pp. 63-64. Fricker was referring to Captain Benjamin Morrell, Jr., *A Narrative of Four Voyages to the South Sea,* etc. (New York, 1832), p. 69.

3. Edouard A. Stackpole, *The Sea Hunters* (Philadelphia, Lippincott, 1953). Also *The Voyage of the Huron and the Huntress,* Marine Historical Association Publication, No. 29, Mystic, Conn., 1955.

4. Mrs. Krueger is the great-granddaughter of Elof Benson (anglicized from the Swedish Berndtson) who was first mate on the *Hersilia* and *Catharina* and captain on the *Adventure.* All three logbooks are in Captain Benson's handwriting. The logbooks of the *Hersilia* and *Catharina* are in one volume. Only a few unbound pages remain of the logbook of the *Adventure.* Microfilm copies of the logbooks are available in Yale University Library.

5. Letters, August 17 and September 4, 1820, from James Byers of New York to Brig. Gen. Daniel Parker, Adjutant and Insp. Gen., U. S. Army, Washington. Records of the Department of State, Misc. Letters, August-October, 1820, Record Group 59, U. S. National Archives.

6. This spelling conforms to Captain Brunow's signature on Custom House documents. Newspapers invariably spelled it Bruno.

7. According to Byers' letter of September 4, 1820, to Gen. Parker, this 40-ton vessel had been assembled earlier at the Falklands from prefabricated parts carried on board a larger vessel. This apparently accounts for the fact that there is no record of its registry among the records of the New York Custom House. In some of the news reports the tender is referred to as the *Sally,* but since this is the diminutive for Sarah, it is safe to assume that the *Sarah* and the *Sally* are the same vessel.

8. Capt. Christopher Burdick, from the logbook of the *Huntress,* as quoted by Stackpole, *op. cit.,* p. 37.

9. See the letter of Daniel W. Clark to the editor of the *Connecticut Journal,* Chap. 4, p. 80.

10. Stackpole, *op. cit.,* p. 66.

11. Capt. John Davis, Logbook of the *Huron.* See the entry for Saturday, January 27, 1821.

12. Christopher Burdick, from the Logbook of the *Huntress,* as quoted by Stackpole, *op. cit.,* p. 47.

13. See pp. 93-94. For a more complete account see Stackpole, *op. cit.,* pp. 44-46.

14. MacKay's name is also sometimes spelled McKay. His role is not entirely clear, since of all the New York vessels at the South Shetlands in 1820-21 only the *Henry's* crew list has been found among the records of the New York Custom House. He seems to have been aboard the *Sarah* on some of her cruises, but apparently was aboard the *Charity* on the voyage to the

Falklands in April 1821. In the logbook of the *Huron*, Capt. Davis refers to him as "Captain MacKay." Dr. S. L. Mitchill also refers to him as "Captain MacKay."

15. John Torrey, M. D., "Description of a New Species of Usnea, from New South Shetland," *American Journal of Science*, vol. 4, No. 1, January, 1823, pp. 104-106. Mitchill's letter transmitting the specimens to Torrey is included in the article. In it Mitchill discusses the special public interest in the natural history specimens brought home by several mariners from the South Shetlands.

16. Samuel L. Mitchill, "Notice of Some of the Things Received into my Museum and Library," *The New York Medical and Physical Journal*, vol. 1, No. 4, December, 1822, pp. 510-513.

17. Samuel L. Mitchill, *Catalogue of the Organic Remains which with other Geological and Some Mineral Articles were Presented to the New York Lyceum of Natural History, in August, 1826, by their Associate, Samuel L. Mitchill* (New York, 1826), 40 pp.

18. Capt. Charles H. Barnard, *A Narrative of the Sufferings and Adventures of Captain Charles H. Barnard in a Voyage Round the World, During the Years, 1812, 1813, 1814, 1815 & 1816*, etc. (New York, 1829), p. 207. Barnard is referring to James Weddell's *A Voyage Towards the South Pole Performed in the Years 1822-24* (London, 1825).

19. *New England Palladium & Commercial Advertiser*, Boston, June 12, 1821.

20. *Boston Patriot and Daily Mercantile Advertiser*, June 9, 1821.

21. Davis, *op. cit.*, March 24, 1821.

22. These dates are taken from the logbook of the *Huron*. Newspaper accounts give April 8 as the date on which the *Sarah* was lost. If the latter is correct, it is probably the date on which the *Sarah* was given up for lost.

23. Clark, *op. cit.*, pp. 406, 448; Stackpole, *op. cit.*, pp. 16, 35-36, 58-59.

24. Although she was registered as the *Catharina* and her name is so spelled in the logbook, newspaper accounts invariably referred to the brig as the *Catherine*.

25. *New England Palladium and Commercial Advertiser*, May 18, 1821.

26. Burdick, as reported by Stackpole, *op. cit.*, p. 58.

27. Registration documents for the ship *Esther* have not been found among records of the Ports of Boston and Providence.

28. *New-York Gazette & General Advertiser*, June 4, 1821.

29. *American Statesman*, Boston, June 12, 1821.

30. *New England Palladium & Commercial Advertiser*, Boston, June 12, 1821.

31. So indicated on an attachment to the surrendered copy of the ship's certificate of registration. Register No. 168, September 6, 1820, Port of Boston, Vessel Documentation Series, Records of the Bureau of Marine Inspection and Navigation, Record Group 41, U. S. National Archives.

32. Published in the *New-York Columbian*, June 11, 1821. Samuel Topliff (1789-1864) for many years operated a news-gathering service in Boston. He specialized in marine and commercial news, but also had foreign correspondents. He sold his service to Boston, New York, Philadelphia, and other newspapers who published his by-line. As early as 1820 he had a 92-foot signal staff on an island in Boston Harbor, by which his men signaled the approach of a vessel, which would then be met by one of his two boats to gather news and pick up bills of lading. In 1821 he operated merchants' reading rooms in the Exchange Coffee House and in Merchants Hall.

33. *Boston Patriot and Daily Mercantile Advertiser*, June 6, 1821.

34. *Essex Register*, Salem, May 29, 1822.

35. *New England Palladium & Commercial Advertiser*, Boston, April 24, 1821. "Port Praya" is probably Praia on the island of São Tiago of the Cape Verde Islands, a common resort of the whalers.

36. Alexander Starbuck, *History of the American Whale Fishery*, Washington, 1878, Appendix A, I, Misc. Sen. Doc. 107, 44th Congr., 1st Sess., 1878, pp. 232-233.

37. Temporary Register No. 18, August 19, 1820, District of Nantucket, Mass., Vessel Documentation Series, Records of the Bureau of Marine Inspection and Navigation, Record Group 41, U. S. National Archives.

38. Starbuck, *op. cit.*, pp. 232-233.

39. *New England Palladium & Commercial Advertiser*, Boston, May 15, 1821.

40. *Boston Patriot & Daily Mercantile Advertiser*, June 21, 1821.

41. *Boston Patriot & Daily Mercantile Advertiser*, May 23, 1821.

42. *New England Palladium & Commercial Advertiser*, Boston, June 12, 1821.

BIBLIOGRAPHY

PUBLISHED MATERIAL

The American, New York, July 1, 1820.

American Statesman, Boston, June 12, 1821.

Barnard, Charles H., *A Narrative of the Sufferings and Adventures of Captain Charles H. Barnard, in A Voyage Round the World, during the Years 1812, 1813, 1814, 1815 and 1816,* etc. (printed for the author by J. Lindon, New York, 1829), vii and 266 pp., 6 plates, map.

Boston Patriot and Daily Mercantile Advertiser, August 12, 16, 21; September 2, 25; October 7; November 4, 1820. May 3, 5, 12, 19, 23, 25; June 6, 9, 12, 16, 20, 21, 23; July 4, 1821. April 22, 25; May 4, 28; June 8, 10, 13, 17, 1822.

Clark, Alonzo Howard, "The Antarctic Fur-seal and Sea-elephant Industries," *The Fisheries and Fishery Industries of the United States,* U. S. Bureau of Fish and Fisheries. Sen. Misc. Doc. 124, 47th Congr., 1st Sess., 1887, Sec. V, vol. 2, pp. 400-467.

Dictionary of American Biography (New York, Charles Scribner's Sons, 1936), vol. 18, p. 592; vol. 13, 1934, pp. 69-71.

Duychinck, Evert A., and George L. Duychinck, *Cyclopedia of American Literature* (New York, Charles Scribner, 1856), vol. 1, pp. 517-524.

Essex Register, Salem, Mass., June 9, 1821; April 20, 1822.

Fricker, Dr. Karl, *The Antarctic Regions* (New York, Macmillan, 1900), xii and 292 pp., map, illus.

Meisel, Max, *Bibliography of American Natural History, the Pioneer Century, 1769-1863* (Brooklyn, N. Y. , Premier Publishing Co.). 3 vols.: vol. 1, 1924, 244 pp.; vol. 2, 1926, xii and 741 pp.; vol. 3, 1929, xii and 749 pp.

Mitchill, Dr. Samuel L., *Catalogue of the Organic Remains which with other Geological and Some Mineral Articles were Presented to the New York Lyceum of Natural History in August, 1826, by their Associate, S. L. Mitchill* (printed by J. Seymour, New York, 1826), 40 pp.

——, "Notice of Some of the Things Received into my Museum and Library," *The New York Medical and Physical Journal,* vol. 1, No. 4, December, 1822, pp. 510-513.

National Advocate, New York, July 3, 4; October 9, 1820; May 12, 1821; April 26, May 16, 22, 1822.

New England Palladium & Commercial Advertiser, Boston, September 26, 1820; April 24; May 4, 8, 15, 18, 22, 29; June 8, 12, 15, 19, 1821.

New-York Columbian, June 15, 1820; May 12, 23; June 11, 1821.

New-York Commercial Advertiser, May 12, 1821.

New-York Gazette & General Advertiser, May 12, 16, 22; June 4, 1821.

New-York Statesman and Evening Advertiser, April 26; May 16, 22, 1822.

Niles Weekly Register, Baltimore, vol. 20, No. 15 (whole No. 509), June 9, 1821, pp. 237-238.

Republican Advocate, New London, July 26, 1820; May 2, 16, 1821; April 17, May 1, 15, 22, 1822.

Stackpole, Edouard A., *The Sea-Hunters* (Philadelphia, Lippincott, 1953), 510 pp.

——, *The Voyage of the Huron and the Huntress,* Publication No. 29, Marine Historical Association (Mystic, Conn.), 1955, 86 pp.

Starbuck, Alexander, *History of the American Whale Fishery, from its Earliest Inception to the Year 1876* (privately printed, Waltham, Mass., 1878), 768 pp., 6 plates. Also published as Report of the Commissioner of Fish and Fisheries for 1875-76. Appendix A, I, Misc. Sen. Doc. 107, 44th Congr., 1st Sess., 1878.

Torrey, John, "Description of a New Species of Usnea, from New South Shetland," *American Journal of Science,* vol. 6, No. 1, January, 1823, pp. 104-106.

MANUSCRIPT MATERIAL

Benson, Elof, Logbook of the brig *Catharina,* Stonington, Conn., Joseph Henfield, Master, 1820-1821. (Benson was First Mate.) Formerly the property of Mrs. Theodore H. Krueger, Stratford, Conn., who gave it to the Yale University Library. Microfilm copies in Yale University Library and in the Library of the Marine Historical Association, Mystic, Conn.

Byers, James, Letters of, August 17, August 25, and September 4, 1820, to Brig. Gen. Daniel Parker, Adjutant and Insp. Gen., U. S. Army, Washington. Records of the Department of State, Misc. Letters, August-October 1820, Record Group 59, U. S. National Archives. These letters have been microfilmed by the National Archives as part of microcopy M-179, roll 49.

Crew List of the schooner *Henry* of New York, June 24, 1820-May 16, 1822, Capt. Benjamin J. Brunow, Custom House Records, Port of New York, Crew Lists, Record Group 36, Legislative and Fiscal Records Branch, U. S. National Archives.

Davis, Capt. John, Logbook of the ship *Huron*, New Haven, Conn., January 18, 1821-April 27, 1822. Formerly the property of Alexander O. Vietor, Curator of Maps, Yale University Library, who has given it to the Library.

Palmer, Capt. Nathaniel B., Logbook of the sloop *Hero*, Stonington, Conn., 1820-1821. Marine Misc., Acc. 3680, Manuscript Division, Library of Congress, Washington.

Ship Registrations: Vessel Documentation Series, Records of the Bureau of Marine Inspection and Navigation, Record Group 41, U. S. National Archives.

Port of Boston:
Permanent Register No. 98, May 12, 1818, ship *O'Cain*.
Permanent Register No. 168, September 6, 1820, brig *Emerald*.

District of Nantucket:
Permanent Register No. 2, March 14, 1815, schooner *William and Nancy*. Registry Book also contains information for Permanent Enrollment No. 14, June 1, 1819, but document missing.
Temporary Register No. 18, August 17, 1820, schooner *Harmony*.
Permanent Register No. 20, August 23, 1820, brig *Diana*.
Data in Registry Book; actual document missing. Document for August 9, 1821, is on file.
Temporary Register No. 27, July 3, 1815, ship *Samuel*. Data in Registry Book; actual document missing.

District of New Bedford:
Temporary Register No. 16, March 30, 1815, ship *Samuel*.
Permanent Register No. 12, May 12, 1818, brig *Gleaner*.

District of New London:
Permanent Register No. 7, July 17, 1820, brig *Catharina*.
Permanent Register No. 8, July 17, 1820, brig *Emeline*.
Permanent Register No. 12, August 2, 1820, ship *Clothier*.

Port of New York:
Permanent Register No. 170, July 1, 1819, brig *Jane Maria*.
Permanent Register No. 144, June 24, 1820, schooner *Henry*.
Data from Registry Book; actual document missing.
Permanent Register No. 152, July 1, 1820, brig *Aurora*.
Permanent Register No. 214, October 7, 1820, schooner *Venus*.
Data from Registry Book; actual document missing.
Permanent Register 141, June 16, 1821, schooner *Wasp*.
Permanent Register No. 144, May 27, 1822, brig *Charity*.

District of Salem:
Permanent Register No. 22, July 13, 1818, schooner *Governor Brooks*.
Permanent Register No. 28, August 15, 1818, ship *General Knox*.
Permanent Register No. 21, August 11, 1820, brig *Nancy*.

7

THE FANNING-PENDLETON SEALING FLEET, 1821-1822

ORGANIZATION AND ACCOMPLISHMENTS

SIGNIFICANCE OF THE FLEET

During the austral summer of 1820-21 the South Shetland Islands had been thoroughly explored by the sealers from 30 American vessels and from at least 24 British vessels. In their search for seal rookeries several vessels had approached the Antarctic Peninsula, and at least two landings had been made on it.[1] So thoroughly had the seals been hunted in what was apparently near the southern limit of their range that they were decimated. Further slaughter in 1821-22 contributed to their ultimate extinction in the South Shetlands.

In the austral summer of 1821-22 it was soon apparent that new rookeries would have to be found if the operations were to be financially successful. Visits to the shores of the Antarctic Peninsula had produced none. For that reason the joint cruise of Nathaniel B. Palmer in the sloop *James Monroe* and the British sealer George Powell in the sloop *Dove* was made to the east. The result was the discovery of the South Orkney Islands, geographically the most significant result of the operations during the entire 1821-22 season. Because of the meager returns, the Fanning firm was dissolved following this venture, and until 1829 subsequent American operations were confined to single vessels.

ESTABLISHMENT AND COMPOSITION OF THE FLEET

The Fanning-Pendleton sealing fleet of 1821-22 was organized by Edmund and William A. Fanning and Benjamin Pendleton. Pendleton and the elder Fanning signed the instructions to the captains of the vessels of the fleet as "Agents for the Concern." William A. Fanning, however, was heavily involved, financially as well as personally.[2]

Although the *Hersilia* in 1819-20 and the five vessels of the Fanning-Pendleton fleet of 1820-21 had been very successful financially, there was abundant evidence before the fleet left for the United States in 1821 that the fur seals had been almost wiped out at the South Shetlands. In fact, the *Hersilia* would not have sailed for the coast of Chile in 1821 but would also have returned home, if she had had a full cargo. In spite of these indications of impending failure, however, the Fannings and Pendleton sent out six vessels in 1821, adding the brig *Alabama Packet* and the sloop *James Monroe* to the fleet. Perhaps the addition of the latter, making two sloops in the fleet, was a concession to the prospects of having to range far and wide for new rookeries.

Data pertaining to the six vessels comprising the fleet, obtained from the certificates of registry filed at the New London Custom House and now deposited at the Federal Records Center, Waltham, Massachusetts, are contained in the following table:

Name of Vessel	Type of Rig	Length	Tonnage	Place and Date of Construction
Frederick	brig	67' 8"	147	Guilford, Conn., 1815
Alabama Packet	brig	....	...	
Express	schooner	76' 9"	138	Hudson, N. Y., 1816
Free Gift	schooner	50' 7"	52	Pawcatuck, R. I., 1807
James Monroe	sloop	....	80	
Hero	sloop	47' 3"	45	Groton, Conn., 1800

The brig *Frederick* was flagship of the fleet. The registries show William A. Fanning and Benjamin Pendleton to be among the owners of the *Frederick*, the *Free Gift*, and the *Hero*. Nathaniel B. Palmer also was a part owner of the *Hero*. In 1821 Benjamin Pendleton was listed as sole owner of the *Express*.

The 85 men who manned the Fanning-Pendleton fleet of 1821-22 were assigned as indicated in the following table:

Name of Vessel	Master	Number in Ship's Company*
Frederick	Benjamin Pendleton	21 men
Alabama Packet	William A. Fanning	21 men
Express	Thomas Dunbar	17 men and a boy
Free Gift	Benjamin Cutler	10 men and a boy
James Monroe	Nathaniel B. Palmer	7 men
Hero	Harris Pendleton	7 men

*These approximate figures are from three sources, none of which is complete and which do not entirely agree. This is due to unrecorded discharges or desertions between departure and return. There were apparently no deaths. These sources are a note among the Palmer Papers in the Manuscript Division of the Library of Congress, the letter of William A. Fanning of January 27, 1822, *op. cit.*, and the "Return of Names of Seamen...." filed at the New London Custom House upon return, now on deposit in the Federal Records Center, Waltham, Mass. The crew lists filed on departure have been lost.

Benjamin Pendleton was designated senior commander and was given direction of operations at the South Shetlands. William A. Fanning was second in command and was to take charge in case of Pendleton's incapacitation.

OBJECTIVES AND ACCOMPLISHMENTS

Commercially, the venture of the Fanning-Pendleton fleet of 1821-22 was successful only owing to the persistence of William A. Fanning and Benjamin Pendleton, who took three of the vessels into the Pacific to hunt off the Chilean coast for the hair seal, whose pelt was inferior to the fur seal. However, as the two letters from William A. Fanning to his father indicate, the profit margin was very narrow, considering the investment, the time, and the risks involved.

Geographically, the major accomplishment was the discovery of the South Orkney Islands, December 6, 1821, during a joint cruise by Nathaniel B. Palmer and the British sealer, George Powell. Whatever additional discoveries, if any, may have been made in cruises by the *Hero* and the *Free Gift* are now unknown.

DETAILED RECORD OF OPERATIONS

The logbooks of the *Hero* and the *Alabama Packet* record the departure of these two vessels in company with the brig *Frederick,* the schooner *Express,* and the sloop *James Monroe* at 8 a. m., Wednesday, July 25, 1821. Their departure was marred by the *Express* going aground as they sailed out of Stonington harbor, but she got free later in the day. The sixth vessel, the schooner *Free Gift,* apparently left as much as 10 or 12 days earlier, for her papers were filed at the New London Custom House on July 10. Sailing instructions from Edmund Fanning and Benjamin Pendleton to Nathaniel Palmer, which are among the latter's papers in the Manuscript Division of the Library of Congress, directed him to proceed to Staten Island and from there to Deception Island, which it had been decided would be the fleet's base of operations in the South Shetlands for 1821-22.

The outward passage of four of the vessels was a slow one due to calms and light, baffling winds north of the equator. The *Express,* however, seems to have made a reasonably good passage in these same latitudes and consequently arrived at Deception Island ahead of the other vessels with which she set out. The other four vessels managed to sail in company until one day north of the Falkland Islands, when they were separated in a gale. The *Alabama Packet* sought shelter in a bay on New Island of the Falklands where the men restowed the hold and took on water and wood. Two days later, while making ready for sea, they saw the *Hero* and the *James Monroe* pass the island. The brig overtook the two sloops during the night and the next day the three vessels proceeded in company to Staten Island, where they found the *Frederick* already at anchor. After two days spent in getting wood and water the fleet set out for the south. Five days later Smith Island was sighted. According to instructions, the vessels proceeded directly to Deception Island (Fig. 3).

At 2 p. m., November 7, the *Hero* arrived in Deception Island. The logbook reports that the *Express* and the *Free Gift* were at anchor. Between then and the arrival of the *Alabama Packet* at 4 p. m. the *Frederick* and the *James Monroe* also entered the harbor formed by the breached caldera of Deception Island which after 1829 became known as Port Foster. The logbook of the *Alabama Packet* documents the presence of the fleet at Deception Island:

> On 6th November Made the Island of Pisga [Mt. Pisgah Island, now called Smith Island] on our Lee bow - Stood off under Short Sail all Knight [sic] next day parted Company with the frederick found plenty of floating ice thick Snow Storm at 4 p. m. Came a Anchor in Deception Harbour now called port Dunbar - found laying at this Harbour Brig Frederick Schooner Express Sloop James Monroe Schooner Freegift And Sloop Hero all of Stonington

The dates of arrival of the *Free Gift* and the *Express* at Deception Island are unknown. In view of the former's earlier departure from Stonington, it probably was the first to arrive. Captain John Davis of the *Huron* was an early arrival at the South Shetlands in 1821-22, having entered Yankee Harbor with much difficulty on October 21. The harbor was "about half frozen over." The next day he reported in the logbook that the harbor was blocked and what looked like the

Free Gift of Stonington was trying to get in. On the next day he wrote, ". . . Ascertained the sch^r that arrived yesterday to be the Free Gift, Captn Chester of Stonington." Several other vessels arrived at Yankee Harbor from October 21 to 23, and since Davis made no further mention of the *Free Gift* it is assumed that Captain Cutler must have sailed for Deception when he saw the bad ice conditions at Yankee Harbor.

The scarcity of seals forced Pendleton to devote much more of his manpower to exploration for seal rookeries in 1821-22 than had been the case a year earlier, when only the *Hero* was so employed. This year the *Free Gift* cruised the shores of King George Island while the *Hero* and the *James Monroe* ranged over a greater territory, mainly northeastward from King George Island to Elephant and Clarence Islands but also along the shores of the Antarctic Peninsula.

EXPLORATION IN THE *HERO*

From the brief entries of the logbook of the *Hero,* kept by Phineas Wilcox, the first mate, it would appear that in addition to cruises about the South Shetlands, two cruises were made across Bransfield Strait to the shores of the Antarctic Peninsula.

On November 11, the *Hero* was at anchor in Deception Island. The logbook entries for that day and for November 12 record the first part of the cruise:

Sunday
Nov the 11 Commences with Light Brease from the Northward Got under way on a Cruse to the Southward Light Brease all Day

Monday
Nov the 12 Commences with Light Brease from the West Ward and pleasant A crusing along Shore on Discover Saw nothing But snow and Ice Latter part calm
Lat By Obs 64.20 S

The observed latitude on November 12 is open to question, for it places the *Hero* at the mouth of Hughes Bay. Considering the severe ice conditions reported by others and the relatively early date, it is doubtful that she could have been that far south. This is supported by the fact that on November 13 the *Hero* was heading for an island to the southwest. It is not otherwise identified except that she found no seals there. If this was Hoseason Island (63°44' S, 61°41' W), which is a strong possibility, the observed latitude for November 12 would have been too far south.

Finding no seals on the unidentified island, Harris Pendleton sailed for "Shoe Island," a name which is referred to in no other logbook or narrative. On November 14, the *Hero* was bound for "Pisga" [Smith Island]. Therefore, if the unidentified island where he found no seals on November 13 is Hoseason Island, "Shoe Island" would be Low Island, for it lies between Hoseason Island and Smith Island (Fig. 4).

A similar cruise may have been made by Harris Pendleton in the *Hero* beginning on December 30. He again stopped at "Shoe Island" and went from there to Smith Island. However, the entries in the logbook are so vague that it

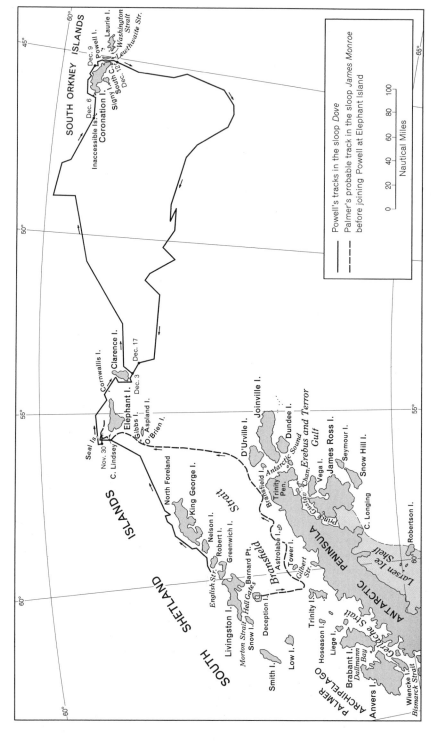

FIGURE 5. Joint Cruise of Powell and Palmer Resulting in the Discovery of the South Orkney Islands, 1821.

is difficult to determine whether the *Hero* sailed south from Livingston Island or from Deception Island. In the former case, he would not have gone as far south as he would have if he had started from Deception.

EXPLORATION IN THE *JAMES MONROE*

Since a major function of the *James Monroe* was to serve as an exploring vessel for the Fanning-Pendleton fleet and since seals were scarce, it is logical to assume that Nathaniel B. Palmer spent considerable time during the 1821-22 season on exploring cruises. The available evidence indicates that such was the case, but the evidence is so incomplete that it is impossible to give an accurate or complete account of the movements of the *James Monroe*.

Only for the joint cruise of Palmer and the British sealer George Powell is there an accurate account of the former's activities and of the movements of the *James Monroe*. On this cruise eastward from Elephant Island the South Orkney Islands were discovered on December 6, 1821 (Fig. 5). The logbook of the *James Monroe* has been lost, but fortunately Powell's brief narrative contains a precise account of the joint cruise which began November 30 and ended at Clothier Harbor December 22.[3] Presumably the vessels were more or less in company during the entire time, but Powell fails to mention the *James Monroe* specifically after December 11.

Powell in the sloop *Dove* set out from the South Shetlands to search for Bransfield's Seal Islands which supposedly lay to the eastward.[4] Upon reaching Elephant Island on November 30, 1821, he found the *James Monroe* already there with a boat crew ashore looking for seals. Palmer accepted Powell's suggestion that they join forces in a joint cruise to the eastward in search for new sealing grounds, such a cruise into unknown waters being less dangerous for two vessels than for one.

The two vessels worked around the north side of Elephant Island and, passing small Cornwallis Island, came upon neighboring Clarence Island where men were put out in boats to examine the beaches. No seals were found. At 10 p. m. on December 3, the two vessels sailed from Cape Bowles, the southern tip of Clarence Island. Their course took them along the east side of the island and then eastward. Foggy weather prevailed, and their position the next noon was 60°38′ S, 50°44′ W by dead reckoning, having covered 92 miles since leaving Cape Bowles. The foggy weather continued so that visibility was poor. Many penguins were seen in the water, an indication of land nearby. At 10 p. m., December 4, the two captains hove to because of the danger of ramming unseen floating ice but also for fear of missing land they were out to find. At 3 p. m. on December 5 the weather began to clear. By 4 p. m. the two sloops got under way under easy sail to the eastward. Forty minutes later the weather had cleared sufficiently to permit Powell to take a sight on the sun, from which he determined his longitude to be 49°7′ W. After 32 miles on an easterly course they steered southeastward to avoid a great deal of floating ice. "At 3 a. m. [December 6] the man at the masthead discovered land and ice, bearing E. by S.; at this time the James Monroe was about four miles a-stern of us; I shortened sail for her, and hailed her; they had not seen it until close up with us, and then Captain Palmer doubted whether it was land or ice; but, at all events, he said he would follow me:" Thus Powell describes the discovery of the South Orkney Islands.[5]

The two sloops had to avoid several icebergs as they worked in toward the land. At 9 a. m. they were close up and found it to be three small rocky islets which Powell appropriately named Inaccessible Islands. From here, however, they could easily see Coronation Island, the largest of the South Orkney group. Loose pack ice made the approach to the island difficult, but about 2 p. m., December 6, Powell landed on the western end of the island and took possession in the name of King George IV, naming the island in honor of his monarch's recent coronation. The two vessels worked slowly along the north side of Coronation Island, obstructed by numerous icebergs and hampered by foggy weather. At 3:30 p. m. December 9, the *Dove* joined the *James Monroe* at the northern end of the passage between Coronation and Powell Islands which Powell named Lewthwaite Strait. After a reconnaissance by Powell in a boat the two sloops entered the strait and came to anchor in a protected harbor (Spence Harbor) at 5 p. m., December 9. Here they waited out a gale. At 4 a. m., December 11, the *Dove* sent out two boats in charge of the first mate to explore to the southern end of the strait and then eastward. Another boat put out from the *James Monroe* to go to the southern end of the strait and then work along the coast of Coronation Island to the westward. The American crew returned at 9:30 a. m. after having reached the southern end of the strait, where they found no sign of seals. The two boats from the *Dove* returned at 8 p. m. after having crossed the southern portal of Washington Strait and reaching the icebound shore of Laurie Island.

A breeze having sprung up from the northward, the two sloops hove anchor and sailed south through Lewthwaite Strait at 4 p. m. on December 12. Provisions now being short, Powell, and presumably Palmer, were forced to discontinue the cruise to the eastward. Powell reports that he sailed south to the edge of firm ice about 62°30' S. He then coasted westward along the edge of the pack ice, reaching Clarence Island on December 17.

Shortly after the *James Monroe* returned to Stonington, April 17, 1822, the following article appeared in the *Connecticut Gazette:*

Continent of New South Iceland

We have been favoured with interesting particulars respecting a Southern Continent, by Capt. Nathaniel B. Palmer, of the Sloop James Monroe, lately arrived at Stonington, from the South Shetlands.

Capt. Palmer proceeded in the James Monroe, from the Shetland Isles to the continent, and coasted it, from abreast of the Isles, to the Eastward, as far as 44° West Longitude, keeping as near to the shore as the edge of firm ice would admit. At some places he could not approach nearer than from one to five or six leagues, owing to the firm and fast ice; although it was midsummer there at the time, being in November, December, and January.

In 61°41' South Latitude, 45°27' West Long. from Greenwich, the coast was clear of firm ice, and here they discovered a fine harbour, lying about one mile within the entrance of Washington Strait, which harbour was named Palmer's Harbour, where he came to anchor. He found not the least appearance of vegetation on the land excepting the wintermoss. Neither did he here discover any animals, only a few Sea-Leopards, beautifully spotted. Of birds, there were Penguins, Port Egmont, or Sea Hens, White Pigeons, and Gulls.

There is now no doubt, that there exists a *South Continent,* and that Capt. Cook's "Southern Thule" belongs to it. Capt. Palmer could discern the mountains covered with snow, in the interior, as he sailed along the coast.[6]

This newspaper article, which was reprinted in several other American newspapers in 1822, was apparently the basis for an almost identical account published by Edmund Fanning in 1833.[7]

The third paragraph of the above quotation obviously applies to Palmer's joint cruise with Powell to the South Orkneys which began at Elephant Island. The article, however, implies that this was part of a longer cruise which began off the Antarctic Peninsula to the south of South Shetlands. It is possible to reconcile this with other known facts, but the newspaper account also implies that Palmer reported that the Antarctic Peninsula and the South Orkneys were all part of the same land area, and that he had sailed along the entire coast. Undoubtedly the editor misunderstood the information that Palmer gave him, for it is difficult to believe that Palmer held such a view or mistook the edge of the pack ice for the coast. From his own explorations and from the reports of other sealers the previous season, he must have known that the Antarctic Peninsula is a mountainous area with ice attached to the shore at times and not a relatively flat-surfaced region as the pack ice would have been.

In accord with the report in the *Connecticut Gazette,* it is quite probable that some time shortly after his arrival on November 6 Palmer took the *James Monroe* south from the base at Deception Island to the edge of the consolidated pack ice fringing the Antarctic Peninsula. From this point he apparently coasted the edge of the pack ice to the eastward. Since ice conditions were reportedly severe in 1821-22, he would have been less likely at such an early date in the season to find his way open to the southwestward. Since there are numerous prominent peaks on the Antarctic Peninsula and Mount Percy, on Joinville Island, is over 3000 feet high, Palmer would have been aware of the fact that he had come abreast of the end of the mountainous terrain as he sailed eastward, even if he were several miles off shore. This fact and perhaps a northward bulge in the edge of the pack ice may have caused him to steer northeastward toward Elephant Island, where Powell found him on November 30.

That Palmer had been away from the base at Deception Island for some time when he joined forces with Powell is indicated by the fact that he was running short of water. While they were lying to waiting for the fog to lift on December 5, Powell reported in his journal that "We supplied the James Monroe with 120 gallons of water, their stock being almost exhausted."[8]

In the sense that he did not return to Deception Island after completing the cruise along the ice-bound edge of the Antarctic Peninsula and before embarking on the joint cruise with Powell, Palmer may have considered these two exploratory efforts as one operation and so reported it to the editor. It is difficult to believe, however, that he considered the South Orkney Islands to be a part of a continuous shoreline connected with the Antarctic Peninsula.

If further information, such as another logbook, journal, or contemporary correspondence relating to the activities of the Fanning-Pendleton fleet of 1821-22 is ever forthcoming, it may be possible to describe in more detail the explorations carried out on cruises by the *Hero* and the *James Monroe*. Until then the accomplishments of Harris Pendleton and Nathaniel B. Palmer in 1821-22 will have to remain obscure.

Until the fleet left Deception Island on January 30, 1822, the *James Monroe,* the *Hero,* and the *Free Gift* were continuously employed in visiting the sealers' camps and looking for new rookeries. Upon leaving Deception Island the *Express,* the *James Monroe,* and the *Free Gift* sailed for home, arriving at Stonington on April 16, 17, and 27, 1822, respectively. The other three vessels sailed into the Pacific, looking for hair sealskins to fill out their cargoes. In a letter to his father, dated January 27, 1822 at the South Shetlands, William A. Fanning wrote:

> . . . having got only about 1000 skins --1100 Bbls oil no prospect of seal we have thought best to send home the Express, Fr. G. & J. M. & proceed with the others round Cape Horn where we shall endeavor to fill the Frederick this season & send her home, the Alabama & Hero must remain as long as their resources will hold out, I am in hopes that we shall do well, I bought some salt from English vessels in this country giving drafts on you at sight you will receive an acct. . . . as to myself I should have returned home had we obtained enough to fill the Frederick & cleared ourselves, as it is when I shall return I know not, on closing the concern which I hope will be done as soon as possible I should wish my funds to be secured at interest, & not ventured again in any expedition, whatever, . . .[9]

The *Frederick* sailed from Isla Santa Maria on the coast of Chile on or soon after August 8 with 24 or 25 thousand hair sealskins. At that time there were 11,000 hair sealskins aboard the *Alabama Packet,* and William A. Fanning was hoping to get a total of 20,000 before he sailed for home not later than five months after the departure of the *Frederick.*[10] The *Frederick* reached Stonington on November 1, 1822. The *Alabama Packet* did not arrive home until June 17 or 18, 1823. The sloop *Hero* was sold at Coquimbo, Chile, October 11, 1822, and the crew was put aboard the *Alabama Packet.*

NOTES

1. One was made on February 7, 1821, in the vicinity of Hughes Bay by men from the *Cecilia,* commanded by Capt. John Davis of New Haven (see Chapter 5). The second was made by a crew in command of Capt. McFarlane of the British brig *Dragon.* The date and place of the latter are unknown.

2. See letters, January 27, 1822, from the South Shetlands and August 8, 1822, from St. Mary's Island (Isla Santa Maria) from William A. Fanning to Edmund Fanning. Edmund Fanning papers, American Geographical Society, New York.

3. George Powell, *Notes on South-Shetland, . . . printed to Accompany the Chart of these Newly Discovered Lands, which has been constructed from the explorations of the sloop Dove by her commander George Powell* (London, printed for R. H. Laurie, 1822). Prof. William H. Hobbs has included excerpts from Powell's narrative, covering the joint cruise, in his "The Discoveries of Antarctica within the American Sector, as Revealed by Maps and Documents," *Transactions of American Philosophical Society,* new series, vol. 31, Part I (Philadelphia, January, 1939), pp. 27-30.

4. They are, as Bransfield showed them on his map, a group of small, rocky islets immediately northwest of Elephant Island.

5. Powell's dates are according to the then common nautical procedure of the day beginning at noon and ending at noon, mentioned earlier. Consequently, his p. m. hours are one day early by the calendar while his a. m. hours conform to the civil calendar. In this account his dates have been corrected to conform to the civil calendar.

6. *Connecticut Gazette,* New London, April 24, 1822.

7. Edmund Fanning, *Voyages Round the World* (New York, 1833), pp. 438-440.

8. Quoted from excerpts of Powell's journal reprinted in Hobbs, *op. cit.,* p. 27.

9. Letter, January 27, 1882, from William A. Fanning to Edmund Fanning, *op. cit.*

10. Letter, dated St. Marys, August 8, 1822 from William A. Fanning to his father, *op. cit.*

BIBLIOGRAPHY

PUBLISHED MATERIAL

Christie, E. W. Hunter, *The Antarctic Problem* (London, Allen & Unwin, 1951), Chap. 6: "The Sealers at the South Shetlands," pp. 83-98.

Connecticut Gazette, New London, April 17 and 24, 1822.

Fanning, Edmund, *Voyages Round the World* (New York, Collins and Hanney, 1833), 499 pp. The account of this voyage, pp. 438-440, is similar to that given in the article in the *Connecticut Gazette.*

Hobbs, William Herbert, "The Discoveries of Antarctica within the American Sector, as Revealed by Maps and Documents," *Transactions of the American Philosophical Society,* vol. 31, Part I (Philadelphia, January, 1939). See pages 25-31. A biased, often intemperate account. Excerpts from Powell's Journal are reprinted on pp. 27-30.

Mill, Hugh Robert, *The Siege of the South Pole* (London, Alston Rivers, Ltd., 1905), Chap. V: "American Sealers in the South," pp. 91-113.

Morse, Jedediah and Richard C., *New Universal Gazetteer or Geographical Dictionary,* 4th ed. (New Haven, 1823), p. 525.

Powell, George, *Notes on South-Shetland, . . . printed to Accompany the Chart of these Newly Discovered Lands, which has been constructed from the explorations of the sloop Dove by her Commander George Powell* (London, printed for R. H. Laurie, 1822). Excerpts from Powell's Journal are printed on pages 27-30 of the paper by Hobbs (above).

Spears, John Randolph, *Captain Nathaniel Brown Palmer, An Old-Time Sailor of the Sea* (New York, Macmillan, 1922).

MANUSCRIPT MATERIAL

Fanning, Edmund, Papers of; American Geographical Society, New York.

Logbook of the brig *Alabama Packet,* 1821-23; Marine Historical Association, Mystic, Conn.

Logbook of the sloop *Hero,* 1821-23, Manuscript Division, Library of Congress.

Logbook of the ship *Huron,* 1821-22, Sterling Memorial Library, Yale University.

Palmer, Alexander S., and Nathaniel B., Papers of; Manuscript Division, Library of Congress.

United States Custom House Records, Port of New London, Conn., 1822. On file at the Federal Records Center, Waltham, Mass.

8

CAPTAIN BENJAMIN MORRELL AND THE VOYAGE OF THE *WASP*, 1822–1823

ORGANIZATION AND ACCOMPLISHMENTS

SIGNIFICANCE OF THE VOYAGE

Captain Benjamin Morrell's *Narrative of Four Voyages* was published in 1832.[1] One of the four voyages he described was to the Antarctic, in 1822-23, in the *Wasp*. His account is one of the very few contemporary reports on sealing voyages, and it is one of only three books by Americans who had been in the Antarctic in the first part of the 19th century. Consequently, Morrell's voyage in the Antarctic was given early and widespread publicity. Since many have taken issue with statements and claims made by Morrell, this voyage has become as controversial as any in Antarctic history. For this reason, no account of American activity in the Antarctic can ignore the voyage of the *Wasp* although its results, in terms of discovery and geographic information, were less than several other American voyages of the time.

ESTABLISHMENT AND COMPOSITION

The schooner *Wasp* was owned by James Byers, Benjamin W. Rogers, William McIntire, and Walter Nexson, New York merchants long associated in the sealing business. The sealing voyage on which they dispatched the vessel to the Antarctic in 1822 was one of many that the firm organized during the early part of the 19th century. On the maiden voyage of the *Wasp* in 1821-22, Morrell had served as first mate to Captain Robert Johnson. The voyage of 1822-23 was projected as a two-year voyage and the vessel was stocked accordingly. Captain Johnson was given command of the schooner *Henry* for a similar voyage, and while the two vessels were not necessarily to sail in company, it was expected that they might on occasion operate jointly.

The *Wasp*, a two-masted schooner of 123 tons, was built at East Haddam, Connecticut, in 1821. She was 76′6″ long and had a single deck.[2] Morrell, the son of a Stonington shipbuilder, had first gone to sea in 1812 at the age of 17. After having served as first mate on the *Wasp* in 1821-22, he was given command of the vessel, his first, in 1822. The crew list for this voyage has not been found, and Morrell gave no statement as to the number or composition of the crew. A vessel of this size, however, would normally carry a company of 18 to 20 men and officers on a sealing voyage. From his statements it can be assumed that the ship was adequately provisioned and equipped for a sealing voyage, but Morrell frequently voiced regrets that he lacked the proper instruments for scientific exploration. There is now no evidence, however, that he had been trained or was able to use anything more sophisticated than the basic navigational instruments with which commercial vessels of the day were equipped.

OBJECTIVES AND ACCOMPLISHMENTS

Morrell stated that Byers offered him command of a vessel on "a South Sea voyage for the purpose of sealing, trading, and making new discoveries."[3] No doubt the principal objective of James Byers and his associates was the procurement of a cargo of sealskins within the two years or less of the projected voyage. Being aware, however, of the rapid and marked decline in the number of seals resulting from their indiscriminate slaughter by the sealers, Byers no doubt expected and encouraged the captains of his ships to explore for new sealing grounds whenever they felt the occasion demanded or success seemed promised.

Morrell also reported, "When the two vessels were properly fitted for sea . . . we commenced taking in provisions and salt for a sealing voyage, which it was calculated would occupy about two years; while both commanders were vested with discretionary powers to prosecute new discoveries, and to trade for the benefit of all concerned."[4] Such an assignment no doubt suited the imaginative mind of Morrell, who expected to use his discretionary powers to the fullest. One wonders, however, whether Byers and his associates fully shared Morrell's feeling that "One great object of that voyage was to acquire a more accurate knowledge of the Antarctic Seas, and to ascertain the practicability, under favourable circumstances, of penetrating to the South Pole."[5]

In his account of the voyage, Morrell is often vague as to dates and positions. At other times his longitude or latitude, or both, are obviously in error. From his frequent reference to the works of others, it is obvious that Morrell was well acquainted with books of travel and exploration by his predecessors in these regions. Unfortunately, in his descriptions of places and features he does not always make a clear distinction between his own discoveries and the reports of others. He is sometimes careless in the accuracy of his dates when referring to earlier explorations. He is careless, too, in spelling proper names, but in this many of his contemporaries were equally guilty. In some of his accounts Morrell is obviously romanticizing. For these reasons and because of the remarkably short time he records for sailing over known distances, some authorities have been inclined to discredit Morrell completely.[6] Yet there is enough substance to Morrell's account to cause others to give it serious consideration as a contribution to Antarctic exploration. Captain R. V. Hamilton made a strong case for Morrell.[7] H. R. Mill was "inclined to believe that he did make a passage from somewhere near the meridian of Kerguelen toward Weddell Sea at a high latitude," but regarded Morrell's claims as "not proven."[8] The whole matter was appraised in a fair-minded manner by Edwin S. Balch who, admitting Morrell's shortcomings, found much in his favor.[9]

Major criticism of Morrell antedates most of the exploration of the 20th century and therefore some of the arguments, both pro and con, have been nullified by subsequent discoveries. In view of our present-day knowledge of the Antarctic, it is possible that Morrell, as he claimed, did (1) make a fruitless search for the Aurora Islands, (2) did make a landing on Bouvet Island, (3) did penetrate far into the Weddell Sea, and (4) did sail within sight of a part of the east coast of the Antarctic Peninsula.

DETAILED ACCOUNT OF THE VOYAGE

New York to the Falkland Islands

The *Wasp* set sail from New York harbor on June 30, 1822, and the next day, after discharging the pilot off Sandy Hook Light, Morrell set a course toward the southeast. By July 22 the *Wasp* was in the middle of the North Atlantic, and after following a south-southeasterly course it crossed the equator on August 12 at 26°42′ W. From here Morrell steered southwestward to cruise along the coast of Brazil, arriving at Rio de Janeiro on September 4 and departing on September 7. Ten days later he was off the coast of Argentina, south of Rio de la Plata. From this point southward Morrell carried on more or less of a running survey of the coast. In many of the bays a crew in a whaleboat followed along the shore while the schooner stayed offshore in deeper water. A number of landings were made for fresh provisions, wood, and water. Game appears to have been plentiful, and a number of hunting excursions were made to provision the schooner. In mid-October the *Wasp* reached Cape Virgenes, the northeast portal of the Strait of Magellan. On October 16 Morrell set a course for the Falkland Islands, arriving at New Island two days later. Here they found two crewmen and the second mate of the schooner *Henry*, Captain Johnson being away in the schooner on a six-week cruise searching for the Aurora Islands.

At the Falklands the men were put to work making necessary repairs on the schooner and gathering eggs and other provisions and supplies in preparation for a voyage south. Captain Johnson returned to New Island on October 23, having failed to find the elusive Aurora Islands. On October 26 Morrell took the *Wasp* into Berkeley Sound. Here they succeeded in killing eight bullocks and 841 geese, which were to supply food on the long cruise in Antarctic waters.

The Search for the Aurora Islands

In spite of Captain Johnson's failure to find the Auroras, Morrell sailed on what seems like a useless cruise in search of the same islands. The *Wasp* sailed from Berkeley Sound on November 2, and the same evening Captain Johnson was to sail westward on an exploratory cruise in that direction.[10] Running on a course essentially eastward from the Falklands, on November 6 Morrell crossed the supposed position of the Auroras without seeing any indication of land. Following an easterly course on the parallel of 52°45′ S as far as 43°50′ W, Morrell then steered northward to 52°30′ S and then westward along that parallel to 50°22′ W. Running south to 53°10′ S, Morrell next set a course eastward along that parallel to 40°00′ W. In all three east-west traverses across the supposed longitude of the Auroras, a man was kept continually on the lookout at the masthead, but no sign of land was seen. During this time Morrell states that he kept his positions "by double altitude, every opportunity both morning and evening, and meridian altitudes of the moon and different planets."[11] If his reported positions are correct, Morrell sailed approximately 1200 nautical miles in 16 days. This does not count the tacks that were necessary to sail against the wind. This is remarkably fast for some one on the lookout for islands, and who would therefore presumably lay to during hours of darkness. He would have had to have averaged five knots per hour for 15 or more hours a day, but this was not impossible, considering that he was in a latitude where strong west winds prevail.

AT SOUTH GEORGIA

On November 18, having concluded that the Auroras did not exist, Morrell set a course for South Georgia, where he arrived on November 20. The *Wasp* was anchored on the north side of the island in a bay which Morrell called "Wasps Harbor" and which he located as being in 54°58′ S, 38°25′ W.[12] Here is an example of the unreliability of some of Morrell's positions, for although there is no reason to believe that he did not visit South Georgia, which by then had been regularly visited by sealers for years, the position he gives for his "Wasps Harbor" is farther west and farther south than any part of the island (Fig. 10). There are more than a score of bays on the north shore of South Georgia, and Morrell's description gives no clue as to the identity of "Wasps Harbor." He sent men out in boats in search of seals. In three days, Morrell claims, they returned to the schooner, having circumnavigated the island without finding any. Presumably the boats were rigged with sails, but even with this aid the time required to circumnavigate the island would seem to be much greater than three days. Without entering any of the bays, it is a cruise of roughly 250 miles.

THE LANDING ON BOUVET ISLAND

On November 24, 1822, Morrell left South Georgia and set a course to the eastward toward the reported position of Bouvet Island, which had been discovered by J. B. C. Bouvet de Lozier January 1, 1739, and resighted again in October 1808 by Captains James Lindsay and Thomas Hopper in the British whaling ships *Swan* and *Otter*. Morrell gave the island's position as 54°15′ S, 6°11′ E, which is remarkably close to its actual position,[13] but he does not indicate whether he determined this position or whether this is what he understood it to be from other sources. The cruise from South Georgia to Bouvet was marked by "occasional heavy weather attended with much snow and hail."[14] Therefore they were fortunate when Bouvet Island was sighted on December 6, bearing ESE, one league distant. Morrell sought shelter among a number of grounded icebergs on the west side of the island, coming to anchor in 17 fathoms of water about a half mile from shore near the northwest side. Early on December 7 the second mate was sent in charge of a boat crew to look for seals. They succeeded in landing, and returned with 80 skins and favorable reports of more, which subsequently proved to be overly optimistic. A boat trip around the island revealed that the initial landing had been made at what appeared to be the only accessible place, the rest of the shoreline being formed by precipitous cliffs. On December 8, after taking only 192 skins, the *Wasp* sailed from Bouvet Island, with a fine southwest breeze and fair weather, on a course to the southeast.[15]

CRUISE TO KERGUELEN ISLAND

As they proceeded southeastward from Bouvet Island the weather continued fair until December 12, when a northeast wind brought a thick snow storm. The next day, when the weather cleared, Morrell found himself in a great field of pack ice with icebergs in every direction. He reported his position as 60° 11' S, 10° 23' E.[16] From our present knowledge of the Antarctic it would appear that the *Wasp* might ordinarily have encountered the pack ice north of 60° S in early December, but there are other indications that this was an open year in the Antarctic. Morrell was alarmed by the perilous position in which he found himself, but the pack was so confining that he could do little about it until December 15 when the leads began to open up enough to permit the *Wasp* to move northward to freedom. Except for the copper on the hull being cut as the schooner was crowded against the ice in making her escape from the pack, she suffered little damage.

Since it was apparently still too early in the season to proceed farther south, Morrell decided to sail for Kerguelen Island, where he could repair the sails and rigging. On the course east-northeast toward Kerguelen the *Wasp* experienced contrary winds and frequent gales of moderate force, attended with squalls of rain and hail. On December 25, 1822, Morrell reported his position as 50° 30' S, 50° 41' E. On December 31 the *Wasp* anchored in Christmas Harbor (Baie de L'Oiseau, Port Christmas) near the northern extremity of Kerguelen Island (Fig. 9).

Morrell gives the following report of his activities for the next ten days:

January 1st, 1823.--At 4 A. M. I took the boats, with the second officer, and went in search of seal, leaving the first officer and three men to take care of the vessel and repair her sails and rigging, which were very much out of order from the almost continual gales of wind we had experienced since our departure from the Falkland Islands on the 2d of November.

In our search for seal we were occupied more than a week, rowing and sailing around the island, and examining every beach; but our labours were not crowned with any great success. We did not see in our whole survey more than three thousand fur-seal, of which we took two hundred. On the west side, however, we saw about four thousand sea-elephants, and about fifteen hundred on the east side. On the former side we found many excellent harbours. We returned to the vessel on Friday, the 10th.[17]

Here, again, Morrell lays himself open to criticism. Perhaps he did not mean literally that he sailed around the island, for he does not describe the south side. To circumnavigate Kerguelen Island, without entering any of the numerous bays, is a cruise of over 300 miles. Morrell could hardly have done this in an open whaleboat in ten days and still make anything but a cursory examination of the headlands.

CRUISE TOWARD WILKES LAND

At 6 p. m., January 11, 1823, the *Wasp* sailed out of Christmas Harbor, coasted along the north shore of Kerguelen Island, and then headed southeastward into the southern Indian Ocean. Morrell continued his course to the southeastward for ten days. He was favored by a fine breeze from the west-southwest, but visibility was impaired by a succession of light snow squalls. When the *Wasp* reached a position reported as 62° 27' S, 94° 11' E, further progress southward was prevented by an extensive field of pack ice. Moreover, numerous icebergs were in sight. We now know that ice conditions vary a great deal from year to year, but heavy pack ice is often met in this vicinity or even farther north. Ellsworth met it about 400 miles farther north in December 1938, a year of bad ice conditions. The icebergs, too, are to be expected in this vicinity, being calved from the Shackleton and West Ice Shelves about 200 miles farther south (Fig. 26).

Blocked by the pack ice which extended indefinitely to the east and to the west, Morrell took the *Wasp* northward to 58°42' S where, on January 22, he was able to sail eastward again. The *Wasp* was kept on an eastward course between this latitude and 60° to the 117th meridian, east. Here the schooner was headed south again. February 1 came in clear, the second such day since the *Wasp* sailed from Kerguelen on January 11. For days Morrell had been sailing by dead reckoning; now at noon on February 1 he was able to take an observation and reported a position of 64°52' S, 118°27' E.

The *Wasp* was now off the Sabrina Coast of Wilkes Land. Some of Morrell's critics have claimed that he should have seen land here, since both Wilkes and Balleny did so some years later. The British sealer reported the appearance of land to the south on March 2, 1839, when his ships, the *Eliza Scott* and *Sabrina,* were in about 65° S, 121° E,[18] and on March 3, when they were in about 65°10' S, 117°04' E.[19] Balleny's attempt to get closer to the land on the latter date was nullified by the pack ice. Morrell was 40 miles north of Wilkes' position in the U.S.S. *Vincennes,* flagship of the United States Exploring Expedition, on February 11, 1840. On that date Wilkes' logbook records that land was sighted to the southward in the morning before the weather closed in. Another of Wilkes' ships, the U.S.S. *Porpoise,* commanded by Lieutenant Ringgold, on February 8, 1840 reported a position of 65°35' S, 118°30' E, but although they were at the edge of the pack ice, no land was sighted at this point.

We now know that the Sabrina Coast lay about 118 miles due south of Morrell's reported position on February 1, 1823. He was 111 miles north-northeast of Totten Glacier at the western end of the Sabrina Coast, and the high land back of the Budd Coast lay about 150 miles southwest of the *Wasp*'s position. Since on February 1 Morrell was about 40 miles from the edge of the pack ice as indicated by Wilkes, it is not surprising that he reported that the sea was open to the south. From the time he left Kerguelen Island until he reached this position off the Sabrina Coast, there is nothing in Morrell's account that is inconsistent with the facts of geography as they are now revealed. Such, however, is not the case of his report of the cruise from the Sabrina Coast westward to Queen Maud Land.

THE CRUISE WESTWARD FROM THE SABRINA COAST

Although the sea was open to the south of his reported position of 64°52' S, 118°27' E on February 1, 1823, Morrell decided to take advantage of a fresh breeze from the northeast to proceed to the westward. Regarding this part of the voyage Morrell reported:

. . . The wind soon freshened to an eleven knot breeze, and we embraced this opportunity of making to the west; being, however, convinced that the farther we went south beyond lat. 64° the less ice was to be apprehended, we steered a little to the southward until we crossed the Antarctic circle, and were in lat. 69°11′ S., long. 48°15′ E. In this latitude there was no field-ice, and very few ice-islands in sight. We likewise discovered that the winds in this latitude blow three-fourths of the time from the southeast, or the north-east, very light, and attended with more or less snow, every day; and that the westerly winds were accompanied with severe hail-squalls."[20]

Such a brief account hardly suffices for a cruise of roughly 1900 miles. Morrell's brief description of the weather he encountered is not inconsistent with what might be expected under favorable conditions on a passage along the 64th or 65th parallels. North of 60° S he would have experienced prevailing winds from the southwest or northwest, and light winds would not be likely.

In analyzing Morrell's statement it is difficult to decide whether he was making a much too sweeping generalization of his cruise westward or whether he meant that he steered southward only after crossing, perhaps, the 50th meridian, east. The latter could be the case, for he said "In this latitude there was no field-ice, and very few ice-islands in sight." Yet, when he was summarizing near the end of the voyage on March 19 he said,

From the second day after we left the "Island of Desolation," up to this date, March 19, we have not passed a day without seeing fields of broken ice, or ice-islands, or both combined; and during all that period of sixty-six days, we have had, every day, more or less snow or hail.[21]

This would seem to indicate that he was making a distinction between the conditions on February 1 and those for the voyage as a whole.

An examination of the map will quickly show that Morrell in his passage from Wilkes Land could have gotten south of the Antarctic Circle at only a few places and in all probability would have had to get as far north as 64°S to have passed the iceberg zone north of the Shackleton Ice Shelf and as far as 65°S to have rounded Enderby Land without seeing it. If, as he said, he experienced "more or less snow, every day," it is most likely that he was sailing by dead reckoning a great part of the time and was never sure of his position. Under those conditions it is not unlikely that the greater part of the cruise was made somewhere along the 65th parallel. In the month of February such a course would be north of the outer edge of the pack ice but near enough to have patches of loose pack, or "fields of broken ice," in sight each day (Fig. 24).

By the time the *Wasp* had rounded Enderby Land and reached the 50th meridian, Morrell would have been able to get farther south without hindrance, but not as far as he reported on February 1. His reported position for that day, 69°11′S, 48°15′E, would have placed the *Wasp* 120 miles inland of Amundsen Bay in Enderby Land. Morrell does not state whether this obviously erroneous position was determined by dead reckoning or by observation.

Morrell continued his course westward and on February 23, at 4 p. m., the *Wasp* crossed the Greenwich meridian at a reported latitude of 69°42′ S. Assuming the longitudes to be roughly accurate, this was a remarkably fast passage of approximately 3000 miles in 23 days, but it is not impossible. Morrell's reported latitude when crossing the 0° meridian is too far south. Although for most of the length of Queen Maud Land the known edge of the land is slightly south of the 70th parallel, several areas of shelf ice and glacier tongues which project north from the coast would have prevented the *Wasp* from sailing westward along such a high latitude. The fact that he reported seeing penguins and other birds would indicate that the schooner was not too far from land.

Morrell now began to steer toward the South Sandwich Islands, discovered by Captain James Cook on January 30, 1775. On February 24 his position was reported as 68°12'S, 4°17'W, which is entirely plausible. He hoped to find, in addition to seals, some driftwood, for his fuel supply was practically exhausted. Land was sighted on February 28, and as they approached nearer, Morrell identified it as Candlemas Island. He gave its position as 57°10'S, 26°59' W (actual position 57°03' S, 26°40' W), but he confuses the situation by saying that it is the northernmost island of the South Sandwich group, which it is not. Morrell described the volcanic nature of these islands in rather exaggerated terms, which is not too noteworthy considering his lack of scientific training. The *Wasp* coasted south among the islands to the Southern Thule islands, and again Morrell gave a fairly accurate position for Thule Island, the westernmost one. His stated position was 59°35'10"S, 27°42'30"W; the actual position is 59°27'S, 27°19' W. On the northeast side of the island he reported a good harbor. Unfortunately for Morrell and his crew, the "entirely barren" islands yielded neither fur seals nor wood.

Morrell's Farthest South

On March 6, 1823, the *Wasp* sailed from Thule Island on a course to the south and west. The wind was from the west-northwest, and they experienced frequent squalls of hail and rain. This course was continued until March 10, when the *Wasp* apparently encountered a belt of loose pack ice stretched across that part of the Weddell Sea. Morrell describes the situation thus:

. . . we found ourselves once more in a very dangerous situation, being hemmed in on every side by field-ice. After exerting ourselves, however, for about twenty-four hours, in a thick snow-storm, we made our escape into an open sea, entirely free of ice. This was in lat. 64°21' S., long. 38°51' W. We then took the wind from the west, and stood to the south under double-reefed sails, until Friday the fourteenth, when our latitude was 70°14' S., long 40°3' W.[22]

The temperature was unbelievably mild, 47° F for the air and 44° F for the water; the sea was clear of pack ice, and Morrell was sure he could have penetrated "as far as the eighty-fifth degree of south latitude." He was almost out of fuel, however, and had water for only 20 days. Lacking proper mathematical and nautical instruments, he decided to abandon the opportunity for making a "bold advance directly to the south pole." Turning about, he set the *Wasp* on a course to the northwest.

This part of Morrell's voyage has also come in for criticism, even to the extent of doubting that it ever was made. Experience has shown that the Weddell Sea, because of pack ice and shelf ice, is a difficult and dangerous sea in which to navigate. We now know, however, that at intervals great masses of ice go out of the Weddell Sea, leaving a much greater area of open water for a few years until the ice builds up again. It is not unlikely that Morrell chanced to sail into the sea during one of those open periods. James Weddell had sailed the brig *Jane* of Leith even farther south in these same waters, less than a month earlier; on February 20, 1823, he reported his farthest south as 74°15'S, 34°16'45" W. Weddell's straightforward account describes conditions similar to those reported by Morrell, who has been accused of borrowing from Weddell's experience, since the British sealer's book was published six years earlier.[23]

New South Greenland

Having turned northwestward on March 14, 1823, from a reported position of 70°14' S, 40°3' W, land was sighted the next afternoon from the masthead, bearing west, distant three leagues. Morrell stated that this was the land that Captain Johnson had previously discovered and called New South Greenland. The *Wasp* drew close in to the land, and the boats went out after seals. As the boats worked along the shore, the schooner coasted farther out. Together they worked southward to 67°52' S, 48°11' W by 4 p. m. on March 17. From this point they thought they could see mountains 75 miles to the south. Again, although the sea was open to the south, Morrell felt compelled to turn northward because of his lack of wood and water. On March 19 the *Wasp* was close in to what Morrell considered "the north cape of New South Greenland." He assigned it a position of 62°41' S, 47°21' W by dead reckoning, since he had not had an observation for three days. The land trended to the south and south by west.[24]

This part of Morrell's account has come in for severe criticism, for there is no land anywhere near the position he gives. The Antarctic Peninsula is too far to the west to be seen from Morrell's reported positions unless by the aid of a superior mirage. Due to the fact that Morrell often had to rely on dead reckoning, some of his positions are undoubtedly in error. A faulty chronometer may be responsible for other errors. Neither of these explanations, however, appears adequate to account for the magnitude of the apparent error. Morrell's positions at the South Sandwich Islands were too nearly accurate to make this plausible. If, as Morrell reported, his men skirted the shore of "New South Greenland" in a boat, even a mirage cannot be used to explain the error unless he and his men confused the pack ice as the shoreline of a distant mirage. Taking all factors into consideration, one wonders if Morrell was not here weaving into his account of the voyage of 1822-23 incidents which occurred the previous year when he was first mate to Captain Robert Johnson. According to Morrell, they then discovered an island to the south and east of the Seal Islands.[25] If Morrell assumed that this island was part of a land extending southward for an unknown distance, his account for 1822-23 would have seemed plausible to him. This would explain the poor reconciliation on Morrell's reported positions and the location of land known to exist.

Conclusion of the Voyage

On March 19 Morrell sailed the *Wasp* north and west toward Staten Island where, on March 24, the schooner came to anchor in East Harbor. Here he met

Captain James Sheffield in the brig *Hersilia*.[26] On March 28 they sailed in company for the Falkland Islands.

Seals being scarce at the Falklands, Morrell on March 31 again headed the *Wasp* south and westward on a cruise beyond the South Shetlands. On April 3 he reported a position of 62°08′ S, 66°14′ W. This was another case of unbelievably fast sailing. The westward course was continued to 65°42′ S, 110°16′ W. By April 24 the *Wasp* was back at Staten Island, no land having been discovered during the cruise.

On April 29 the *Wasp* again sailed from Staten Island and began a passage through the Strait of Magellan. After sealing along the coast of Chile and offlying islands, the *Wasp* reached Valparaiso on July 26, 1823. Here Morrell applied for a loan from the American Consul, Michael Hogan, to buy copper and other materials necessary to repair the *Wasp*. He sailed to Coquimbo, where the vessel was repaired, and, after several months' further sealing off the coast of South America, returned to Valparaiso on February 22, 1824. Here he sold the schooner to Mr. Hogan. The cargo of sealskins was shipped home on the ship *Endeavor* of Salem, which happened to be in the harbor, and Morrell and the crew took passage for home.

Critics have challenged Morrell's facts and questioned his veracity. There is no doubt that he indulged his fancy in some of his accounts, and his assumptions are not always distinguishable from fact. It is interesting to note, however, that James Byers and his associates retained confidence in him and offered him other commands. In view of the severe charges made against him by latter-day critics, an effort has been made to find in what light Morrell was held by his contemporaries. The most severe criticism was contained in a letter written by Jeremiah N. Reynolds on August 10, 1834, to Nathaniel B. Palmer. Reynolds, of whom much more will be said in the next chapter, made many caustic remarks about several persons in his letter. Among these was the following: "Morrell who always sees through a glass dimly has described south sea penguin rookeries — but his descriptions have more poetry than truth."[27] Reynolds, however, did not hesitate to include discoveries by Morrell in his "A Report of in Relation to Islands, Reefs, and Shoals in the Pacific Ocean, &c." published as House Document 105 of the 23rd Congress, 2nd Session, in 1836. The bibliography of this chapter contains reference to two reviews of Morrell's *Narrative of Four Voyages*. Neither was unfavorable.

Regardless of what his critics might say, Morrell took himself seriously. On December 23, 1831, Edmund Fanning addressed a letter to the Secretary of the Navy, Mr. Levi Woodbury, forwarding a memorial addressed to the Secretary by Morrell and which was apparently meant to be presented to Congress. In this memorial Morrell briefly repeated, among others, many of the accomplishments described above. He requested assistance of not over $30,000 to fit out an exploring vessel which he would command.[28] Nothing having come of this request, Morrell on January 30, 1833, wrote an appeal to President Andrew Jackson to borrow the instruments that had been procured for the proposed government-sponsored Antarctic expedition of 1829. Jackson forwarded the request to the

Secretary of the Navy with a notation that he knew of no law which empowered him to give the instruments to a private individual.[29]

NOTES

1. Benjamin Morrell, Jr., *A Narrative of Four Voyages to the South Sea,* etc. (New York, 1832). Other editions were published in 1841 and 1850.

2. Ship enrollment No. 141 in Coast Trade and Fisheries of the United States, issued at New York, June 16, 1821, Vessel Documentation Series, Records of the Bureau of Marine Inspection and Navigation, Record Group 41, U. S. National Archives.

3. *Ibid.,* p. xxvii.

4. *Ibid.,* p. xxvii.

5. *Ibid.,* p. 30

6. Karl Fricker, *The Antarctic Regions* (London and New York, 1900), pp. 62-64. Morrell was condemned by Comdr. J. E. Davis and Mr. Charles Enderby, and others, in a discussion following a paper read before the Royal Geographical Society in London by Capt. R. V. Hamilton. See *Proceedings of the Royal Geographical Society,* vol. 14, 1870, pp. 152-155.

7. Capt. R. V. Hamilton, "On Morrell's Antarctic Voyage in the year 1823, with Remarks on the Advantages Steam will Confer on Future Antarctic Expeditions," *Proceedings of the Royal Geographical Society,* vol. 14, 1870, pp. 145-156.

8. Hugh Robert Mill, *The Siege of the South Pole* (New York, 1905), p. 111.

9. Edwin Swift Balch, *Antarctica* (Philadelphia, 1902), pp. 100-107.

10. No account of the nature or results of this cruise by Captain Johnson is known to exist.

11. Morrell, *op. cit.,* p. 57.

12. *Ibid.,* p. 58.

13. Bouvet Island is centered in 54°26′ S, 3°24′ E. It is roughly five miles long and four miles wide.

14. Morrell, *op. cit.,* p. 58.

15. Morrell's account of Bouvet Island is highly credible. Lars Christensen, whose expeditions visited the island several times between 1927 and 1933, landing in 1927, 1928, and 1929, credits Morrell with the first landing. See Lars Christensen, *Such Is the Antarctic,* translated by E.M.G. Jayne (London, 1935), pp. 125, 129.

16. Morrell, *op. cit.,* p. 59.

17. *Ibid.,* pp. 61-62.

18. Mill, *op. cit.,* p. 170.

19. *The Antarctic Pilot,* 2nd ed., 1948, British Admiralty (London), p. 312.

20. Morrell, *op. cit.,* p. 65.

21. *Ibid.,* p. 70.

22. *Ibid.,* p. 66.

23. James Weddell, *A Voyage Towards the South Pole Performed in the Years 1822-24,* etc. (London, 1825).

24. Morrell, *op. cit.,* p. 69.

25. *Ibid.,* pp. xxiv-xxvii.

26. This was a new ship built at Stonington in 1822 to replace the vessel of the same name that had been captured and burned in May 1821 at Arauco, Chile. The new *Hersilia* was registered at New London on December 9, 1822. Permanent Register No. 23.

27. Letter filed with the Palmer Papers, Library of Congress, Manuscript Division, Acc. 3807.

28. Miscellaneous Letters Received by the Secretary of the Navy, December, 1831. Record Group 45, Naval Records Collection of the Office of Naval Records and Library, U. S. National Archives.

29. Miscellaneous Letters Received by the Secretary of the Navy, January, 1833, Record Group 45, Naval Records Collection of the Office of Naval Records and Library, U. S. National Archives.

BIBLIOGRAPHY

PUBLISHED MATERIAL

Anonymous, "Art III. — A Narrative of Four Voyages to the South Sea, North and South Pacific Ocean, etc., By Capt. Benjamin Morrell, Jr., 8vo, New York: 1832," *American Quarterly Review,* vol. 13, No. 24, June, 1833, pp. 314-336. (A review.)

Anonymous, "Article III. — A Narrative of Four Voyages to the South Sea, North and South Pacific Ocean, etc., by Capt. Benjamin Morrell, Jun., 8vo, one thick vol. New York, J. & J. Harper, 1832," *The Monthly Review*, vol. 3 (new, 4th series) October, 1833 (London, G. Henderson).

Balch, Edwin Swift, *Antarctica* (Philadelphia, Allen, Lane and Scott, 1902) 230 pp. (See pages 100-107.)

Christensen, Lars, *Such is the Antarctic*, translated by E.M.G. Jayne (London, Hodder and Stoughton, 1935), xiii and 265 pp., maps, illus.

Fricker, Karl, *The Antarctic Regions* (New York, Macmillan, 1900), xii and 292 pp. (See pp. 62-64.)

Hamilton, Captain R. V., "On Morrell's Antarctic Voyage in the Year 1823, with Remarks on the Advantages Steam will confer on future Antarctic Expeditions," *Proceedings of the Royal Geographical Society*, vol. 14, 1870, pp. 145-156.

Mill, Hugh Robert, *The Siege of the South Pole* (New York, Frederick A. Stokes, 1905), xvi and 455 pp. (See pp. 104-111.)

Morrell, Benjamin, Jr., *A Narrative of Four Voyages to the South Sea, North and South Pacific Ocean*, etc. (New York, J. & J. Harper, 1832), xxvii and 492 pp.

Reynolds, J. N., *A Report of in Relation to Islands, Reefs, and Shoals in the Pacific Ocean &c.*, Referred to Committee on Commerce January 27, 1835, House Doc. 105, 23rd Congr., 2nd Sess. (See p. 27.)

MANUSCRIPT MATERIAL

Ship enrollment No. 141 in Coast Trade and Fisheries of the United States, issued at New York, June 16, 1821, Vessel Documentation Series, Records of the Bureau of Marine Inspection and Navigation Record Group 41, U. S. National Archives.

Memorial of Benjamin Morrell, addressed to Secretary of the Navy, Levi Woodbury, December 23, 1831, Miscellaneous Letters Received by the Secretary of the Navy, December, 1831, Record Group 45, Naval Records Collection of the Office of Naval Records and Library, U. S. National Archives.

Letter of Benjamin Morrell addressed to President Andrew Jackson, January 30, 1833, Miscellaneous Letters Received by the Secretary of the Navy, January, 1833, Record Group 45, Naval Records Collection of the Office of Naval Records and Library, U. S. National Archives.

9

JAMES EIGHTS AND THE PALMER-PENDLETON EXPEDITION OF 1829-1831

ORGANIZATION AND ACCOMPLISHMENTS

SIGNIFICANCE OF THE EXPEDITION

The combined sealing and exploring expedition of 1829-31 in the brigs *Annawan* and *Seraph* and the schooner *Penguin* marked the first time that an American scientist entered Antarctic regions, resulting in the remarkably advanced reports of Dr. James Eights. As a private enterprise organized by Edmund Fanning and his associates, the expedition was related to the earliest American activity in the Antarctic. At the same time it was a forerunner of the U. S. Exploring Expedition of 1838-42 under Lieutenant Charles Wilkes for, although it was privately financed, it was given government sanction and was organized only after a proposed U. S. naval expedition was canceled. Jeremiah N. Reynolds, a member of the expedition, had been a leading promoter of the proposed government expedition. He helped solicit private funds for this expedition and later actively promoted what eventually became the U. S. Exploring Expedition.

ORGANIZATION AND COMPOSITION OF THE EXPEDITION

Following the wholesale slaughter of the fur seals on the South Shetlands in the early 1820s, these animals became so scarce that few voyages in this once fabulously profitable business were successful. Since it was thought that the seals were seen in as great numbers as ever in the open sea it was assumed that they were resorting to some as yet undiscovered islands. This idea was supported by the unverified reports of islands existing to the west of the South Shetlands. Fanning reported that an island had been seen by Captain James C. Swain of Nantucket in 1800 in 59°31' S, 100° W.[1] A different version has Captain Swain of the *Alliance* returning to Newport, R. I., on May 21, 1824, from a whaling voyage in the Pacific and reporting that while rounding the Horn farther south than usual he had seen an island "covered with snow and abounding with sea dogs and foul" in 59° S, 90° W. A similar report was made in 1825 by Captain Richard Macy of Nantucket who discovered an island four or five miles in extent in 59° S, 91° W. He claimed to have passed close enough to it to have seen the breakers. He also reported an abundance of seals.[2] It was felt that if these islands could be definitely located, the sealing industry would have a new lease on life, and in some quarters a government expedition was proposed to search for and chart these and many of the islands in the whaling grounds of the south Pacific frequented by New England whalers.

The proposition that the government should send an exploring expedition to the high southern latitudes was not new and, if it was not at first widely popular, the idea had strong proponents. In fact, Edmund Fanning, long an advocate of a government-sponsored expedition, had been commissioned by President James Madison, March 17, 1812, to command an exploring expedition to the far south and to the Pacific Ocean. As the two vessels, the *Volunteer* and the *Hope*, were about to sail, however, the project was canceled due to the outbreak of the War of 1812.

A well-documented account of the various steps leading to the organization of the proposed government expedition and its eventual cancellation in 1829 has been given by Harley Bartlett.[3] Jeremiah N. Reynolds of Wilmington, Ohio, was the most persistent and effective figure of that day in arousing public opinion in support of a government exploring expedition to the south polar regions and the Pacific Ocean.

While temporarily residing in Baltimore in 1827, Reynolds began a campaign for political pressure on Congress to authorize an exploring expedition which he argued would promote American commerce and advance American prestige among foreign nations. This resulted in a letter from Reynolds being presented to the House of Representatives on January 21, 1828, with memorials from citizens of several States urging Congress to give favorable consideration to an exploring expedition.[4] President John Quincy Adams was favorably disposed to the idea. In his message to Congress on December 6, 1825, he had recommended that a government expedition be organized to explore the northwest coast of North America.[5] Newspapers in the eastern port cities were much in favor of a government-sponsored exploring expedition. Until 1828, however, Congress did not get beyond the discussion stage.

After a favorable report from Secretary of the Navy Samuel L. Southard on the feasibility of an expedition, the House Committee on Naval Affairs, on March 25, 1828, reported a bill authorizing an expedition. No action was taken on the bill in the rush of business toward the end of the session, and a substitute resolution was drawn up on May 21. This passed a few days later, resolving that the President be requested to send one of the small naval vessels to the Pacific Ocean and the "South Seas" to examine and chart coasts, islands, and reefs, providing this could be done without an additional appropriation during the year.[6]

The Secretary of the Navy authorized Reynolds to visit the New England seaports as a government agent to collect preliminary information through interviews with whalers and sealers and from examination of logbooks and journals. These data were apparently used on the subsequent expedition of 1829-31 and were published in support of the establishment of the U. S. Exploring Expedition as House Document 105, 23d Congress, 2nd session, January 27, 1835, and as Senate Document 262, 24th Congress, 1st session, March 21, 1836.

The sloop-of-war *Peacock,* then at New York, was selected as the smallest vessel suitable for the expedition. Since she had been scheduled for repairs, her conditioning for the expedition was begun immediately at the Brooklyn Navy Yard. Thomas ap Catesby Jones was given command, and J. N. Reynolds was authorized to procure a second vessel as a supply ship. For this purpose he obtained the brig *Seraph,* owned and commanded by Captain Benjamin Pendleton of Stonington. The *Seraph* was then loaded with a cargo for Malaga which had to be removed and the ship put in condition for the Antarctic. Lieutenant Charles Wilkes, who had been selected to be the astronomer on the expedition, was ordered to procure instruments, part of which he purchased at his own expense. A crew was enlisted, and officers were placed in readiness. Scientific personnel were contacted so as to be signed up when the expedition was ready to sail.

The Navy Department felt that, if possible, two or perhaps three of its vessels should be sent on the expedition, to insure greater safety and efficiency of operation. Additional money was needed for running expenses beyond the amount that normally could be charged to Navy funds. Consequently, when Congress met again, the old expedition bill was taken up and passed in the House. The Naval Affairs Committee of the Senate, however, on February 23, 1829, although approving the expedition in principle, decided to delay action.

On March 4, 1829, Andrew Jackson became President. As a matter of economy he vetoed the whole exploring project, and the new Secretary of the Navy, John Branch, disallowed Lieutenant Wilkes' bill for instruments. The *Seraph* was turned back to Pendleton, who was forced to apply to Congress for relief.[7]

Although the prospect of a government expedition was thus lost, enough interest had been generated to make possible a privately financed expedition. The manner in which the Jackson administration disposed of the expedition was resented in New England where, regardless of political leanings, the discovery of new sealing islands and the charting of unknown dangers in the Pacific were matters of practical importance. As a consequence, a South Sea Company was formed to sponsor a private expedition in which sealing, to help make expenses, would be combined with exploration. Associated in the Company were Edmund Fanning, who acted as agent, James E. Bleecker and a Captain Leslie of New York, Benjamin Rodman of New Bedford, Benjamin Pendleton, and Nathaniel B. Palmer.[8] Whether Jeremiah N. Reynolds was actually a member of the company is not known, but he participated in the organization and promotion of the expedition. In a letter to Alexander S. Palmer on August 14, 1829, Fanning, who was then living in New York, said, ". . . Mr. Reynolds has just received a letter from the owner of the Brig *Annawan* at N. Bedford saying he was going in the country for 10 days, and the *Annawan* would be left to be delivered to our order, at the price we have named, if the Captain call'd for her, But as Mr. Baldwin or Mr. R. has got no further on with subscription funds, for outfits, I am afraid there is now no prospect for the Discovery, or Exploring Expedition."[9] Funds were contributed, however, for as Fanning later testified, "Those two brigs were taken up and fitted out of, and by . . . a contribution of patriotic citizens residing in several of our commercial cities and towns. . . ."[10] If Reynolds was not directly responsible for these contributions, his promotional work had certainly aroused public interest to the point where people were willing to contribute.

The scientific program of the expedition was sponsored by the Lyceum for

Natural History of the City of New York. Newspapers encouraged private citizens to lend books, charts, and instruments to the expedition, and when the *Annawan* sailed it was said to have on board a fine collection of instruments and several hundred books.[11]

All contemporary published references to the expedition mention only the *Seraph* and *Annawan,* yet in actual operations the *Annawan* sailed in company with the 84-ton schooner *Penguin.* The latter, as shown by a contract between Alexander S. Palmer and Trudon Trumbull dated September 29, 1829,[12] was engaged in a private sealing voyage, but it would appear from implications in Fanning's letter of August 14, 1829, to Alexander Palmer that there was an understanding between them that the *Penguin* would work in company with the expedition ships.

Although this was a private expedition, it did receive specific government sanction. At the suggestion of the Department of State a special committee inspected the vessels before departure, and Foreign Service personnel and naval officers stationed in foreign ports were notified that the government regarded the expedition favorably.[13]

Officially, the expedition consisted of the brigs *Seraph* and *Annawan.* During the entire period in the Antarctic, however, the *Penguin* did sail in company or operated in conjunction with the *Annawan.* Benjamin Pendleton was principal owner of the *Seraph,* and the *Annawan* was owned by Nathaniel B. Palmer and other members of the company sponsoring the expedition. The *Penguin* was partly owned by Trudon Trumbull and Ephraim Williams of Stonington.

Fanning reported that 55 men were engaged in the expedition.[14] To this must be added the 16 men aboard the *Penguin.* The *Seraph* carried a company of 22 men under the command of Benjamin Pendleton, with William Noyes as first mate. Aboard the *Annawan,* commanded by Nathaniel B. Palmer, were the five members of the scientific corps and a crew of 28.[15] The *Penguin* was commanded by Alexander S. Palmer, brother of Nathaniel Palmer, and Phineas Wilcox was first mate. Benjamin Pendleton was technically field commander of the expedition, but exploration was actually carried out independently by Pendleton and Nathaniel B. Palmer.

The so-called scientific corps consisted of James Eights of Albany, N.Y., John Frampton Watson of Philadelphia, Jeremiah N. Reynolds, and two unidentified assistants. Of this group only Eights, who had been trained as a physician and who became a competent geologist, could be considered a scientist. Contemporary news accounts at first referred to Reynolds as leader of the expedition. It is natural that the public should have been confused as to his position in view of the active part he had taken in promoting the proposed government expedition. More properly, he was historiographer and commercial investigator of the expedition.

OBJECTIVES AND ACCOMPLISHMENTS

Edmund Fanning laid out an ambitious program for the expedition. Upon leaving separately from New York and Stonington the two brigs were to rendezvous four leagues south of Montauk Point, the eastern extremity of Long Island. Failing this they were to attempt a meeting at Port Hatches on the north coast of Staten Island at the eastern tip of Tierra del Fuego. From here they were to spend a short time sealing in the vicinity of Cape Horn and in the South Shetland Islands, in an effort to defray expenses. Since the crew had signed to the usual terms, the only pay they would receive was in the form of shares. After leaving the South Shetlands, the vessels were to sail westward in search of the islands reported in about 59° S and 90° W by Captains Swain, Gardiner, and Macy. If these were found, it was felt that an abundance of sealskins would be obtained. The skins were to be shipped home from either Talcahuano or Valparaiso, Chile. After refreshing the crews and replenishing the supplies, the ships were to cruise in the north Pacific Ocean, the waters off the coast of Japan, and eastern Asia in general. Here it was proposed to chart islands, reefs, and shoals which were dangerous to whaling ships. The findings of Reynolds, in his inquiries as an agent of the Navy Department, were to serve as a guide. Sealing grounds and areas where whales might abound were to be sought. By the beginning of the Southern Hemisphere summer the ships were to return to the Antarctic for further exploration, perhaps making a high southern latitude, for it was felt that Weddell had shown that if one could penetrate the outer icy barrier surrounding the polar region he would find conditions much less severe in the areas nearer the pole. Following this venture, whatever sealskins that could be obtained would be stowed, and the expedition would return home.

It is difficult to imagine such an ambitious program being accomplished by such a small expedition in so short a time, even under the most favorable conditions. That they failed to do so is not surprising. No doubt much depended on the rediscovery of the islands reported by Captains Swain, Gardiner, and Macy, for this would have assured the financial success of the expedition. A great part of the month of March was spent cruising in the reported vicinity of these islands without finding them. The reports apparently must have been in error, for no other navigator to this day has seen any trace of land in this area.

This expedition marked the first time that an American scientist entered the Antarctic and, although no land was discovered, significant contributions were made to scientific knowledge in the form of seven papers published by Dr. James Eights. They represent the first scientific writing on the Antarctic by an American. The high degree of competence which Dr. Eights reveals in his papers is gratifying to an American reader more than a century later. Martin has pointed out that nine years before Charles Darwin published his widely noted statement on the importance of erratic boulders found in Antarctic icebergs, Eights in 1830 had appreciated their significance as indicators of the nature of the bedrock on the Antarctic continent and had published his views in 1833, six years before Darwin.[16] Eights' conclusions were noted by the French geologist Cordier, but otherwise little attention was paid to them.[17]

This surprising neglect of Eights' work has been discussed by two modern scientists who were sufficiently impressed with his work to write a brief account of his scientific career.[18] Dr. W. T. Calman, whose paper was given as a presidential address before the Linnean Society of London, was most impressed by Eights' discovery of the 10-legged "sea spider" (*Decolopoda australis*), generally not given full credence in Europe until W. S. Bruce discovered a member of the same species in the South Orkney Islands in 1903. Eights published an account of his discovery in 1837.[19] With regard to Eights' "remarks" on the natural history of the South Shetlands[20] Dr. Calman comments, "Probably owing to the fact that they were appended to a paper of systematic zoology, these remarks do not seem to have received the attention they deserve. They give the earliest attempt at a scientific account of this important group of islands. . . . Eights' 'Remarks' are written in a style which, if somewhat florid for modern taste, is by no means devoid of literary merit, and I am assured by members of the Discovery staff who are familiar with the islands that his descriptions are vivid and apt."[21] Calman concludes with this compliment, "More than half a century has passed away since James Eights went to his grave a broken and disappointed man. It is fitting that we should pay tribute to the memory of one who . . . was an accurate observer, a trustworthy recorder, and a pioneer in the natural history of Antarctica."[22]

In view of the fact that Eights' writings are published in journals which are today available in few libraries, excerpts from his "remarks" on the natural history of the South Shetlands are included here that the reader may judge the work for himself:

The geological features that these islands present in those highly favored situations, where the continuous power of the winds has swept bare the rocks, correspond in a great measure with their desolate and dreary aspect. They are composed principally of vertical columns of basalt, resting upon strata of argillaceous conglomerate. . . . (p. 61)

A few rounded pieces of granite are occasionally to be seen lying about, brought unquestionably by the icebergs from their parent hills on some far more southern land, as we saw no rocks of this nature *in situ* on these islands. In one instance, I obtained a boulder nearly a foot in diameter from one of these floating hills . . . . (pp. 61-62)

The color of the basalt is generally of a greenish black. The prisms are from four to nine sides, most commonly however of but six, and from three to four feet in diameter. . . . (p. 62)

. . . The effect produced upon it by the action of the file is very slight; the steel elicits no sparks; the fragments are angular with an imperfect conchoidal fracture; its structure coarsely granular and uneven, and is composed essentially of hornblende, feldspar and a greenish substance in grains much resembling epidote; crystals of leucite of a yellow and reddish tinge are disseminated through the mass whose fractured surfaces strongly reflect the rays of light to the eye; in some places it sensibly affects the needle, owing no doubt to its iron. Veins of quartz frequently traverse the fine variety, some of them containing beautiful amethysts. (p. 63)

The basis of these islands, as far as I could discover, is the conglomerate which underlies the basalt. It is composed most generally of two or three layers, about five feet in thickness each, resting one on the other and dipping to the southeast at an angle of from twelve to twenty degrees . . . (p. 63)

The upper portion of this conglomerate for a few feet is of a dirty green color, and appears to be constructed by the passage of the amygdaloid into this rock, the greenish fragments predominating, and they are united to each other principally by zeolite of a beautiful light red, or orange color, together with some quartz and chalcedony. . . . (p. 63)

The only appearance of an organized remain that I anywhere saw was a fragment of carbonized wood imbedded in this conglomerate. It was in a vertical position, about two and a half feet in length and four inches in diameter; its color is black, exhibiting a fine ligneous structure, the concentric circles are distinctly visible on its superior end, it occasionally gives sparks with steel, and effervesces slightly in nitric acid. (p. 64)

Embraced within these drifting icebergs, rocky fragments, varying greatly in size, are not unusually to be seen, sometimes rounded into the boulder form, but for the most part angular, and so arranged as to present a dark striped, or partially stratified appearance, strikingly visible from the contrast of their darker hues, with those of the lighter tints of the ice in which they are inclasped. The origin of these last is extremely obvious, and admit of a simple explanation. In many places, isolated masses of the rock that constitute the land, are observed to penetrate and protrude far above the general level of the surrounding snows; portions of these are almost continually falling, from the expansive power of the congealing water among their fissures: these fragments are thrown upon the indurated surface of the snows, and are then slidden to some considerable distance from whence they were derived; upon these the falling snows soon accumulate to a sufficient depth to retain them in their places, until they become firmly embraced within the mass. When portions of these glaciers are detached, and tumble into the sea, icebergs bearing rocky fragments are then produced. . . . (p. 64)

It is worthy of note that, as shown in the next to the last quotation above, James Eights should be credited with the first discovery of a fossil in Antarctica, a distinction generally accorded Captain C. A. Larsen who recovered some fossils of molluscs and petrified wood from Seymour Island in 1892.

While no land was discovered on the exploratory cruise to the west of the Antarctic Peninsula, Dr. Eights felt that several lines of evidence pointed to its existence to the south of the ships' tracks.

The existence of a southern continent within the Antarctic circle is, I conceive, a matter of much doubt and uncertainty, but that there are extensive groups, or chains of islands yet unknown, I think we have many indications to prove, and were I to express an opinion, I would say that our course from the South Shetlands to the southwest, until we reached the 101° of west longitude, was at no great distance along the northern shores of one of these chains. The heavy clouds of mist which encircled us so often could arise from no other cause than that of the influence of large quantities of snow and ice, on the temperature of the atmosphere; the hills of floating ice we encountered, could not form elsewhere than on land. The drifting fuci we daily saw, grow only in the vicinity of rocky shores, and the penguins and terns, that were almost at all times about us, from my observations of their habits, I am satisfied never leave the land at any great distance. During our cruise to the southwest above the 60° of south latitude, we found the current setting continually at a considerable rate towards the northeast, bearing the plants and ice along in its course, some of the latter embracing fragments of rock, the existence of which we could discover no where on the islands we visited. When the westerly winds drew well toward the south, we were most generally enveloped in banks of fog, so dense it was with difficulty we could distinguish objects at the distance of the vessel's length. When Palmer's Land becomes properly explored, together with the known islands situated between the longitude of Cape Horn and that of Good Hope, I think they will prove to be the northeastern termination of an extensive chain, passing near where Capt. Cook's progress was arrested by the firm fields of ice in latitude 71°10' S. and west longitude about 105°; had that skillful navigator succeeded in penetrating this mass of ice, he would unquestionably in a short time have made the land upon which it was formed.[23]

Although it does not pertain to Antarctic exploration, it must be pointed out in dealing with the accomplishments of the expedition that Fanning and Pendleton placed considerable importance on the contacts that were made with the Araucanian Indians by Reynolds and Watson.[24] The journal which Reynolds proposed to publish, however, never materialized.

Upon its return the expedition deposited 13 chests of natural history specimens with the Lyceum of Natural History in New York, and two chests were sent to Philadelphia. Reynolds gave his personal collection to the Boston Society of Natural History, and Eights' specimens were given to the Albany Institute.

DETAILED ACCOUNT OF OPERATIONS

The leader of the expedition, Captain Pendleton, left New York with the *Seraph* on August 31, 1829, calling at Stonington to complete the outfitting of the vessel. The *Penguin* sailed from Stonington on October 2, 1829. Captain Palmer sailed from New York on the *Annawan* on October 17 with the intention of meeting the *Seraph* four leagues south of Montauk Point, the eastern tip of Long Island. Although the *Seraph* was ready for sea on October 16, she was held in port at Stonington by an easterly gale. Leaving three days later, the *Seraph* missed the rendezvous with the *Annawan*.

On October 31 the *Penguin* was in sight of the Cape Verde Islands. From November 4 to 6 the vessel was at the island of Boa Vista taking on salt, fresh water, and fresh food. Eights describes a visit to the island, indicating that the *Annawan* also called there for salt and fresh water. Presumably the *Seraph* did likewise.

From the Cape Verde Islands the *Penguin* sailed southward, skirting the east coast of South America. Except for gales between December 3 and 12, while passing between 25° S and 35° S, a reasonably good passage was experienced. On December 24 the *Penguin* arrived at Port Hatches on the north coast of Staten Island. When the weather permitted, crews took to the boats in search of seals. At other times the vessel was made ready for the rough weather anticipated in Antarctic waters. En route from the Cape Verde Islands the *Annawan* put in at the mouth of the Rio Negro, where a landing was made on the coast of Patagonia.[25] On January 5 the *Annawan* arrived at Port Hatches.

On January 14, 1830, the *Annawan* and the *Penguin* sailed out of Port Hatches after having spent the time since the arrival of the former in readying the vessels for the Antarctic. If weather permitted, the crews hunted for seals. The vessels sailed southeastward, sighting drift ice as they arrived off Elephant Island on January 20 (Fig. 6). The passage was marked by relatively fine weather with only a few squalls of rain and snow. In the meantime the *Seraph* arrived at Port Hatches, where she remained until January 22. Failing to contact the *Annawan,* Captain Pendleton left on that day for the South Shetlands. The crews of the *Penguin* and the *Annawan* began sealing on the Seal Islands, lying northwest of Elephant Island. On January 22 a party which included J. N. Reynolds landed in two boats on Elephant Island, where they were forced to remain because of fog or wind or icebergs which prevented the vessels from picking them up until late on January 26. They spent the nights under their overturned

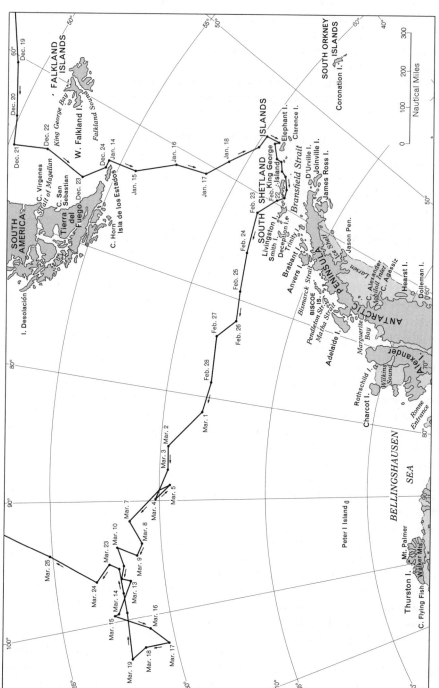

FIGURE 6. Track of the Schooner *Penguin*, 1829-1830.

boats and cooked their meals on a fire made from elephant seal blubber.[26] During the day they reconnoitered the coast of Elephant Island, including the strait between it and Clarence Island.

Late on January 28 the *Annawan* and the *Penguin* left Elephant Island en route for King George Island, passing O'Brien Island on January 29. The next day fog caused the vessels to heave to off the east coast of King George Island. At 8 p. m. on January 31 the vessels came to in Potter Cove on the southwest end of King George Island. During the next three weeks the combined crews hunted for seals in the South Shetlands. During this time the *Annawan* seems to have remained at anchor in Potter Cove while the *Penguin* cruised along the beaches looking for seals. At Potter Cove they found a shallop which had been left by a James Johnson. This the crew of the *Annawan* might well have rigged and used to cruise along the beaches. Some time during the first week in February the *Annawan* or perhaps this shallop must have visited Deception Island, for James Eights describes conditions that he saw on the island.

On February 6 the *Penguin* set out from Potter Cove on a cruise to the western end of the South Shetlands, and it would appear that Eights was on this cruise, giving us some idea of the extent of the islands that he saw firsthand. The logbook of the *Penguin* for the latter part of February bears the following:

Latter part winds from W. NW. passing squals of fog. Working through King George Straits [now called Nelson Strait]. Towed clear of several Ice bergs. Landed on one & got a speciman of rocks which are not found at Shetlands we found.

Since the *Penguin* had taken aboard a boat's crew from the *Annawan*, it is very likely that Eights was aboard the vessel on this cruise, for as Martin has pointed out, he was the only one who could have recognized the importance of an erratic boulder in an iceberg.[27] On February 7 the schooner put in at Harmony Cove where a landing was made the next day.

On February 9 the *Penguin* emerged from the north end of Nelson Strait, and at 4 p. m. made for Clothier Harbor on the northern side of Robert Island. Thick snowfall and many icebergs caused Captain Palmer to put away from the land without trying for an anchorage. The next day the schooner struck bottom several times while trying to enter a small bay at the northern end of McFarlane Strait, before withdrawing. Later that day the *Penguin* was anchored in Shirreff Cove. On February 11 a landing was made here, and apparently a little geographical reconnaissance was carried out in addition to looking for seals. In the logbook Captain Palmer recorded, "Walking over the Icebergs I fell down in a crack in the ice but ascended without much trying." It would appear that the mate or the captain, and perhaps Eights, were climbing over the foot of a glacier although it might have been a stranded iceberg. There were a great many icebergs floating about. Sealers generally referred to glaciers as icebergs and to icebergs as ice islands.

At 4 p. m., February 11, the schooner got under way for Rugged Island where she was anchored that night. February 12 was spent walking the beaches of Rugged Island. At 6 a. m. the next day they got under way, sailing eastward along the north shore of Livingston Island. The water was calm enough later in the day to permit a landing at Cape Shirreff. From here the schooner proceeded eastward to Nelson Strait and then southeast to Potter Cove, where she arrived on February 17.

On February 20, 1830, the *Annawan* and *Penguin* got under way for the cruise to the westward in search of the islands reported by Captains Swain, Macy, and Gardiner. Beating northward through Nelson Strait, the vessels left the South Shetlands on February 22. Heywood Island was taken as the point of departure. The weather was fitful with strong winds, mostly from the west-northwest, which kept the vessels under close reefed sails a great part of the time. Rain and snow squalls were common, punctuated by spells of good weather. The sea was usually rough, and icebergs were frequently seen. Until March 1 the course was westward along the 62nd parallel. By March 7 the vessels had moved north of 60°S, and the winds began to blow more often from west-southwest. Three days were spent tacking between 88°W and 90°W in latitude 60°S in a fruitless search for the islands reported to be in this vicinity. On March 7 a great number of penguins and many pieces of kelp were seen. On March 9 a wind-shift from the northwest to the southwest ushered in a heavy gale when the vessels were in about 59° S, 94° W. The next day, however, was clear. Another gale began on March 12 and ended March 17. So much did the men suffer from exposure that several of the crew were unfit for duty on March 15. Penguins and kelp were seen on several days in this week. One day's fine weather was followed by another gale which began at 6 p. m. on March 18. A heavy sea struck the schooner on March 19, and a boat was stove in and damage was done to the vessel itself. On this day, however, the farthest western point of the cruise was reached, 58°01′ S, 103°03′ W. On March 21 the weather was much improved, but the next evening a heavy gale set in again, lasting through March 23. By now "Captain Nat" and "Captain Alex" decided they had done the best they could in the search for the islands. The season was now much advanced, and they set a course for the coast of Chile.

As the vessels moved northeastward the weather improved steadily, and every opportunity was made to press more sail. Finally, on April 2, the island of Mocha was sighted. On the next day both vessels were at anchor. This ended the exploring cruise, for from now on the crews were interested only in getting seal-skins to make a cargo sufficiently large that each might have a worthwhile share at the end of the voyage.

After leaving Staten Island on January 22, 1830, the crew of the *Seraph* spent a month sealing on the South Shetlands. The *Seraph* then left on a westward cruise in search of the islands reported to exist there. Captain Pendleton kept a course to the south of 60°S, and reached as far westward as 101°W without sighting land. The cold wet weather and a succession of gales had by then worn out his crew, and evidences of scurvy were apparent. He decided to retreat to the northward, reaching the coast of middle Chile early in May. Here he found the *Annawan* and *Penguin*.

When Captains Palmer and Pendleton talked of further exploration in the

Pacific the crews threatened to mutiny because they had not been able to take enough seals up to that time to make their shares commensurate with the toil and danger they had had to experience. Consequently the leaders agreed to seal along the coast of Chile and the off-lying islands in the hopes of getting an adequate cargo. Reynolds and Watson were put ashore and made a successful trek through the territory of the then warlike Araucanian Indians, with whom they were able to deal on peaceful terms.

When exploration was again discussed, the crews continued to refuse to go, and the captains were forced to conclude the voyage as a sealing venture only. In this activity they ranged as far to the northwest as the islands of San Felix and San Ambrosio, where they had to be content to take the skins of the hair seal rather than the more valuable fur seal. Reynolds remained in Chile, where he joined the U. S. Frigate *Potomac* as private secretary to Commodore Downes in October 1832. The *Penguin* also continued sealing along the coast of Chile, spending the following summer months in the vicinity of Cape Horn. On Tuesday, April 26, the schooner left the Falkland Islands for Stonington, where she arrived on June 22, 1831. The *Annawan* left Talcahuano, Chile, on May 23, 1831, and arrived in New York on August 6. Rounding Cape Horn, heavy weather was experienced and three boats were lost. The *Seraph* arrived at Stonington early in August, Captain Pendleton reporting at the Custom House on August 8, 1831 that six members of his crew had deserted during the voyage.

NOTES

1. Edmund Fanning, *Voyages Round the World; with selected sketches of voyages to the South Seas, North and South Pacific Oceans, China, etc.* (New York, 1833), p. 447.

2. American State Papers, Naval Affairs, vol. 4, pp. 695-698. Alexander Starbuck, *History of American Whale Fishery* (Waltham, Mass., 1878), pp. 243-246.

3. Harley Harris Bartlett, "The Reports of the Wilkes Expedition, and the Work of the Specialists in Science," *Proceedings of the American Philosophical Society*, vol. 82, No. 5, June, 1940, pp. 602-611.

4. "Letter from J. N. Reynolds to the Speaker of the House of Representatives . . .," *Journal of the House of Representatives*, 20th Cong. 1st Sess., Washington, 1828, House Doc. 88.

5. *Niles Weekly Register*, vol. 29, No. 743, December 10, 1825, p. 239. The message is printed in full on pp. 233-240.

6. J. N. Reynolds, *Address on the Subject of a Surveying and Exploring Expedition to the Pacific Ocean and South Seas; Delivered in the Hall of Representatives on the Evening of April 3, 1836* (New York, Harper and Bros., 1836), 300 pp. The whole procedure is reviewed on pp. 25-30.

7. John R. Spears, *Captain Nathaniel Brown Palmer, An Old-Time Sailor of the Sea* (New York, Macmillan, 1922), pp. 116-118; Bartlett, *op. cit.*, pp. 607, 610; petition of Benjamin Pendleton, May 31, 1830, House of Representatives, Report 418, 21st Congr., 1st Sess.

8. *Morning Courier and New York Enquirer*, October 20, 1829.

9. Palmer Papers, Acc. 3807, Box 1, Add. 1, Manuscript Division, Library of Congress.

10. "Memorial of Edmund Fanning to Illustrate the views in a petition presented Congress . . .," December 18, 1833, Sen. Doc. 10, 23d Congr., 1st sess., p. 3.

11. *Morning Courier and New York Enquirer* (1829), September 23, 24, 25, p. 2; October 17, p. 2; October 20, p. 1.

12. Palmer Papers, Acc. 3807, Box 1, Manuscript Division, Library of Congress.

13. Fanning, *Voyages Round the World* . . ., *op. cit.*, p. 488; "Memorial of Edmund Fanning . . .," *op cit.*, p. 3.

14. "Memorial of Edmund Fanning . . .," *op. cit.*, p. 6.
15. Determined from an account in the *Morning Courier and New York Enquirer*, October 20, 1829. The crew list for the *Annawan* has not been located.
16. Lawrence Martin, "James Eights' Pioneer Observations and Interpretations of Erratics in Antarctic Icebergs," *Bulletin, Geological Society of America*, vol. 60, No. 1, January, 1949, pp. 177-182.
17. P. L. A. Cordier, "Expéditions Scientifiques: Voyage au pôle austral, Géologie," *L'Institut, Journal Général des Sociétés et Tr. sci. de la France et de l'Entranger*, vol. 5, No. 219, Sect. I, Paris, p. 283.
18. John M. Clarke, "The Reincarnation of James Eights, Antarctic Explorer," *The Scientific Monthly*, vol. 2, 1916, pp. 189-202; W. T. Calman, "James Eights, A Pioneer Antarctic Naturalist," *Proceedings of the Linnean Society of London*, session 149, Part 4, 1937, pp. 171-184.
19. James Eights, "Description of a New Animal Belonging to the Arachnides of Latreille; Discovered in the Sea Along the Shores of the New South Shetland Islands," *Boston Journal of Natural History*, vol. 1, pp. 203-206 and Plate 7, 1837.
20. James Eights, "Description of a New Crustaceous Animal Found on the Shores of the South Shetland Islands, with Remarks on their Natural History," *Transactions of the Albany Institute*, vol. 2, article 4, pp. 53-69, 1833-52 communicated July 10, 1833).
21. W. T. Calman, "James Eights, a Pioneer Antarctic Naturalist," *Proceedings of the Linnean Society of London*, session 149, Part 4 (1937), pp. 176-177.
22. *Ibid.*, p. 181.
23. Eights, "Description of a New Crustaceous Animal . . .," *op. cit.*, pp. 68-69.
24. Edmund Fanning, "Memorial of Edmund Fanning and Benjamin Pendleton," November 7, 1831, House Ex. Doc. 61, 22nd Congr., 1st Sess., Serial 217, pp. 3-4; "Memorial of Edmund Fanning . . . *op. cit.*,", p. 3.
25. James Eights, "Notes on Natural History," *American Journal of Agriculture and Science*, vol. 5, No. 5, May, 1847, pp. 248-259.
26. J. N. Reynolds, "Leaves from an Unpublished Journal," *New York Mirror*, vol. 15, No. 43, April 21, 1838, pp. 340-341.
27. Martin, *op. cit.*, p. 179. At a later date on the westward cruise Martin places Eights aboard the *Seraph*. This was impossible, for contemporary newspaper accounts previously cited, Custom House documents, and two letters later written by Eights prove he was aboard the *Annawan*, which did not contact the *Seraph* at any time in the Antarctic.

BIBLIOGRAPHY

PUBLISHED MATERIAL

Almy, Robert F., "J. N. Reynolds: A Brief Biography with Particular Reference to Poe and Symes," *The Colophon*, new series, vol. 2, No. 2 (Winter 1937), pp. 227-245.
Bartlett, Harley Harris, "The Reports of the Wilkes Expedition, and the Work of the Specialists in Science." *Proceedings of the American Philosophical Society*, vol. 82, No. 5, June, 1940, pp. 601-705. See also pp. 605-612, which outlines the steps leading to organization of the Palmer-Pendleton Expedition of 1829-31.
Calman, W. T., "James Eights, a Pioneer Antarctic Naturalist," *Proceedings of the Linnean Society of London*, session 149, Part 4 (1937), pp. 171-184.
Clarke, John M., "The Reincarnation of James Eights, Antarctic Explorer," *The Scientific Monthly*, vol. 2, No. 2, February, 1916, pp. 189-202.
Eights, James, "Description of a New Animal Belonging to the Arachnides of Latreille; Discovered in the Sea Along the Shores of the New South Shetland Islands," *Boston Journal of Natural History*, vol. 1, 1837, pp. 203-206 and plate 7.
——, "Description of a New Animal Belonging to the Crustacea, Discovered in the Antarctic Seas by the Author," *Transactions of the Albany Institute*, vol. 2, article 16 (1833-52), pp. 331-334.
——, "Description of a New Crustaceous Animal Found on the Shores of the South Shetland Islands, with Remarks on their Natural History," *Transactions of the Albany Institute*, vol. 2, article 4 (1833-52), pp. 53-69 (Communicated July 10, 1833).
——, "Notes on Natural History," *American Journal of Agriculture and Science*, vol. 3, No. 2 April, 1846, pp. 219-223. Refers to frost action on basalt at South Shetlands, and to observations on the voyage across the Atlantic while on the exploring expedition in 1829.
——, "Notes on Natural History," *American Journal of Agriculture and Science*, vol. 5, No. 5,

May, 1847, pp. 248-259. Pertains to observations off the Rio de la Plata, and to investigations in Patagonia after landing at Rio Negro.

——, "On the Icebergs of the Antarctic Sea," *American Journal of Agriculture and Science,* vol. 4, No. 1 (July 1846), pp. 20-24.

——, "The South Exploring Expedition, from the [New York] *Mercantile Advertiser* and *Advocate.* Extract from report of Dr. James Eights, naturalist to the late American exploring expedition of brigs *Seraph* and *Annawan,*" *Niles Weekly Register,* vol. 46, No. 1, 180 [4th series, vol. 10, No. 10] May 3, 1834, pp. 167-168. Much the same as his paper, with technical geological and biological material omitted.

Fanning, Edmund, "Memorial of Edmund Fanning and Benjamin Pendleton," House Ex. Doc. no. 61, 22d Congr., 1st sess., November 7, 1831, serial 217. 10 pp. Contains a report of the expedition written by Pendleton to Fanning.

——, "Memorial of Edmund Fanning to Illustrate the Views of, in a Petition Presented to Congress, Praying that a National Discovery and Exploring Expedition be Sent to the South Seas, etc., December 18, 1833," Sen. Doc. 10, 23d Congr., 1st sess., serial 238, 15 pp. Contains a report on the expedition of 1829-31 along with Pendleton's account included in the House document of 1831 (above).

——, "Memorial of Edmund Fanning on the Exploration of the South Seas, January, 1840," House Doc. 57, 26th Congr., 1st Sess., serial 364, 11 pp.

——, *Voyages Round the World; with selected sketches of voyages to the South Seas, North and South Pacific Oceans, China, etc.* (New York, Collins & Hannay, 1833), 499 pp. See Chap. 24, pp. 478-491 which describes the 1829-31 expedition.

Hobbs, William Herbert, "The Discoveries of Antarctica within the American Sector as Revealed by Maps and Documents," *Transactions, American Philosophical Society,* new series, vol. 31, Part I, January, 1939, 71 pp. See pp. 53-54 for a brief account of the expedition.

"Marine Journal," *New York American:* Monday, October 12, 1829; Friday, August 5, 1831.

Martin, Lawrence, "Early Explorations and Investigations in Southern South America and Adjacent Antarctic Waters," *Proceedings, 8th American Scientific Congress,* Washington (1940), vol. 9, History and Geography, pp. 43-46, 1943.

——, "James Eights' Pioneer Observations and Interpretations of Erratics in Antarctic Icebergs," *Bulletin, Geological Society of America,* vol. 60, No. 1, January, 1949, pp. 177-182.

Meisel, Max, *A Bibliography of American Natural History, the Pioneer Century, 1769-1863* (Brooklyn, Premier Publishing Co.), 3 vols.: vol. 1, 1924, 244 pp.; vol. 2, 1926, xii, 741 pp.; vol. 3, 1929, xii, 749 pp.

Morning Courier and New York Enquirer, September 23, 24, 25, 1829; p. 1; October 17, 1829; October 20, 1829; August 5, 1831. The "Marine List" article of October 20, 1829 appears to have been inspired by Fanning and corrects several errors about organization and personnel appearing in the October 17 issue.

Niles Weekly Register, Baltimore, vol. 36, No. 911, February 28, 1829, pp. 7-12. (Progress report of Secretary of Navy Samuel L. Southard.) Also vol. 37, No. 942, October 3, 1829 and No. 945, October 24, 1829, pp. 86 and 132. (News accounts of preparation and departure.) See also James Eights, "The South Exploring Expedition, etc." (above).

Pendelton, Benjamin, "Petition of Benjamin Pendelton, May 31, 1830," House of Representatives, 418, 21st Congr., 1st Sess.

Reynolds, J. N., "Leaves From an Unpublished Journal," *New York Mirror,* vol. 15, No. 43, April 21, 1838, pp. 340-341.

——, "Mocha Dick: or the White Whale of the Pacific; a leaf from a manuscript journal," *The Knickerbocker or New York Monthly Magazine,* vol. 13, May, 1839, pp. 377-392. Also published as *Mocha Dick, or the White Whale of the Pacific* (Lowell LeRoy Balcom, ed.) (New York, Charles Scribner's Sons, 1932), 7-90 pp.

Spears, John R., *Captain Nathaniel Brown Palmer, An Old-Time Sailor of the Sea* (New York, Macmillan, 1922), 252 pp.

MANUSCRIPT MATERIAL

Journal of the Schooner *Penguin* Bound to the Falkland Islands and Cape Horn on Sealing Voyage in the Year 1829, Alex S. Palmer, Master, Phineas Wilcox, Mate, etc., Library of Congress, Manuscripts Division, Marine Misc., Acc. 3680.

Palmer Papers, Alexander S. and N. B., Library of Congress Manuscript Division, Acc. 3807. (18 boxes. See especially Add. 1, Box 1, folders for 1827-34.)

The papers of Edmund Fanning, American Geographical Society of New York.

Port of New York, Foreign Clearances, 1829-31, Book 7, Record Group 36, Records of Bureau of Customs, Fiscal Section, Legislative and Diplomatic Branch, U. S. National Archives.

Port of New York, Index of Foreign Entrances, 1831-32, Book 22, Record Group 36, Records of Bureau of Customs, Fiscal Section, Legislative and Diplomatic Branch, U. S. National Archives.

Port of Stonington, Conn., Custom House Records: Crew lists and outward cargo manifests for the schooner *Penguin* and the brig *Annawan* on file in the Federal Records Center, Waltham, Mass.

Wilkes U. S. Exploring Expedition, letters pertaining to received by the Secretary of the Navy, vol. 1, May to December 1836. Record Group 45, Naval Records Collection of the Office of Naval Records and Library, U. S. National Archives. See letter written by James Eights, Aug. 2, 1836, to Benjamin F. Butler, U. S. Attorney General, asking Butler to support his application for a place in the scientific corps of the Wilkes Expedition. Here he speaks of his experience on the *Annawan*.

PLATE I. Nathaniel B. Palmer. Photograph of portrait at the American Geographical Society.

PLATE II. Charles Wilkes. U. S. Bureau of Ships, Photo No. 19-N-13802 in the National Archives.

10

THE UNITED STATES EXPLORING EXPEDITION
1838-1842

ORGANIZATION AND ACCOMPLISHMENTS

SIGNIFICANCE

The United States Exploring Expedition of 1838 to 1842, often referred to as the Wilkes Expedition, is a milestone in American science. It had a marked effect on the scientific activity of the young republic, and to a great degree American science attained its majority in this effort. The expedition brought back to the United States, from its four-year cruise, such a wealth of geological, botanical, zoological, anthropological, and other materials that they served as a foundation of much of American science, and it indirectly exerted a major influence on the form of organization of the Smithsonian Institution. At least three of the civilian scientists of the expedition gained international reputations as a result of their work.

Authorized by Congress in response to popular demand, the expedition carried out investigations in such widely separated areas as the Atlantic Ocean, Brazil, Tierra del Fuego, Antarctica, Chile, the Pacific Ocean, Australia, New Zealand, the west coast of North America, the Philippines, and the East Indies. The two thrusts into Antarctic waters in February and March, 1839, and January and February, 1840, were only part of a much larger program chiefly centered in the Pacific. Yet, on the basis of its Antarctic accomplishments, the expedition ranks as one of the major South Polar expeditions. As a result of sighting land at several points as he cruised for 1500 miles along the edge of the Antarctic pack ice south of Australia, Wilkes was the first to provide proof of the existence of an Antarctic continent, and he was the first to recognize this fact. Moreover, the Wilkes Expedition demonstrated continued American interest in South Polar regions at a time when two of the leading nations of the world, France and the United Kingdom, also had expeditions in Antarctica.[1]

ESTABLISHMENT AND COMPOSITION OF THE EXPEDITION

The popular demand for a government-sponsored exploring expedition, so vigorously promoted by Jeremiah N. Reynolds in the 1820s, was not satisfied by the indifferent success of the private expedition led by Benjamin Pendleton and Nathaniel Palmer in 1829-31, nor were the hopes of the New England sealers and whalers fulfilled. Soon after the return of that expedition, Edmund Fanning and Benjamin Pendleton sent a memorial to Congress in the form of a report of the expedition and included a petition for reimbursement from the government for losses sustained.[2] This was also included in a second petition by Fanning two years later, in which he argued the impracticability of a privately sponsored expedition and urged Congress to authorize a national exploring expedition.[3] He outlined in detail the need for such an expedition and the commercial benefits that might be expected.

This second petition was followed by other petitions by Fanning on the same theme, and the correspondence files of the Secretary of the Navy, now in the National Archives, contain many letters from Fanning concerning a national exploring expedition. Fanning's letters were especially numerous once Congress began to take action, for he had very definite ideas of what should be done. While Jeremiah N. Reynolds was completing his duties as secretary to Commodore John Downes of the U. S. Frigate *Potomac,* his report being published in 1835,[4] he took up again the cause of a national exploring expedition. Apparently as a result of his experience in the South Shetlands and Chile and later on the *Potomac,* he was now more concerned with the Navy and a naval expedition as an instrument for the promotion of national glory than as a scientific undertaking.

Although Fanning actively continued to promote the idea of an expedition, he worked more or less alone and his letters and petitions represented mainly his own thoughts. Reynolds, on the other hand, knew how to reach the public, who soon accepted his ideas as their own, and once public opinion had been developed, he knew how to marshal it and bring it to bear on public officials. Petitions and memorials favoring a national exploring expedition were submitted in great numbers by individuals and groups. Congress responded by a series of favorable committee reports. The data which Reynolds had collected from New England whaling and sealing skippers in preparation for the proposed government expedition of 1829 were now published as Congressional documents.[5] By virtue of a resolution passed by the House of Representatives, Reynolds was permitted use of the House Chamber for a public address on the exploring expedition.[6]

On May 18, 1836, Congress passed an amendment to the Naval Appropriations Bill authorizing the President to "send out a surveying and exploring expedition to the Pacific Ocean and the South Seas," and a total of $300,000 was appropriated for the purpose. In its final form the amendment passed the Senate 26 to 3, but considerable opposition to the expedition was voiced in the House, where the final vote was 79 to 65.[7] The exploring expedition was by then a national issue in which various groups were actively interested although for different reasons, and the project was not without opposition in some quarters: all of which contributed to the controversy which gradually surrounded it.

The primary purpose of the expedition was to aid commerce and navigation, but it was also supposed "to extend the bounds of science and to promote knowledge." That these purposes might be fulfilled, Secretary of the Navy Mahlon Dickerson invited suggestions from various organizations regarding the formulation of the program of operations to be drawn up for the expedition. Among the organizations consulted were the East India Marine Society of Salem, Massachusetts; the Lyceum of Natural History of New York; the United States Naval Lyceum, also of New York; the American Philosophical Society of Philadelphia; and the Academy of Natural Sciences of Philadelphia. In this way the scientists of the country entered actively into the planning of the scientific program and in the selection of the scientific staff.

President Jackson, as shown by letters relating to the expedition addressed to the Secretary of the Navy, took an active interest in the undertaking. This interest is well illustrated in a letter hurriedly drafted in his own hand as he was about to leave Washington on July 9, 1836, of which the following is an excerpt:

> About to leave the City for a short time, and feeling a lively interest in the exploring expedition . . . the Executive is anxious that nothing should be wanting on our part to secure its success; and if unsuccessful that no blame should rest upon us--it is my desire that ample means as authorized by Congress be furnished, and prompt measures taken to prepare and compleat [sic] the outfit . . .[8]

The President hoped that, if at all possible, the expedition should sail in October 1836.

Mr. Dickerson and some officers of the Navy, however, appear not to have shared the President's feelings of urgency or his aspirations for the success of the expedition. A series of disputes over objectives, personnel, and the selection of vessels was permitted to delay its organization. As a consequence, by the time the expedition finally sailed on August 18, 1838, it had become deeply involved in personal and official controversy. Ostensibly due to the illness of Secretary of the Navy Dickerson, the organization of the expedition was transferred in 1837 from him to Secretary of War Joel R. Poinsett. Responsibility for the expedition was later returned to Dickerson's successor, James K. Paulding.[9]

A frigate, two brigs, a schooner, and a supply ship were originally assigned to the expedition. Incidents occurred during preparations for the expedition which raised serious doubts regarding the fitness of these particular vessels for exploration in the stormy seas of the far south. A board of inquiry appointed by the Secretary of the Navy recommended, July 31, 1837, that the vessels undergo additional alterations to make them more suitable. A considerable part of the appropriations had now been spent, and the expedition was still not ready to sail. The Secretary, whom some accused of opposing the expedition, sought to effect economies by reducing both the size and number of vessels. Finally in April, 1838, four naval vessels were assigned to the expedition, with the *Vincennes,* a sloop of war of 780 tons, designated as the flagship. Other vessels were the *Peacock,* a sloop of war of 650 tons, the *Porpoise,* a brig of 230 tons, and the store ship *Relief.* Two New York pilot boats, the 110-ton schooner *Sea Gull* and the 96-ton schooner *Flying Fish,* were purchased for the expedition to be used as survey vessels close in to shore. Of the vessels originally assigned to the expedition, only the *Relief* remained.

Since the three larger ships were regular naval vessels with sides punctured for gun ports, they were not well suited for the heavy seas and cold weather of the Antarctic although they might otherwise serve well enough. Alterations made to provide greater protection and comfort for the crew proved to be not particularly effective in high southern latitudes. When Wilkes took command of the vessels, he was much concerned about their poor condition, but being determined that the squadron should sail without further delay, he decided to make what repairs he could during the expedition rather than wait for reconditioning in port.[10] The *Peacock,* especially, was in need of an overhaul, and the poor condition of the vessel continued to be a problem during the expedition. The *Relief* proved to be such a slow sailer that Wilkes separated her from the squadron at Callao in July 1839 so as not to reduce the speed of the other vessels. The *Sea Gull* was presumably lost in a gale about May 1, 1839, shortly after leaving Tierra del Fuego en route to Valparaiso. In July 1841, the *Peacock* was wrecked on the bar at the mouth of the Columbia River. The *Flying Fish,* being in poor condition due to her hard usage, was sold at Singapore in February 1842, near the close of the expedition.

No aspect of the organization of the United States Exploring Expedition was more involved in controversy than was the selection of personnel. At the outset President Andrew Jackson appointed Captain Thomas ap Catesby Jones to command the expedition. Since J. N. Reynolds had played such a prominent role in promoting the expedition, it was generally conceded that he would be given an important position. On July 9, 1836, Jackson appointed Reynolds corresponding secretary to the commander of the expedition, with a salary of $2000. The appointment stated: "His duties shall be to collect such information as shall be given to his charge; and to condense the reports made to the Commander, by the scientific members of the expedition; to be transmitted to the Head of the Navy Department." Knowing of the differences between Reynolds and Dickerson, President Jackson, in his letter to the latter on July 9, 1836, added the following postscript: "It will be proper that Mr. Reynolds go with the expedition--this the publick [sic] expects-- A. J."[11]

Reynolds, however, seems to have had an ill-disguised ambition for greater things, and this aroused the opposition of both naval officers and scientists. The naval officers were unwilling to accept a position wherein they might find themselves subordinate to a civilian at sea, and they were suspicious of any arrangements by which civilian scientists of the expedition would take over work such as astronomy and magnetism, which they regarded as being strictly within the province of the Navy. Consequently, several officers rejected appointments to serve on the expedition. John Torrey, a leading American botanist, wrote to Secretary Dickerson on November 24 asking for a clarification of Reynolds' status, and stated that the majority of the scientists would reject their appointments rather than serve under Reynolds. He added, "He [Reynolds] is utterly unacquainted with Natural History & no man of science who is possessed of the least self respect will accept of a situation under him."[12]

Meanwhile Reynolds had been carrying on a heated correspondence with Secretary Dickerson as to his appointment, accusing the Secretary of ignoring his appointment, of withholding his salary, and of trying to kill the expedition altogether. The feud broke out in the open when Reynolds published a series of anonymous letters over the pseudonym of "Citizen" in the *New-York Times* in July, August, and September 1837, and in the New York *Courier and Enquirer* in December 1837 and January 1838. In these letters Reynolds, whose identity was generally known, bitterly belabored the Secretary, who in turn replied under the pseudonym of "Friend of the Navy." As a result, Reynolds did not go on the expedition.

Harried by the controversies that delayed the expedition and dissipated its appropriation, Captain Jones resigned as commander in December 1837. From its inception he had been almost continuously at odds with Dickerson over the objectives of the Expedition and the appointment of subordinate officers. The uncooperative attitude and jealousies of his fellow officers had added to his woes. When a succession of senior officers declined the appointment to succeed Jones as commander of the Expedition, Joel Poinsett, Secretary of War, who was then in charge of the project, turned to men of junior rank. One of the best qualified of this latter group was Lieutenant Charles Wilkes, whom Secretary Dickerson had previously proposed as commander of one of the ships but whom Captain Jones had wanted aboard the flagship in charge of instruments and surveying.

Wilkes, known as an excellent mathematician and one of the best physical scientists among the naval officers, in 1834 became head of the Navy's Depot of Charts and Instruments, forerunner of the present Oceanographic Office. In this capacity he had been sent to Europe to purchase instruments for the Exploring Expedition. He spent more than $19,000 for the best available in England, France, and Germany. Some were also of American manufacture. In 1837, upon his return from Europe, Wilkes was given command of the *Porpoise* and ordered to make a survey of Georges Bank off the coast of New England with some of the newly procured instruments. Such was the background of the man who, on March 20, 1838, was given command of the Exploring Expedition.

Second in command of the expedition and captain of the *Peacock* was Lieutenant William L. Hudson, who accepted his post on June 16, 1838. Hudson, since he was Wilkes' senior in point of service, accepted the position only after assurances from Secretary Poinsett that service in the expedition, which was divested of military character, would not jeopardize his seniority. The store ship *Relief* was under command of Lieutenant A. K. Long, and the brig *Porpoise* was in charge of Lieutenant Cadwalader Ringgold. The *Sea Gull* was commanded by Lieutenant Robert E. Johnson and Passed Midshipman James W. E. Reid, the latter being in command when the vessel was lost. The *Flying Fish* was commanded most of the time by Lieutenant Samuel R. Knox, but Lieutenant William M. Walker was in charge of the vessel during the joint cruise with the *Peacock* from Tierra del Fuego toward the Antarctic. The following season Lieutenant Robert F. Pinkney commanded the *Flying Fish* on the Antarctic cruise south of Australia.

As it sailed from Norfolk in 1838, the Exploring Expedition included 83 officers and 342 enlisted men. The naval officers were charged with the responsibility for all the survey work, geography, hydrography, and all work pertaining to meteorology, astronomy, and terrestrial magnetism. Special commendation was later given by Wilkes to Lieutenant Overton Carr, Passed Midshipmen Henry Eld and Simon F. Blunt, Captain's Clerk James R. Howison, and Assistant Surgeons J. L. Fox and Silas Holmes, for their assistance and zeal in carrying out scientific investigations.[13] At the close of the expedition Lieutenants

Overton Carr, Thomas A. Budd, George M. Totten, and Henry Eld, and Captain's Clerk Frederick D. Stuart were continued on the expedition rolls under Lieutenant Wilkes' supervision to prepare final drafts of the numerous surveys for the engravers.

By the time Lieutenant Wilkes assumed command, two years of delay had so dissipated the resources of the expedition that strict economies were in order. This meant that the civilian scientific staff had to be reduced in size. At this stage the work in meteorology, astronomy, and magnetism was transferred to the naval officers, where Wilkes no doubt wished it to be under any circumstances. W. R. Johnson, who had resigned his professorship at the Franklin Institute in Philadelphia to accept an appointment to the scientific staff in 1837, and who had spent the intervening months in preparation for taking charge of the work in magnetism, electricity, and astronomy, was summarily discharged. Reynell Coates, then a prominent Philadelphia naturalist, also lost his appointment.

Among those dropped from the expedition was Dr. James Eights of Albany who, by virtue of his experience and fine work on the Palmer-Pendleton Expedition of 1829-31, certainly deserved a place. Eights had sought an appointment as a geologist, but the committee of the Lyceum of Natural History of New York recommended James D. Dana for that position. From a letter written by John Torrey to Secretary Dickerson on December 3, 1836, in which he insisted Eights be appointed zoologist rather than geologist, he made it clear that other scientists of influence also preferred Dana as geologist.[14] As a consequence, Eights was appointed zoologist on December 28, 1836. He was later assigned the field of paleontology, but was dropped from the staff as the expedition was about to sail.

When the expedition finally sailed, the civilian staff consisted of seven scientists, two artists, an instrument maker, an assistant taxidermist, and an interpreter. The two naturalists, Dr. Charles Pickering and Titian R. Peale, were from Philadelphia, as was William D. Brackenridge, the horticulturist. Joseph P. Couthouy, conchologist, was from Boston. Horatio E. Hale from Newport, New Hampshire, who graduated from Harvard College in 1837, was appointed philologist. James D. Dana, geologist, was an assistant to Professor Benjamin Silliman at Yale. William Rich, botanist, was from Washington, D. C. and the two artists, Joseph Drayton and Alfred T. Agate, were from Philadelphia and New York respectively. John G. Brown was named instrument maker and John W. W. Dyes was assistant taxidermist. F. L. Davenport, who was appointed interpreter, left the expedition at Rio de Janeiro.

OBJECTIVES AND ACCOMPLISHMENTS

Exploration of the Antarctic was only one phase of the extremely broad program of the expedition, which called for surveys and scientific observations extending from the Atlantic across the far reaches of the Pacific to the Sea of Japan and the Sulu Sea, and from the Pacific coast of North America to Australia. Investigations were proposed in practically all phases of the physical and natural sciences of the day. The emphasis on the Pacific and surveying was expressed in the opening paragraph of the instructions which Mr. J. K. Paulding, the Secretary of the Navy, gave to Lieutenant Wilkes upon his assumption of command.

The Congress of the United States, having in view the important interests of our commerce embarked in the whale-fisheries, and other adventures in the great Southern Ocean, by an act of the 18th of May, 1836, authorized an Expedition to be fitted out for the purpose of exploring and surveying that sea, as well to determine the existence of all doubtful islands and shoals, as to discover and accurately fix the position of those which lie in or near the track of our vessels in that quarter, and may have escaped the observation of scientific navigators.[15]

That scientific investigation was not to be neglected was definitely borne out, however, by another part of the instructions:

Although the primary object of the Expedition is the promotion of the great interest of commerce and navigation, yet you will take all occasions, not incompatible with the great purposes of your undertaking to extend the bounds of science, and promote the acquisition of knowledge.[16]

The instructions which Wilkes received were specific as to the major objectives and policy, but within this framework he was fortunately granted a considerable degree of latitude in the execution of the program.

After ascertaining the position of Cabo Frio and of Rio de Janeiro and surveying the Patagonian coast in the vicinity of the Rio Negro, Wilkes was instructed to proceed to Tierra del Fuego, where most of the squadron would moor in a safe harbor. Here the officers were to make surveys of the bays, harbors, and inlets while the scientists carried on their investigations. In the meantime Wilkes was to

. . . proceed with the brig Porpoise, and the tenders, to explore the southern Antarctic, to the southward of Powell's Group, and between it and Sandwich Land, following the track of Weddell as closely as practicable, and endeavouring to reach a high southern latitude; taking care, however, not to be obliged to pass the winter there and to rejoin the other vessels between the middle of February and the beginning of March.

You will then, on rejoining the vessels at Tierra del Fuego, with all your squadron, stretch towards the southward and westward as far as the Ne Plus Ultra of Cook, or longitude 105° W. and return northward to Valparaiso, where a store-ship will meet you in the month of March, 1839.[17]

From the coast of South America Wilkes was directed to proceed across the Pacific, conducting surveys and scientific investigations in the Navigator's Group, possibly if time permitted in the Society Islands, and in the Fiji Islands. From the Fiji Islands, where he was expected to conclude his work by the end of October 1839, he was ordered to proceed to Sydney, New South Wales, to prepare for the third thrust into the Antarctic. His instructions read as follows:

From thence [Sydney] you will make a second [actually the third] attempt to penetrate within the Antarctic region, south of Van Diemen's Land [Tasmania], and as far west as longitude 45° E., or to Enderby's Land, making your rendezvous on your return at Kerguelen's Land, or the Isle of Desolation, as it is now usually denominated, and where you will probably arrive by the latter end of March, 1840.

From the Isle of Desolation you will proceed to the Sandwich Islands, by such route as you may judge best. . . .[18]

From the Hawaiian Islands Wilkes was directed to proceed to the west coast of North America, where he was to make a survey of the coast of what is now Washington and Oregon, of the Columbia River, and of the coast of California, particularly in the vicinity of San Francisco Bay. This being concluded by October 1840, he was directed to sail for the Sea of Japan and the Sulu Sea, where the program would be concluded in April 1841.

Almost all of the extensive program outlined above was completed, although it took an extra year to accomplish the task. Wilkes fulfilled his instructions completely, for in those instances where circumstances compelled him to shorten his assigned tasks, the instructions were contingent on time and circumstances. During the three years and ten months that the expedition was away, about 280 islands were surveyed, the position of many of them being accurately fixed for the first time. Surveys of the west coast of North America covered 800 miles of coast and inland waters, including Puget Sound, the lower Columbia River, the Willamette River, San Francisco Bay, the lower Sacramento River, and the lower San Joaquin River. Inland parties explored the Columbia Plateau and traversed the country from the Columbia River to San Francisco Bay. At least 220 maps were published, but it is probable that even more were prepared for publication.[19] The care and skill which Wilkes exercised in his surveys is reflected in the fact that charts based on his surveys which were used in military operations in the Pacific in World War II were found to be accurate.

The scientific work of the expedition was published in 22 large quarto volumes and 12 atlases. At least three volumes were prepared for publication but were never printed, and one volume of the reports was suppressed after publication and replaced by another.[20] Several of the published volumes are monumental works, still valuable 100 years after they were written. The scientific work of the expedition was evaluated by participants in the centenary celebration held at the American Philosophical Society in 1940.[21]

The most noteworthy achievement of the Antarctic phase of the expedition was the cruise by the *Vincennes* and the *Porpoise* for a distance of 1500 miles along the edge of the Antarctic pack ice south of Australia. As a result of sighting land at several points on this cruise, Wilkes concluded that an Antarctic continent existed beyond the icy barrier of the pack. The first to reach such a conclusion on the basis of actual field observation, Wilkes vigorously maintained his stand in the face of contradictions by others, including Sir James Clark Ross.

The atlas accompanying Wilkes' *Narrative* contains a map of the Antarctic coastline between 93° E longitude and 179° E longitude. Although explorers who followed Wilkes disparaged his delineation of the coast, the greater part of his map, when compared with modern maps based on aerial photography, is essentially correct. Surveys and scientific observations in Tierra del Fuego resulted in important contributions to knowledge, but the simultaneous operations in Antarctic waters in February and March 1839 were begun too late in the season to result in any great accomplishment. Meteorological, hydrographical, and magnetic data were collected, however, and the equipment and men were given a test in preparation for the more prolonged operations a year later. The cruise of the *Peacock* and the *Flying Fish* to the southwestward resulted in no discovery, but it did push back the curtain of the unknown in the area to the north of Thurston Island.

The Antarctic cruises were well reported by Wilkes in Volumes I and II of the *Narrative*.[22] The meteorological data were incorporated in Volume XI of the scientific reports,[23] and part of the data were also included in brief tables in the *Narrative* (vol. II, pp. 459-460, 464). Participating in the Centennial of the Expedition, Dr. F. W. Reichelderfer, then chief of the United States Weather Bureau, referring to Wilkes' Volume XI on meteorology, said, "In reviewing the meteorological results of the Expedition, one is impressed by their far-reaching influence and by the information still to be gleaned from Wilkes' records in the light of modern observations from regions crossed by the Expedition."[24]

Wilkes was personally very much interested in terrestrial magnetism, and personally prepared the report on physics, which was to have been Volume XXIV of the Scientific Reports. Unfortunately this volume still remained unpublished when Congress, in 1874, decided to spend no more money on the Exploring Expedition. If Wilkes did complete the manuscript, it has been lost, but his *Chart of the Antarctic Continent* does show isogonic lines. Some of Wilkes' geophysical data were recovered many years later from his descendants and have been evaluated in two papers.[25] G. W. Littlehales, hydrographic engineer with the United States Hydrographic Office, found that it was possible "to extract from them [Wilkes' papers] the material for a complete representation of the lines of magnetic inclination and declination in the approaches to the South Magnetic Pole and along the borders of the Antarctic Continent. . . ." He concluded that the results indicate "that the south magnetic pole was not then a mere point, but that there must have been a large irregular area over which the dipping needle stood vertical or very near vertical. . . . The computed position of the magnetic pole, from a combination of groups [of data] B and C was 68°56' 15" S, 135° E, and from a combination of groups C and D, 68"42'07" S, 135" E."[26]

DETAILED RECORD OF OPERATIONS

OPERATIONS FROM TIERRA DEL FUEGO

As a token of the administration's interest in the expedition, President Martin Van Buren, Secretary of War Joel Poinsett, and Secretary of Navy James K. Paulding visited the squadron lying in Hampton Roads on July 24, 1838. This helped to restore the morale of the crew, which was at low ebb due to exasperating delays and dwindling public confidence in the expedition. Some of the men had signed up almost two years earlier and were impatient to sail or be discharged.

Finally, on August 18, 1838, five months after Wilkes was appointed commander and almost two years later than President Jackson had intended, the squadron sailed out of Hampton Roads. The vessels called at Madeira and the

Cape Verde Islands en route to Brazil. The scientific program and repairs to the *Peacock* prevented the squadron from leaving Rio de Janeiro until January 6, 1839. The slow-sailing *Relief,* which had been sent ahead of the other vessels, arrived at Orange Harbor,[27] Tierra del Fuego, on January 30. The rest of the squadron, stopping at the Rio Negro en route, did not arrive until February 17. This late arrival left too little time to carry out entirely the original plan of the operations for this area.

As planned, the officers and crews of the *Relief* and *Vincennes* were detailed to survey areas in the vicinity of Orange Harbor and adjacent parts of Tierra del Fuego. With the exception of Titian R. Peale, the scientists were also to work in this area. Meanwhile, Lieutenant Wilkes and Lieutenant Ringgold were to sail in the *Porpoise,* accompanied by the *Sea Gull,* commanded by Lieutenant Robert E. Johnson, for the South Shetlands and "Palmer's Land." Since it would be much too late for the entire squadron to sail toward Cook's Ne Plus Ultra (71°10' S, 106°54' W) after Wilkes' return from a projected cruise into the Weddell Sea, he simultaneously dispatched the *Peacock* and the *Flying Fish* toward the southwest.

Early on February 25 the *Porpoise* and the *Sea Gull* sailed out of Orange Harbor and set a course south-southeast toward the South Shetlands. They encountered their first iceberg on March 1, and at noon of that day were in sight of Ridley Island off the north coast of King George Island. They could not land, but set out a boat to try the current, which was found to be setting north-northwest at 2 fathoms per hour.[28] That evening they were off North Foreland, the northeastern extremity of King George Island. The next morning O'Brien Island and Aspland Island were sighted to the east, but they stood south for Bridgeman Island, which could be seen dimly through the fog. As they approached the island Wilkes deduced its position to be 62°06' S, 57°10' W.[29] The fog suddenly became so dense that preparations for a landing had to be abandoned. As they neared the volcanic island Wilkes thought he detected smoke rising from the island through the wisps of fog. Later, after a vain wait for the fog to lift, they sensed a distinct sulphurous odor when passing to the leeward of Bridgeman.

The next morning, March 3, the two vessels were working among icebergs at the northeastern end of the Antarctic Peninsula within sight of two large peaks, one of which Wilkes identified as Mount Hope, now known as Mount Bransfield. Wilkes had intended to work down along the eastern side of "Palmer's Land," but he found the pack ice too solid and icebergs too numerous to permit this. After some hours spent maneuvering among the icebergs, Wilkes decided to withdraw to a less dangerous position, and the vessels moved southwestward some distance off shore. Due to thick weather and icebergs, they lay to during the short period of darkness. A snow storm was followed by a strong gale from the southwest which lasted until March 5, by which time the vessels appear to have been carried eastward to a position northeast of Joinville Island. The decks were covered with ice and snow and the rigging was sheathed in ice. The men suffered from the cold due to the inadequacy of the clothing which had been provided and which proved to be of shoddy stuff, much inferior to that which was supposedly contracted for.[30] Wilkes concluded that it was too late in the season to hope to get farther south. Consequently, he directed the *Sea Gull* to return to Orange Harbor via Deception Island while the *Porpoise* worked northward to examine the more easterly islands of the South Shetlands.

As the *Porpoise* sailed northward on March 6 and 7, the weather continued poor with rain, snow, and fog. On the latter date the fog lifted just in time to prevent the vessel from being wrecked on Elephant Island. They passed between it and neighboring Cornwallis Island, but high seas prevented a landing on either. They made the eastern end of Tierra del Fuego on March 14, where they carried out investigations in Estrecho de la Maire. A storm delayed the return to Orange Harbor, which they reached on March 30. Wilkes had tried the current in several places on the cruise, and on numerous occasions, even under difficult conditions, the temperature of the water had been taken both at depths and at the surface. Soundings, too, had been made at a number of places.

After the *Sea Gull* parted company with the *Porpoise* on March 5, Lieutenant Johnson set a course for Deception Island. As in the case of the *Porpoise,* gales, snow, and sleet lashed the schooner. At times, the vessel was so sheathed with ice that it was almost impossible to work the sails. Deception Island was sighted March 8, but because of bad weather Lieutenant Johnson kept the vessel standing off and on rather than attempting to make the narrow harbor entrance. Finally, on the morning of December 10 they entered Port Foster, the body of water within the breached volcanic crater, and anchored in Pendulum Cove. A week was spent here during which Lieutenant Johnson, Assistant Surgeon J. S. Whittle, and Passed Midshipmen James W. E. Reid and Frederick A. Bacon made excursions about Port Foster.[31] A small secondary crater and a hot spring were visited and specimens of ash and scoria were collected. A fruitless search was made for the self-registering thermometers left by the *Chanticleer* expedition in 1829. During the stay at Deception Island the party was plagued by bad weather which prevented them from getting soundings and temperature readings of the waters of Port Foster. All of March 13 the men were busy at the mooring lines trying to keep the schooner from going aground in a gale which left several inches of snow on deck. A supply of penguins and other fowl was procured for the galley and as living specimens for the naturalists. After placing a record of the visit to the island in a bottle at the foot of a flagstaff which they erected, the party sailed out of Deception on March 17. The *Sea Gull* arrived at Orange Harbor, after a stormy passage, on March 22, 1839.

Three hours after the departure of the *Porpoise* and the *Sea Gull* on February 25, the *Peacock,* commanded by Lieutenant William L. Hudson, and the *Flying Fish,* commanded by Lieutenant William M. Walker, sailed out of Orange Harbor. On board the former was naturalist Titian R. Peale, the only civilian scientist to make any of the Antarctic cruises of the expedition. A heavy squall from the southwest and thick weather soon caused the vessels to retreat to the shelter of the outer harbor. The next morning they were able to get under way again under orders to sail westward "as far as the *Ne Plus Ultra* of Captain Cook, in longitude 105° W. [71°10' S, 106°54' W; January 30, 1774], and thence you will extend your researches as far to the southward and eastward as you can reach."[32] It is also interesting to note that Hudson was also instructed to return, if possible, by the south and eastern side of "Palmer's Land," an indication that Wilkes thought it at most a large island or archipelago that could be circumnavigated, rather than a part of a continent. He also thought that it extended much farther west than it had been then mapped, in order to account for the large number of icebergs north and west of Cape Horn, since those from the South Shetland Islands drifted to the east.

The two ships separated in a gale the first day out and did not meet again until they were about to return on March 25. Alternately battered by gales, enshrouded in fog, and plagued by snow and ice, the two ships independently sailed southwestward. On March 9, William Steward, captain of the maintop on the *Peacock,* was knocked off the yard into the sea. Although he was rescued, he was so badly injured in the fall that he died two days later. As the vessels sailed southward, approaching the edge of the pack ice, frequent spells of bad weather and the presence of large numbers of icebergs forced them to lay to for hours at a time. Whenever weather permitted they got under way again. On March 18, the logbook of the *Peacock* reveals, the sides and bow of the vessel were covered with from 5 to 6 inches of ice and "even the gun deck is slightly glazed with it." Opportunities for trying the current and for taking soundings were taken while the vessels were lying to in fog. Temperature of the air and of the water was recorded daily. On March 20 the *Peacock* reached 68° S, 90° W, and at noon, March 25, she was at 68°05' S, 96°06' W.[33] That afternoon the *Peacock* met the *Flying Fish,* which had succeeded in penetrating still farther south, after their separation.

The *Flying Fish* had experienced even greater hardship than the *Peacock.* Heavy seas had smashed some of her boats, carried away the larboard binnacle, and caused other damage on deck. The jib had been split, repaired, and split again, and other sails were damaged. Water was frequently shipped in heavy seas so that the quarters of men and officers were wet and damp. Supplies of bread had to be shifted in the hold to keep them dry. Each of the appointed rendezvous was kept without seeing the *Peacock,* and after each, in spite of adverse circumstances, Lieutenant Walker decided to push on toward the assigned objective.

On March 20 at 4:00 a. m. those on board the *Flying Fish* noticed the water was discolored as though near land, and Lieutenant Walker noticed an earthy stain on some ice. A sounding, however, showed no bottom at 100 fathoms. The schooner was lying to at the time, due to heavy fog. When it lifted at 8:00 a. m. the way to the south was blocked by a wall of ice 15 to 20 feet high, stretching as far as the eye could see. They first worked westward and then eastward along the edge of the pack. At 9:00 a. m. their location was 67°30' S, 105° W. They continued working along the edge of the pack ice, first eastward then westward and back to the north, then pushing south as the ice and weather dictated. The water was frequently discolored as though land were near. At noon, March 21, they had reached 68°41′ S, 103°34′ W, and twenty-four hours later they had reached 70° S, 101°16′ W, approximately 110 nautical miles north of Thurston Island. While this position was somewhat short of Cook's farthest south, we now know that it was actually slightly nearer the coast since it was farther east. On March 23, after with difficulty getting free from the pack ice and closely spaced icebergs, they were in 69°17′ S, 100°30′ W, and Lieutenant Walker reported, "In the afternoon stood southward and eastward and for three hours observed appearances of land . . ."[34] Later discolored water was noted. The next day they reached 69°06′ S, 96°50′ W. After almost being ice-bound a second time, and the ship being in poor condition, with from two to three men on the sick list each day and fuel running low, Lieutenant Walker decided to return north and on March 25 met the *Peacock*. After consultation with Walker, Lieutenant Hudson decided that nothing further could be accomplished, and they sailed northeastward together until April 1, when the *Peacock* headed north for Valparaiso while the *Flying Fish* continued toward Orange Harbor, which was reached on April 11, 1839.

On April 17 the *Vincennes* and the *Porpoise* left Orange Harbor for Valparaiso. The *Flying Fish* and the *Sea Gull* were ordered to await the return of the *Relief,* which with the naturalists on board had left on February 26 for a cruise into the Strait of Magellan via Cockburn Channel. The *Relief,* however, having failed to achieve its objectives by March 21 and having lost all but one of its anchors, proceeded directly to Valparaiso. On April 28, because the *Relief* had failed to return to Orange Harbor, the *Sea Gull* and the *Flying Fish,* under the command of Passed Midshipmen James W. E. Reid and Samuel R. Knox, respectively, set out for Valparaiso. The *Sea Gull* was lost sight of during the night. The next morning strong squalls increased to a furious gale, and at 1 p. m. Mr. Knox decided to seek a harbor to ride out the storm, which lasted until the morning of May 1. The *Flying Fish* then set out again for Valparaiso, arriving on May 17. No trace was found of the *Sea Gull,* and it was presumed that she was lost with all hands during the gale.

From Valparaiso the squadron sailed for Peru. Here the *Relief* was detached and sent to depot supplies for the expedition in Hawaii and Australia before returning home via Cape Horn. The squadron left Callao on July 13. The next four months were spent in the South Pacific, where surveys were made of the Tuamotu Archipelago, Society Islands (Tahiti), and the Samoan Islands. On the evening of November 29, 1839, the squadron anchored in the harbor of Sydney, New South Wales.

OPERATIONS IN THE INDIAN OCEAN

At Sydney, Wilkes and the naval officers, with the permission of the governor, set up an astronomical and magnetic observatory at Fort Macquarie while the civilian scientists pursued investigations in their respective fields. Meanwhile the vessels were prepared for the rigorous Antarctic cruise they were about to undertake. Two new masts were installed on the *Flying Fish*. The *Peacock* should have been put into drydock for a complete overhaul, but this would have prevented her from making the Antarctic cruise. Consequently, only the most necessary repairs that could be completed in the limited time were made. The gun ports on the three naval vessels were sealed, and all of the vessels were calked and tarred and all openings made as weather-tight as possible.

With the cheers of the Australians spurring them on, the squadron departed for the Antarctic on December 26, 1839. Wilkes was in command of the *Vincennes*, Hudson commanded the *Peacock*, Ringgold was in charge of the *Porpoise*, and the *Flying Fish* was commanded by Lieutenant Robert F. Pinkney. The civilian scientists were left at Sydney from whence they were to sail for New Zealand, where they would meet the squadron on its return from Antarctica. In view of the division of labor between the naval officers and the civilians, Wilkes felt that the greater part of the scientific work on the Antarctic cruise would be within the province of the former and that the latter would have a much greater opportunity to pursue their work in then little-known Australia and New Zealand than on the Antarctic cruise. In this view the civilian staff concurred, and considering the overall objectives of the expedition, it was an entirely logical conclusion.

As early as January 1, 1840, with a storm brewing, the *Flying Fish* became separated from the squadron. The ship was in great difficulty; with a sail split and with part of its undermanned crew on the sick list it could not keep up with the rest of the squadron. On January 3 the *Peacock* was separated in a storm. The *Vincennes* and the *Porpoise* then made for Macquarie Island, the first rendezvous, but since the vessels were blown to the leeward of that island on January 7, they did not wait for the other two ships, and if they had done so, the predetermined 24 hours would not have sufficed. The *Peacock* made Macquarie Island (54°37′ S, 158°54′ E) on January 10, and two men succeeded in getting ashore. On January 11, just as the *Peacock* was pulling away from the island, the *Flying Fish* arrived, but did not succeed in signalling the *Peacock*. The next day the *Flying Fish* landed two men on the island at a different spot, before pulling away to the south. The second rendezvous also failed because Emerald Island (circa 57° S, 163° E), which had been selected as the meeting place, was found not to exist.[35] The *Vincennes* in company with the *Porpoise,* and the *Peacock* and *Flying Fish* independently, therefore proceeded to the edge of the pack ice in the vicinity of the Balleny Islands which, then unknown to Wilkes, had been discovered the previous year by John Balleny, an English sealer in the employ of the Enderby Brothers.

The *Vincennes* and the *Porpoise* first encountered the pack ice on January 11, 1840, and found themselves in a great embayment at the edge of the ice in about 64°11′ S, 164°30′ E, from whence they began beating westward along the ice front. On January 13, when the *Porpoise* was about 65°08′ S, 164°30′ E, Ringgold thought he saw land. The supposition was supported by the fact that the water was discolored, there were many birds about, and the men killed an elephant seal on an ice floe. Ringgold could not confirm the landfall, however, because ice prevented the ship from approaching nearer to it. From his recorded position it is possible that he saw the distant loom of the Balleny Islands. The

Peacock reached the ice edge on January 15 in about 65°45′ S, 158°30′ E. The *Flying Fish* did not encounter the pack (in about 65°20′ S, 159°36′ E) until January 21.

Because of the wretched condition of its crew, the *Flying Fish* was able to pursue the Antarctic cruise only until February 5. From its position of January 21, the little schooner sailed westward close in against the pack ice until January 29. On January 23, when in about 66°S, 158°E, the crew saw what they thought were rocks appearing as specks on the distant ice, but they were inaccessible. While in the Antarctic, the *Flying Fish* was buffeted so severely by gales that the hull was leaking badly. The small crew was so incapacitated by sickness that even with the help of the officers they could not properly manipulate the sails. As a result, the vessel was often carrying too much sail in strong gales, causing great strain on the hull, which was responsible for leaking seams. The crew was moved into the officers' ward room which was drier than their own quarters, but in spite of this they were continuously wet for seven days. Under such conditions there was little hope of being able to carry on any significant amount of exploration. Finally, on February 5, when in 66°S, 143°E, in response to a petition from the crew, Lieutenant Pinkney headed the vessel north for New Zealand[36] and on March 9, 1840, the *Flying Fish* arrived at the Bay of Islands. This was the designated rendezvous for the squadron, on the extreme northeast coast of North Island, about midway between present-day Auckland and North Cape.

CONTROVERSIAL EASTERN LANDFALLS

On January 12 the *Vincennes* became separated from the *Porpoise*. The latter, however, met the *Peacock* on January 15, and on January 16 the three ships were together again in about 157° E. In his *Narrative,* Wilkes reported that men on all three vessels on this day saw what they believed to be land in the distance.[37] There were many birds about, and the water had an olive green color. The *Peacock* sounded to 850 fathoms, however, without reaching bottom. Because these landfalls, "Eld's Peak," "Reynolds' Peak," and "Ringgold's Knoll," were unconfirmed until recently and positions given for them by Wilkes were sailed over by subsequent British expeditions, they became the subject of much controversy.

In view of this controversy it is interesting to note that the records reveal considerable disagreement as to whether or not land was seen on this date. As shown by his report to Wilkes, which included entries from his journal and from the logbook of the *Porpoise,* Lieutenant Ringgold was very certain of seeing land on January 16.[38] No mention of an appearance of land, however, is contained in the entries for this date in Wilkes' journal, in the logbook of the *Vincennes,* or in the logbook of the *Peacock.* Yet some of the junior officers of these vessels were so confirmed in their belief, as revealed in their testimony at the court-martial following the close of the expedition, that Wilkes apparently felt justified in reporting the fact in his *Narrative.*

Since the appearance of land on January 16 was the subject of some of the questioning at the court-martial, pertinent testimony is given below.[39] On August 29, 1842, Lieutenant William Reynolds, who had been a Passed Midship-man on the expedition, testified as follows:

QUESTION: State whether you saw land on the 16th of January, if you made a report of it, and how that report was received.
ANSWER: I was on board the *Peacock*. I did see what I supposed to be land on the morning of the 16th. I saw it from the masthead. I was up there nearly an hour with Mr. Eld. Before I went on deck to make a report we procured a spy glass from deck. We became satisfied that it was land. I went below and reported it to the officer of the deck. Mr. Eld went below and reported it to Captain Hudson. I could see the land from the deck, but not so distinctly as from aloft. I pointed out the direction of the land to Lt. Budd; he did not seem to think that it was land, and did not send anyone to the masthead to make any further examination. There was no lookout at the masthead to the best of my belief. I waited on deck some time for Captain Hudson to come up. He did not come. I went below, tacked ship and steered off the barrier. No mention was made in the logbook of the appearance of land or of the report--much to my disappointment and mortification.
QUESTION: Were you then, and are you now confident that it was land you saw?
ANSWER: I was convinced then as far as I could judge, and am still convinced. I never have doubted it was land.

Lieutenant Hudson later testified on the same day that "Two officers reported land on the 16th. I looked at it, but could not make it out. Mr. Eld made the report."

On August 30, 1842, Passed Midshipman Henry Eld was called upon and testi-fied as follows:

QUESTION: Did you see land on any day prior to the 19th and when?
ANSWER: I saw it on the 16th between 10:00 and 11:00 a. m. I went to the main top-mast crosstree in company with Lt. Reynolds as it was my custom to do every day while cruising in those seas. We both of us immediately exclaimed and I believe simultaneously, "There is the land." There were three remarkable peaks, one conical and two more of a dome-like appearance, much like mountains of volcanic formation. After looking at it for some time we sent down for a spy glass, and examined it very closely, and came to the conclu-sion that it could be nothing else but *terra firma*. This, like the land I have spoken of on the 19th, was very much higher than any ice island, and a very strong reason I would give for it being land that all ice islands before being detached from the shore or barrier are invariably table-topped in large square masses. . . .
QUESTION: How did Lt. Hudson receive your report of land on the 16th and what could he have done to verify your report?

ANSWER: I reported to him that I had seen the land from the main topmast crosstrees, and he immediately remarked that he believed it was land and had not the slightest doubt of it, and that he also believed that the many large islands of ice about us were aground, but the wind was light, the swell setting on to the barrier and he deemed it necessary either to go no nearer, or to put the ship about, but at all events we should see more of it in two or three days. I went soon after and spoke to Mr. Reynolds upon the subject. We remarked that it was strange that he did not come up (the conversation with Lt. Hud-son having occurred in the cabin) or send any person aloft to examine this appearance of land, and I felt extremely mortified that he did not do so.

Lieutenant Hudson was later recalled to the stand, and the following testimony resulted:

QUESTION: It was stated to the court by Lt. Reynolds and Passed Midshipman Eld that they reported to you on the 16th January that they had discovered land from the masthead of the *Peacock* in the southern quarter. Did you believe at the time that it was land, and do you now believe so?

ANSWER: I did not think it was land at the time. I do think so now.

QUESTION: Did you not tell Mr. Eld at that time you had no doubt that it was land?

ANSWER: I rather think not, for I had doubts, and I could not tell him I had no doubts.

On January 17 it was decided not to try to stay together because much valuable time was being lost in so doing. On January 19 the *Peacock* entered a deep bay in the ice front where the water was dark green with a muddy appearance. From this point, 66°20′ S, 154°30′ E, land which Wilkes called Cape Hudson was visible to the south and southwest. This became a controversial feature as soon as the ships reached Sydney. There it was learned that the French expedition under Dumont d'Urville had landed on some islands off the Antarctic coast in about 140° E on January 21, but had first sighted the land on January 19 in the afternoon. Since Wilkes claimed to have seen land from the *Vincennes* on the morning of the 19th, an international rivalry for priority of discovery hinged on this landfall. The controversy broadened when Assistant Surgeon Charles F. B. Guillou charged in the court-martial that Wilkes had falsely reported to the Secretary of the Navy the discovery of land on January 19.

Testimony with regard to the landfalls of January 19, as in the case of that pertaining to those of the 16th, was conflicting. Lieutenant James Alden of the *Vincennes* testified that he had the watch, and that shortly after 8:00 a. m. he had sent word to Lieutenant Wilkes, calling his attention to something that looked like land. The fog had lifted a little to make the view possible. He felt that at the time Lieutenant Wilkes was not much impressed. During the questioning Lieutenant Alden on three different occasions definitely stated that he had no confidence in the fact that they had sighted land on the morning of the 19th. Lieutenant A. L. Case, who relieved Lieutenant Alden on the morning watch, was even less certain of land having been seen. On the other hand, John G. Williamson, gunner on the *Vincennes,* testified as follows:

On the morning of the 19th I was standing in the larboard gangway. Captain Wilkes was on deck at the time. He came to me and asked me what I thought of the appearance of the land. My answer was, if it was not land, I had never seen land. Then the conversation ended. This conversation was between 9:00 and 10:00 in Lieutenant Case's watch.

Except for Lieutenant Hudson, those on board the *Peacock* were more certain of sighting land on the 19th, but in the afternoon. Passed Midshipman Alonzo B. Davis, promoted to lieutenant by the time of the court-martial, testified that he had seen strong appearances of land and had so noted in the logbook. Lieutenant Hudson, however, had ordered him to erase the entry, stating that the appearance of land proved to be an iceberg. On further questioning, Lieutenant Davis said that he thought then and still believed that what he had seen was land. Lieutenant Reynolds testified that the appearance of land on the 19th had caused excitement on board the *Peacock,* while such was not the case on the 16th. Passed Midshipman Henry Eld was much more specific. He testified:

I was attached to the *Peacock* and to the best of my knowledge saw land late in the afternoon of that day [January 19, 1840]. There was at all events considerable excitement among the officers. I was at the masthead at least two or three hours during that day, and what I saw was much higher than any icebergs or island I have ever seen. I had been cruising two years south. The form also of this appearance of land was very different from any ice island.

When questioned about his order to Mr. Davis to erase his notation of having seen land, Lieutenant Hudson stated, "I gave Mr. Davis no order about the logbook. Mr. Davis told me that he had put the appearance down as land. I told him that it might be land, but that we ought to be very certain before we put down positively. I did not tell him what to put down." He went on to say that the general impression on board was that what they saw was land.

The logbook of the *Vincennes* records the discovery of land on January 19, and the following is an excerpt from the logbook of the *Peacock* for that day:

Sea unusually smooth. Ran about 25 miles into a Bay formed by large Ice Bergs & drift Ice with many detached pieces scattered through the whole space ... while working up to windward searching for an opening in the Barrier to the South an appearance of land was made to the Sd & Wd distant about 30 miles apparently of considerable height and covered with snow. Worked up to within 25 miles of it which left no doubts of it being land but unfortunately we could not get any nearer. . . .[40]

The controversy over Cape Hudson continued until February 21, 1959, when Phillip G. Law, leader of the Australian National Antarctic Research Expedition, made a flight from the *Magga Dan* to discover Mawson Peninsula, the tip of which he later identified as Wilkes' Cape Hudson.[41] Hobbs had suggested that the men on the *Peacock* saw by means of a superior mirage what is now known as Cape Freshfield,[42] but Mawson, who discovered Cape Freshfield, took exception to this view.[43]

On January 23 the *Peacock* penetrated deeply into a large embayment in the pack ice which the *Vincennes* had also entered on January 19. Bottom was sounded at 320 fathoms, and the next day a second sounding reached bottom at 800 fathoms. On January 24 the *Peacock* penetrated still deeper into this embayment to 65°55'20" S, 151°18'45" E. Here the ship, in making a tight maneuver, went astern against the closely packed ice, damaging the rudder so badly as to make it useless. As the crew tried to control the rudderless vessel by manipulating the sails and by putting out ice anchors, the ship was further damaged by several hard bumps against the ice. Severe damage occurred as the vessel swung against the overhanging side of an iceberg. The rudder was finally unshipped and brought on deck where the carpenters worked for 24 hours without relief to effect repairs. Meanwhile, in spite of unceasing efforts of the officers and men, the vessel continued to thump against large floes which surrounded her. When the sea began to rise it was apparent that the *Peacock* must somehow be forced into more open water if she were to be saved. The first bump had been sustained at 8:30 a. m. on January 24. By the next afternoon the crew had succeeded in getting the ship into clearer water where the vessel was hove to until the rudder could be reshipped. By the morning of January 26 they had worked their way through a narrow opening in the ice embayment and reached a comparatively open sea. In its crippled condition, however, the ship could no longer be risked along the gale-swept, ice-infested Antarctic coast.[44] It was also necessary that repairs be completed in time to permit the *Peacock* to participate in the work scheduled for the Pacific following the Antarctic cruise. Consequently, after consultation with his officers, Lieutenant Hudson set a course for Sydney, which was reached on February 21. Here the necessary repairs were accomplished by March 30, in the process of which it was found that the stem of the *Peacock* had been chafed to within 1½ inches of her wood ends.

After leaving the *Peacock* on January 19 the *Vincennes* sailed westward, and on January 23 the appearance of land was again seen to the east and west. The *Vincennes* came upon and entered a large embayment about 25 miles wide in about 67°04′30″ S, 147°30′ E. In fine weather, Wilkes pushed his ship among the icebergs about 15 miles into the embayment until he was sure that ice blocked his way to the south. Because of closely spaced icebergs he could not approach what appeared to be land on either side. On the morning of January 24 Wilkes sailed out of what he appropriately called "Disappointment Bay."

This "bay" in which Wilkes was probing was thought by many to have been the deep embayment between the Ninnis and Mertz Glacier Tongues, discovered by Mawson in December 1912, for these ice tongues would have appeared as snow-covered land to him. However, as a result of exploration along this coast by Phillip G. Law and the Australian National Antarctic Research Expedition in 1958, and the aerial photography of the U. S. Navy Antarctic Developments Project, 1946-47, we now know that there is a major embayment, Cook Ice Shelf, corresponding to Wilkes' "Disappointment Bay." The Ninnis and Mertz Glacier Tongues have lost much of their seaward projection since their discovery, and if they were likewise in a diminished state in 1840, Wilkes would not have seen them at all.

The *Vincennes* was back in "Disappointment Bay" on the afternoon of January 24. To the eastward, the *Peacock* was being disabled by the thumping ice floes. Taking advantage of fine weather, men were landed from the *Vincennes* to make magnetic observations on an iceberg in "Disappointment Bay," and a supply of ice was also procured to fill the water tanks. On the evening of January 25, the *Vincennes* moved out into the open sea, but a thick snow storm soon forced Wilkes to heave to until morning. Shortly after making sail on the morning of January 26, the *Porpoise* was sighted and hailed, and the chronometers on the two ships were compared.

CRUISE OF THE *PORPOISE*

From this point the two vessels continued their cruise westward, but at noon on January 27 lost sight of one another. From this point Ringgold, under the mistaken assumption that the prevailing winds were westerly, decided to take advantage of a fair easterly wind to sail westward farther north, where he would be free of ice. Upon reaching the 105° E meridian he would then return eastward along the edge of the pack ice, favored by the prevailing wind. As a consequence, for the remainder of the cruise the *Porpoise* was often too far from the coast for the men to have seen an appearance of land, although there were also many days when they cruised amongst icebergs at the edge of the pack ice.

On the afternoon of January 30 two strange ships were sighted. They proved to be two corvettes, the *Astrolabe* and *Zélée,* of the French explorer Admiral Dumont d'Urville. Ringgold and d'Urville both wished to bear up and speak the other. Yet, each misunderstanding the maneuvers of the other, the three vessels bore away without making contact.

From January 30 through February 2 the *Porpoise* worked through great numbers of icebergs close to the edge of the pack ice. Part of the time she was lying to in a gale with heavy snowfall, which ended on January 31. On February 1 they sailed along a solid ice front 150 to 180 feet high, behind which shone a bright iceblink. On the next day the *Porpoise* worked south into a deep embayment in the ice until progress was blocked at about 65°24'S, 130°36'E.[45] The current in the embayment was found to be setting to the southeast at about one mile per hour. Penguins and seals were present in great numbers. This embayment, to the west of Cape Carr, was later named "Porpoise Bay" by Wilkes. While the position given by Ringgold is slightly too far north and east, the embayment conforms so well in relative position to the present Porpoise Bay in 66°25' S, 128°30' E that it is most likely they are the same feature.

After leaving Porpoise Bay on the evening of February 2, a gale with heavy falls of snow forced Ringgold to lay to under close-reefed sail until February 4. Getting under way on February 4, the *Porpoise* remained well north of the pack ice until February 8. On the latter date Ringgold again directed the brig southward to the edge of the pack ice in 65°35' S, 118°30' E.

From this position westward to 64°15' S, 100°07'40" E, where on February 14 he turned his ship eastward again, Ringgold directed a course close to the edge of the pack ice. The current was tried on both the 9th and 10th, and on the latter date a magnetic observation was also made. The weather was favorable until February 12. On that day, while sailing across the northwest part of what is now known as Vincennes Bay, they encountered numerous flat-topped icebergs, many of them bearing sand and mud as though having been recently detached from a glacier. A boat was put out to examine a stratified piece of ice; it was found to be composed of alternating layers of ice and snow and from it the men obtained pieces of "granite and red clay." A sounding of 200 fathoms failed to reach bottom. Ringgold reported "the weather was misty, affording little opportunity for observation; many strong indications of land presented themselves. The barrier assumed a dark discoloured appearance, with numerous stratified veins of earth and rocks, and with lofty and conical peaks, remotely placed along its southern portion; the impression of land, surrounded and covered by field-ice, was often strongly urged."[46] He was undoubtedly viewing the high land behind the Knox Coast which was a little later seen more distinctly from the *Vincennes.*

After being under snug sail during the night due to thick weather and snow, the cruise westward was continued on February 13. Numerous icebergs containing great masses of earth and rock were observed, and Ringgold correctly assumed that they were overturned icebergs. Additional samples of "red earth, granite and sandstone" were obtained. On February 14, having reached 100°07′ 40″ E, Ringgold had fulfilled his assigned objective and headed the *Porpoise* eastward, with the intention of filling in gaps left on the outward leg of the voyage.

On the eastward track Ringgold kept north of 64° S, far from the edge of the pack ice, until February 19, when he headed south. On February 20 the ship reached 65°15′ S, 121°30′ E and was close to the pack for a few hours before pulling away again. The next day snow and rain coated the brig with ice. On February 24 the ship was again in sight of the pack, this time at 64°29′ S, 126° E. Bad weather was now more prolonged and intervals of good weather less frequent. Feeling that he had carried out his instructions, Lieutenant Ringgold decided at this point to turn the ship northward and a course was set for New Zealand. After a stop at Auckland Island on March 7, the *Porpoise* reached the Bay of Islands on March 26, sighting several whaling ships en route.

SEPARATE CRUISE OF THE *VINCENNES*

On January 26, after comparing chronometers with the *Porpoise* in about longitude 148° E, Wilkes had directed the *Vincennes* westward. He tried to stay close to the edge of the pack ice, but a long north-south line of hundreds of tabular icebergs forced him to detour to the northward to approximately 65°30′ S. On January 28 a southeast wind enabled the *Vincennes* to push rapidly south again, this time through hundreds of tabular bergs from one-quarter to 3 miles in length. Land was sighted at 9:30 a. m. By 11:00 it was in plain view, but the weather which up to now had been clear began to thicken. The position recorded in the logbook of the *Vincennes* for noon, January 28, 1840 (66°32′45″ S, 140°24′ E), indicated clearly that they were indeed only two or three miles off the Adélie Coast near Cape Bienvenue. The weather continued to deteriorate rapidly, and to remain among the icebergs meant destruction. In the thick weather only a sharp lookout and a quick helm kept them from colliding with the bergs that pressed in upon the ship from all sides. By 8:00 p. m. a very strong gale was blowing and the snow was falling heavily. Spray was coating the ship with ice. During the dark, stormy, and perilous night all hands were called to work the ship, which seemed almost certainly doomed. After several hours of successive hair-breadth escapes, the *Vincennes* reached the comparative security of more open water at about 5:00 a. m., January 29.

On the afternoon of January 29, however, the weather cleared up, and Wilkes decided to return south to try for a landing. On the morning of January 30 they were proceeding south under a brisk easterly breeze with all sails set, bearing first to the left, then to the right, to avoid collision with the numerous icebergs. At 5:00 a. m., high mountains covered with snow were sighted to the south from the masthead. By 8:00 a. m. the *Vincennes* was against the solid edge of the pack ice. Wilkes forced the ship through an open lead into a bay formed partly by rocky islets which protruded from the ice and partly by grounded icebergs. The land behind rose to elevations of about 3000 feet and could be seen both to the east and the west for a distance of 60 miles. Hard bottom was sounded at 30 fathoms. Wilkes named this bay, which is located in 66°43' S, 140°17' E, "Piner's Bay" after Thomas Piner, signal quartermaster on the *Vincennes*.[47]

Wilkes intended to attempt a landing here, but decided against it when a storm suddenly threatened.[48] A gale was soon blowing, and shortly after noon a driving snow storm set in. This time Wilkes decided not to risk the ship among the icebergs but to take his chances in the short choppy waves in the stretch of open water between the coast and the pack ice. By 1:00 a. m., January 31, however, ice floes began to close in about the ship, and Wilkes had to take her through the two-mile-wide channel to the outer edge of the pack. Here the same perilous experience with the icebergs of two days earlier was repeated. The thirty-hour gale finally began to moderate about 6:00 p. m., January 31, by which time Wilkes had once more managed to get the ship through the icebergs to comparatively open water.

He was now ready to attempt another effort to get south. The crew, however, was thoroughly exhausted by their second struggle with icebergs in a gale-tossed sea, within a period of 72 hours. Assistant Surgeons J. L. Fox and J. S. Whittle reported 15 men on the sick list and many others in less than fit condition. They felt that a few days more of such exposure would so reduce the crew as to hazard the safety of the ship. Wilkes sought the opinion of the officers and found that they were essentially in agreement with the doctors. Nevertheless, since his personal observations were contrary to the report of the medical men, he felt that he was duty bound to pursue the exploration of the coast "until the ship should be totally disabled, or it should be evident to all that it was impossible to persist any longer."[49]

Wilkes accordingly set a course to the southwestward. At noon on February 1, 1840, according to the logbook, the *Vincennes* was in 65°52'36" S, 137°51'30" E. At 4:00 p. m. land was in sight from the west-southwest to the southeast, and it was reported again at 8:00 p. m. At 3:00 p. m. the next day, February 2, the *Vincennes* was at the edge of ice cliffs 150 to 200 feet high about 60 miles west of Piner Bay. From this position, 66°12' S, 137°02' E, they reported seeing snow- and ice-covered land rising beyond the ice, but no bare rock could be seen. The weather was bright, with the temperature reaching a maximum of 38° F. The water was discolored, but no bottom was reached at 150 fathoms. The trend of the ice edge forced the ship northwestward on February 3, and another gale with snow squalls made them retreat still farther to 63°49' S, 134° E by dead reckoning. Although the gale moderated, thick weather with occasional heavy snow squalls kept the ship under close-reefed sails as Wilkes maneuvered to stay clear of icebergs. The sick list increased to 30, and stoves were lighted on the gun deck and those on the berth deck and in galleys were kept burning continuously to keep the men's clothes dry. When the weather cleared on February 6 they were slightly farther south and in sight of the pack ice. The nights were now becoming noticeably longer, and Wilkes found it expedient to lay to on this and succeeding nights from 10:00 p. m. to 2:00 a. m. because of darkness.

Early on February 7 they began again to skirt the high ice cliffs. Land was "well distinguished in the background." At 6:00 p. m. the trend of the ice front changed sharply from westerly to southerly. This change in the coastline Wilkes named Cape Carr for Overton Carr, first lieutenant on the *Vincennes*.[50] On February 8 Wilkes set a course to the south. They were now entering Porpoise Bay, but pack ice barred the way almost 30 miles north of the position attained by the *Porpoise* on February 2. Wilkes suspected that a deep bay lay beyond his position, for he could no longer see land to the south. The weather was thick for most of the rest of the day, but at 7:00 p. m. they "had strong indications of land; the barrier was of the former perpendicular form, and later the outline of the Continent appeared distinct though distant."[51] They lay to during a dark and unpleasant night.

February 9 and 10 brought clear, bracing weather, the finest that had yet been experienced on the Antarctic cruise. During daylight the ship cruised along the cliffed ice front. The water was a dirty green and no current was perceptible. A magnetic observation gave a variation of 32°45′ westerly; the dip was 3′15″. Numerous icebergs were in sight during the two days, and there was a considerable amount of open floe ice. On February 10 the appearance of land was seen indistinctly to the southward in the direction of "Tottens High Land" of Wilkes' "Chart of the Antarctic Continent."[51] The noon position was 65°27′ S, 121°32′ E, the compass variation 44°30′ westerly. The next day brought thick weather with occasional snow falls, but before the visibility was obscured the appearance of land was reported in the logbook to the westward. The water was discolored and many birds were in sight. The trend of the edge of the solid pack now forced the ship again to the northwest. The noon position recorded in the logbook was 65°04′50″ S, 116°20′30″ E.

In clear weather on February 12 Wilkes continued to work the ship through open floes as they skirted the edge of the pack ice, which was now trending southwestward again. He tried in vain to find an opening to permit him to approach nearer the land, which could be seen distinctly, "from eighteen to twenty miles distant, bearing from south-southeast to southwest, --- a lofty mountain range, covered with snow, though showing many ridges and indentations."[53] Wilkes based his estimate on a noon position of 64°57′ S, 112°16′12″ E. It is quite clear from the map (Fig. 7), showing both Wilkes' and the most recent delineation of the coast along which he cruised, that he was viewing the Budd Coast, named by him "Budd's Highland," for Thomas A. Budd, acting master on the *Peacock,* who assisted Wilkes in the preparation of the charts and reports at the close of the expedition. Wilkes hove to for about three hours in very clear weather to examine the coast and take a sounding, which failed to reach bottom at 250 fathoms.

After lying to until daybreak at 2:00 a. m., February 13, the *Vincennes* got underway, proceeding southwestward into a deep embayment in the edge of the ice front corresponding closely to the present Vincennes Bay. The bay contained

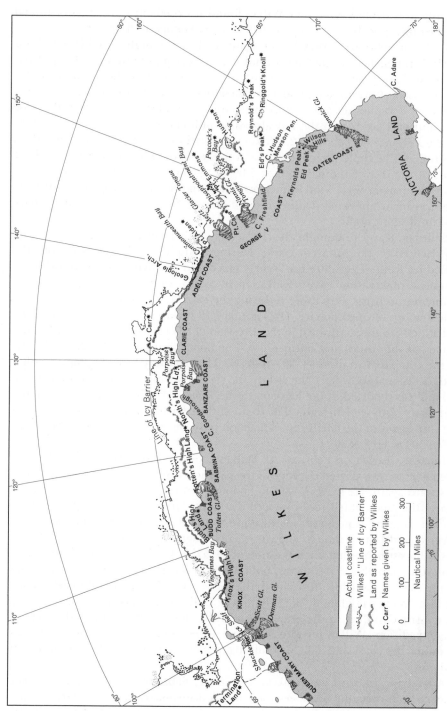

FIGURE 7. Wilkes Land and Adjacent Areas, with Features as Mapped by Wilkes.

many tabular icebergs. At 6:30 p. m. Wilkes calculated his position to be 65°57′ S, 106°40′ E, from where he estimated the land to be 12 miles distant.[54] A sounding of 300 fathoms failed to reach bottom. After retreating northward, where he hove to for the night, Wilkes returned again to the edge of the land on the morning of February 14. At 11:00 a. m. the *Vincennes* reached impenetrable pack ice about seven or eight miles from the edge of the snow-covered land, which Wilkes estimated rose to an elevation of 3000 feet.[55] Being unable to reach land due to the pack ice, Wilkes sent four boats to land on a nearby iceberg to obtain some geological specimens and to make magnetic observations. They returned with samples of sandstone, basalt, gravel, and clay which were embedded in "extremely hard and flint-like" ice.[56] The largest boulder they had seen, some five or six feet in diameter, was unobtainable. The ship was watered from a pond of meltwater on the berg. The men erected a flag on the berg and left a message for the other vessels of the squadron should they happen to see the flag. Specimens of minute marine life and some small crustacea were also collected. Wilkes named this landfall "Knox's High Land," now known as Knox Coast, for Lieutenant Samuel R. Knox, acting master on the *Vincennes* during the Antarctic cruise.

At 8:00 p. m., February 14, the *Vincennes* got under way toward the northwestward, following the edge of the pack ice out of Vincennes Bay. Wilkes continued to sail northwestward along the edge of the pack ice until February 17 when, in a position of 64°01′ S, 97°37′ E, he found the way to the westward barred by ice. He was then in a great embayment in the pack ice, the sides of which extended to the northeast and to the southeast, from which he had just come. Icebergs were numerous, and whales and penguins were present in great numbers, both apparently attracted by the abundance of small shrimp in the water. Detecting the appearance of land to the eastward, Wilkes named the supposed land "Termination Land." Captain John K. Davis, however, in the *Aurora* in February 1912, found here a great ice tongue which Mawson named Termination Ice Tongue on the assumption that it was what Wilkes had taken to be land. In 1931 Mawson discovered that the ice tongue no longer existed. If such were the case in 1840, however, the Shackleton Ice Shelf immediately to the westward would have served as a barrier against which pack ice and bergs would have lodged to block Wilkes' westward progress.

Blocked to the westward, Wilkes temporarily set a course to the northeast in an effort to sail around the barrier to the northwestward. He kept amongst the numerous icebergs that bordered the pack on the theory that land, if it were present, would be to the inside of the fringing bergs. The smooth sea that had prevailed for several days seemed to indicate that the vessel was entirely embayed or cut off by a line of pack ice from the open sea. A slight swell encouraged the men on February 20; a sounding to 850 fathoms failed to reach bottom.

On February 21 the weather began to deteriorate, and a westerly wind held down progress to the westward. At noon the vessel was at 61°34′ S, 100°49′ E. Considering all aspects of their situation, the lateness of the season, and the fact that they were nearly 3000 miles from the rendezvous with the other vessels in

New Zealand, Wilkes decided to return northward. All hands were called, congratulated on their good work, and informed that the cruise was concluded.

Several gales were experienced in the first part of the return voyage, but except for a shortage of water on board, no particular difficulty was experienced. On March 11, 1840, the *Vincennes* anchored at Sydney, where the *Peacock* was found undergoing repairs. The Antarctic phase of the U. S. Exploring Expedition was now concluded, but more than two years of exploration and surveying in uncharted waters remained before the *Vincennes* and the *Porpoise* would return to New York, their mission accomplished.

EVALUATION OF WILKES' ANTARCTIC DISCOVERIES

CONDITIONS UNDER WHICH DISCOVERIES WERE MADE

In any evaluation of Wilkes' Antarctic accomplishments, consideration must be taken of the fact that he was exploring what may well be the stormiest coast in the Antarctic. Mawson has aptly termed it "The Home of the Blizzard." Wilkes sailed in ships which, even by the standards of his day, were poorly suited for polar work. In spite of all the makeshift arrangements to provide for their greater comfort, the men were wet and cold a good part of the time. The ships being unfortified for the ice, Wilkes had to avoid contact with large floes and any but the loosest of pack ice. Without mechanical power to drive his ships he could not force his way into narrow leads in the pack ice, and since he depended only on sails, it was important that he keep his ships in a maneuverable position at all times.

Wilkes was also exploring what has proven to be one of the more inaccessible coasts of Antarctica. Beginning with Dumont d'Urville's landing on January 21, 1840, a number of landings have been made in the area where the Adélie Coast and the George V Coast join (between 140° E and 142°40' E). Two bases have been established in the vicinity, one by the Australasian Antarctic Expedition under Mawson (1911-14) and the other by Expéditions Polaires Françaises for a series of operations from 1950 to 1953. Mawson landed here again on January 7, 1931. With these exceptions, prior to the preliminary stages of the preparatory activity for the International Geophysical Year, the only other landings in the great 1800-mile sweep of the Antarctic coast from Cape Adare (71°17' S, 170°14' E) to Farr Bay (66°35' S, 94°23' E) were made in 1947 and 1948. Landings in 1947 on the Knox Coast and on the Knox and Budd Coasts in 1948 by personnel of U. S. Navy expeditions (see Chapters 22 and 24) were made from ship-based aircraft. In 1948, helicopters were flown from icebreakers.

WILKES' EASTERN LANDFALLS CONFIRMED

All of the earlier discoveries of Wilkes, east of 148° E, were disputed by later British explorers who sailed over or near his eastern landfalls without seeing land. They were therefore inclined to discredit all of his discoveries.[57] These included Ross (1841), Borchgrevink (1899), Scott (1904, 1912, 1913), and Shackleton (1909, 1915). Hobbs explained this situation by pointing out that

Wilkes was deceived by the great distance that one can see in the dust-free air of the Antarctic on a clear day. He also called attention to polar looming or superior mirage caused by refraction of light during periods of temperature inversion as a factor in explaining how Wilkes could have seen distant landmarks invisible to others who followed him.[58]

In support of his contention that looming is probably the answer to the elusiveness of some of Wilkes' landmarks, Hobbs has pointed out that Commander J. R. Stenhouse of Shackleton's 1914-17 expedition saw very clearly a mountain which he took to be Cape Hudson when drifting in the ice in 1915 about 20 miles from the position of the *Peacock* on January 19, 1840. Yet on the following day Stenhouse could see no evidence of land.[59]

Confirmation of Wilkes' eastern landfalls has at last been achieved as a result of the work of the Australian National Antarctic Research Expedition under the leadership of Phillip G. Law in 1958 and 1959. A reconnaissance was made by air and from the sea from Horn Bluff, approximately 150° E, to approximately 160° E on the Oates Coast. Aerial photographs were made of parts of the coast and an astro-fix was obtained at Magga Peak on the coast at 69°09' S, 157° 08' E.[60] Aerial photography of this area by the U. S. Navy Antarctic Developments Project ("Operation Highjump") in 1947 was much obscured by clouds, greatly reducing its value; however, it has served to supplement the Australian photography. A Soviet expedition also explored in this area in 1958. The results of both expeditions have appeared on maps which confirm the accuracy of the work of the two expeditions.[61]

In comparing Wilkes' map with the map resulting from their discoveries, Law and Lambert were able to make a substantial confirmation of Wilkes' eastern landfalls.[62] From Wilkes' description and panoramic sketches they concluded that he had in fact seen the tip of the newly discovered Mawson Peninsula when he named a feature Cape Hudson, and they applied that name in recognition of his first sighting it. They converted a copy of the relevant portion of Wilkes' chart to the scale and projection of their own map, over which they superimposed it. The following is quoted from their conclusions (pp. 7-8):

Examination of the two maps in this position . . . showed that:

(a) Wilkes's headland around Point Emmons agreed very well with Mawson's Cape Wild — Horn Bluff — Cape Freshfield feature.

(b) Wilkes's Peacock Bay agreed in general with the shape of the coast shown on the new provisional map.

(c) When directions were extended from the position of the "Peacock" on January 16, 1840, through the plotted positions of Reynolds Peak and Eld Peak, these rays went very close to the hills now mapped to the west of the glacier, but chart distances from the "Peacock" to the Peaks were short.

(d) When the chart direction from the position of "Vincennes" on 16 January through Ringgold Knoll was extended it passed near the Wilson Hills, but a similar extension of the direction from the position of the "Porpoise" on that day did not go near any newly-mapped feature.

Reference to Wilkes's Narrative showed that the recorded description of the hills seen by Reynolds and Eld was in accord with the photographs of the hills to the west of the glacier, but it was impossible to pick out which two particular peaks were the prominent features to which names were given by Wilkes.

Having regard to all these factors it is suggested that:

(a) The point of the peninsula stretching north-westerly from the vicinity of the Wilson Hills is Wilkes's Cape Hudson.

(b) On 16 January 1840:

    (i) Eld and Reynolds, on the "Peacock," sighted the hills to the west of the glacier.

    (ii) Wilkes himself, on the "Vincennes," may have seen a peak in the Wilson Hills group.

However, it has not been possible to locate any feature to correspond with that reported to have been sighted by Ringgold from the "Porpoise" on 16 January 1840.

In view of these considerations, two peaks in the western group of hills and one in the Wilson Hills have been arbitrarily selected and shown on the provisional map as Reynolds and Eld Peaks and Ringgold Knoll respectively.

The longitudinal differences between Wilkes's chart and the new provisional map are understandable.

The consistent difference in latitude and the underestimated distances from the ship to the Reynolds and Eld Peak and to Ringgold Knoll are both thought to be due to abnormal atmospheric refraction existing at the time of observation.

From the above quotation, it is apparent that Lambert and Law agree with Hobbs' explanation for Wilkes' errors in latitude.

WILKES' WESTERN LANDFALLS CONFIRMED

Sir Douglas Mawson, whose Australasian Antarctic Expedition of 1911-14 explored the Antarctic coast from 89° E to 153° E, at first denied the existence of all of Wilkes' discoveries except that of Knox Coast and of the coast in the vicinity of Piner Bay.[63] Later, following his British-Australian-New Zealand Antarctic Research Expedition of 1929-31, Mawson made a critical analysis of Wilkes' discoveries in the light of his own work during the two expeditions.[64] In this he rejected all of Wilkes' landfalls east of Point Alden (66°48' S, 142°02' E) on the Adélie Coast. Although he thought that Wilkes' "Disappointment Bay" is the indentation between the Ninnis and Mertz Glacier Tongues, he rejected "Point Emmons" and "Point Case" because they could only be the ends of the Ninnis and Mertz Glacier Tongues, respectively, and not land as Wilkes supposed. Mawson agreed that Wilkes definitely saw the Adélie Coast and the Knox Coast, and that he could have seen the Budd Coast and Norths Highland. Cape Carr and "Termination Land" he rejected as having been seaward projections of the edge of the pack ice. He pointed out that in a lecture in August 1932 before the Geographical Section of the Australian and New Zealand Association for the Advancement of Science, he had stressed "the fact that in light of the now very substantial knowledge gained of the ice features of Antarctica and of the peculiar atmospheric effects at times prevailing, Wilkes had come in for an undue amount of censure."[65]

The three papers by Hobbs dealing with Wilkes' discoveries have already been noted with reference to the eastern landfalls. In regard to those west of 147° E, it is Hobbs' contention that Mawson's own work confirms that of Wilkes, and he supports his contention with a map in which Mawson's delineation of the coast is superimposed over Wilkes' "Chart of the Antarctic Continent."[66]

As a result of aerial photography made by the U. S. Navy Antarctic Developments Project, 1946-47 (see Chapter 22), and ground control and supplementary photography obtained by the U. S. Navy Second Antarctic Developments Project, 1947-48 (see Chapter 24), to supplement already available and subsequently obtained geographic positions determined by others,[67] a reasonably accurate delineation of the coast of Antarctica from the Davis Sea to Mertz Glacier Tongue is now available. The first delineation was made on a scale of 1:1,000,000 by Gardner D. Blodgett of the Office of Geography, U. S. Department of Interior, under a contract with the Office of Naval Research (ONR Project 388-008). Blodgett's unpublished manuscript sheets were used in the compilation of "U. S. Hydrographic Chart of Antarctica," No. 2562 (1:11,250,000), 2d edition, and "Air Navigation Chart" No. V30-SP 9 (1:2,188,800), 1st edition, issued by the U. S. Hydrographic Office in 1955.[68]

In 1956 the U. S. Geological Survey issued eight sheets of its "Antarctic Reconnaissance Map" (1:500,000) based on the same data plus six additional geographical positions that had not been available to Blodgett. Six of the published sheets, E2-64-10, E2-64-11, E2-66-7, E2-66-10, E2-66-11 and E2-66-12, cover part of the area in question.

Because of the fact that Blodgett was working with six fewer geographical positions than was the Geological Survey, there is a discrepancy between the two compilations in the area of Totten Glacier of about 25 minutes of latitude. In the vicinity of Cape Carr there is a 13-minute discrepancy, and on the Budd Coast there is a difference of 12 minutes. In each instance the Geological Survey has placed the coast farther south than did Blodgett. There is a long stretch, from 111° E to 136°42' E, where no control is available, and it is possible that both compilations are slightly out of position in the middle sections. The degree of accuracy which has been attained can be determined only when additional ground control is available.

The two compilations cover 1200 miles of Antarctic coast, and the small discrepancies noted above should not be permitted to detract unduly from the otherwise high quality and general usefulness of the maps. Even where the latitude may be in error, the configuration of the coast is still accurately portrayed, and the relation of one feature to another in the same locality is correct. Since Blodgett's coastal delineation is more extensive than the Geological Survey's, it is necessary to use both for complete coverage. Both have been used on the 3rd edition, 1956, of H. O. Chart 2562 (1:11,250,000) and in the compilation of H. O. Charts 6643, 6644, and 6645 (1:2,000,000), 1st edition, published by the U. S. Hydrographic Office in 1956. As a result of the coastal delineation by Blodgett and the maps published by the U. S. Geological Survey, it is now, after more than 100 years, at last possible to test, thoroughly and objectively, the accuracy of Wilkes' mapping of the Antarctic coast.

An examination of Wilkes' "Chart of the Antarctic Continent" will show that he adhered to high standards of cartographic integrity. He clearly distinguished between land and ice, and although he assumed the land to be continuous, he did not show it on his map where he did not see it.

Wilkes' landfalls and his "line of icy barrier" have been redrawn on Figure 7, which in the east follows mainly Australian, New Zealand, and Russian sources. Most of the coastline is based on Blodgett's map or the Geological Survey series. The cartographic result of this superposition, more eloquently than words, shows how closely Wilkes' map conforms to reality west of 147° E. Admittedly he mistook a glacier tongue or the Shackleton Ice Shelf for land in the case of "Termination Land." There is, however, a definite break in the coast corresponding closely in general configuration to his Cape Carr and Porpoise Bay, although located 60 miles south and 15 miles west of the position Wilkes assigned to them. In the case of Norths Highland, Wilkes erred in latitude by from 25 to 30 miles, not a serious discrepancy in view of the confusing atmospheric phenomena that prevail in the Antarctic. It is an error which has been exceeded by others using far better and more modern equipment than Wilkes had. "Totten's High Land" is the weakest point in Wilkes' western landfalls. Here he was in error approximately 35 to 40 miles, and there is no distinctive break in the coastline, such as in the case of Cape Carr, to serve as a confirming feature. The break which Wilkes shows between "Totten's High Land" and Norths Highland is, however, understandable when it is realized that the position is occupied by relatively low-lying Reynolds Trough. As Figure 7 shows, Wilkes' demarcation of the Budd and Knox Coasts was remarkably accurate, especially considering the conditions under which he was operating.

Wilkes' investigation and survey work during the expedition in areas outside of the Antarctic have proven to be exceptionally accurate, justifying the reputation that he had earned by the time he assumed command of the squadron. That he should therefore have erred in the Antarctic raises two important points. Errors in longitude in high latitudes have always been more common than mistakes in latitude, yet Wilkes' errors in longitude are relatively minor — much less serious than his errors in latitude. Wilkes did not err in latitude when he was close to land, as in the case of Knox Coast and Piner Bay. His errors were all made in estimating the distance between his ship and distant snow-covered land. This bears out Hobbs' contention that Wilkes was deceived by the great distance that one is able to see in the dust-free Antarctic air on a clear day. Lambert and Law agree that atmospheric conditions were responsible in the case of the landfalls east of 147° E.

WILKES' CONCEPT OF AN ANTARCTIC CONTINENT

Wilkes was not the first to sight Antarctic land, and no member of the expedition set foot on the mainland. Wilkes, however, was the first to discover that Antarctica was a continent. Captain James Cook, by circumnavigating the world in high southern latitude in his second voyage, 1772-75, had disproved the then popular fancy of "Terra Australis," a great southern continent suitable for European settlement. Little was known of the Antarctic region. By sailing along its margin for approximately 1500 miles, Wilkes provided proof of the existence of a great south polar continent, and he was astute enough to recognize the fact and to maintain it in the face of formidable opinion to the contrary.

At the time that Wilkes entered the Antarctic in 1839, land had been discovered, with four exceptions, only in the South American quadrant. These four exceptions were: Biscoe's discovery of Enderby Land in about 53°00′ E in 1831; Kemp Coast in about 58°00′ E by Peter Kemp in 1833; the Balleny Islands, astride the Antarctic Circle in 162°50′ E, and the Sabrina Coast in 119°30′ by John Balleny in 1839. Until he returned to Australia in 1840, Wilkes did not know of Balleny's discoveries. Even with Balleny's landfalls, however, knowledge of the Antarctic consisted only of isolated landfalls separated by great distances. Landings had been made only on the Antarctic Peninsula, the South Shetlands, the South Orkneys, and South Georgia. Landfalls in other areas were generally seen at some distance for a short time from a sailing ship held off by pack ice. At the most these might be considered separate archipelagoes. It is true that sealers spoke of the Antarctic Peninsula as part of a continent, but they had no proof for it. From his instructions to Hudson in February, 1839, we know that Wilkes apparently considered "Palmer's Land" an archipelago around which it might be possible to sail. Consequently, Wilkes firmly believed that after having sighted land at frequent intervals for 1500 miles he had proven the existence of an Antarctic continent. Of this he said:

The evidence that an extensive continent lies within the icy barrier, must have appeared in the account of my proceedings, but will be, I think, more forcibly exhibited by a comparison with the aspect of other lands in the same southern parallel. Palmer's Land, for instance, which is in like manner invested with ice, is so at certain seasons of the year only, while at others, it is quite clear, because strong currents prevail there, which sweep the ice off to the northeast. Along the Antarctic Continent for the whole distance explored, which is upwards of fifteen hundred miles, no open strait is found. The coast, where the ice permitted approach, was found enveloped with a perpendicular barrier, in some cases unbroken for fifty miles. If there was only a chain of islands, the outline of the ice would undoubtedly be of another form; and it is scarcely to be conceived that so long a chain could extend so nearly in the same parallel of latitude. The land has none of the abruptness of termination that the islands of high southern latitudes exhibit; and I am satisfied that it exists in one uninterrupted line of coast, from Ringgold's knoll, in the east [c. 159° E], to Enderby's Land, in the west [c. 50° E]; that the coast (at longitude 95° E) trends to the north, and this will account for the icy barrier existing, with little alteration, where it was seen by Cook in 1773. The vast number of ice-islands conclusively points out that there is some extensive nucleus which retains them in their position; for I can see no reason why the ice should not be disengaged from islands, if they were such, as happens in all other cases in like latitudes. The formation of the coast is different from what would probably be found near islands, soundings being obtained in comparatively shoal water; and the colour of the water also indicates that it is not like other southern lands, abrupt and precipitous. This cause is sufficient to retain the huge masses of ice, by their being attached by their lower surfaces instead of their sides only.[69]

Wilkes' idea of an Antarctic continent was not acceptable to all. No less an authority than Sir James Clark Ross disputed Wilkes' claim. He wrote:

There do not appear to me sufficient grounds to justify the assertion that the various patches of land recently discovered by the American, French, and English navigators on the verge of the Antarctic Circle unite to form a great southern continent. The continuity of the largest of these, "Terre Adelie" of M. D'Urville, has not been traced more than three hundred miles, Enderby's land not exceeding two hundred miles; the others being mostly of inconsiderable extent, of somewhat uncertain determination, and with wide channels between them, would rather lead to the conclusion that they form a chain of islands. Let each nation therefore be contented with its due share, and lay claim only to the discovery of those portions which they were the first to behold.[70]

Time and subsequent exploration have substantiated Wilkes' claim of an Antarctic continent and confirmed his landfalls. After more than a century, during which disparagement was most often his reward, there can now no longer be any doubt of the greatness of his achievement.

NOTES

1. The French expedition, commanded by Dumont d'Urville, explored the Antarctic Peninsula from January to March 1838, and landed on the Adélie Coast, on the other side of Antarctica, in January 1840. The British Expedition under Sir James Clark Ross explored the Ross Sea in 1840-41 and returned there again the following year, before sailing for the Falkland Islands. The 1842-43 season was spent on the margin of the Weddell Sea.

2. "Memorial of Edmund Fanning and Benjamin Pendleton," November 7, 1831, House Exec. Doc. 61, 22nd Congr., 1st Session, 10 pp., Serial 217.

3. Edmund Fanning, "Memorial of Edmund Fanning to Illustrate the Views in a petition presented to Congress praying that a National Discovery and Exploring Expedition be sent out to the South Seas, etc.," December 18, 1833, Sen. Doc. 10, 23rd Congr., 1st Sess. 15 pp., Serial 238.

4. J. N. Reynolds, *Voyage of the United States Frigate Potomac, under the command of Commodore John Downes, during the Circumnavigation of the Globe in the years 1831, 1832, 1833, 1834*, (New York, Harper & Bros., 1835), 560 pp.

5. Letter from the Secretary of the Navy, transmitting a report of J. N. Reynolds, in relation to islands, reefs, and shoals in the Pacific Ocean, etc., Referred to the Committee on Commerce, January 27, 1835, House Doc. 105, 23rd Congr., 2nd Sess., 1835. (Signed by Reynolds, September 24, 1828.)

Dutee J. Pearce, "Report from the Committee on Commerce, praying that an Exploring Expedition to the Pacific Ocean and South Seas may be authorized by Congress," House Report No. 94, February 7, 1835, 23rd Congr., 2nd Sess., (A favorable committee report containing memorials and statements from organizations, naval officers and private citizens. Reynolds' report "In Relation to islands, reefs, and shoals, etc." also included.) A revised version of Reynolds' report, prefaced by several memorials in favor of an expedition and including Secretary of the Navy Southard's report of 1829 costs of preparations, was printed as Sen. Doc. 262, 24th Congr., 1st Sess., March 21, 1836, 87 pp., Serial No. 281. The original manuscript of Reynolds' report, entitled "Report of J. N. Reynolds of facts obtained at Nantucket of South Sea and Pacific Ocean," is filed in Record Group 45, Naval Records Collection of the Office of Naval Records and Library, U. S. National Archives.

6. For the resolution, see *Journal of the House of Representatives*, 24th Congr., 1st Sess., April 1, p. 613.

J. N. Reynolds, *Address on the Subject of a Surveying and Exploring Expedition to the Pacific Ocean and the South Seas*. Delivered in the Hall of Representatives on the evening of April 3, 1836, with correspondence and documents (New York, Harper & Bros., 1836). Although he has sometimes been mistakenly referred to as such, Reynolds was never a member of Congress.

7. *Journal of the Senate*, p. 341, and *Journal of the House of Representatives*, pp. 804-805, 24th Congr., 1st Sess.

8. Letters received by the Secretary of the Navy pertaining to the U. S. Exploring Expedition, 1838-1842, Record Group 45, Naval Records Collection of the Office of Naval Records and Library, U. S. National Archives.

9. The controversies are discussed rather fully by Philip L. Mitterling, *America in the Antarctic to 1840* (Urbana, University of Illinois Press, 1959), pp. 105-128, and by David B. Tyler, "The Wilkes Expedition," *Memoirs of the American Philosophical Society*, vol. 73, Philadelphia, 1968, pp. 7-29. The latter is especially thorough on the personal animosities both during the preparations for and throughout the course of the expedition. The former treats very fully the part of J. N. Reynolds in the inception of the expedition, beginning on p. 82.

10. Charles Wilkes, *Narrative of the United States Exploring Expedition, During the*

years 1838, 1839, 1840, 1841, 1842 (Philadelphia, Sea & Blanchard, 1845), vol. 1, pp. xvi, xvii, 370-372.

11. Letters received by the Secretary of the Navy pertaining to the U. S. Exploring Expedition, 1838-1842, Record Group 45, Naval Records Collection of the Office of Naval Records and Library, U. S. National Archives.

12. *Ibid.*

13. Wilkes, *op. cit.*, vol. 1, p. xvii.

14. Letters Received by the Secretary of the Navy Pertaining to the U. S. Exploring Expedition, 1838-1842, *op. cit.* See also Misc. Letters Sent ("General Letter Book") by the Secretary of the Navy, June 1798-November 1886, Record Group 45, National Archives. See especially folio September 28, 1836-August 21, 1837, p. 123 for the letter, December 28, 1836 to James Eights notifying him of his appointment to the expedition's scientific staff, and p. 478 for the letter, August 2, 1837, to Eights asking him to attend a meeting of the zoological staff of the scientific corps, to be held at Philadelphia.

15. Wilkes, *op. cit.*, vol. 1, p. xxv. The instructions were partly written by Wilkes himself.

16. *Ibid.*, p. xxix.

17. *Ibid.*, p. xxvi.

18. *Ibid.*, p. xxvii.

19. Kenneth J. Bertrand, "Geographical Exploration by the United States," *The Pacific Basin*, Herman R. Friis, ed., American Geographical Society, Special Publication No. 38, New York, 1967, p. 271.

20. Max Meisel, *A Bibliography of American Natural History, the Pioneer Century, 1769-1865* (Brooklyn, 1926), vol. II, p. 655, 31-110; Daniel C. Haskell, *The United States Exploring Expedition, 1838-1842, and its Publications, 1844-1874* (New York, New York Public Library, 1942), pp. 18-19.

21. Various authors with separate titles, "Centenary Celebration of the Wilkes Exploring Expedition of the United States Navy 1838-1842 and Symposium of American Polar Exploration, February 23-24, 1940, "*Proceedings of the American Philosophical Society*, vol. 82, No. 5, June, 1940, pp. 517-800. See especially Harley Harris Bartlett, "Reports of the Wilkes Expedition and the Work of the Specialists in Science," pp. 601-705.

22. Wilkes, *op. cit.*, vol. 1, pp. 131-161, 394-400, 405-414; vol. II, pp. 279-365, 457-473.

23. Charles Wilkes, *United States Exploring Expedition, 1838 to 1842*, vol. XI, *Meteorology* (Philadelphia, 1851).

24. F. W. Reichelderfer, "The Contributions of Wilkes to Terrestrial Magnetism, Gravity and Meteorology," *Proceedings of the American Philosophical Society*, vol. 82, No. 5, June, 1940, p. 598.

25. G. W. Littlehales, "The South Magnetic Pole," *Bulletin of the American Geographical Society*, vol. 42, No. 1, January, 1910, pp. 1-8; C. C. Ennis, "Magnetic Results of the United States Exploring Expedition, 1838-1842, Lieutenant Charles Wilkes, Commander," *Terrestrial Magnetism and Atmospheric Electricity*, vol. 39, No. 2, June, 1934, pp. 91-100.

26. Littlehales, *op. cit.*, pp. 3, 8.

27. A small bay (Bahia Orange), about five miles wide, located in about 55°31' S, 68°00' W on the east side of Peninsula Hardy, about 38 miles northwest of Cape Horn.

28. Wilkes, *Narrative . . ., op. cit.*, vol. I, p. 135.

29. *Ibid.*, p. 136. Modern surveys show the position of the island to be 62°04' S, 56°40' W, which bears witness to the accuracy of Wilkes' navigation.

30. *Ibid.*, p. 137. Complaints about the equipment are also noted in some of the private journals of other officers.

31. Journal of Lt. Robert E. Johnson, August 18, 1838-November 23, 1839. (See entries for March 10 to 17, 1839, inclusive.) Filed with Journals and Logs of the United States Exploring Expedition, Record Group 37, Records of the Hydrographic Office, U. S. National Archives. These journals and logs have been microfilmed by the National Archives as Micro-copy M-75, rolls 7-25.

32. Wilkes, *Narrative . . ., op. cit.*, vol. I, p. 394.

33. This position taken from the logbook of the U. S. S. *Peacock*, Logs of United States Naval Ships and Stations, 1801-1946, Record Group 24, Records of the Bureau of Naval Personnel, U. S. National Archives. Wilkes in his *Narrative* (vol. I, p. 153) gives the longitude as 97°58' W.

34. Wilkes, *Narrative . . ., op. cit.*, vol. I, p. 413. They were then about 140 miles from land, and if they actually saw land, it could only have been by the aid of looming or a superior mirage.

35. "Emerald Island (E. D.)" [Existence Doubtful] has only recently been removed from the charts.

36. Wilkes *Narrative . . ., op. cit.*, vol. II, pp. 357-359.

37. *Ibid.*, p. 292.

38. *Ibid.*, pp. 469-470.

39. Wilkes was an able, forceful, and resolute man. Since he was also a stern and strict disciplinarian, open animosity developed between him and a number of his subordinates. Some were crew members who had been punished for their offenses; some were officers whom he had reprimanded or discharged for shortcomings in line of duty. These malcontents, a few of whom had been sent home during the expedition, found encouragement in Washington, where Wilkes, "the stormy petrel" of the Navy, had enemies as well as friends among his brother officers. Moreover, a new political party now controlled the national administration, and there was no interest in promoting the accomplishments of the preceding administration. The result was that shortly after the squadron returned to New York in June 1842 Wilkes was brought before a court-martial on charges of oppression, cruelty, disobedience of orders, violence against native peoples, falsely claiming to have seen land, and wearing the uniform and flying the emblem of a captain when he did not hold that rank. He was acquitted of all except excessive punishment of his men and was given a public reprimand. The records of the trial proceedings are on file with Records of Proceedings of General Courts-Martial, Courts of Inquiry, Boards of Investigation, and Boards of Inquest, Record Group 125, Records of the Office of the Judge Advocate General (Navy), in the Washington National Records Center, Suitland, Md. The 1842 court-martial records relating to Wilkes have been microfilmed by the National Archives as microcopy M-75, roll 27.

40. Logbook of the U. S. S. *Peacock,* Sunday, January 19, 1840, *op. cit.,* U. S. National Archives.

41. Phillip Law, "Australian Coastal Explorations in Antarctica," *Geographical Journal,* vol. 127, Part 4, December, 1961, pp. 432-433.

42. William Herbert Hobbs, "Discovery of a New Sketch of Cape Hudson in the Antarctic," *Geographical Review,* vol. 24, No. 1, January 1934, pp. 115-118.

43. Sir Douglas Mawson, "Wilkes's Antarctic Landfalls," *Proceedings, Royal Geographical Society of Australia,* South Australian Branch, vol. 34, 1934, pp. 89-94.

44. Wilkes, *Narrative . . ., op. cit.,* vol. II, pp. 299-306, 464-468; Logbook of the U. S. S. *Peacock, op. cit.,* January 24-26, 1840.

45. Wilkes, *Narrative . . ., op. cit.,* vol. II, p. 345.

46. *Ibid.,* p. 471.

47. *Ibid.,* pp. 316-317. The name officially approved by the U. S. Board on Geographic Names is Piner Bay.

48. A few days earlier, January 21, 1840, Dumont d'Urville landed a party on some islets (Dumoulin Islands, 66°37′ S, 140°04′ E) in the vicinity, near what he called "Pointe Géologie."

49. Wilkes, *Narrative . . ., op. cit.,* vol. II, p. 320.

50. *Ibid.,* p. 321.

51. *Ibid.,* p. 322.

52. The chart was first issued in the atlas accompanying Wilkes' *Narrative . . ., op. cit.* It was later issued as U. S. Hydrographic Chart No. 70.

53. Wilkes, *Narrative . . ., op. cit.,* vol. II, p. 324. If Wilkes position was correct, the distance to the coast was actually twice as great as he estimated. About 25 miles back from the coast, the land, which rises as a great ramp from the shoreline, reaches an elevation of 4000 feet.

54. *Ibid.* Reference to Figure 7 will show Wilkes' estimate to be essentially correct.

55. Sheet E2-66-10, Antarctic Reconnaissance Map (1:5,000,000) by the U. S. Geological Survey, 1956, shows the land rising rapidly from the coast. The 4000-foot contour is approximately 20 miles from the shoreline. Since by noon, when the vessel was at 65°59′40″ S, 106°18′42″ E, Wilkes had retreated northwestward some miles, his estimate of seven or eight miles would appear to be essentially correct.

56. Wilkes, *Narrative . . ., op. cit.,* vol. II, p. 325.

57. William H. Hobbs, "Wilkes Land Rediscovered," *Geographical Review,* vol. 22, No. 4, October, 1932, pp. 639-646. A well-documented summary of the dispute.

58. William Hobbs, "The Discovery of Wilkes Land, Antarctica," *Proceedings of the American Philosophical Society,* vol. 82, No. 5, 1940, pp. 561-563, 569-581. It should be pointed out, however, that Wilkes was not unaware of this phenomenon, but was perhaps unprepared for the extent to which it can occur in the Antarctic. Wilkes refers to looming on page 295 of vol. II of his *Narrative.* Looming was one of the atmospheric phenomena dealt with in the recommendations for the scientific program supplied by the American Philosophical Society. See Edward G. Conklin, "Connection of the American Philosophical Society with our First Na-

tional Exploring Expedition," *Proceedings of the American Philosophical Society*, vol. 82, No. 5, 1940, p. 523.

59. William Hobbs, "Discovery of a New Sketch of Cape Hudson in the Antarctic," *Geographical Review*, vol. 24, No. 1., January, 1934, pp. 115-117.

60. Phillip G. Law, "Australian Coastal Explorations in the Antarctic," *op. cit.*, pp. 427-435.

61. "Antarctica," Coastal Region Between Longitudes 148° E. and 162° E., NMP|59/137.1. Division of National Mapping, Department of National Development, Canberra, October, 1959. 1:1,500,000.

"Australian Antarctic Territory," Sheet SR 56-57, Compiled to 1961, Division of National Mapping, Department of National Development, Canberra. 1:1,000,000.

"Pacific Ocean-Antarctic Coast, King George V Coast to New Zealand," Scale, 1:2,500,000 U. S. S. R. Chart 5996, Publication of the Office of the Chief of Hydrographic Service of the Navy, U. S. S. R., July, 1959.

62. B. P. Lambert and P. G. Law, "A New Map of the Coastline of Oates Land and Eastern King George V Land," Australian Paper read at the Antarctic Symposium in Buenos Aires, November, 1959. See also, A. Grenfell Price, *The Winning of Australian Antarctica* (Sydney, Angus and Robertson, 1962) Reports, B. A. N. Z. Antarctic Research Expedition, 1929-31, Series A, vol. 1, xvii and 241 pp., maps and illus. See pp. 180-181 for a discussion of the work of Lambert and Law, including a quotation similar to that on pp. 185-186.

63. Sir Douglas Mawson, *The Home of the Blizzard* (London, 1915), vol. 1, pp. 9-10, 50.

64. Mawson, "Wilkes' Antarctic Landfalls," *op. cit.*, pp. 70-113.

65. *Ibid.*, p. 80. Reviewed by A. Grenfell Price, *op. cit.*, pp. 174-180.

66. Hobbs, "Wilkes Land Rediscovered," *op. cit.*, Plate V. See also A. Grenfell Price, *op. cit.*, Map 11 for a composite map of the coastline as now known, and the discoveries of Wilkes and Mawson.

67. Positions in the Commonwealth Bay area and on the Queen Mary Coast were determined by the Australasian Antarctic Expedition, 1911-14. Positions on the Wilhelm II Coast were determined by Drygalski and the German South Polar Expedition, 1901-03. Those on the Adélie Coast were determined by members of the expeditions, 1950-53, sponsored by Expéditions Polaires Françaises.

68. Ozalid copies of Blodgett's compilation were also supplied to the American Geographical Society and to the Antarctic Division of the Australian Department of External Affairs. They were used in the preparation of the American Geographical Society map of Antarctica (1:3,000,-000 in 4 sheets) prepared for the Antarctic Committee of the United States National Committee of the IGY. A one-sheet version of the map (1:6,000,000) has also been published for public sale. Blodgett's work was also incorporated in the map of Antarctica (1:10,000,000) published in 1955 by the Antarctic Division of the Australian Department of External Affairs.

69. Wilkes, *Narrative . . ., op. cit.*, vol. II, pp. 334-335. Wilkes may also have been influenced by the fact that stones recovered from icebergs were identified by the scientists as granitic and dense sandstone, and therefore probably of continental origin. Rocks of volcanic origin were thought to have been more likely from oceanic island chains. It is worthy of note that Bellingshausen, although he made no such claim in his narrative report, actually thought he saw land near the Greenwich meridian on January 28, 1820 (January 16 by the Julian calendar). Although this was not known outside of Russia, he so reported on April 8, 1820 to the Minister of the Navy. He and the officers of the Russian expedition called Antarctica the "Ice Continent." See V. L. Lebedev, "A New Basis for the Solution of Controversial Aspects of Antarctic History," *Antarctica Commission Reports*, 1962, Akademiya Nauk SSSR, Interdepartmental Commission on Antarctic Research, (Izdatel'stvo Akademii Nauk SSSR, Moskva, 1963), pp. 182-3. Translated from Russian for the National Science Foundation, Washington, D. C. by the Israel Program for Scientific Translations, Jeruselm, 1969. Bellingshausen's narrative was not published in English until 1945. See note 28, Chapter 4. Frank Debenham, the editor, speculated on why Bellingshausen did not claim having seen land on January 16 and 17, on pages xviii and xix of his introduction.

70. James Clark Ross, *A Voyage of Discovery and Research in the Southern and Antarctic Regions During the Years 1839-43* (London, 1847), vol. 1, p. 275.

BIBLIOGRAPHY

PUBLISHED MATERIAL

Bartlett, Harley Harris, "The Reports of the Wilkes Expedition, and the Work of the Specialists in Science," Centenary Celebration of the Wilkes Exploring Expedition of the United States Navy, 1838-1842, *Proceedings of the American Philosophical Society*, vol. 82, No. 5,

June, 1940, pp. 601-705. Contains a well-documented summary of the problems concerning the organization of the expedition. Many of the scientific results are evaluated.

Bryan, Capt. George S., "The Purpose, Equipment and Personnel of the Wilkes Expedition," Centenary Celebration, The Wilkes Exploring Expedition of the United States Navy, 1838-1842, *Proceedings of the American Philosophical Society,* vol. 82, No. 5, June, 1940, pp. 551-560.

Callahan, James Morton, *American Relations in the Pacific and the Far East, 1784-1900* (Baltimore, 1901). Johns Hopkins University Studies in Historical and Political Science, Series XIX, Nos. 1-3. Chapter V deals with the U. S. Exploring Expedition in a superficial way. A general account is given of the whole expedition. Many careless errors of fact, and outdated by more recent and more detailed studies.

Conklin, Edwin G., "Connection of the American Philosophical Society with our First National Exploring Expedition," Centenary Celebration, The Wilkes Exploring Expedition of the United States Navy, 1838-1842, *Proceedings of the American Philosophical Society,* vol. 82, No. 5, June, 1940, pp. 519-541.

Cooley, Mary E., "The Exploring Expedition in the Pacific," Centenary Celebration, the Wilkes Exploring Expedition of the United States Navy, 1838-1842, *Proceedings of the American Philosophical Society,* vol. 82, No. 5, June, 1940, pp. 707-719.

Debenham, Frank, "Names on the Antarctic Continent," *Geographical Journal,* vol. 81, No. 2, February, 1933, pp. 145-148.

Ennis, C. C., "Magnetic Results of the United States Exploring Expedition, 1838-1842, Lieutenant Charles Wilkes, Commander," *Terrestrial Magnetism and Atmospheric Electricity,* vol. 39, No. 2, June, 1934, pp. 91-101.

Fanning, Edmund, "Memorial of Edmund Fanning to Illustrate the Views in a petition presented to Congress praying that a National Discovery and Exploring Expedition be sent out to the South Seas, etc.," December 18, 1833, Sen. Doc. 10, 23rd Congr., 1st Sess., 16 pp., Serial 238.

Fanning, Edmund, and Benjamin Pendleton, "Memorial of Edmund Fanning and Benjamin Pendleton," November 7, 1831, House Exec. Doc. 61, 22nd Congr., 1st Sess., 10 pp., Serial 217.

Haskell, Daniel C., *The United States Exploring Expedition, 1838-1842, and Its Publications, 1844-1874* (New York, New York Public Library, 1942, xii and 188 pp., plates. An annotated bibliography containing over 500 entries which gives a detailed and complete treatment of the many bibliographic problems pertaining to the publications of the expedition. An excellent history is given of the publication of the scientific reports. Separate papers by the scientists and congressional actions pertaining to the expedition are included in the bibliography. The present library location of each of the copies of the official reports is given.

Henderson, Daniel, *The Hidden Coasts: A Biography of Admiral Charles Wilkes,* (New York, William Sloane, 1953), 306 pp. An accurate biography with major emphasis on Wilkes' connection with the expedition.

Hobbs, William H., "Wilkes Land Rediscovered," *Geographical Review,* vol. 22, No. 4, October, 1932, pp. 632-655. Deals at some length with the dispute concerning Wilkes' eastern landfalls. Plate V consists of a superposition of Mawson's delineation of the coast on Wilkes' *Chart of the Antarctic Continent.*

——, "Discovery of a New Sketch of Cape Hudson in the Antarctic," *Geographical Review,* vol. 24, No. 1, January, 1934, pp. 115-117.

——, "Conditions of Exceptional Visibility Within High Latitudes, Particularly as a Result of Superior Mirage," *Annals of Association of American Geographers,* vol. 27, No. 4, December, 1937, pp. 229-240.

——, "The Discovery of Wilkes Land, Antarctica," Centenary Celebration, the Wilkes Exploring Expedition of the United States Navy, 1838-1842, *Proceedings of the American Philosophical Society,* vol. 82, No. 5, June, 1940, pp. 561-582.

Lambert, B. P., and P. G. Law, "A New Map of the Coastline of Oates Land and Eastern King George V Land," Australian Paper read at the Antarctic Symposium, Buenos Aires, November, 1959.

Law, Phillip G., "Australian Coastal Exploration in Antarctica," *Geographical Journal,* vol. 127, Part 4, December, 1961, pp. 427-435.

Littlehales, G. W., "The South Magnetic Pole," *Bulletin of the American Geographical Society,* vol. 42, No. 1, January, 1910, pp. 1-8. Based on an analysis of unpublished data collected on the expedition.

Mawson, Sir Douglas, *The Home of the Blizzard* (London, William Heinemann, 1915), 2 vols: vol. 1, xxx and 349 pp., maps and illus.; vol. 2, xiii and 337, maps and illus.

——, "Wilkes's Antarctic Landfalls," *Proceedings, Royal Geographical Society of Australia*, South Australian Branch, Sess. 1932-33, vol. 34, 1934, pp. 70-113.

——, "Geographical Narrative and Cartography, Australasian Antarctic Expedition, 1911-14," *Scientific Reports*, Series A, vol. 1, Sydney, 1942.

Meisel, Max, *A Bibliography of American Natural History, the Pioneer Century, 1769-1865*, vol. II (Brooklyn, Premier Publishing Co., 1926), xii and 741 pp. (See pp. 650-673.)

Palmer, James, *Thulia: A Tale of the Antarctic* (New York, Samuel Colman, 1843), 72 pp., illus. Appendix, pp. 65-72, is an account of the Antarctic cruise of the *Flying Fish* based on journals of the vessel.

Palmer, James C., *Antarctic Mariner's Song* (New York, Van Nostrand, 1868), 92 pp., illus. A revised version of the James Palmer book, above. The appendix consists of an account of the Antarctic cruise of the *Flying Fish*, February-March, 1839, based on logbooks and journals. Palmer was acting surgeon on the *Relief* and later on the *Peacock*.

Pearce, Dutee J. (Comm. Chairman), "Report from the Committee on Commerce, praying that an Exploring Expedition to the Pacific Ocean and the South Seas may be authorized by Congress," House Report No. 94, February 7, 1835, 23rd Congr., 2nd Sess., 43 pp., Serial 276.

Poesch, Jessie, "Titian Ramsay Peale, 1799-1885, and His Journals of the Wilkes Expedition," The American Philosophical Society, *Memoirs*, vol. 52, Philadelphia, 1961.

Price, A. Grenfell, *The Winning of Australian Antarctica*, B. A. N. Z. Antarctic Research Expedition, 1929-31, Reports, Series A, vol. 1 (Sydney, Angus and Robertson, 1962) xvii and 241 pp., maps and illus.

Rehn, James A. G., "Connection of the Academy of Natural Sciences of Philadelphia with our First National Exploring Expedition." Centenary Celebration, the Wilkes Exploring Expedition of the United States Navy, 1838-1842, *Proceedings of the American Philosophical Society*, vol. 82, No. 5, June, 1940, pp. 543-549.

Reichelderfer, F. W., "The Contributions of Wilkes to Terrestrial Magnetism, Gravity and Meteorology," Centenary Celebration, the Wilkes Exploring Expedition of the United States Navy, 1838-1842, *Proceedings of the American Philosophical Society*, vol. 82, No. 5, June, 1940, pp. 583-600.

Reynolds, J. N., "A Report of in relation to Islands, Reefs, and Shoals in the Pacific Ocean &c.," Referred to Committee on Commerce January 27, 1835, House Doc. No. 105, 23rd Congr., 2nd Sess., 28 pp., Serial 273. An abridged and revised version is published in Sen. Doc. 262, March 21, 1836, 24th Congr., 1st Sess., 87 pp., Serial 281. Several memorials favoring an exploring expedition are included as a preface.

——, *Address on the Subject of a Surveying and Exploring Expedition to the Pacific Ocean and the South Seas*, Delivered in the Hall of Representatives on the evening of April 3, 1836, with correspondence and documents (New York, Harper & Bros., 1836), 300 pp.

Ross, Capt. Sir James Clark, *A Voyage of Discovery and Research in the Southern and Antarctic Regions, During the Years 1839-43* (London, John Murray, 1847), 2 vols. (See vol. I, pp. 273-276, 285-299, 346-359.)

Tyler, David B., "The Wilkes Expedition," The American Philosophical Society, *Memoirs*, vol. 73 (Philadelphia, 1968).

Wilkes, Charles, U. S. N., *Narrative of the United States Exploring Expedition During the Years 1838, 1839, 1840, 1841, 1842* (Philadelphia, Sea & Blanchard, 1845), vols. I to V and Atlas: vol. I, lx and 434 pp., illus., 8 plates, map; vol. II, xv and 475 pp., illus., 28 plates, 3 maps; vol. III, xv and 438 pp., illus., 12 plates; vol. IV, xvi and 539 pp., illus., 15 plates, map; vol. V, xv and 558 pp., illus., 15 plates, 4 maps, index.

——, *United States Exploring Expedition During the Years 1838, 1839, 1840, 1841, 1842*, vol. XI, *Meteorology* (Philadelphia, C. Sherman, 1851), viii and 726 pp., 24 plates, 1 map.

MAPS

Blodgett, Gardner D. Five preliminary reconnaissance work sheets showing the delineation of the coast of Antarctica from 84° E to 146° E. Compiled by the Division of Geography, U. S. Department of Interior, as part of Office of Naval Research Project ONR 388-088 from "Operation Highjump" photographs (January-February 1947) and photographs and control data of "Operation Windmill" (1947-48). Scale 1:1,000,000, Lambert conformal conic projection. March to June, 1955. Restricted ozalid copies for official distribution.

"Antarctic Reconnaissance Map." Scale 1:500,000, contour interval 1000 feet, preliminary base. Polar stereographic projection. U. S. Geological Survey. Compiled from aerial photographs of U. S. Naval Task Force 68, 1946-47, and supplementary photography and geographic control by U. S. Naval Task Force 39, 1947-48. Sheets E2-64-10, E2-64-11, E2-66-7, E2-66-10, E2-66-11 and E2-66-12. 1956. (In spite of differences in designation, the source materials for both compilations above are the same.)

"Air Navigation chart" No. V30-SP 9. Scale 1:2,188,800, transverse Mercator projection. U. S. Hydrographic Office, 1955. (Based in part on Blodgett's coastal delineation and compilation.)

"Antarctica, Davis Sea to Porpoise Bay." Scale 1:1,5000,000, Lambert conformal conic projection. U. S. Hydrographic Office, Chart No. 6644, 1st edition, 1956.

"Antarctica, Porpoise Bay to Cape Adare." Scale 1:1,500,000, Lambert conformal conic projection. U. S. Hydrographic Office Chart, No. 6645, 1st edition, 1956.

Wilkes, Charles, "Chart of the World Shewing the Tracks of the U. S. Exploring Expedition in 1838, 39, 40, 41 & 42." Mercator projection. [Map 1] in *Atlas, Narrative of the United States Exploring Expedition During the years 1838, 1839, 1840, 1841, 1842*. (Philadelphia, Sea & Blanchard, 1845.)

"Chart of the Antarctic Continent Shewing the Icy Barrier Attached to It. Discovered by the U. S. Ex. Ex., Charles Wilkes, Esq., Commander, 1840." Mercator projection. [Map 2] in *Atlas, Narrative of the United States Exploring Expedition During the Years 1838, 1839, 1840, 1841, 1842* (Philadelphia, Sea & Blanchard, 1845. (Also published as the second map in *Atlas of Charts*, vol. 1, of *United States Exploring Expedition During the Years 1838, 1839, 1840, 1841, 1842, Hydrography*, by Capt. Charles Wilkes, U. S. N., 1850. Later printed as "U. S. Hydrographic Chart No. 70" and finally as "Historical Chart No. 70.")

"Antarctica, Coastal Region Between Longitudes 148° E and 162° E." Scale 1:2,000,000. Lambert conformal conic projection. NMP/59/138, Division of National Mapping, Department of National Development, Canberra, Australia, October, 1959. Shows control and air photography used in compilation.

"Antarctica, Coastal Region Between Longitudes 148° E and 162° E." Scale 1:1,5,000,000, Lambert conformal conic projection. NMP/59/137.1, Division of National Mapping, Department of National Development, Canberra, Australia, October, 1959. Special Map. "Pacific Ocean — Antarctic Coast, King George V Coast to New Zealand." Scale 1:2,500,000 at Latitude 66°, Mercator projection. Publication of the Chief of Hydrographic Services of the Navy (USSR), Chart 5996, New edition, July 1958 [translated from the Russian].

"Australian Antarctic Territory." Scale 1:1,000,000, Sheet S. R. 56-57, Compiled to 1959, Division of National Mapping, Department of National Development, Canberra, Australia.

MANUSCRIPT MATERIAL

Alden, James, Journal of Lt. James Alden kept aboard U. S. S. *Vincennes*, Library of the Mariners Museum, Newport News, Virginia. Very full entries.

Briscoe, William, Journal of William Briscoe, armorer, aboard U. S. S. *Relief*; transferred to *Vincennes* at Callao, June 20, 1839. August 18, 1838-March 23, 1842. Entries not continuous; occasional summaries for several days. Journals and Logs Kept by Members of the Wilkes Expedition, 1838-42, Record Group 37, Records of the Hydrographic Office, National Archives.

Dickerson, Mahlon, Letters from the Secretary of the Navy, Mahlon Dickerson, to various individuals. Misc. Letters Sent ("General Letter Book") by the Secretary of the Navy, June 1798-November 1886, Record Group 45, National Archives. See especially the folio for September 28, 1836-August 21, 1837. The "General Letter Book" has been microfilmed by the National Archives as microcopy M-209.

Hartsene, Henry J., Journal of Lt. Henry J. Hartsene aboard U.S.S. *Porpoise* and *Relief*, August 14, 1838-March 23, 1840; transferred to *Relief* June 21, 1839, at Callao. Complete daily entries for the first cruise of the squadron to the Antarctic. Journals and Logs Kept by Members of the Wilkes Expedition, 1838-42, Record Group 37, Records of the Hydrographic Office, National Archives.

Johnson, Robert, Journal of Lt. Robert Johnson aboard the *Vincennes*, the *Peacock*, the *Sea Gull* and the *Porpoise*, August 18, 1838-November 23, 1839. Journals and Logs Kept by Members of the Wilkes Expedition, 1838-42, Record Group 37, Records of the Hydrographic Office, National Archives. Contains an account of the voyage of the *Sea Gull* into Antarctic water in 1839.

Letters Received by the Secretary of the Navy Pertaining to the U. S. Exploring Expedition, 1838-1842, Record Group 45, Naval Records Collection of the Office of Naval Records and Library, National Archives.

Logbook of the U. S. S. *Peacock* kept by Captain's Clerk F. D. Stuart, August 19, 1838-July 18, 1841. Logs of United States Naval Ships and Stations, 1801-1946, Record Group 24, Records of the Bureau of Naval Personnel, National Archives.

Logbook of the U. S. S. *Vincennes*, 1838-1842. [Improperly labeled journal.] Logs of the United States Naval Ships and Stations, 1801-1946, Record Group 24, Records of the Bureau of Naval Personnel, National Archives.

Lyceum of Natural History of New York, Report of the Committee of the Lyceum of Natural History, New York, October 2, 1836, to the Secretary of the Navy. Letters Received by the Navy Pertaining to the U. S. Exploring Expedition, 1838-1842, Record Group 45, Naval Records Collection of the Office of Naval Records and Library, National Archives.

Records of the Court Martial of Lt. Charles Wilkes, 1842, Proceedings of General Courts Martial, Courts of Inquiry, Boards of Investigation, and Boards of Inquest, Record Group 125, Records of the Office of the Judge Advocate General (Navy) in the Washington National Records Center, Suitland, Md. The 1842 court-martial records relating to Wilkes have been microfilmed by the National Archives as microcopy M-75, roll 27.

Sanford, Joseph P., Journal of Passed Midshipman Joseph P. Sanford aboard U. S. S. *Relief, Vincennes* and *Porpoise,* August 19, 1838-July 22, 1841. Served aboard the *Vincennes* on the Antarctic cruise of 1840. Made concise and significant daily entries. Journals and Logs Kept by Members of the Wilkes Expedition, 1838-1842, Record Group 37, Records of the Hydrographic Office, National Archives.

Sinclair, George T., Journal of Acting Master George T. Sinclair, aboard the *Relief,* December 19, 1838-June 15, 1839, aboard the *Porpoise,* August 13, 1839-September 6, 1839; aboard the *Flying Fish,* September 15, 1839-September 25, 1840. Gives account of conditions on the *Flying Fish* in the Antarctic, January 1840. Journals and Logs Kept by Members of the Wilkes Expedition, 1838-1842, Record Group 37, Records of the Hydrographic Office, National Archives.

Wilkes, Charles, Journal of Charles Wilkes aboard the U. S. S. *Vincennes* and *Porpoise,* August 10, 1838-June 9, 1842. 3 vols. Very complete. Contains many diagrams and sketches. Obviously the basis for the *Narrative* of the Expedition. Journal form frequently interspersed with lengthy expositions concerning a special point of interest. Journals and Logs Kept by the Members of the Wilkes Expedition, 1838-1842, Record Group 37, Records of the Hydrographic Office, National Archives.

11

MAURY AND SMYLEY, SCIENTIST AND
SEALER IN MID-CENTURY

SIGNIFICANCE OF THEIR CONTRIBUTIONS

Although neither of them played an active part in a major exploring expedition, two Americans gained international recognition for their roles in unveiling the Antarctic during the middle of the 19th century. They were Lieutenant Matthew Fontaine Maury and Captain William H. Smyley. Each represented one of the two elements which were responsible for the early presence of the United States in Antarctica.

Maury, Superintendent of the United States Navy Depot of Charts and Instruments and of the Naval Observatory and Hydrographical Office from 1842 to 1861, gained world renown for the compilation of his *Wind and Current Charts* which drastically changed the conventional routes of sailing ships throughout the world. In the compilation of his charts Maury was confronted with a lack of data for high southern latitudes which he felt held the key to the weather of the entire southern hemisphere. Consequently, he advocated a great international undertaking in the exploration of the Antarctic. Although the American Civil War blighted his hopes, a century later his dream materialized in the International Geophysical Year, 1957-58.

William H. Smyley of Newport, Rhode Island, was the captain of a number of sealing voyages to sub-Antarctic and Antarctic waters in the second quarter of the 19th century. He reported to Lieutenant Charles Wilkes at the New York Navy Yard in 1842 his recovery of the maximum and minimum thermometers left at Deception Island by Captain Henry Foster of H.M.S. *Chanticleer* in 1829. He also gave the first description of Deception Island in a state of eruption. Both facts were published by Wilkes, and for half a century Smyley's name was associated with the lowest temperature recorded in Antarctica, −5° F. Smyley was one of the many commercial mariners who supplied Maury with information for his charts and for his widely disseminated *Sailing Directions,* where Smyley's name appeared in association with the material he contributed. From 1850 until his death in 1868 he was the United States Commercial Agent at Port Stanley in the Falkland Islands.

MAURY AND THE ANTARCTIC

BACKGROUND

Matthew Fontaine Maury was born near Fredericksburg, Virginia, in 1806, and grew up on a farm near Nashville, Tennessee.[1] When he was 19, he was appointed a midshipman in the United States Navy. Most of his active duty was with the Pacific Squadron on the west coast of South America. Briefly he held appointments on the *Relief*, then on the *Macedonian,* and finally as astronomer on the expedition while the U. S. Exploring Expedition was in the initial stages of its organization under Captain Thomas ap Catesby Jones. However, after Jones resigned and Lieutenant Charles Wilkes was appointed commander, Maury asked to be detached from the expedition.[2] In October 1839, while traveling from his parents' home in Tennessee to report for active duty aboard ship in New York, he was injured when a stagecoach overturned in Ohio. He was left with a permanent limp and never again served aboard ship.

By this time Maury had written two articles which had been published in the scholarly *American Journal of Science and Arts,* and he was also the author of a textbook on navigation, copies of which were on every ship in the Navy.[3] The former had been written while he was serving as acting sailing master aboard the U. S. S. *Falmouth* (1831-33) of the Pacific Squadron. The textbook stemmed from his dissatisfaction with the kind of schooling he had received as a midshipman. It had consisted mostly of committing to memory large parts of Nathaniel Bowditch's *American Practical Navigator* and had emphasized the practical aspects of navigation without the underlying mathematical theory.[4] During his enforced idleness following the accident, Maury wrote articles on many subjects which were published in various journals and newspapers. Some, under pseudonyms, were critical of naval training, wastefulness and inefficiency, and advocated organizational reform and the establishment of a naval academy similar to the Army's West Point.[5]

In 1842 Maury was appointed Superintendent of the Navy's Depot of Charts and Instruments. Founded in 1830, it was the forerunner of the former Hydrographic Office and the present Naval Oceanographic Office. His three predecessors had all been able men. The second was Lieutenant Charles Wilkes. Also in 1842, Congress authorized the construction of a naval observatory in Washington, and one of Maury's tasks was to supervise its construction. On October 1, 1844, he was appointed the first Superintendent of the Naval Observatory. Until 1866 the observatory and the depot were under a single head. The combined organization was officially designated the United States Naval Observatory and Hydrographic Office in 1854, but it was usually referred to as the "Naval Observatory."

WIND AND CURRENT CHARTS

At the Depot of Charts and Instruments, Maury found in 1842 a great store of logbooks of naval vessels which had been filed there following each cruise. Upon examination of some of them he realized that in the more or less systematic recording of winds, current, and weather, they contained the information which he had sought in vain when he had become acting sailing master of the *Falmouth* in 1831. He devised a plan by which the data contained in the logbooks could be systematically tabulated on charts representing quadrangles of 5 degrees of longitude by 5 degrees of latitude. For example, the direction of the wind was tabulated according to the 16 points of the compass for each of the 12 months of the year.[6] The data thus summarized and generalized were plotted on maps, using pictorial symbols for each of the 5-degree quadrangles. This was the basis for his *Wind and Current Charts,* the first of which was of the Atlantic, issued in 1847.[7]

Soon after beginning work on the logbooks at the Depot, Maury recognized that additional sources would be needed. First, by his urgent request, naval commanders were ordered late in 1842 to send navigational, hydrographic, and meteorological information to Maury at the Depot. Knowing that whalers and sealers often cruised in waters far from the regular tracks of merchant or naval vessels, Maury had associates in New England search for logbooks of such voyages from which they extracted data for his charts.

On the basis of the information revealed by the first chart, Maury suggested changes in the tracks generally followed by sailing vessels. When his suggested track to Rio de Janeiro was tested in a voyage from Baltimore and proved to save 17 days on the outward voyage and 35 on the round trip, the news spread rapidly among mariners.[8] Maury's *Wind and Current Charts* were soon in great demand, but they could not be purchased.

Maury needed a wider source of information, and much time could be saved in extracting the data if a uniform system of reporting could be established. Consequently, he devised a standard form which he called the abstract log. On this the latitude, longitude, the direction and rate of the current, the barometric reading, the temperature of air and water, the clouds, the condition of the weather, the magnetic variation, and the direction and velocity of the winds were to be recorded systematically. A somewhat more demanding form was devised for use on naval vessels.

A set of the wind and current charts and a copy of the *Sailing Directions,* which explained how the charts should be used and advised navigators on courses to steer and dangers to avoid, were given to any mariner who requested them providing he agreed to keep an abstract log on his next voyage and send the completed log to the Naval Observatory when he returned. He would then get a revised set of charts and another abstract log. On the basis of the data gleaned from thousands of abstract logs Maury was continually revising and perfecting his charts and the *Sailing Directions.*[9]

Maury's fame spread and he became known internationally as more and more mariners used his *Wind Charts* and *Sailing Directions.* His work was a great boon to shipping companies and insurance companies, to navigators, and even to the ordinary seaman. As time at sea was cut, the cost of ocean voyages decreased. Clipper ships, aided by Maury's charts and sailing directions, were setting unbelievably fast records for sailing voyages, speeds which even the steamboats of that day could not match. In 1853 Maury was authorized to offer the charts and sailing directions to the navies and to merchant ships of certain foreign countries interested in cooperating.[10] His recommendation to go into higher latitudes in the Indian Ocean on a great circle course to Australia resulted in the discovery of Heard Island on November 25, 1853, and in 1854 McDonald Island was discovered and Heard Island was sighted by four different vessels on this course.

As a result of a proposal by Maury, the first International Maritime Meteorological Conference, in which he played a leading part, was held in Brussels in
1853. At this conference the delegates of 10 maritime nations agreed to cooperate on a system of observations based on abstract logs patterned after Maury's. It
was made mandatory for naval vessels but remained optional for merchant ships.
Following the conference Maury received citations and honors from scientific
organizations or the governments of several countries.

As an observant farm youth, Maury had developed a curiosity about nature.
He became a keen observer of the weather and of the sea as a midshipman and
later as acting sailing master on the *Falmouth,* and it was natural for him to
speculate about the causes. When the data from the logbooks and abstract logs
were plotted on the charts, Maury was fascinated by the patterns of distribution
that began to be revealed, and he attempted to explain them in numerous
papers read before scientific groups. These papers were subsequently published
in one form or another, including his *Physical Geography of the Sea*.[11] Here
the inadequacies in his education in basic physical theory betrayed him.[12]

Maury's great contribution to science was his method for gathering the information about the sea and the atmosphere and placing it on maps from which
patterns of winds, currents, and temperature distribution could be discerned.
For this as well as for the practical results to shipping he was acclaimed by the
public and the scientific community alike. As the numerous editions and print-
ings of *The Physical Geography of the Sea* testify, the public accepted it un-
critically. However, a number of contemporary scientists at home and abroad
were critical of his explanations and rejected some as unsound.[13]

ANTARCTIC EXPLORATION

Maury became interested in polar regions for a number of reasons. He was
getting data from logbooks of whalers who in the 1840s and 1850s were pushing
through the Bering and Davis Straits into Arctic waters. In the compilation of
his *Whale Chart* he discovered that the Right whale of the northern hemisphere
is different from that of the southern, and that neither crosses the tropical
waters.[14] He was intrigued by other differences between the Arctic and the Antarctic that his research was revealing. He also had a hand in the planning of two
Arctic expeditions sponsored by Henry Grinnell, led by Lieutenant Edward J.
De Haven, USN, (1850-51) and by Dr. Elisha Kent Kane, USN (1853-55).

The development of Maury's concern with the Antarctic is well illustrated in
successive editions of his *Physical Geography of the Sea,* reflecting successive
editions of the *Sailing Directions* from which the material was taken. In the first
edition, published in 1855, and in the 5th edition, published in 1856, references
to the Antarctic are infrequent and merely incidental to some other topic.
Maury added a paragraph to one or another topic in the numerous reprintings,
enlargements, and revisions as new material became available. Finally, in the
eighth and last American edition, published in 1861, Maury included for the
first time a separate chapter on Antarctica. A large part of another chapter was
also devoted to Antarctica.[15]

In his discussion of Antarctica, Maury is trapped by the fact that he had few reports from south of 60° S. His data correctly show a generalized pressure gradient descending from between 20° to 25° S to 60° S.[16] Unfortunately, he projected this all the way to the South Pole to a mean barometric pressure of 28.1 inches. He lacked the data that would have shown a polar high or the trough of low pressure at about 60° S, which is the track of a succession of cyclonic storms.

Maury's whole concept of the Antarctic is summed up in the opening paragraph of Chapter 21:

> During our investigations of the winds and currents, facts and circumstances have been revealed which indicate the existence of a mild climate--mild by comparison-- within the antarctic circle. They plead most eloquently the cause of exploration there. The facts and circumstances which suggest mildness of climate about the south pole are these: a low barometer, a high degree of aerial refractions, and strong winds from the north.

His explanation of this combination of observed facts and supposed conditions is difficult to document without long and disjointed quotations or without numerous citations because of the organization of the book which scatters the various parts of his presentation on any topic over several pages. In short, he argued that the westerly winds (he called them the counter-trades) blow across vast expanses of ocean and therefore carry much water vapor. These winds blow to a low pressure center in the polar area where there is much precipitation. The amount of this precipitation is increased due to the fact that the winds must rise up over the highlands which have been discovered to form the margin of Antarctica. The large number and great size of the Antarctic icebergs are proof of the large amount of precipitation in the south polar region. The latent heat of condensation released by this copious precipitation in the polar region rises somewhat in the effect of a flue, causing the low pressure near the pole. On the southern or inner side of the marginal highlands descending winds (presumably he inferred a foehn effect with adiabatic heating) help to raise the temperature in the polar area and lower the pressure still further.

In developing his explanations for the oceanic and atmospheric circulation, Maury recognized that he was handicapped by lack of data for high latitudes, particularly for Antarctica. Captains of merchant ships who on his advice had taken the great circle course beyond the 50th parallel en route to Australia complained about running into easterly winds, stormy weather, and floating ice. At that time, activity in the Arctic was being spurred by the search for Sir John Franklin, but Antarctica was being neglected. These were compelling reasons for renewed exploration in the far south.

Maury's major contribution to science had come about through cooperative effort. Through his official position he had numerous foreign contacts, but he had gained even more through his *Wind and Current Charts.* The pinnacle of his career probably had been the International Maritime Meteorological Conference at Brussels in 1853, an excellent example of international cooperation. It was natural, therefore, for him to think in terms of an international cooperative effort in the Antarctic.

The last three paragraphs of Chapter 21 of Maury's last edition of the *Physical*

Geography of the Sea were a plea for Antarctic exploration, but not yet a co-operative effort.

These facts . . . plead the cause of antarctic exploration. Within the periphery of that circle is included an area equal in extent to one sixth part of the entire landed surface of our planet. Most of this immense area is as unknown to the inhabitants of the earth as is the interior of one of Jupiter's satellites. With the appliance of steam to aid us, with the lights of science to guide us, it would be a reproach to the world to permit such a large portion of its surface any longer to remain unexplored. For the last 200 years the Arctic Ocean has been a theatre for exploration; but as for the antarctic, no expedition has attempted to make any *persistent* exploration or even to winter there.

England through Cook and Ross; Russia through Bellingshausen; France through D'Urville; and the United States through Wilkes; have sent expeditions to the South Sea. They sighted and sailed along the icy barrier, but none of them spent the winter or essayed to travel across and look beyond the first impediment. The expeditions which have been sent to explore unknown seas have contributed largely to the stock of human knowledge, and they have added renown to nations, lustre to diadems. Navies are not all for war. Peace has its conquests, science its glories; and no navy can boast of brighter chaplets than those which have been gathered in the fields of geographical exploration and physical research.

The great nations of the earth have all with more or less spirit undertaken to investigate certain phenomena touching the sea, and, to make the plans more effectual, they have agreed to observe according to a prescribed formula. The observations thus made have brought to light most of the facts and circumstances which indicate the existence within the antarctic circle of a mild climate--mild by comparison. The observations which have led to this conclusion were made by fellow-laborers under all flags. It is hoped that this circumstance may vindicate, in the eyes of all, the propriety of an appeal in this place for antarctic exploration, and plead for it favorable consideration among all nations.[17]

Maury always had been firm in his convictions and persistent in pressing them, and in the matter of Antarctic exploration he appears to have been acting with a special urgency. He was deeply concerned about the future of the country as the differences between the North and the South grew more ominous. The ideas he expressed in Chapter 21 of *The Physical Geography of the Sea* were repeated in one form or another several times in 1860 and 1861.

Early in 1860 he prepared an article for publication by the American Geographical and Statistical Society.[18] On March 31, 1860, he sent a letter to Isaac Toucey, Secretary of the Navy, pointing out what had been revealed by the research under his direction, the vast unknown area within the Antarctic Circle, emphasizing the need for further exploration and urging him to encourage it by official action.

This circumstance suggests the importance of further Antarctic exploration. Perhaps the Honourable Secretary may think it proper to encourage it by official action.

The improved appliances, with the information which present skill and research afford, would seem to promise a degree of success now that was beyond the reach of previous exploration in that quarter.[19]

Maury was not hopeful of action by the United States, and he began to press harder and more specifically for international cooperation. On May 20, 1860, he wrote to his friend Lord Wrottesley, President of the British Association for the Advancement of Science, urging him to use his "influence with her Majesty's

Government and the English people in the cause of Antarctic exploration."[20] Maury also enclosed a paper, "On the climates of the Antarctic Regions, as Indicated by Observations upon the Height of the Barometer and Directions of the Winds at Sea," which was read at the 1860 meeting of the Association at Oxford. In this paper he pointed out that the steamship now made it possible to do much more than had been possible for former explorers dependent on only sailing ships, and he recommended:

> For many reasons this exploration should be a joint one among the nations that are concerned in maritime pursuits. The advantages are manifold; each one of the cooperating powers, instead of equipping a squadron at its own expense, would furnish only one or two steamers, and these should not be large nor should their cost be extravagant. Thus the expense of a thorough Antarctic exploration like those for carrying on the "Wind and Current Charts" may be so subdivided among the nations concerned, as literally to be "almost nothing" . . ., such an Expedition would have several centres of exploration. The officers and men under each flag would naturally be incited by the most zealous and active emulation. They would strive so much the more earnestly not to be outdone in pushing on the glorious conquest.[21]

Late in 1860 Maury was in England regarding the copyright on the British editions of *The Physical Geography of the Sea and Its Meteorology* and was invited to read a paper before the Royal Geographical Society in London.[22] The paper was well received and Maury was lauded at the close of the session, but nothing came of his plea for Antarctic exploration.

Back in Washington in mid-winter of 1861, Maury was caught up again in the great controversy between the states. One after another, the southern states were seceding. With war imminent it was obvious that the United States government had no interest in Antarctic exploration. Other countries would have to carry out his plan. In April 1861 Maury figuratively passed the torch in letters addressed to the Ministers in Washington from Austria, France, Great Britain, Italy, the Netherlands, Portugal, Russia, and Spain urging international cooperation in the exploration of Antarctica.[23] These were accompanied by a 44-page proposal for an international Antarctic exploring expedition, including specific scientific objectives. That addressed to Lord Lyons of Great Britain was forwarded by him to the Foreign Office, from where it reached the Admiralty and in turn the Secretary of the British Association for the Advancement of Science. It was placed before the Department of Meteorology of the Association at the Manchester meeting in September 1861.[24] The paper reiterated much that was contained in the earlier one to Lord Wrottesley.

Conditions in 1861 were not auspicious for an international undertaking in Antarctica. Civil war commenced in the United States with the bombardment of Fort Sumter on April 12. The Virginia Convention passed an ordinance of secession on April 17, and Maury with heavy heart resigned his commission as Commander of the United States Navy on April 20, 1861. (He had been promoted by recommendation of President Buchanan with the concurrence of the Senate as of September 14, 1855 on January 18, 1858.) He was well aware that his resignation meant the end of his work in oceanography and perhaps as a scientist, but he felt a greater obligation to his native state than to his career.

None of the foreign governments whom Maury had contacted took any action regarding Antarctic exploration, although he planted a seed which would eventually germinate. Maury was a man of international renown, and his persistent recommendation of a cause had to have some impact. Some scientists had rejected his explanations of the circulation of the atmosphere and of the ocean currents, but he was still honored for his very substantial and original contributions. During the war he was labeled a traitor in the North, and he had many enemies in the South. However, in 1861 Grand Duke Constantine, brother of the Czar, invited Maury and his family to live in Russia and he had a similar invitation in 1866 from Napoleon III to live in France. In 1868 Cambridge University conferred on him the honorary LL.D. Degree. Hugh Robert Mill, a geographer of world recognition for his work in many fields, including oceanography, climatology, and the history of Antarctic exploration, in his classic *Siege of the South Pole,* published in 1905, said of Maury:

All the same there were not wanting men who, . . . saw the immense importance of increasing our fragmentary knowledge of the remotest south. First amongst these stands Matthew Fontaine Maury, an officer of the United States Navy, a profound scientific investigator, and the most brilliant writer who ever attempted to put into words the wonders of the sea as they are revealed to an appreciative mind by the patient study of facts. Maury's "Physical Geography of the Sea" is so full of charm, so permeated by his own enthusiasm that even now, after the data have been corrected almost beyond recognition by subsequent research, and the theories shown to be fallacious or imperfect, the book remains the most popular treatise on the oceans.[25]

Indirectly, Maury's influence extended to the first International Polar Year, 1882-83.[26] Conceived by Lieutenant Karl Weyprecht, Austrian naval officer, scientist, and Arctic explorer, he and Dr. Georg von Neumayer, director of the oceanographical institute (Deutsche Seewarte) at Hamburg, had leading roles in its organization. Neumayer was president of the International Polar Conference at Hamburg in 1879 at which the Polar Year's organization was begun. As a young man Dr. Neumayer was greatly influenced by Maury, and as the first director (1857-1862) of the Flagstaff Observatory near Melbourne, Australia, he had cooperated with Maury in the collection of meteorological data.[27] Emphasis was placed on simultaneous and coordinated meteorological and magnetic observations in both the Arctic and the Antarctic. Fifteen stations were proposed. Of the four proposed for the Antarctic, however, only the German station at Royal Bay, South Georgia, was established. The United States confined its efforts to the Arctic.[28]

Since the end of the precedent-setting First International Polar Year a number of organizations have been established and have functioned for varying lengths of time in the promotion of international cooperation in various polar activities.[29] It is doubtful that Maury's plea for international cooperation in the exploration of the Antarctic in 1860 and 1861 extended beyond whatever influence it might have had on Dr. Neumayer. Such activity steadily increased through the first half of the 20th century, and after the magnificent example of the International Geophysical Year of 1957-1958, it is bound to increase even more in the future. In his fondest dreams, Matthew Fontaine Maury could not have imagined the extent and magnitude of the operations during the IGY, when 12 nations established and maintained some 60 bases on the continent and its surrounding islands.

CAPTAIN WILLIAM H. SMYLEY

SMYLEY THE SEALER

Other than that he was a resident of Newport, Rhode Island, nothing is now known of the early life of William H. Smyley. He engaged in sealing off the coast of Patagonia, the Falkland Islands, the Cape Horn region, and the South Shetland Islands from about 1828 to 1850. We have his word that, "I have spent 22 years of my life mostly from South Shetlands to the River La Plata, and I once remained six years without coming north of 41° S."[30]

The record reveals that Smyley was a man of good repute, highly regarded by his contemporaries. From his letters it is obvious that he was largely self-educated, and it is also apparent that he was a man of intelligence. It is interesting to note the improvement in his letters between 1842 and 1867. He possessed an intellectual curiosity about nature, especially about things pertaining to the sea. And he was a remarkable sailor. Before Maury recommended that sailing ships en route from the United States to Rio de Janeiro and Cape Horn keep close in to the "hump" of Brazil instead of taking the conventional track close to the African coast, Smyley was doing it and making remarkably fast passages as a result. He was not afraid to deviate from the beaten track of navigators nor from time-honored practices. He usually had good reasons, however, for such deviations. He was a keen observer and was quick to translate his observations into practical seamanship, as is borne out by the following:

My voyages being principally made for sealing or whaling, caused me to keep close into the coast whereby I had the best opportunities for observing the weather, currents, tides, &c.; in fact my voyages depended partly on these and it stood me in hand to make myself acquainted with them.[31]

The ship registers and enrollments for the Custom House at Newport, Rhode Island, list William H. Smyley as part owner at one time or another of five different vessels. This does not include vessels owned after 1850 while stationed at Port Stanley.

It appears that Smyley's first voyage to the South Shetlands as master of a ship was made in 1836 in the schooner *Sailor's Return*. Fragmentary evidence indicates that he made seven other sealing voyages between then and 1850. From these bits of information we have some insight into the man.

In the first of two voyages in the *Sailor's Return* Smyley sailed from Newport on July 3, 1836, accompanied by the schooner *Geneva* commanded by Captain A. Padack. Keeping close in to the "hump" of Brazil, he reached Puerto Deseado (47° 38' S, 66° W) in the Province of Santa Cruz, Argentina, on September 6. Here he waited 20 days for the *Geneva* which had taken the conventional sailing route. Sealing was carried on at both the Falklands and the South Shetlands. The next year Smyley left Newport on September 22, and 30 days later the *Sail-*

or's Return was wrecked on a reef as he was rounding Cabo de São Roque (Cape St. Roque), "bound in to Rio Grande North," (probably modern Natal) to repair the sheathing on the schooner.[32]

As master and part owner of the schooner *Benjamin de Wolf,* Smyley sailed from Newport on April 2, 1839, bound for the Falkland Islands. Sailing between the islands of Fernando de Noronha and the mainland, he made a very fast passage, reaching Port Egmont in the Falklands on June 1, 41 days and eight hours out of Newport. He ended the season on the coast of Patagonia, where he found no other American vessel. He left Pernambuco (Recife), Brazil, on February 19, and on March 27, 1840, sailed into Newport with 1375 fur sealskins and 150 hair sealskins. The sealing industry was at a low ebb during the years that Smyley was engaged in it. As a result of the heavy slaughter in the South Shetlands from 1820 to 1822, the fur seals were decimated. After the boom had collapsed in the 1820s the number of sealing vessels declined to one or two a year and sometimes none. Thus, the fur seal was able to make a partial recovery only to become almost extinct following the slaughter in the 1870s. Smyley's report of no American vessels on the coast of Patagonia and his comparatively small cargo are a reflection of the state of the business in the late 1830s. Smyley made a second voyage in the *Benjamin de Wolf* in 1840-41, apparently to the coast of Patagonia and the Falklands.

Smyley made two voyages in the schooner *Ohio.* The first, in 1841-42, will be discussed in more detail below. For the second voyage, Smyley became part owner of the schooner and of her consort, the 60-ton schooner *Sarah Ann* which was commanded by Captain Richard Sydney Gough. They sailed from Newport on September 29, 1842, and Smyley, unlike Gough, took his usual course close in to the "hump" of Brazil. He passed between Atol des Rocas and Cabo de São Roque and was eight miles off the coast at Recife in 30 days from Newport. Thirty days later, after two stops on the coast of Brazil, totaling six days, he was at the mouth of the Rio Negro. On this voyage he made a search for the La Agle Shoal. He did not report whether this was in the hope of finding seals on rocks that might be above water or whether it was merely to locate definitely a reported danger. He reported to Maury:

I have cruised for the above mentioned shoal several times, taking a good departure from the Jasans and from New Island in the Falklands, and crossed to Cape Virginis and back in the long summer days, seeing no signs of it. In 1842, I left East Harbor Staten Land, with my consort in company, and steered for the shoal, keeping about eight miles apart, the weather was clear. I kept men at the mast-heads, and saw nothing of it. My observations were to be relied upon; for I had on board three chronometers, which had been well proved at Cape St. John. I kept on for Rio Negro, and on my arrival, again tried my chronometers and found them correct. I am well aware that no such shoal exists.[33]

At the close of the season, on March 27, 1843, the *Ohio* was wrecked on the coast of Rio Negro. Three men were lost and a fourth died later.

Following the loss of the *Ohio,* Smyley apparently stopped sealing and engaged in merchant shipping, for he was both owner and master of the 216-ton brig *America.* At least he was the registered owner when a new register was issued at Newport on August 28, 1845, after the rigging was altered from brig to bark. James W. Smyley was listed as master.[34]

Sailing from Newport on September 10, 1845, Smyley returned to the South Shetlands in the schooner *Catherine*. She was wrecked in 1846, apparently being driven against the cliff-like face of a glacier in a gale. His last sealing voyage was made in the pilot boat *John E. Davidson,* which sailed from New York for Patagonia on July 5, 1849. On the outward voyage part of the crew mutinied, nearly killing the mate and shooting Smyley. He claimed they had shipped at New York with that intent. They did not succeed, however, and he turned the mutineers over to the U. S. Consul at "St. Catherines" (perhaps a port on the province of Santa Catarina, Brazil). Despite his difficulty, he was on the coast of Rio Negro on September 16.

VOYAGE OF THE *OHIO*, 1841-42

As previously stated, the voyage of the *Ohio* to the South Shetlands in 1841-42 has become historically important because of Smyley's discovery of the thermometers left by Captain Foster. The *Ohio* was a 126-ton, two-masted schooner built in Baltimore in 1840.[35] On this voyage Gilbert Chase of Newport was the sole owner. Smyley had no shallop as consort; the *Ohio* being a rather small schooner, a tender was not necessary, especially since seals were too scarce to make it feasible to anchor at one place for several weeks. The ship's company, including Smyley, consisted of 16 men, all residents of Newport.

Captain Smyley sailed from Newport, Rhode Island, July 14, 1841, on his first voyage in the *Ohio*. He set his course for Cabo de São Roque. He kept a sharp lookout for the offlying Atol das Rocas as he approached the cape because of the fog, but he failed to see these low-lying islands. He stopped on the coast of Brazil to pick up recruits. These men apparently were not seamen, but men to do some of the labor of killing and skinning the seals and of salting their skins. He probably followed his usual course, that which he recommended to Maury, staying close to the shore of Patagonia.

> Then I endeavor to keep near enough to see the land until I get well to the south, so as to pass close by Staten Land [Isla de los Estados at the tip of Tierra del Fuego], . . . When bound to the Shetlands from the Cape or from Staten Land (which is our rendezvous on account of getting wood there to last until our return), . . .[36]

It is not known whether Smyley proceeded directly to the South Shetlands from Staten Island or hunted seals for a time on the coast of Tierra del Fuego. Lieutenant Wilkes stated that Smyley was at Deception Island in February 1842.[37] He must have known this from Smyley's visit with Commodore Perry at the New York Navy Yard, for Smyley gives no date in the letter he sent to Wilkes.

Lieutenant Robert E. Johnson was in command of the *Sea Gull* of the U. S. Exploring Expedition when it visited Deception Island in March 1839. Wilkes had ordered Johnson to search for the maximum and minimum thermometers which had been left there in 1829 by Captain Henry Foster of the British *Chanticleer* expedition. Lieutenant Johnson failed to find the thermometers, but he left a bottle containing a record of his visit, tied to a flagstaff. It was this bottle which Captain Smyley found in 1842 which led him to search for and find the thermometers, and through Johnson's message he knew of Wilkes' interest in them.

When Captain Smyley picked up the maximum thermometer, the indicator slipped, thus making the reading unreliable. Handling the minimum thermometer more carefully, he was able to get an accurate reading of $-5°$ F. On his return northward Captain Smyley left the message of Lieutenant Johnson with Commodore Morris, commandant of the South Atlantic Squadron of the Navy, based at Rio de Janeiro. At New York he gave the bottle to Commodore Perry and apparently related his experience to him. In reply to an inquiry by Wilkes, Smyley wrote him a letter containing an account of his visit to Deception Island. From this Wilkes extracted the facts which he published in his *Narrative* of the U. S. Exploring Expedition.[38] In this way the scientific world learned of the fact that Smyley had found the thermometers. Until 1898 the minimum temperature of $-5°$ F reported by Smyley was the lowest temperature recorded in Antarctica.[39] Consequently, the incident of Smyley's visit to Deception Island was often referred to, giving him a place in Antarctic history (Fig. 3).

Another fact reported by Smyley concerning this visit has further insured his place in history. As he left Deception Island it was in a state of eruption, and his description, reported by Wilkes, is the first we have of such an event on this breeched volcanic caldera: ". . ., the whole side of Deception Island appeared as if on fire. He counted thirteen volcanoes in action. He is of opinion that the island is undergoing many changes."[40]

Beginning with Captain Robert Fildes in 1821, many visitors to Deception Island, sealers, explorers, and scientists, have described the hot springs, fumaroles, and other evidences of volcanism found there. Therefore, it might be thought that Smyley's description was just another layman's (and therefore exaggerated) account in which fumaroles were confused with volcanic vents. Geological investigations in recent years and eruptions in 1967 and 1969, however, show Smyley's description to be quite plausible, and geologists now credit him with having witnessed the first of three volcanic eruptions of Deception Island in historic time.[41]

The initial stages of the eruption which began December 4, 1967 were witnessed by personnel at Argentine, British, and Chilean bases located on the shores of Port Foster before they were evacuated. The principal result of the 1967 eruption was the formation in Telefon Bay of an oval-shaped island, about a half mile (934 m) long and a third of a mile (366 m) wide, consisting of three closely spaced craters. The central and principal crater is 550 feet (170 m) in diameter and rises 200 feet (62 m) above sea level. A fourth crater developed on the shore of Telefon Bay, 1.2 miles east of the new island.[42]

The eruption which began on February 21, 1969, was witnessed by five members of the British Antarctic Survey at Whalers Bay before they were evacuated by a Chilean helicopter crew. Smyley's description of the 1842 eruption has relevance to the 1969 eruption which developed along a great fissure, 8 miles (5 km) long, about 1000 feet (300 m) above sea level on the western slopes of Mount

Pond, i.e., the eastern shore of Port Foster.[43] Some 20 vents erupted along this fissure, giving credibility to Smyley's report of 13 in 1842. Thus, while Smyley's reported temperature is no longer relevant, his account of the eruption at Deception is taking on new significance.

From his letters we know that Captain Smyley was on occasions farther south than Deception Island. At one time he was at least as far south as 66° S. Since he said that he had tried the minimum thermometer later in a higher latitude, we can assume that he went south after he left Deception Island in February 1842. Moreover, since he reported his conclusions regarding "Palmer Land" to Wilkes, it is not improbable that he sailed among the islands of the Palmer Archipelago in February or March 1842, especially since the straits are more likely to be ice-free at this season than at any other.

Smyley said that he had sailed in the straits off "Palmer Land" in sight of Pisgah of the Americans and Smith Island of the English. He said, "This is only a sound, but farther South there is a passage and also one to the Eastward but it is both narrow and Dangerous."[44] Could the passage to the eastward be Gerlache Strait? Gerlache Strait would certainly appear narrow and dangerous. Perhaps what he calls only a sound in sight of Smith Island is Dallmann Bay, and the passage farther south would be Bismarck Strait. In his letter to Maury, Captain Smyley said, "For instance, many suppose that Palmer's Land is a continent, and connects with the land laid down by Wilkes; however, this is not the case, for I have sailed round Palmer's Land and far south of it."[45] In the letter to Wilkes he does not imply that he sailed around the Palmer Archipelago, but only in the straits between the islands. To Wilkes he wrote, "There is in the 66 degree another passage by which you may pass and from there shape your course to Cape Horn as I have done myself when I left the Isle of Deception."[46] This is difficult to interpret, but like his statement that he had tried the minimum thermometer at a higher latitude, it indicates that after leaving Deception Island in 1842 Captain Smyley sailed southwesterly along the Palmer Archipelago. The passage in latitude 66° S would have to be Pendleton Strait, and Captain Smyley implies that he sailed from there to Cape Horn after he had been at Deception. If he actually entered Pendleton Strait and sailed north inside the Palmer Archipelago, he must have had very favorable ice conditions. In that case, of course, he would have sailed through Gerlache Strait. It is difficult, though, to see how he could have thought of the Antarctic Peninsula as anything but a part of the mainland unless the numerous bays and coves gave the same impression as the channels between the islands of the Palmer Archipelago.

Captain Smyley must not have had very good luck finding seals to have gone so far afield in search of them. He probably combed his old hunting ground, the coast of Patagonia, on his voyage home. He arrived at Rio de Janeiro April 2, 1842. We do not know what he did there, but he remained until June 22, during which time four men deserted. There must not have been much of value in the cargo to be shared for them to have deserted at this point. While at Rio Smyley picked up a cargo of coffee, another indication that he did not have a hold full of sealskins. It is improbable that Brazil, with its tropical climate, would have afforded much of a market for furs. We cannot tell how much coffee he carried, for the Foreign Tonnage Book of the New York Custom House listed 126 tons, which was the capacity of the schooner. The inward cargo manifests which should give more details apparently have been lost. The record gives no indication of the nature of the cargo, but the "Marine List" of the *New York Express* for July 28, 1842, notes the arrival of the schooner *Ohio* from Rio with coffee. At the time Smyley left Rio de Janeiro there was a great deal of civil unrest in the city due to a reported insurrection in São Paulo. This, too, was reported in a separate article in the *Express*.

Captain Smyley arrived at New York on July 28, 1842. Here he reported to the Navy Yard and turned in the bottle he had found at Deception Island, at the same time giving an account of the voyage. He later took on a cargo of corn and arrived with it back in Newport on August 13, 1842.

Smyley's voyages to the southern hemisphere between 1842 and 1850, including two shipwrecks, have already been mentioned. In 1850 Smyley's career took what a century later appears to have been a sudden and surprising turn.

SMYLEY, COMMERCIAL AGENT

On September 12, 1850, Secretary of State Daniel Webster appointed William H. Smyley of Newport, Rhode Island, United States Commercial Agent at Port Stanley in the Falkland Islands. Strangely, the record of his appointment is not accompanied by a written application by Smyley nor by letters recommending him for the position. A search of the records of the Department of State where such documents would likely be found in the National Archives has uncovered none. It is possible that Smyley was in Washington in the summer of 1850 and made an application in person, but available information does not indicate this. The lack of recommendations can partly be explained by the fact that there would be no competition for a post as unattractive as Port Stanley. Also, Smyley was not unknown in official Washington in 1850, as a letter from Elisha Whittlesey, Comptroller of the Treasury, to Lieutenant Maury indicates. (See Appendix B of this chapter.)

Smyley's claim for reimbursement for $287.50, due him from the United States under the Distressed Seaman's Act, for expenditures for relief of his crew of the *Ohio* after it was wrecked in 1843 was not settled until the summer of 1850.[47] Correspondence between Smyley and Whittlesey indicates that Smyley intended to sail again for the southern hemisphere in the early autumn of 1850. So does Smyley's letter of September 2, 1850, to Maury.[48]

Smyley's service as Commercial Agent at Port Stanley had no direct connection with the Antarctic, and only a brief summary can be given here. His letters to the Department of State, generally two or three a year, are a record of his activities and of his observations of affairs at the Falklands and of that whole region.[49] His reports indicate that he was accepted socially on a personal basis by settlers and officials at Port Stanley, but officially he seems to have been kept in some state of unrecognized limbo as a reaction to the United States' not recognizing British sovereignty over the Falkland Islands. Not many American vessels called at Port Stanley between 1850 and 1868, and those that did were generally in a condition of distress. Whalers and sealers were more likely to put in to some harbor a long way from the settlement. They sought water, an opportunity to repair their vessels, and supplies of fresh meat and eggs. The latter items were obtained by hunting wild waterfowl, rabbits, and semiwild bullocks. This was declared illegal by the Governor although, as Smyley explained to Secretary of State William L. Marcy, they were the offspring of animals left by Americans.[50] Smyley was informing the Secretary of the arrest of Captain Clift of the ship *Hudson* of Mystic, Connecticut, one of two guano boats that had reached the Falklands in distress in October 1853. Smyley had defended Clift, insisting the captain had paid for the bullocks. He also considered the Governor's decree unjust.

During his years at Port Stanley, Smyley maintained his own vessel on which he cruised from Cape Horn to the Rio Negro on the coast of Patagonia, aiding shipwrecked seamen. There were a considerable number of shipwrecks along the coast of South America, and other vessels came into whatever harbor they could make in the Falklands in such poor shape as to be condemned. Smyley used his vessel to take crews from such vessels to Montevideo for passage home. In other cases he obtained supplies for the repair of ships that were not available at Port Stanley. Although he was a United States Commercial Agent, his assistance was given to all. For rescuing a lone survivor of the Belgian ship *Leopold* in 1858 he received an engraved spyglass from the Belgian government. For going to the aid of British missionaries on Tierra del Fuego he was given an inscribed copy of the Scriptures by a London missionary society.

Smyley's family lived with him at Port Stanley. He made two visits to the United States, one in 1855-1856 and another in 1863. He died suddenly of cholera at Montevideo on February 15, 1868. At the time he owned two schooners and two houses in Port Stanley.

APPENDIXES

APPENDIX A*

Letter from Smyley to Wilkes

NEWPORT, R. I. *Aug. 15th 1842*

MY DEAR SIR: The letter you Sent to Me Reached me but yesterday I Did not leave New York until the last of the week and I hope you will not think [me] Neglegent for twas out of my power to answer you before the thermometer when I took it up Stood at five Deg. below zero the heat could not be ascertained accurate as the note fell Some Degrees whilst lifting it up — the Cold May be Depended on for I found it to work and perform well afterwards in a higher Latitude. The land to the Southward Called palmers land is not a Continent but Composed of islands for I have sailed in the Strates off in sight of pisgy [Mount Pisgah Island] of the Americans & Smith Island of the English this is only a Sound but farther South there is a passage and also one to the Eastward but it is both narrow and Dangerous there is in the 66 Deg. another passage by which you may pass and from there Shap [shape] your course to Cape horn as I have Done myself When I left the Isle of Deception the South Side of the Isle was all on fire there being 13 volcanoes and many other places where you might pick up the

Sinders the water was boiling hot in many places in the harbour. I find the Isle is much altered Since my last voige [voyage] and the former I made to that place. I am bound in a short time to that part of the world again an should you want me to see to anything out in that part of the world pleas let me know and If it is in my power to do it it will be Done with pleasure. My voige is for Seal & Eliphant Oil and perhaps it might be in your power to give me Some information if you fell in with any and if not it might Save me much labour and trouble if you Should Even tell me if there is not any in your rout [route] I will Do any thing for the benefit of you or the government and would be glad to Receive any information appertaining to my voig which you may have in your power to give me — the bottle I brought away from the Shetlands I gave to Commodore Perry at New York the Letter left by the Sea Gull is I presume in Washington as I gave it to Commodore Morris at Rio Janeiro I will sail in about Three weeks so if you have any Commands please forward and they will be attended to with pleasure

I remain Your Most Obedient Servant

W. H. SMYLEY

Captain Charles Wilkes US Navy

APPENDIX B*

Letter From Whittlesey to Maury

TREASURY DEPARTMENT
COMPTROLLERS OFFICE
August 23, 1850

Lieut. MATTHEW F. MAURY
United States Navy
at the Observatory

SIR: Captain W. H. Smyley of Newport Rhode Island has navigated the South Seas for twenty two successive years — and has been so far as to latitude 76 degrees. He sets sail again, in a few days, and he offers to render any service for his country that it may be in his power to perform. I have no personal acquaintance with him, but I was led to form a very favorable opinion of him from a letter he wrote to me on business. Mr. Gordon formerly and Mr. Parks more recently consul at Rio Janiero were acquainted with him at their consulates, and they speak of him in the highest terms of commendation, for his strong, good, and unerring sense, for his humanity, fidelty, energy, and fearless courage. Can he be of any service to you, by collecting information? Can you render him any assistance by charts or other publication. His frankness gained my confidence.

Most Sincerely
Yours

ELISHA WHITTLESEY.

APPENDIX C*

Letter From Smyley to Whittlesey

NEWPORT, R. I. *Aug the 30 1850*

Mr. Whittlesey

DEAR SIR: I have just arrived from a Short Cruise of three Days in my vessail. I found your letters waiting for me. I also Rec'd the Charts of Lieut. Maury. I will send

* Letter files of area 9, Naval Records Section, Collection of the Office of Naval Records and Library, Record Group 45, U. S. National Archives. All apparent errors checked and the above was found to be an exact copy of the original letter. Brackets are inserted by the author.

him what Information I can. I am Sorry I have not log books to Send him but as he is a Sailor & a man of Experience he will Consider this a sufficient Excuse. I was Cast away in the Sailors Return in 1838 on the Shoals of Cape St. Roque given me scarce time to save my crue. I was Cast away in the Schooner Ohio on the Coast of Patagonia in 1843 with Bare time to Save my Crue and only succeeded in Doing So by taking part of them on the spars of the vessail nine miles. in 1846 I was Drove on shore in a tremendous Gale parting both Chains the sea swept both Boats off Deck & Drove the vessail against the Ice Bergs Causing almost Instintaneous loss. however I have Some journals and Memorandums as soon as I can find them I will give him what information I can. As for my passages they stand unrivaled for shortness through out the world. Even my last passage home is the quickest they have had Except what I have made my Self. I have bare time to Send you this you can send it to Mr. Maury & twill do to let him know that I have Re'd the Charts & that I will send him what Information I can

Please Excuse My Scrawl as it is done in haste & Believe Me Dear Sir to be your Most Obedient Servant.

W. H. SMYLEY

To The Honorable
ELISHA WHITTLESEY *Comptroller*

NOTES

1. Maury had distinguished forebears, and among his relatives were prominent and successful planters and professional men. Three of several biographies of Maury are listed in the bibliography of this chapter. The most recent and most complete is by Frances Leigh Williams, *Matthew Fontaine Maury, Scientist of the Sea* (New Brunswick, N. J., 1963).

2. *Ibid.*, p. 119.

3. "On the Navigation of Cape Horn," *Amer. Jour. of Science and Arts.*, vol. 26, July, 1834, pp. 54-63; "Plan of an Instrument for Finding the True Lunar Distance," *Ibid.*, pp. 63-65; *A New Theoretical and Practical Treatise on Navigation, . . .* (Philadelphia, 1836). In 1844, by order of the Secretary of the Navy, a second edition (1843) became the standard textbook for midshipmen.

4. Williams, *op. cit.*, pp. 53-54, 69-70, 87, 97-98, 103.

5. *Ibid.*, pp. 125-143.

6. Matthew Fontaine Maury, *The Physical Geography of the Sea* (New York, 1856) 5th ed., pp. 257-258 and Plate V.

Matthew Fontaine Maury, *The Physical Geography of the Sea and Its Meteorology*, edited by John Leighly (Cambridge, 1963), pp. 373 and Plate II. This is a republication of the 8th and last American edition, 1859, and is hereinafter referred to as John Leighly.

7. *Wind and Current Charts*, Series A. *Track Charts, Atlantic Ocean North*, Sheet 1, 1847. Ultimately there were 6 series of charts: A. *Track Charts*, B. *Trade Wind Charts*, C. *Pilot Charts*, D. *Thermal Sheets*, E. *Storm and Rain Charts*, and F. *Whale Chart of the World*, issued between 1847 and 1860, with as many as 1 to 8 charts in a series. See Williams, *op. cit.*, pp. 693-696.

8. Williams, *op. cit.*, pp. 179-180.

9. *Explanations and Sailing Directions to Accompany the Wind and Current Charts*, 3rd ed. (Washington, 1851). The first and second editions are considered to be *Notice to Mariners* (Washington, 1850), 18 pp. and (Washington, 1850) 51 pp., respectively. Numbered editions followed annually from the 3rd in 1851 to the 7th in 1855. The 8th edition was published in two volumes, volume 1 in 1858, and volume 2 in 1859. All were published in Washington except the 6th, which was published in Philadelphia in 1854.

10. Williams, *op. cit.*, p. 218 and footnote 116, p. 546.

11. *Ibid.*, pp. 696-701; Maury, *The Physical Geography of the Sea, op. cit.* Several American and foreign editions were published and reprinted from 1855 to 1883.

12. See Leighly, *op. cit.*, pp. xxi, xxviii-xxix. Harpeth Academy at Franklin, Tennessee, which Maury attended for four years prior to entering the Navy, apparently was a good school

---

* File of miscellaneous letters to the Director of the Naval Observatory, Aug. 1, 1850-Mar. 11, 1851, part 1, Records of the Naval Observatory, Record Group 78, U. S. National Archives.

for its time. Neither there nor as a midshipman did Maury receive training in basic physical theory. He tried to compensate for this by private study from whatever textbooks were available to him, but this was inadequate for the level on which Maury was working.

13. *Ibid.*, pp. xvi-xxix.

14. *Whale Chart of the World*, Series F (of Wind and Current Charts) Sheet 1, (Washington, 1852) Sheets 2, 3, and 4, n.d.; Maury, *Physical Geography of the Sea, op. cit.*, pp. 146-147; *Leighly, op. cit.*, pp. 371-372.

15. Leighly, *op. cit.*, Chap. 21, "The Antarctic Regions and Their Climatology," pp. 406-418. Chap. 20, "Winds of the Southern Hemisphere," pp. 389-405 involves Antarctica to a considerable extent. Antarctica is also discussed on pages 166-167 and 323-325. Plate X is a map of the southern hemisphere south of 40°S on a polar equidistant projection. See also Fig. 2, p. 154. As Leighly points out (pp. xv-xvi), none of the editions of *The Physical Geography of the Sea* is well organized, and there is a great deal of repetition.

16. *Ibid.*, figs. 13 and 14, p. 409.

17. *Ibid.*, pp. 417-418.

18. Herman R. Friis, "Matthew Fontaine Maury, Captain U. S. Navy, American Pioneer in Polar Research and Progenitor of the International Geophysical Year Program in the Antarctic, 1840-1860," *Bulletin, U. S. Antarctic Projects Officer*, vol. 1, No. 6, February, 1960, pp. 23-29 (see p. 26).
   Matthew Fontaine Maury, "On the Physical Geography of the Sea, in Connection with the Antarctic Regions," Amer. Geogr. and Stat. Soc. *Proceedings*, vol. 5, 1861, pp. 22-26.

19. Friis, *ibid.*, p. 26. For this and other correspondence on this subject, see Registry of Letters Sent, Records of the Naval Observatory, Record Group 78, U. S. National Archives.

20. *Ibid.*, p. 27.

21. *Ibid.*, p. 28. See also *Report of the 30th Meeting of the British Association for the Advancement of Science*, 1860, vol. 30, Notices and Abstracts, Section on Meteorology (London, 1861), pp. 44-48. Includes 2 charts, 1 graph, and 2 maps, similar to those published in the last American edition of *Physical Geography of the Sea*. Maury's letter to Lord Wrottesley, pp. 44-46.

22. Hugh Robert Mill, *Siege of the South Pole* (New York, 1905), p. 336. See also Williams, *op. cit.*, pp. 350-351.

23. Williams, *op. cit.*, p. 360.

24. Mill, *op. cit.*, pp. 336-338. A partial quotation of the paper. Matthew Fontaine Maury, "On Importance of an Expedition to the Antarctic Regions for Meteorological and other Scientific Purposes," *Report of the 31st Meeting of the British A.A.S.*, vol. 31, Notices and Abstracts, Section on Meteorology (London, 1862), pp. 65-72.

25. Mill, *op. cit.*, p. 334. Mill's long years of personal acquaintance with Antarctic explorers can be judged by reading Chap. 7, p. 159, of *Hugh Robert Mill, an Autobiography* (London, 1951). Mill (1861-1950) wrote "It is a wonderful thought that I knew Joseph Hooker, who sailed for the Antarctic in 1839, when only sailing-ships could be used for travelling or carrying communications, and that I lived to hear in my own study the very voice of Admiral Byrd on the loudspeaker of my radio-set from the remoteness of his winter-quarters whither he had travelled by tractor and aeroplane."

26. The international undertaking for the observation of the transit of Venus (see Chapter 14 for the United States role) in 1874 stemmed from activity in the 18th century, and Maury had no relation to it.

27. Mill, *op. cit.*, pp. 340-342, 364-365; Jannette Mirsky, *To the Arctic* (New York, 1948), pp. 185-186; A. W. Greeley, *Handbook of Polar Discoveries* (Boston, 1910) 5th ed., pp. 221-222; Georg Neumayer, *Results of the Meteorological Observations Taken in the Colony of Victoria during the Years 1859-1862* (Melbourne, 1864).

28. One station was located at Point Barrow, Alaska, under Lt. P. H. Ray. The other was established on Ellesmere Island by Maj. A. W. Greeley. Because of mismanagement and poor leadership of the proposed relief expedition, 20 of the 26 men under Greeley perished.

29. For a brief summary of these activities see Brian Roberts, "International Organizations for Polar Exploration," *Polar Record*, vol. 5, Nos. 37-38, January-July, 1949, pp. 332-334.

30. Maury, *Sailing Directions, op. cit.*, 5th ed., 1853, p. 411. From a letter and communication from Smyley to Maury, dated Newport, Rhode Island, September 2, 1850, written on the abstract log forms. Original in Abstract Log Collection of Matthew Fontaine Maury, Record Group 27, Records of the Weather Bureau, U. S. National Archives.

31. *Ibid.*

32. *Ibid.*, p. 408.

33. *Ibid.*, p. 411.

34. *Ship Registers and Enrollments of Newport, Rhode Island, 1790-1939, Ship Documents of Rhode Island,* vol. I., Works Progress Administration (Providence, 1941), p. 26.

35. *Ibid.*, p. 474.

36. Maury, *Sailing Directions, op. cit.*, p. 411.

37. Charles Wilkes, *Narrative of the United States Exploring Expedition During the Years 1838, 1839, 1840, 1841, 1842* (Philadelphia, 1845), vol. 1, p. 144.

38. *Ibid.*, pp. 144-145. Unfortunately, in Wilkes' *Narrative* the name is misspelled Smiley, and until *Geographic Names of Antarctica,* Gazetteer No. 14, U. S. Board on Geographic Names (Washington, 1956), was published all subsequent writers, with the exception of Maury, used the incorrect form.

39. The first scientific expedition to winter in the Antarctic was the Belgian expedition led by Lt. Adrien de Gerlache when his ship, the *Belgica,* was beset within sight of Alexander Island and drifted across Bellingshausen Sea from March 3, 1898 to March 14, 1899, before it was freed. A minimum temperature of ⁻45.6°F was recorded on September 8, 1898.

40. Wilkes, *Narrative, op. cit.,* p. 145. Smyley's letter to Wilkes is included in the appendix to this chapter to provide a copy of his own words describing the eruption and because there has been speculation concerning what the letter contained relative to other matters.

41. Raymond J. Adie, "Geological History," *Antarctic Research,* Sir Raymond Priestley, Raymond J. Adie, and G. DeQ. Robin, eds. (London, 1964), pp. 136-137; D. D. Hawkes, "Geology of the South Shetland Islands: II, The Geology and Petrology of Deception Island," *Falkland Islands Dependencies Survey Scientific Reports,* No. 27, 1961, 43 pp. It was formerly thought that the caldera resulted from the collapse of a cone built from a single vent. Evidence cited by Hawkes supports his contention that it was formed by eruptions from as many as four vents, followed by collapse along a series of arcuate faults. Three later eruptions have occurred along these faults.

42. "Volcanic Activity at Deception Island, South Shetland Islands, 1967," *Polar Record,* vol. 14, No. 89, May, 1968, pp. 229-230; Eduardo Valenzuela A., Leonidas Chavez B., and Francisco Munizago V., "Informe Preliminar Sobre La Erupcion de Isla Decepcion Ocurrida en Diciembre de 1967," *Instituto Antartico Chileno, Boletin* No. 3, Mayo 1968, pp. 5-16; P. E. Baker, "Investigations of the 1967 and 1969 Volcanic Eruptions on Deception Island, South Shetland Islands," *Polar Record,* vol. 14, No. 93, September, 1969, pp. 823-827.

43. Baker, *Ibid.,* pp. 825-826; "Deception Island Eruption," *Antarctic Journal of the United States,* vol. 4, No. 3, May-June, 1969, pp. 87.

44. Letter of August 15, 1842, from Smyley to Wilkes. See Appendix A of this chapter.

45. Maury, *Sailing Directions, op. cit.,* p. 413.

46. Letter of August 15, 1842, *op. cit.*

47. Report No. 7537, Diplomatic and Consular Accounts, Fifth Auditor's Office, Legislative and Fiscal Records Section, U. S. National Archives, Record Group 36.

48. This letter accompanied material on Abstract Log forms but was not published in the *Sailing Directions.* See note 30, above.

49. See Despatches from United States Consuls in Port Stanley, Falkland Islands, vol. 1, May 8, 1851-December 31, 1875. General Records of the Department of State, Record Group 59. These despatches have been microfilmed by the National Archives as Microcopy T-480, Roll 1.

50. *Ibid.,* letter dated March 20, 1854.

BIBLIOGRAPHY

PUBLISHED MATERIAL

Anonymous, "Volcanic Activity at Deception Island, South Shetland Islands, 1967," *Polar Record,* vol. 14, No. 89, May, 1968, pp. 229-230.

——, "Deception Island Eruption," *Antarctic Journal of the United States,* vol. 4, No. 3, May-June, 1969, p. 87.

Adie, Raymond J., "Geological History," *Antarctic Research,* Sir Raymond Priestley, Raymond J. Adie, and G. deQ. Robin, eds. (London, Butterworths, 1964), pp. 118-162. (See pp. 136-137.)

Arctowski, Henry, "The Antarctic Voyage of the 'Belgica' During the Years 1897, 1898, and 1899," *Geographical Journal,* vol. 18, No. 4, October, 1901, pp. 353-390. (See page 368.)

Baker, P. E., "Investigations of the 1967 and 1969 Volcanic Eruptions on Deception Island, South Shetland Islands," *Polar Record,* vol. 14, No. 93, September, 1969, pp. 823-827.

Balch, Edwin Swift, *Antarctica* (Philadelphia, Allen, Lane and Scott, 1902) 230 pp., map. (See pp. 186-187, 190-191.)

Christie, E. W. Hunter, *The Antarctic Problem* (London, George Allen & Unwin, 1951) 336 pp., maps. (See page 124.)

Fricker, Karl, *The Antarctic Regions* (New York, Macmillan, 1900) xii, 292 pp., map. (See pp. 117-118.)

Friis, Herman R., "Matthew Fontaine Maury, Captain U. S. Navy, American Pioneer in Polar Research and Progenitor of the International Geophysical Year Program in the Antarctic, 1840-1860," *Bulletin, U. S. Antarctic Projects Officer,* vol. 1, No. 6, February, 1960, pp. 23-29.

Hawkes, D. D., "Geology of the South Shetland Islands: II, The Geology and Petrology of Deception Island," *Falkland Islands Dependencies Survey Scientific Reports,* No. 27, 1961, 43 pp.

Hobbs, William Herbert, "The Discoveries of Antarctica within the American Sector, as Revealed by Maps and Documents," *Transactions, American Philosophical Society,* new series, vol. 31, Part I, January, 1939, 71 pp., 31 plates. (See pp. 61-62.)

Jahns, Patricia, *Matthew Fontaine Maury & Joseph Henry, Scientists of the Civil War* (New York, Hastings House, 1961) xii and 308 pp.

Lewis, Charles L., *Matthew Fontaine Maury, The Pathfinder of the Seas* (Annapolis, United States Naval Institute, 1927) xviii and 263 pp., illus.

Maury, Matthew Fontaine, "On the Navigation of Cape Horn," *American Journal of Science and Arts,* vol. 26, July, 1834, pp. 54-63.

——, "Plan of an Instrument for Finding the True Lunar Distance," *American Journal of Science and Arts,* vol. 26, July, 1834, pp. 63-65.

——, *A New Theoretical and Practical Treatise on Navigation; . . .* (Philadelphia, Key and Biddle, 1836).

——, *Explanations and Sailing Directions to Accompany the Wind and Current Charts,* Fifth ed. (Washington, C. Alexander, 1853), pp. 492, plates; Supp. xxxx and 8 plates.

——, *The Physical Geography of the Sea,* Fifth ed., enlarged and improved (New York, Harper & Brothers, 1856) pp. xxiv and 287 pp. consecutive pagination, 8 plates.

——, "On the Physical Geography of the Sea, in Connection with the Antarctic Regions," *American Geographical and Statistical Society Proceedings,* vol. 5, 1861, pp. 22-26.

——, "On the Climates of the Antarctic Regions, as Indicated by Observations Upon the Height of the Barometer and Directions of the Winds at Sea," *Report of the 30th Meeting of the British Association for the Advancement of Science, 1860,* vol. 30 (London, 1861), pp. 44-48.

——, "On Importance of an Expedition to the Antarctic Regions for Meteorological and other Scientific Purposes," *Report of the 31st Meeting of the British Association for the Advancement of Science,* 1861 (London, 1862), pp. 65-72.

——, *The Physical Geography of the Sea and Its Meteorology,* edited by John Leighly (Cambridge, Harvard University Press, 1963) republication of eighth ed., 1859, xxxii and 432 pp. 10 plates.

Mill, Hugh Robert, *The Siege of the South Pole* (New York, Frederick A. Stokes, 1905), xvi, 455 pp., map. (See pp. 223, 334-342.)

Murray, George, ed., *The Antarctic Manual* (London, Royal Geographical Society, 1901), xvi and 586 pp., map, biblogr. (See pp. 43-45.)

New York Express, July 28, 1842.

The Newport Mercury, July 30, 1842.

Ship Documents of Rhode Island, vol. I, *Ship Registers and Enrollments of Newport, Rhode Island, 1790-1939* (Providence, 1941), The National Archives Project, Works Progress Administration, vii, 810 pp., mimeographed. (See p. 474.)

Wilkes, Charles, *Narrative of the United States Exploring Expedition During the Years 1838, 1839, 1840, 1841, 1842* (Philadelphia, Sea and Blanchard, 1845), 5 vols., vol. I, xii, 434 pp. (See pp. 144-145.)

Williams, Frances Leigh, *Matthew Fontaine Maury, Scientist of the Sea* (New Brunswick, Rutgers University Press, 1963), xxii and 720 pp. illus., bibliogr.

MANUSCRIPT MATERIAL

Crew list of the schooner *Ohio,* surrendered at the custom office in New York, July 28, 1842. Custom House Records, New York, crew lists, Records of the Bureau of Customs, Record Group 36, U. S. National Archives.

Foreign Tonnage Book, Arrivals, Port of New York, 1841-1842. Records of the Bureau of Customs, Record Group 36, U. S. National Archives.

Letter from William H. Smyley to Lt. M. F. Maury, September 2, 1850, including lengthy comments on his several voyages. Filed with Maury's Abstract Logs with the Records of the Weather Bureau, Record Group 27, U. S. National Archives. These comments were published by Maury in his *Explanations and Sailing Directions . . .*, listed above.

Letter from William H. Smyley to Elisha Whittlesey, Comptroller, and forwarded to Lieutenant Maury, August 30, 1850. (See Appendix C of this chapter.) Miscellaneous letters to the Director of the Naval Observatory, August 1, 1850-March 11, 1851, Part I, Records of the Naval Observatory, Record Group 78, U. S. National Archives.

Letter from William H. Smyley to Lt. Charles Wilkes, Navy Yard, New York, August 15, 1842. (See Appendix A of this chapter.) Letter File, Area 9, Naval Records Collection of the Office of Naval Records and Library, Record Group 45, U. S. National Archives.

Letter from Elisha Whittlesey, Comptroller, to Lieutenant Maury, Director of the Naval Observatory, August 23, 1850. (See Appendix B of this chapter.) Miscellaneous Letters of the Director of the Naval Observatory, August 1, 1850-March 11, 1851, Part 1, Records of the Naval Observatory, Record Group 78, U. S. National Archives.

Statement of the Account of William H. Smyley for the relief of the crew of the schooner *Ohio*, which vessel was lost on the coast of Patagonia in March 1843. Report No. 7537, Diplomatic and Consular Accounts, Fifth Auditor's Office, Records of the United States General Accounting Office, Record Group 217, U. S. National Archives. This file contains a sworn testament by the mate and a seaman commending Smyley very highly for his conduct at the time the schooner *Ohio* was wrecked in March, 1843, off the mouth of the Rio Negro.

Despatches from United States Consuls in Port Stanley, Falkland Islands, vol. 1, May 8, 1851-December 31, 1875. General Record of the Department of State, Record Group 59. These despatches have been microfilmed by the National Archives as Microcopy T-480, Roll 1.

Letters from M. F. Maury to various individuals at different dates. See Registry of Letters Sent, ("Letter Book," "Record," or "Records."), July, 1842-November 1862. Records of the Naval Observatory, Record Group 78, National Archives.

See also Letters Received, March, 1840-January, 1885, Records of the Naval Observatory, Record Group 78, U. S. National Archives.

12

VOYAGE OF THE BARK *ORIENTAL* AND THE DISCOVERY OF HEARD ISLAND BY CAPTAIN JOHN J. HEARD, 1853

ORGANIZATION AND ACCOMPLISHMENTS OF THE VOYAGE

ESTABLISHMENT AND SIGNIFICANCE OF THE VOYAGE

The voyage of the bark *Oriental* from Boston to Melbourne was essentially a commercial operation, but insofar as Captain John J. Heard was testing the subpolar great circle route recommended by Matthew Fontaine Maury it was a pioneering venture. This penetration into uncharted Antarctic waters resulted in the discovery of Heard Island, which in a few years became the center of an important American sealing industry.

Captain Heard was in the employ of Robinson, Wiggin and Company of Boston, who owned the bark *Oriental.* The voyage of 1853-54 to Melbourne and the East Indies was one of many commercial voyages Captain Heard made for the company to all parts of the world.

Born in Boston in 1809, Captain Heard went to sea as a cabin boy at the age of 12. He rose in the merchant marine to the position of master with the reputation of being a careful, reliable, and efficient sailor.

The ship's company totaled 20, including three passengers, the Captain's wife and two young men, Henry Beal and William Kimball. Mrs. Fidelia Heard kept an interesting diary of the voyage.

The previous chapter has discussed the work of Lieutenant Matthew Fontaine Maury, Director of the U. S. Naval Observatory, who had published his first "Wind and Current Chart of the North Atlantic" in 1847, and early the next year had issued what he called an "Abstract Log for the Use of American Navigators." Devised to secure the cooperation of navigators in gathering information for perfecting the charts, the first edition consisted of some blank forms and ten pages of interpretation and instruction. This publication was later expanded into the "Sailing Directions" which were issued in several editions of hundreds of pages.[1] As we have seen, merchant captains all over the world were immediately impressed by the practical utility of Maury's charts because the routes he recommended greatly shortened the passages between the most frequented ports. Hundreds of the more conscientious mariners agreed to furnish the required data on their future voyages in return for the charts and sailing directions. One of these was Captain Heard.

Common practice at this time in sailing from Europe or the United States to Australia was to round Africa close in to the Cape of Good Hope. Maury, on the other hand, recommended that ships sail south through the mid-Atlantic so as to pass close in to Cape St. Roque, on the "hump" of Brazil, and thence

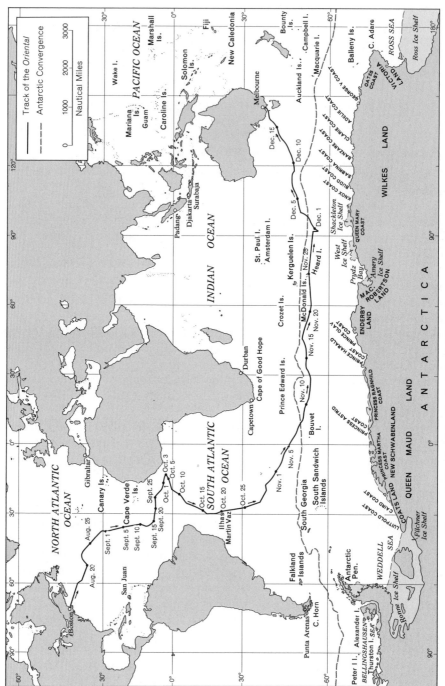

FIGURE 8. Track of the Bark *Oriental* from Boston to Melbourne, 1853.

southeastward past Tristan de Cunha on a great circle route penetrating beyond 50° S. This route was 600 to 800 miles to the west and far to the south
of the Cape of Good Hope.²

OBJECTIVES AND ACCOMPLISHMENTS

On this voyage from Boston to Melbourne, Australia, it was Captain Heard's
intention to follow the new route suggested by Maury and to try for a fast passage.³ As a result, his course in the Indian Ocean was laid far to the south of the
ordinary paths of merchant ships, and even south of the areas frequented by
whalers working out of Kerguelen Island (Fig. 8).

The major accomplishment of the voyage was the discovery of Heard Island
on November 25, 1853, a direct result of penetrating south beyond the usual
track of merchant vessels. Captain Heard took bearings on the east and west
ends of the island which he was able to locate with the aid of a good astronomical observation at noon, but he did not take time to land.

Captain Heard, cooperating with Lieutenant Maury, kept an abstract log
in the prescribed manner. This he sent from Melbourne to Maury at the Naval
Observatory in Washington, where the data would be used for refinement of
subsequent editions of the wind and current charts. Abstract logs for the remainder of the voyage were submitted later.

In the abstract log, as well as in the regular logbook, Captain Heard recorded in tabular form the temperature of the air, the direction of the wind,
and the reading of the barometer at 8 p. m., midnight, 8 a. m., and noon each
day. The position of the ship according to latitude and longitude was given
each noon, and at 8 a. m., daily, the temperature of the water was recorded.
The strength of the winds and the nature of the weather were recorded in the
general remarks. There is an almost daily notation of the direction of the current, and if any current was perceptible, its rate in knots per hour was indicated.
He also noted any special marine phenomena such as the presence of birds,
whales, kelp, or discoloration of the water. Astronomical phenomena such as
shooting stars and displays of aurora australis were recorded, and the variations
in the compass were noted. Such systematic recording of so much data was not
the usual procedure on merchant ships at this time.

That Captain Heard looked on his voyage as a test of Maury's great circle
route is evident from the comments regarding it in his letter to Maury, sent
from Melbourne and dated January 4, 1854. In regard to the penetration to
high southern latitudes he says, "My passage from 11°00′ E to 100°00′ E was
nearly all fog, and the winds irregular. I should not recommend any one coming down at the same season of the year. Since my arrival here I have learned
through several American, and many English shipmasters, that the majority
came along between 40° and 44° S. The steadiness of the winds in these latitudes
are quite an offset to the shorter distance of the Great Circle Route. Icebergs
and foggy weather farther South." [sic]

But many other navigators continued to follow this high southern track, and
several of them also sighted Heard Island. Captain McDonald of the English

ship *Samarang* on January 4, 1854, discovered the McDonald Islands and sighted Heard Island. The latter was also sighted from three other British vessels at the end of 1854: the *Earl of Eglinton,* Captain James S. Hutton, on December 1; the *Herald of the Morning,* Captain John Attwaye, on December 3 and 4; and from the *Lincluden Castle,* Captain Rees, on December 4.[4] In January 1857 Heard Island was sighted again by Captain J. Meyer of the German ship *La Rochelle.*[5] By then, however, the New London sealers had begun operations which were to result in continuous occupation for over 20 years, the first landing being made from the *Corinthian* under Captain E. D. Rogers in March 1855.

Captain Heard's recommendation for not going so far south was subsequently substantiated by the *Challenger* Expedition, which visited Kerguelen and Heard Island in 1874. The following comment appears in the "Narrative" of the expedition.

With reference to the direction of the wind and state of the weather, it may perhaps be as well to draw attention here to the fact that easterly winds seldom if ever blow at Kerguelen Island, but 100 miles south of it and in the neighborhood of Heard Island they are quite common. It would appear, therefore, unadvisable for sailing vessels running down their easting to adopt a route south of Kerguelen, even supposing the chances of meeting icebergs were equal on both sides of the island, but considering the much less danger of meeting those obstructions to navigation on the northern side, there can hardly be a doubt as to which is the preferable route.[6]

ACCOUNT OF THE VOYAGE

The *Oriental* got under way from Boston on Friday, August 12, the towboat and pilot being dropped at 2 p. m. along with a party of well-wishers which included the owners of the vessel.[7] With favorable weather the ship proceeded southeasterly until August 26 by which time it had reached the mid-Atlantic (34°21' W, 42°44' E). From there a southerly course was followed for the next 17 days between 35° to 40° W toward Cape St. Roque, Brazil. The weather was fine, but winds were often light, and for 9 of the 17 days less than 100 miles were logged. Strong breezes on September 8 accounted for 195 miles that day. After the 10th parallel was crossed on September 12 "light airs and calms" permitted little progress. On the 15th, when in 9°04' N, 34°30' W, light airs from the south to west-southwest began. Captain Heard felt that he was then too far westward to tack in that direction and so deviated from Maury's idea of passing close to Cape St. Roque by steering southeastward toward the Gulf of Guinea, getting as far east as 13°32' W before tacking southwestward. The equator was crossed October 8 between 19° and 20° W, 23 days after crossing the ninth parallel. All this time breezes were mostly from a southerly quarter, or calms and light airs prevailed. The ship entered the southeast trades on October 9, and a south-by-west course was laid.

In his letter to Maury from Melbourne (Appendix A) Captain Heard explained why he was forced to deviate from the recommended course, saying, "... I saw some 30 sail in the same fix that I was myself. I think September and October of this year were exceptions to the average, and not any more favorable to your route than to the old, though had I had a clipper ship, I would have risked more and gone to the W. when in 34°."

The *Oriental* sailed in fine weather on a southerly course through the south Atlantic, and the islands of Trinidade and Martin Vas were sighted on October 19. The weather remained such that sails did not have to be taken in or reefed until 2 a.m. October 25. A heavy thunderstorm, including hail, struck the ship in about 36° S, 24° W on the evening of October 27. The next day the course was changed to the southeast so as to pass some distance southwest of Gough Island. The Greenwich meridian was crossed on November 6 about 46° S after having a heavy sea for several days. Fog, sometimes thick, was experienced November 4 through November 8, and on the 8th Captain Heard recorded, "I can't account for fog here unless it be that we have ice not far from us."

Early in the morning of November 9, slightly east of 10° E, the 50th parallel was crossed, and the day was appropriately marked by a heavy sea, strong breezes, spells of fog, and passing snow squalls. That night ice formed on deck. At 5 a.m., November 11, an iceberg, about a quarter mile long and 60 feet high, was seen to the north.

Captain Heard was now sailing an easterly course approximately along the 52nd parallel. Winds were strong, and on only a few days were less than 150 miles logged. On several days, in spite of bad weather, 180 or more miles were covered. The wind shifted from the north-northeast to the southwest on the morning of November 12, and snow fell for 2 hours. From 5 to 6:30 p.m. three icebergs were sighted. Later a gale commenced and there were squalls of snow and a very heavy sea. The next day the wind moderated, but the snow squalls continued, and four more icebergs were seen. The air temperature had been close to freezing for several days, dipping a little below at night and rising a bit above during the day. November 14 and 15 continued with strong winds occasionally rising to gale proportions and interspersed with snow squalls. Four icebergs were seen on the 14th and one on the 15th, when Captain Heard recorded "I should not recommend any one coming down here this month as when it snows you can see but a very short distance. Icebergs are too plenty to run with safety."

Another gale began on the afternoon of November 15, this time from the northwest. The sea was very rough, and snow squalls followed one another in close succession. The gale subsided on November 17, but a thick fog set in and continued through November 19. The weather cleared for a few hours, but on the afternoon of November 20 another snowstorm occurred. The next day was marked by snow squalls with an occasional break in the clouds. Snow squalls, more or less severe, characterized the weather for several days. Such weather made navigation difficult. On November 23 Captain Heard wrote, "I got a moon observation. The first for 14 days." He also closed out that nautical day with a meridian solar observation, the first since November 18, and the latter he considered unreliable. By this time he had been south of the 50th parallel for 14 days, and had only six meridian observations, three of them poor.

The inclement weather was having other adverse effects. In her diary for November 21 Mrs. Heard recorded:

William [presumably William Kimball, one of the passengers] is quite sick with very severe sore throat and dreadful chilblains — he neglected attending to them until they have become very bad. I dressed his feet this morning & the Capt. & I made him a pair of moccasins. His feet are too much swollen to wear his own shoes, neither can he get on a pair of the Captain's.

On Tuesday, November 22, she reported:

An old fashioned snow storm. I hope it will not last a great while. . . . William is much better today. Weather very cold and cheerless, I shall be thankful when we get out of this gloomy latitude.

The next day she wrote:

Same kind of weather that we've had for a month, but we have had good breeses the last 24 hours, & that helps us mightly.

Apparently the crew was also feeling the effect of the weather, for on the night of November 23 the Captain was on deck from midnight until 4:00 a.m. in place of the second mate who had a severe cold. Several hogs had been taken on the voyage to supply fresh meat. One had been butchered on October 16. The voyage through sub-Antarctic waters was apparently pretty hard on the remainder, for on November 23 the logbook reads, "Three of our pigs have died."

If the voyage in the high southern latitudes had been hard till now, a reward was in the offing. The snow squalls had been interrupted briefly by spells of bright sunshine on both November 23 and 24, but Friday, November 25, proved to be exceptionally fine. Had it been otherwise, Captain Heard would probably not have discovered the island which bears his name. For this day the logbook bears the following entry:

Pleasant breeses and passing snow squalls. The latter part clear and the first clear weather that we have had for 20 days. At 8:30 a. m. made the land. First took it for Ice bergs and as no island is laid down on my charts or in the Epitome. At 11:30 a. m. the clouds and hase cleared round and over it revealing it to be an island. At noon the eastern end bore by compass N.N.E., distance 20 miles. The west End bore by compass N. by W. distance about 20. By good observations I make the west end of the Island 74°15′ East, Lat. 53°10′ S. East End Lat. 53°10′ S., Long. 74°40′. Near the center of the Island a High peak 5000 feet. Large quantity of birds about. Lat. Obs. 53°26′ S. Chron. 74°19′ E., Dist by Stat.   149

                                                                            ———
                                                        105 days out   11459

The following is the entry in Mrs. Heard's journal:

Friday 25th. The Sun has been out quite bright nearly all the mor'g which has made us all feel quite elated, but the air is cold yet. At ten o'clk the Capt. was walking on deck, and saw what he supposed to be an immense Iceberg. He came & called me, told me to put on my "chicken fixings," as he called them, dress up warm & come on deck to see it. I hastened to do so, but the atmosphere was hasy & then a heavy snow squall came up which shut it entirely from our view. Not long after the sun shone out again, & I went up again & with the glass tried to get an outline of it to sketch its form, the sun seemed so dassling on the water, & on the tops of the apparent Icebergs covered with snow, that the outline was very indistinct. We were all the time nearing the object & on looking again the Capt. pronounced it to be land. The Island is not laid down on the Chart, neither is it in the Epitome, so we are perhaps the discoverers if so the Capt. will have the privilege of endowing it with a name. I think it must be twin to Desolation Island for it is certainly a Frigid looking place. I suppose it is 15 miles off, & the Capt. judges the height to be 5000 feet — the length of 25 miles.

With reference to Mrs. Heard's remark about the cold, it should be noted that the temperature at noon was 38° F. The sketch which Mrs. Heard made of the island was sent with the abstract log to Lieutenant Maury from Melbourne. Maury mentions receipt of the sketch in his letter to the Secretary of the Navy on June 12, 1854, but it is not now among the records of the Naval Observatory in the National Archives.

Although he does not say so in the logbook, Captain Heard apparently would have liked to examine the island more closely. In a letter, February 6, 1854, to the editor of the Melbourne *Argus,* after describing the island he added, "At such a distance it would be impossible to designate a number of islands lying near together from one large island. Had I discovered it to be land before getting so far to the eastward, I would have neared it and ascertained what dangers were about it; but the weather was rough, and I could not then do so without putting about, and delaying my vessel longer than I felt justified in doing."

In a letter to Gershom Bradford, April 7, 1936, Dr. Mary A. Heard, Captain Heard's daughter, said that it was her father's desire to land and plant the American flag. Since Dr. Heard's knowledge of the event was gained from her mother long after it occurred, it is difficult to distinguish what might have been Captain Heard's intention at the time from what he later fancied he would have liked to do. As it was, he fixed as best he could the location of the eastern and western ends of the island and continued on his voyage.

It is interesting to compare the accuracy of Captain Heard's fixes for the extremities of the island with those obtained by two scientific expeditions and by Captain McDonald. Captain Heard made his fixes by means of compass bearings from a distance of approximately 20 miles. Members of the *Challenger* Expedition landed at Corinthian Bay on February 6, 1874, but weather forced them to leave the next morning before they could survey the island. Captain McDonald sighted the island at 8 p.m., and hove to for the night. By morning, however, he had been blown eastward out of sight of the island. His estimate of the approximate location of the island is, therefore, remarkably accurate. The Australian National Antarctic Research Expedition surveyed the island in 1948 while based there from 1947 to 1949. The results of the survey are incorporated in Aus. Chart 08, "Heard Island," issued by the Department of the Navy, Hydrographic Branch. The various fixes are given in the following table:

LOCATIONS FOR HEARD ISLAND

Source	Date	Eastern extremity	Western extremity	Height of Big Ben
Capt. Heard	1853	53° 10' S. 74° 40' E.	53° 10' S. 74° 15' E.	5,000'
Challenger Exp. . . .	1874	53° 14' S. 73° 52' E.	53° 03' S. 73° 15' E.	6,000'
Aus. Chart 08	1948	53° 07' S. 73° 51' E.	52° 59' S. 73° 15' E.	9,005'
Capt. McDonald . .	1854	53° 03' S. 73° 31' E.		Obscured

The day after the discovery, November 26, was cloudy, raw, and misty with passing snow squalls. November 27 was marked by thick foggy weather with fresh breezes from the northeast. This was one of those days that puzzled Captain Heard, as it has others in sub-Antarctic regions for the first time. The barometer had been falling until at 8 a.m. it registered 28.40 inches, but the weather did not indicate an impending storm. Nevertheless, to be on the safe side, Captain Heard had all light sails taken in and the topsails close-reefed which, of course, cut down his speed. He noted in the logbook, "I do not understand the low state of the barometer with the appearance of the weather. It looks like nothing but a royal topsail breese." He mentioned this problem to Maury in his letter from Melbourne.

The weather on November 28 was a continuation of the previous day with passing snow squalls added. Hail fell at 10 a.m. Although the weather did not look ominous, the barometer did not rise above 28.70 inches. Captain Heard decided to let out the reefs and sails. Icebergs were seen again, and during the night and early morning the ship passed through colored water whose depth the captain estimated at 150 fathoms. The depth in this area is actually over 2000 fathoms. There were a large number of whale birds flying about.

The next day all drawing sails were set to take advantage of a good breeze and reasonably good weather. The afternoon of November 29 ushered in strong winds, increasing to gale proportions by 11 p.m. The barometer stood at 28.54, and the foresail was stowed and the topsails close-reefed. The next morning the wind had dropped to a light breeze with an occasional calm, and all sails were set. Although the weather did not permit an observation, November 30 probably marked the farthest penetration into high latitudes, 54°23′ S by dead reckoning. Four men were placed on the sick list December 1, a large number for so small a crew. For several days the thermometer had dropped to freezing at midnight and rose to 36° F to 38° F at noon.

As he explained in his letter to Maury, Captain Heard had been having trouble with his compasses in high southern latitudes, but in the latter part of the voyage, as he approached closer to the south magnetic pole, the problem became more vexing.

From November 30 until December 4 the distance sailed on three of the five days was cut to less than 100 miles because of poor visibility or light winds. Periods of thick fog and passing snow squalls were the rule. Another large iceberg was reported on December 2. On December 5 strong winds with heavy gusts and squalls, culminating in a gale, split the flying jib in the hems and shredded the inner jib. The gale subsided to strong winds on December 6, and in spite of a thick drizzly day, good progress was made. Since December 1 the ship had been on an east-northeast course, and the 50th parallel was crossed on December 4. As a consequence, temperatures afterward remained above freezing, being mostly in the 40s. Displays of aurora australis were noted on December 3 and 5.

From December 6 to December 12 the weather was mostly favorable. There were spells of thick, drizzly rain and occasional periods of high winds with a heavy sea, but good progress was made on most days. December 11 the 46th parallel was crossed. From here to Melbourne the weather remained pleasant, and the recorded temperatures were always above 50° F. Cape Otway was sighted on

December 20, but light airs and calms held progress to 20 miles. At 4 p.m. on December 22, a pilot was taken on off The Heads, and at 9:30 p.m. the bark was anchored in Hobsons Bay at Melbourne.

Upon his arrival at Melbourne Captain Heard took immediate action to protect the priority of his discovery. The first public announcement of the discovery of Heard Island was contained in the following notice which appeared in the Melbourne *Argus* for December 24, 1853:

> Capt. John J. Heard of the barque Oriental, from Boston to this place, reported having seen in lat. 53°10′ S., long. 74°19′ E. an island not on the chart, 20 miles to the northward, covered with snow. He judged it to be 25 miles from east to west.

On January 4, 1854, Captain Heard wrote a letter to Lieutenant Maury and dispatched it, along with his abstract log, on the bark *Auckland,* bound for San Francisco. In this letter (Appendix A) he discussed his passage, as indicated above, and announced the discovery of the island, which he claimed the privilege of naming for himself. In the seventh edition of his *Sailing Directions,* Maury published a great part of Heard's abstract log, including the complete entry for November 25. The following announcement also appeared:

> Another caution is necessary to navigators in this trade, that have a fancy on the outward passage, to run down their longitude between the parallels of 52° and 53°. There is a group of newly discovered and not accurately determined islands in the way. They are between the parallels 52°53′36″ and 53°12′ S., and the meridians of 72°35′ and 74°40′ E. They were first seen by Captain Heard, of the American barque *Oriental* November 25, 1853. On the 12th June, 1854, the fact was duly reported by me to the government of the United States, and the importance of sending a vessel of the navy to look after them and fix their position was urged upon the Navy Department.[8]

Maury's letter of June 12, 1854, to the Honorable J. C. Dobbin, Secretary of the Navy, reporting the discovery of Heard Island, appears as Appendix B to this chapter.

Captain Heard, who was still in Melbourne at the time, became much concerned when, on February 4, 1854, the Melbourne *Argus,* in a dispatch from Sydney, announced that Captain McDonald in the British ship *Samarang* had discovered on January 4, 1854, islands between 53°00′ S and 53°03′ S and 72°35′ E and 73°31′ E. He wrote a letter, dated February 6, to the editor of the *Argus* disputing the Britisher's claim. He referred to the notice of his discovery in the issue of December 24, and ended with, 'I publish this that Captain McDonald may know, should the land be the same, that my discovery claims the priority by nearly two months' date."

On the same date Heard also wrote to Lieutenant Maury regarding McDonald's claim, saying, ". . ., I am confident that the islands are the same that I reported. Had it been other island or islands, by the position that he gives them, I must have seen them. I do not see fit to give up my claim on the islands to him or to any one else, unless they have seen them prior to me. Should you find that they have not been seen either by England or France, or any of our home marine, previous to my seeing them, I claim them for the United States, and also the privilege of naming the Island or Islands as the case may be."[9]

On April 24, 1854, the *Oriental* sailed from Melbourne for Surabaya (Soerabaya) Roads. After being becalmed for long periods she arrived off the roadstead on Friday, June 16. With the help of a fisherman, Captain Heard finally got a pilot and entered and anchored at 8 a.m., Sunday, June 18. The *Oriental* weighed anchor on August 10, and came to anchor in Batavia Roads (Jakarta) at 2 p.m. on August 15. She sailed again at 7 a.m. on Sunday, August 20, arriving at Padang, August 31. Captain Heard was ready for sea September 14, but lack of wind kept him at anchor until 6 a.m., September 17. From Padang he sailed, via the Cape of Good Hope, for Boston, which he approached in a storm. He moored in Boston Harbor on Friday morning, January 26, 1855, after an absence of 1 year, 5½ months.

CAPTAIN HEARD PRESSES HIS CLAIM

Conscious of the personal honor involved, and undoubtedly inspired by patriotic motives as well as by a hope for possible monetary reward, Captain Heard was very much interested in having the United States recognize his discovery officially and lay claim to the island. Consequently, when he found that no official action was being taken as a result of Maury's letter to the Secretary of the Navy announcing his discovery, he wrote to both the Secretary of the Navy and the Secretary of State regarding his rights. Captain Heard was aware of the money to be made from hunting elephant seals which he suspected abounded on the island, and he thought it likely that deposits of guano were also present. Since he was unable to exploit the island himself, he felt that some bounty was due him from the government for discovering this source of wealth which he felt could be insured for the citizens of the United States if his claim was recognized and acted upon.

He met with little encouragement and much indifference, however, from Federal officials. J. C. Dobbin, Secretary of the Navy, wrote him in November 5, 1856, "In reply to your inquiries of the 28th ult. the Department informs you that it has not been convenient to take steps to investigate the discovery of the island or islands in Lat. 53°25′ S. Long. 74°19′ E. reported as discovered by you. ... I am not aware of any provision made by the government for remunerating persons claiming to have discovered islands." (See Appendix C.) A similar answer was received from George L. Marcy of the Department of State, who rubbed salt in the wounds by speaking of ". . . an alleged discovery of island by you. . . ." (See Appendix D.) Both men pointed out that while the government paid no bounty, according to the Guano Act of 1856, discoverers of guano islands would be protected by the government in their efforts to exploit the deposits providing the conditions of the Act were complied with.

Captain Heard, however, was interested in more than monetary reward. He was concerned lest his claim of discovery be disregarded abroad, and he wrote Maury regarding his fears. On June 11, 1858, Maury answered, "Your claims as the discoverer of Heard's Island have been stated by me fully in the Nautical

Magazine, London. I therefore think it needless for me to say anything to the Admiralty upon the subject." He added, "I have time and again called the attention of our own Navy Department to this matter, and I write again urging the importance of having those islands looked after."

Captain Heard was confirmed in his stand regarding the monetary return to be realized by American interests by his discovery. He noted that newspaper accounts showed that from 1855 to 1860 3,200,000 gallons of elephant seal oil had been sold in the United States for a total of $1,920,000. There is no way of knowing how much of this came from Heard Island, but it is reasonable to assume that a large part of it was produced there.

After Captain Heard's death in 1862, Mrs. Heard apparently continued from time to time to press for recognition of her husband's claim, for on August 30, 1871, she appealed to the President, and on March 24, 1873, to the Secretary of the Navy. Both letters were referred to the Department of State, but the position of the Department remained unchanged from what it had been almost 20 years earlier.

Subsequently two instances have been reported of land having been sighted south of Kerguelen Island prior to Captain Heard's discovery. In each case, however, the evidence is too indefinite to support a positive claim to priority of discovery.

In an article entitled "The Desolation Islands," published in the *New London Day*, May 18, 1869, describing the beginning of elephant sealing on Heard Island, Charles Lanman mentioned that Captain Thomas Long, master of the *Charles Carroll*, reported to his owners in 1849 that he had seen land from the masthead while sailing south of Kerguelen Island.[10] Perhaps this was either Heard Island or one of the McDonald Islands, but it could have been an overturned iceberg with rocks frozen into its basal section. Such ice masses have been mistaken for land by mariners on many occasions. Captain Long may also have seen the distant shore of Antarctica by the aid of looming. Such indefinite evidence, however, can hardly challenge Captain Heard's priority to the discovery of Heard Island.

In 1935 Sir Douglas Mawson published a copy of a manuscript chart on file in the Hydrographic Department of the Admiralty which shows the tracks of the *Tula*, Captain John Biscoe, in 1831, and of the *Magnet*, Captain Peter Kemp, in 1833, south of Kerguelen Island between 45° E and 75° E.[11] On this chart, beside Kemp's track when the vessel was in the indicated position of approximately 52°37' S, 69°15' E, is the notation "Saw land." Shortly before this Kemp had sounded and reached bottom at 55 fathoms. Since the logbook of the *Magnet* has been lost, this chart is the only contemporary record of Kemp's voyage. By a series of unverifiable assumptions, Mawson placed Kemp's track sufficiently farther east from where it is on the chart to make it possible for Kemp to have sighted Heard Island. This tenuous reasoning has apparently been accepted by the Hydrographic Department of the British Admiralty as the basis for the flat statement that Heard Island was first sighted by Peter Kemp.[12]

APPENDIXES

APPENDIX A

MELBOURNE, *Jan. 4th 1854*

Lieut. M. F. MAURY

DEAR SIR: I herein send you my abstract log of Barque Oriental under my command from Boston to Australia. I left Boston August 13th 1853 sea account, with light airs from the West; and took your route as well as the winds would admit, until in the Lon. of 34°00′ W. Lat. 10°00′ N. I had no N.E. trades, all my passage had been light winds, from 10° to 9° 3 days calms and light airs from all round the compass. Sept. 15th Lat. 9°4′ Lon 34°30′ took light airs varying from S. to W.S.W. which put me across the Equator Oct. 8th, being 23 days from Lat. 9°00′ N. in Lon. 20°25′ W., after having been as far E as 13°32′ W. making the passage from Boston to the Equator 57 days. When I took these head winds in 34° I was too far W. to take the larboard tack with a full built vessel like the Oriental, therefore had to keep to my starboard tacks mostly. When the wind was S.S.W. to S. so that my larboard tack was the best, the winds would be so light that I would have hardly steerage way. I did not get the S.E. trades till on the Equator, and did not get the wind E. of S.S.E. until below 5°00′ S. so had I have had the winds in the North Atlantic to have crossed the Equator in 30°00′ W. it would have been impossible for me to have passed Cape St. Roque. When N. of the Equator, I saw some 30 sail in the same fix that I was myself. I think September and October of this year were exceptions to the average, and not any more favourable to your rout than to the old, tho' had I have had a clipper ship, I should have risked more and gone to the W. when 34°. I lost the S.E. trades when in 16° & 17° S. then had the wind from E. round to N. and W. by S. seven days down, to Lat. 28°37′.

Nov. 25th discovered an island which I claim the privilege of naming Heard's Island, as I cannot find it on any chart that I have seen. My observations on that day were the only reliable ones I had got for over 20 days. You will see the particulars of the Island in my Abstract Log, which I send you, also notices of several shoal places. My passage from 11°00′ E. to 100°00′ was nearly all fog, and the winds irregular. I should not recommend any one coming down at the same season of the year. Since my arrival here I have learned through several American, and many English shipmasters, that the majority came along between 40° and 44° S. The steadiness of the winds in these Lat. are quite an offset to the shorter distance of the Great Circle Route. Icebergs and foggy weather farther South. After passing 30° E. to Hobson's Bay my compasses would fly round very much, and along 70° to 110° E. 53° to 47° S. they were very unsteady flying round 4 to 12 points. I put mine in different positions and parts of the ship and the effect was the same. Since my arrival I have heard from those masters who were down S the same complaint. My barometer, in running my Easting up in the high South Latitudes and thick fogs would often be down to 28.30 & 50. and would hang so for two or three days at a time, and we would often have no more than a royal breese. I lost several days run through a low state of the Barometer. From here I proceed to Batavia, thence to Boston or Europe, and on my arrival in the States or in Europe, I will send you the Abstract Log of my passage. I shall send this letter and Abstract Log of passage by the barque Auckland via San Francisco. Hoping to hear from you on my arrival home

I remain Dear Sir,
Yours truly

JOHN J. HEARD
Commander of the barque Oriental

Please address me to care of
Messrs Robinson, Wiggin & Co.
Boston — Mass.

NOTE: Above Captain Heard says, "I left Boston August 13 1853 sea account, . . ." Time of sailing was 2:00 p.m., and since nautical time was advanced 12 hours, the day beginning at noon, his departure according to civil time was 2:00 p.m., August 12.

APPENDIX B

NATIONAL OBSERVATORY
Washington June 12, 1854

SIR: I have the honor to report that in the abstract log kept for this office by Capt. John J. Heard of the American barque "Oriental" on a voyage from Boston to Australia last year mention is made of the discovery of an island as follows, viz.

"Nov. 25th 1853 — Lat 53°26′ South; Long. 74°19′ East, (Noon). Pleasant breezes and passing snow squalls; latter part clear; the first clear weather we have had for twenty days. At 8:30 A.M. made land. At first took it for Icebergs, as no island is laid down on my chart nor in the Epitome. At 11:30 A.M. the clouds cleared around & over it revealing it to be an Island. At noon the Eastern end bore by compass N.N.E. 20 miles. The western end bore by compass N. by W. about 20 miles. By good observations I make the west end of the island in 74°15′ E. long; East end 74°40′ — Lat. 53°10′ South. Near the centre of the island a high peak 5000 feet high. Large number of birds."

Capt. H. sent me a sketch of the island, which in the exercise of the rights which usage gives to discoverers, he claims for the United States, and calls Heard's Island.

I perceive by a slip copied in the Hobartown Argus from the Sydney Morning Herald, that Capt. McDonald of the "Samarang" who passed near the same place 39 days after the Oriental Viz, January 3d, 1854 also reported land in the same vicinity viz

McDonald's Isle 53°00′ S. Longitude 72°35′ E.

Young's Island 53°03′ S. Longitude 73°31′ E.

The nearest land to this, known to Hydrographers is Kerguelen Land which is about 300 miles to the N.N.W.; the difference of latitude being nearly four degrees. It can hardly be supposed therefore, that one could be mistaken for the other.

There is a vast amount of shipping engaged in the Australia trade, and according to the best route as indicated by the wind & current charts this reported discovery lies in the fair way of outward bound vessels, both from this country & Europe to the ports of Australia; and doubt as to the existence or position of dangers in such a commercial thoroughfare as this is, should not be suffered to remain a day too long.

Heard's Island may perhaps prove valuable to the sealing interests; it is not a probable place of resort for the Guano fowls. I hope the department will find it convenient to have all doubts removed at an early day, as to its place & existence.

I beg leave in this connexion to say that the vessel, which by the act of Congress March 3d 1849, the Secretary of the Navy is authorized to employ "in testing the new routes and perfecting the discoveries" made in the course of the investigations carried on at this office, could now be employed with great advantage.

Respectfully Ob.

M. F. MAURY
Lt. U.S.N.

Hon. J. C. DOBBIN
Secty. of the Navy
Washington

APPENDIX C

NAVY DEPARTMENT
November 5th 1856

SIR: In reply to your inquiries of the 28th ult. the Department informs you that it has not been convenient to take any steps to investigate the discovery of the island or islands in Lat. 53°25′ S., Long: 74°19′ E. reported as discovered by you on your last voyage to Melbourne, Aust. Nov. 25th 1853.

I am not aware of any provision made by the government for remunerating persons claiming to have discovered islands. Certain rights are, however, secured to discoverers of islands, rocks, or keys not within the lawful jurisdiction and not occupied by the citizens of any other government, upon which exist deposits of guano. See "An Act to Authorize Protection to be given to Citizens of the United States who may discover deposits of guano." Approved May 18, 1856.

The question relating to the extent of protection that would be afforded you in case you should proceed to, and take possession of the islands to which you allude, is one about which you had better confer with the Department of State.

Very respectfully
Yr. Obt. St.

J. C. DOBBIN

Capt. JOHN J. HEARD
    Care of N.E. Bank Note Coy.
        Boston, Mass.

APPENDIX D

DEPARTMENT OF STATE,
Washington 10th Nov. 1856

To JOHN J. HEARD, Esqre.
    Boston,
        Massachusetts.

SIR: Your letter of the 7th instant relative to an alleged discovery of Islands by you, has been received. In reply, I have to acquaint you, that no reward is promised by the Government for any such discovery. It is, however, authorized to protect the discoverer of deposits of guano upon the conditions prescribed in the Act of Congress, a copy of which is herewith enclosed.

I am Sir, Your obedient Servant

GEO. L. MARCY.

NOTES

1. Charles L. Lewis, *Matthew Fontaine Maury, Pathfinder of the Seas* (Annapolis, 1927), pp. 53-54.

2. Lt. M. F. Maury, *Explanations and Sailing Directions to Accompany the Wind and Current Charts*, 5th ed. (Washington, 1853), pp. 464-466 and supplement pp. xii-xv.

3. In a letter to Gershom Bradford, April 7, 1936, then of the U. S. Hydrographic Office, Dr. Mary A. Heard said, "My father's desire was to land on the island and plant the American flag, but his ship was sailing on a test voyage to prove the theory of a 'circle sailing route,' and no time was allowed for delay." In a letter dated April 19, 1936, she added, "What I know and wrote you, was what my mother had told me, as she was on the voyage with him." Copies of both these letters are in the files of the late Dr. S. W. Boggs, Special Adviser on Geography to the Department of State.

Any idea of setting a record or of testing the route must have been entirely Captain Heard's, for there is no evidence in Maury's official correspondence, on file in the Naval Records Section of the National Archives, that he knew about the voyage until it was over. He encouraged navigators to write to him, however, reporting their experiences.

4. Maury, *op. cit.*, 7th ed., p. 862.

5. Brian Roberts, "Historical Notes on Heard and McDonald Islands," *Polar Record*, vol. 5, No. 40, July, 1950, p. 581.

6. *Report on the Scientific Results of the Voyage of H. M. S. "Challenger" during the years 1873-76, Narrative*, vol. 1, first part (London, 1885), p. 378.

7. *Boston Post*, Saturday morning, Aug. 13, 1853, "Marine Journal." Also *Boston Daily Evening Transcript*, Friday, Aug. 12, "Transcript Marine Journal." According to the logbook of the *Oriental* the departure was on August 13, but Captain Heard, in conformity with the accepted practice of his day, kept the logbook on nautical time which was advanced 12 hours ahead of civil time. The day began at noon, and was divided into first part, middle part, and latter part. According to this method, events occurring in the p.m. hours are advanced one day

over the civil calendar, but those occurring in the a.m. hours are in conformity with the civil calendar. In the account, all times have been converted to the civil calendar.

8. Maury, *op. cit.*, p. 862. The abstract log from October 13 to December 21, inclusive, appears on pp. 763-768.

9. Copies of the letters to Maury and to the editor of the *Argus* are among Capt. Heard's personal correspondence, now the property of David B. Heard.

10. Lanman's article was republished in the *New London Democrat*, May 22, 1869, and in many other New England papers. It was also republished, pp. 55-66, in Lanman's book, *Recollections of Curious Characters and Pleasant Places* (Edinburgh, 1881). Captain Long's report appears on p. 59.

11. Sir Douglas Mawson, "Some Historical Features of the Discovery of Enderby and Kemp Land," *Geographical Journal*, vol. 86, 1935, pp. 526-530.

12. *Antarctic Pilot*, Hydrographic Department, Admiralty (London, 1948), 2nd edition, p. 290.

BIBLIOGRAPHY

PUBLISHED MATERIAL

Anonymous, "Heard Island," *Geographical Review*, vol. 20, No. 4, October, 1930, pp. 683-684. A brief sketch of the history of Heard Island, including a copy of the entry in the logbook of the bark *Oriental* for November 25, 1853, the date of discovery by Capt. Heard.

Balch, Edwin Swift, *Antarctica* (Philadelphia, Allen, Lane and Scott, 1902), 230 pp., map. (See pages 189-192.)

Fricker, Karl, *The Antarctic Regions* (New York, Macmillan, 1900), xii, 292 pp., map. (See pages 119-120.)

Lanman, Charles, *New London Day*, May 18, 1869, "The Desolation Islands."

——, *Recollections of Curious Characters and Pleasant Places* (Edinburgh, D. Douglas, 1881), xiii, 351 pp. Pages 55-66 are a reprint of the article listed just above.

Lewis, Charles L., *Matthew Fontaine Maury, The Pathfinder of the Seas* (Annapolis, United States Naval Institute, 1927), xvii, 264 pp., end papers. (See Chap. V.)

"Marine Journal." *Boston Post*, Saturday, August 13, 1853; Saturday, January 27, 1855.

Maury, Lt. M. F., USN, *Explanations and Sailing Directions to Accompany the Wind and Current Charts*, 5th ed. (Washington, C. Alexander, 1853), 492 pp., 15 plates; supp. xxx and 8 plates.

——, *Explanations and Sailing Directions*, etc., 7th ed. (Philadelphia, E. C. and J. Biddle, 1855), xxxvi. 869 pp., xxii plates, appendix. Heard's abstract log from October 13 to December 21, 1853, inclusive, is published on pp. 763-768.

Mawson, Sir Douglas, "Some Historical Features of the Discovery of Enderby Land and Kemp Land," *Geographical Journal*, vol. 86, 1935, pp. 526-530.

Melbourne Argus, Melbourne, Australia, Saturday, December 24, 1853; February 4, 1854; February 6, 1854. These numbers include the first announcement of Capt. Heard's discovery, of Capt. McDonald's discovery, and of Capt. Heard's reply to Capt. McDonald's announcement.

Mill, Hugh Robert, *The Siege of the South Pole* (New York, Frederick A. Stokes Co., 1905), xvi, 455 pp., map. (See pp. 167, 335-336.)

Roberts, Brian, "Historical Notes on Heard and McDonald Island," *The Polar Record*, vol. 5, No. 40, July, 1950, pp. 580-584.

Tizard, T. H.; H. N. Mosley, J. Y. Buchanan, and John Murray, *Reports on the Scientific Results of the Voyage of H. M. S. "Challenger" During the Years 1873-76, Narrative*, vol. 1, First Part (London, H. M. Stationery Office, 1885), liv. 509 pp., 25 plates, charts.

"Transcript Marine." *Boston Daily Evening Transcript*, Friday, August 12, 1853; Friday, January 26, 1855.

MANUSCRIPT MATERIAL

Correspondence in 1936 between Dr. Mary A. Heard, daughter of Capt. Heard, and Gershom Bradford of the U. S. Hydrographic Office. Copies on file in the office of the Special Adviser on Geography to the Department of State.

Diary of Mrs. Fidelia (Reed) Heard kept on the voyage of the *Oriental*. Now in possession of David B. Heard.

Logbook of the Bark *Oriental* From Boston Toward Melbourne. Capt. John J. Heard. Now in the possession of David B. Heard, Waban, Mass., great-grandson of Captain Heard.

Various letters consisting of the correspondence between Captain Heard and various Government officials, including Lt. M. F. Maury. The collection includes copies of letters sent as well as those received. It also includes those later sent and received by Mrs. Fidelia Heard. These are now in the possession of David B. Heard. Capt. Heard's correspondence with Lt. Maury is also on file in Record Group 78 of the National Archives. His letters to the Secretary of the Navy are filed with Record Group 80.

PLATE III. Matthew Fontaine Maury. Official U. S. Navy photograph, original in the Library of Congress.

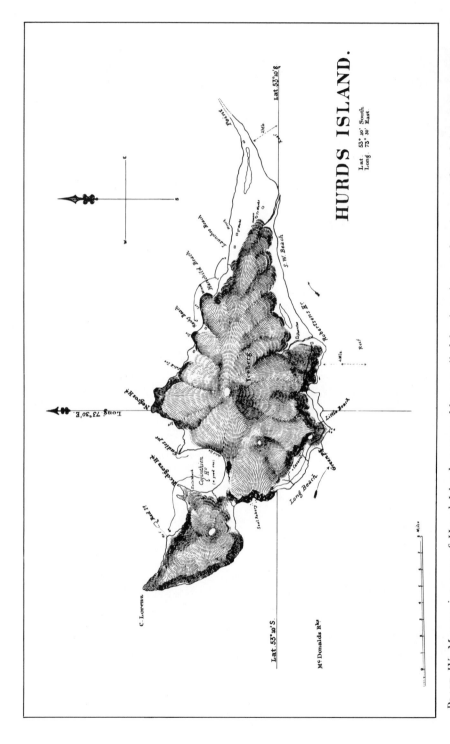

PLATE IV. Manuscript map of Heard Island, presumably compiled by American sealers (see p. 235). Original in the National Archives.

13

NEW LONDON SEALERS ON HEARD ISLAND

SIGNIFICANCE AND DURATION OF THE ACTIVITY

In January 1855, slightly more than a year after its discovery by Captain John J. Heard, Captain Erasmus Darwin Rogers made the first landing on Heard Island. This marked the beginning of elephant sealing on the island and resulted in its continuous occupation by Americans for approximately a quarter of a century. Although precise figures are not available, it is probable that during this period more than 100,000 barrels of elephant seal oil were obtained from the island. In connection with this activity the island was completely explored, and at least two maps by sealers are known to exist. Contemporary watercolor sketches of the island by an American naval officer are also in existence. In addition, a daily report of weather conditions at Heard Island during November and December 1872 was supplied by sealers for use by the United States Commission for the Observation of the Transit of Venus. A manuscript map of "Hurd's Island" is reproduced as Plate IV.

From the time of its discovery until 1880, 48 sealing voyages to Heard Island are registered from United States ports, and it is known that many of the ships which are listed for the same period on 43 voyages to "Desolation Island" also worked at Heard Island. It is probable that very few, if any, operated exclusively at Kerguelen Island. To do more than list most of these 91 voyages is today impossible. Since this chapter is an account of activity extending over a period of 28 years or more, it is organized differently from other chapters which deal with only one voyage or expedition. Concerning the sealers on Heard Island, an account will be given only for those voyages which were significant milestones in the long period of continuous occupation of the island by Americans.

THE NEW LONDON WHALING AND SEALING INDUSTRY

From its very inception and throughout its duration, the sealing industry on Heard Island was very closely related to activity on Kerguelen Island, although for a time during its heyday some voyages covering only a single season were made directly to and from Heard Island, with no stop at Kerguelen. In all instances where it was necessary for the vessel to remain near the sealing grounds during the winter, ships were moored at Kerguelen Island because there was no safe harbor in which a ship could winter at Heard Island. Sealing was an offshoot of the whaling industry. Some whale ships cruising in the Indian Ocean sought to augment their cargo by procuring oil from the great numbers of elephant seals which occupied the beaches of Kerguelen Island from September through December.

The first recorded American sealing on Kerguelen was carried on in conjunction with a whaling voyage in the Indian Ocean by two Nantucket whalemen.[1]

FIGURE 9. Îles de Kerguelen.

The *Asia,* commanded by Captain Elijah Coffin, and the *Alliance,* commanded by Captain Bartlett Coffin, left Nantucket on October 6, 1791. At the island of Mauritius they purchased a schooner which they named the *Hunter,* to act as a tender for a proposed sealing operation at Kerguelen Island. On the voyage south they sighted Kerguelen on December 17, 1792, and two days later all three vessels were moored in Christmas Harbor (Port Christmas, Baie de l'Oiseau).[2] From January 16, 1793, to the middle of February, the *Hunter,* under command of Simeon Starbuck, explored the north coast of Kerguelen, hunting for elephant seals and giving names to several bays and inlets. Captain Bartlett Coffin died at Kerguelen on February 7, being the first of several Americans to be buried on the island. On March 11, 1793, the three vessels left Kerguelen for Mauritius, where the *Hunter* was sold. In February 1794 the *Asia* and *Alliance* returned to Nantucket.

Starbuck reports the voyage of Captain William Swain in the *Nancy* of New Bedford to Kerguelen in 1793.[3] Other so-called "mixed voyages" in which whaling was combined with sealing on Kerguelen Island followed with increasing frequency in the 19th century. According to A. H. Clark, however, it was not until 1837 that American sealing was begun on a big scale at this bleak and stormy island which, like Captain James Cook, the Yankee whalers called "Isle of Desolation" or "Desolation Island."[4]

By 1837 whaling in the Indian Ocean in the vicinity of Kerguelen and sealing on the "Isle of Desolation" had become almost the exclusive province of whaling firms from New London. In the list of sealing voyages from American ports published by Clark, 31 ships between 1844 and 1854 were reported as destined for "Desolation Island."[5] All of them sailed from New London. The whaling industry was established in New London later than in such famous centers as New Bedford and Nantucket, but by 1846 New London had risen to second place among United States whaling ports. In this year 78 New London vessels, totaling 26,200 tons and manned by 2500 seamen, were engaged in the industry.[6] The New London portion of the whaling industry was unique in that a large part of the fleet operated in the south Indian Ocean, particularly in the vicinity of Kerguelen Island, which other American whalers seem to have left pretty much to the New Londoners.

The operations of the New London whalers at Kerguelen were well systematized and coordinated with the seasons. It was customary for each whaling ship to be accompanied by one or two tenders, generally schooners. It was common practice to hunt for whales in the south Atlantic and Indian Oceans en route to Kerguelen. Upon reaching this sub-Antarctic island, the ships made for Pot Harbor, now officially known as Anse Betsy (Betsy Cove), on the north side of the northeastern peninsula (Presqu'île Courbet). The name used by the whalers stemmed from the fact that several iron "try kettles" were to be found here on the beach, left there by departing ships until they should return.

Pot Harbor was the field headquarters in 1853 for at least two of the firms: Perkins and Smith, and E. V. Stoddard. Here surplus supplies and gear were piled in neat rows above the beaches, around hovels partially dug out of the hillside and roofed over with spars and pieces of old sails. Here some of the men spent a part of the year, and here were kept a few livestock to supply some milk and fresh meat, mostly for the officers' mess. Some social life was carried on in Pot Harbor, particularly if some of the captains brought their wives on the voyage. Only at Pot Harbor were circumstances likely to afford an opportunity for fraternization among officers and crews of the rival fleets. From here departing ships carried letters for anyone who wished to write home, regardless of his affiliation, and everyone eagerly awaited mail and packages when a ship arrived from New London.

After unloading supplies and gear at Pot Harbor, the parent ships and schooners spent January and February hunting for whales in the Indian Ocean around

Kerguelen. They might return to the base during these two months or remain away, as occasion demanded. This offshore whaling ended at the beginning of March, however, because the strong winds and frequent storms that prevailed after this date made offshore waters too hazardous for whaling. The parent ship was now moored in Pot Harbor until the following December. Extra-heavy anchors were brought for the purpose, and, if possible, a heavy chain might be made fast to a rock on one side. The sails, spars, and rigging were taken down and sent on shore. Only a skeleton crew remained on board as ship keepers and to render, or as the whalers said, "try out," the blubber and put the oil in casks. The remainder of the crews were divided among the two or three tenders, which were now dispatched to hunt for whales in the protected waters of the bays or fjords which deeply indent the coast of Kerguelen. From March until August the humpback whale, especially, frequented these inshore waters, but other whales were also taken. A keen rivalry existed between competing crews, and rules were agreed upon between the captains of competing firms by which the competition was governed. When a whale was caught by a schooner, the blubber was cut up and put into casks later to be transported to the parent ship at Pot Harbor where it would be "tried out." By the end of August the whales had departed from the fjords, and the inshore whaling came to an end.

The New London whalers did not hunt exclusively for whales. The beaches on the much-indented shores of Kerguelen Island were the habitat during the breeding season of hundreds of thousands of elephant seals. These huge beasts — old bulls may be 20 feet long and weigh 6000 pounds — are very fat when they come onto the beaches in September. From then through December the New London whalers killed the elephant seals and boiled out the oil from the thick layers of blubber under the skin. One old bull seal might yield as much as 100 gallons of oil. Scraps from the "try kettles" and penguin skins were used for fuel along with wood brought from home. By agreement between the captains of rival fleets, the beaches were divided among them and each schooner was assigned its exclusive stretch of coast. Men were stationed at the beaches most frequented by the elephant seals. Here they lived in crude shelters for three or four months, killing the seals as they came upon the beach, skinning the animals, and cutting up the blubber into small strips or cubes that could be pushed through the bunghole of a cask. They also had to drive the seals off beaches from which casks of blubber could not be taken off in a boat, with the hope that the seals would come up again on more accessible spots to be killed.

Meanwhile, some of the men remained on the schooners which patrolled their assigned stretches of the coast. Wherever elephant seals were found, the men landed, if conditions permitted, slaughtered the seals, and put the blubber into casks. They also called at the beaches where men were stationed and picked up whatever blubber had been obtained. The blubber was then transported to Pot Harbor to the parent ship, where it was "tried out." This continued into December when, the young now being old enough, the elephant seals moved out to sea. In less than a month they would begin to return to the beaches again for a time, while they shed their coats, but by then the animals were much thinner and yielded much less oil. When the elephant seals went to sea in December, therefore, the men stationed on the beaches were picked up and returned to Pot Harbor. If a cargo of oil had been obtained, the parent ship prepared to sail for New London. If not, the offshore whaling was now begun again until a cargo was had. If results had been especially good, one or more of the schooners serving as tenders might also return home with a cargo of oil. Otherwise, the tenders remained to continue the cycle of activities with the passing seasons, accumulating a cargo of oil for the next year.

Three New London firms were well known for their operations in the waters of Kerguelen Island during the 1850s. These were Perkins and Smith, Williams and Haven, and E. V. Stoddard. Few firms could entice men on whaling cruises which were mostly limited to the harsh environment of the "Isle of Desolation." By contrast, whaling in the Pacific was considered a pleasant experience. Later, when sealing began on Heard Island, the firms of Thomas Fitch, II, and Lawrence and Company also sent ships there.

Some New England families became well known from the number of men who played a prominent part in the whaling industry. One of these was the Rogers family of Montville, a small town immediately north of New London. Benjamin H. Rogers, Erasmus Darwin Rogers, and James H. Rogers commanded large ships. Charles E., John R., and Henry Rogers were also in the industry.[7] Captain Franklin F. Smith, junior partner of the firm of Perkins and Smith, was reputed to be one of the most successful whaling captains. He also had four brothers and a son who were whalers.[8]

VOYAGE OF THE *CORINTHIAN* AND THE FIRST LANDING ON HEARD ISLAND

The voyage of the *Corinthian* under the command of Captain Erasmus Darwin Rogers, sailing from New London on November 15, 1853, and resulting 14 months later in the first landing on Heard Island, began as just another whaling and sealing expedition to the "Isle of Desolation," according to the pattern described above. The firm of Perkins and Smith of New London had been engaged in whaling in this area as well as in other parts of the world since the company was organized by Elias Perkins and Franklin F. Smith in 1846. Although the voyage which resulted in the first landing on Heard Island began in 1853, it is necessary to go back to the previous voyage of the *Corinthian* which began in 1851 to get the full picture of the overall operation which led to the landing, because two of the tenders to the *Corinthian* sailed from New London in 1851.

THE PERKINS AND SMITH FLEET

In 1847 Perkins and Smith introduced the *Corinthian* as the parent ship of their fleet at Kerguelen Island. She was a square-rigged, double-decked ship of 503 tons built at Baltimore in 1822.[9] In 1847, the vessel was completely overhauled and newly "topped." Originally built as a packet, she had a trimmer line and a more spacious cabin than ordinary whalers.[10] A fast sailer, the *Corinthian* was sold in 1859, withdrawn from the whaling business, and placed in the South American trade.

On the voyage which began in the summer of 1851, the *Corinthian* was served by two tenders, the schooners *Atlas* and *Franklin*. When Captain Rogers began operations on Heard Island in February 1855, however, the *Corinthian* was accompanied by the schooners *Atlas* and *Mechanic,* the latter having sailed from New London in 1853. The *Atlas,* a schooner of 81 tons built in Sussex, Delaware, in 1833, had a single deck and two masts. The schooner *Franklin* was similar, although slightly larger. She was built at Eastport, Maine, in 1833 and was registered as of 99 tons. The *Mechanic,* also a two-masted schooner with a single deck, was a vessel of 89 tons built in Stonington in 1846. Perkins and Smith also owned the bark *Hannah Brewer,* a vessel of 193 tons built at Robbinston, Maine, in 1850. Although the *Hannah Brewer* operated out of Pot Harbor at Kerguelen Island at this time, it was not involved in the initiation of sealing on Heard Island.

The leader of the Perkins and Smith fleet at Kerguelen and captain of the *Corinthian* was Erasmus Darwin Rogers (1817-1906) of Montville. Some confusion has resulted from the fact that Captain Rogers is sometimes referred to as Erasmus D. Rogers and at other times as E. Darwin Rogers. Thus Howard Palmer, in his introduction to Nathaniel W. Taylor's *Life on a Whaler,* states that both Erasmus D. and E. Darwin Rogers were captains of large ships.[11] In trying to trace incidents in Captain Rogers' life, it becomes apparent that E. Darwin and Erasmus D. are the same man. There is no doubt of it in Colby's biographical sketch of Erasmus Darwin Rogers.[12] On Custom House documents concerning his voyages his name appears as Erasmus D. Rogers. His signature, however, is always E. D. Rogers.

A brief and yet exact statement for a specific date, concerning the crew of a vessel engaged in sealing and whaling at the "Isle of Desolation," is practically impossible because of the fact that not all crew lists are still available.[13] Even if they were, the problem would be complicated by the fact that men occasionally shifted from one vessel to another belonging to the same fleet. Unless the shift was permanent, the crew lists would not document it. Even commanding officers were changed during a voyage. It was also common practice for vessels to call at the Cape Verde Islands to recruit additional hands, some of whom were skilled in the business of whaling and sealing. As increasing industrialization offered more remunerative and less arduous if not so adventurous employment at home, it became more difficult to sign on a full crew at New London. After 1849, the promise of adventure and the possibility of quick wealth in the gold fields of California also attracted one type of recruit away from the whaling ships. Thus Cape Verde Islanders came to be relied on to an increasing extent to fill out the crews of whaling vessels in the last half of the 19th century. Crew men were paid in terms of shares of the profits from the voyage, which steadily declined as oil prices dropped in the face of competition from petroleum, and as the growing scarcity of whales made it more difficult to obtain a cargo.

When the schooner *Franklin* sailed from New London on July 29, 1851, with a crew of 16, she was under command of Captain Henry S. Williams of Salem, who was accompanied by his wife and small son.[14] Williams relinquished command sometime in 1852, and his family returned on the *Corinthian* in 1853.[15] At the time operations began on Heard Island, Joshua Starr was master of the *Franklin*. When the schooner *Atlas* sailed from New London on August 12, 1851, it carried a crew of 12 with Henry N. Whipple of Groton, Connecticut, in command. Whipple and several of the crew, however, returned to New London on the *Corinthian* in 1853. Again, at the time operations began on Heard Island, John Edwards was captain of the *Atlas*. When the schooner *Mechanic* sailed from New London on October 26, 1853, as tender to the *Corinthian,* she was in command of Captain John Edwards. The crew list is not available, but from the size of the vessel it can be assumed that it probably carried about 14 men. When the *Corinthian* sailed from New London on November 15, 1853, she carried a crew of 29 officers and men. Three additional hands were signed on at the Cape Verde Islands.

BEGINNING OF THE VOYAGE

The *Corinthian* and the two tenders, the schooners *Franklin* and *Atlas,* sailed separately from New London in the latter part of summer 1851 for the "Island of Desolation and Indian Ocean" on a mixed voyage. The typical operations of such a voyage have already been described. Many of the incidents pertaining to this particular voyage have been related by Taylor.[16] On March 18, 1853, the *Corinthian* sailed from Kerguelen, arriving at New London on June 24 with 2100 barrels of whale oil, 2100 barrels of elephant seal oil, and 10,000 pounds of whalebone.[17] Meanwhile the tenders remained at Kerguelen, continuing the seasonal cycle of activities in the process of procuring the next cargo of oil. The company's bark, *Hannah Brewer,* was also there.

The voyage directly leading to the first landing on Heard Island began with the departure from New London of the schooner *Mechanic,* in command of Captain Edwards, on October 26, 1853. The schooner had been added to the Kerguelen fleet of Perkins and Smith as a tender to the *Corinthian.* On November 15, 1853, the *Corinthian* sailed from New London, and Captain Rogers set a course for the Cape Verde Islands where, at Brava on December 20, he signed on six hands, three for the *Corinthian* and three for the *Atlas*.[18] Available data do not indicate when the *Corinthian* reached Kerguelen Island, but considering the distance to be sailed and the nature of the voyage it must have been some time in February 1854. The procurement of oil being more important than an early arrival at Kerguelen, a sharp lookout was no doubt kept for whales while en route, and an attempt would have been made to take any that were spotted. Whaling continued from Pot Harbor, after arrival, until early in March when frequent storms prevented such operations on the open sea in the region about Kerguelen. The vessel would then have to be moored securely at Pot Harbor until the next January. On March 24, 1854, at Pot Harbor, Ruben Brown was transferred from the *Corinthian* to the bark *Hannah Brewer* upon that vessel's departure for New London with a cargo of oil for Perkins and Smith. On July 15, 113 days later, the *Hannah Brewer* arrived at New London.

Following the usual period of inshore whaling by the three tenders, the *Atlas, Franklin,* and *Mechanic,* from March to September and the elephant sealing from September into December, the *Corinthian* was made ready for sea. In January she was again cruising for whales on the open ocean, where Captain Rogers apparently spoke a vessel from which he learned of the discovery of Heard Island, which he then set out to investigate.

THE FIRST LANDING ON HEARD ISLAND

The actual landing on Heard Island and events that followed are described by Captain Erasmus D. Rogers in a letter which he wrote to A. Howard Clark, who published an excerpt from it in his work on the American seal fishery.

In November, 1853, I left New London in the ship Corinthian, bound on a whaling voyage, and while cruising from Desolation Island in January, 1854, concluded to visit Heard's Island, that I learned had been recently discovered by Captain Heard in a Boston vessel. As soon as we reached the island men were sent ashore and reported a great abundance of sea-elephants, and in fact we could see great numbers of them lying on the beaches. We were the first men, so far as known, that ever landed at this desolate island. As the summer season was fast drawing to a close we concluded to sail immediately to Desolation Island, and, with our tenders, the schooners Atlas and Mechanic, return to Heard's Island and secure some oil. It is only about 300 miles from one island to the other, so that by the first of February we had returned to the new land and anchored in a small bay that we called Corinthian Harbor. The next morning we found our ship had dragged anchor and was almost aground. With much difficulty we got her into deeper water, and having made her as secure as possible with heavy riding anchors, sent ashore about 30 men to examine the place and kill the elephants. We remained at the island about a week, our men going ashore each morning and returning to the vessel at night. There were thousands of the animals upon the sandy beaches, so that there was little difficulty in getting all we wanted. After securing about 500 barrels of the blubber we sailed for Desolation Island and tried it out. As soon as possible we sent word of our good luck to our agents, Messers. Perkins and Smith at New London, Conn., and they purchased the ship Laurens, which was thoroughly equipped, and, under command of Capt. Frank Smith, sailed for this land in September 1855. The island was fully explored by Captain Smith and his men, all the headlands and bays named, and a rough map drawn. A full cargo of elephant oil was obtained, and in May, 1857, the Laurens arrived home at New London with about 4,700 barrels of elephant oil and 500 barrels of whale oil, the entire cargo being valued at $130,000.[19]

This is a very explicit statement, and it is confirmed by H. N. Moseley, who was a member of the party which landed on Heard Island from the British expedition ship *Challenger* on February 6, 1874. The landing party was met on the beach by six sealers. From the boss of the sealers Moseley learned, among other things, that ". . . He had been engaged in sealing about the island since 1854, having landed with the first sealing party which visited the island."[20]

Yet there are compelling reasons for believing that the year of the landing was in fact 1855. Captain Rogers was very highly regarded by his contemporaries as an able and reliable person. He wrote to Clark, however, presumably more than 25 years after the date of the landing on Heard Island, and he could have made an error in the year. A typographical error, by which the year was changed, could also have been made some place in the process of publication of Clark's work. The sealers' boss, too, was speaking 19 years after the event, and his memory could have been faulty. It is worthy of note that in the official narrative of the *Challenger* expedition, of which Moseley was a co-author and which was published six years after his "Notes by a Naturalist," a statement regarding the first landing on Heard Island by Captain Rogers gives the date as 1855.[21]

Charles Lanman wrote the first published account of the first landing on Heard Island, which appeared in the New London *Daily Star,* May 18, 1869, under the title of "Desolation Island." This story was reprinted in other American newspapers and subsequently appeared as a chapter in a book by Lanman.[22] While he goes into some detail on the matter of subsequent events, Lanman neglects to give the date of the first landing although he claims to have had in his possession the logbooks and journals relating to the events. A thorough search for these in all probable places has proved fruitless.

There are four reasons for believing that the year of the landing was 1855. In the first place, even though the *Corinthian* was considered a fast ship, it would have been impossible for Captain Rogers to have been at the Cape Verde Islands on December 20, 1853, and to have reached Kerguelen Island before February 1, 1854. It should be remembered that Captain Heard, when he discovered the island, was 105 days out of Boston and was trying for a fast passage. The following table, compiled from a variety of sources, gives the sailing times for six contemporary voyages between New London and Kerguelen. The larger vessels generally had a longer passage on the outbound voyage because they hunted whales on the way out to Kerguelen. On the way home they had a full cargo. From the days required by other vessels in similar voyages, it seems highly improbable that the *Corinthian* could have left New London on November 15 and reached Kerguelen before February 1.

SAILING TIMES ON VOYAGES BETWEEN NEW LONDON AND KERGUELEN

Vessel	Direction	Departure	Arrival	Number of Days
Ship Julius Caesar	outbound	Aug. 18, 1851	Dec. 29, 1851	134
Ship Julius Caesar	inbound	Mar. 3, 1853	June 4, 1853	94
Ship Corinthian	inbound	Mar. 10?, 1853	June 24, 1853	106±
Ship Peruvian	inbound	Mar. 22, 1852	July 21, 1852	122
Ship Peruvian	outbound	Aug. 19, 1852	Jan. 1, 1853	136
Schooner Exile	inbound	Mar. 22, 1852	July 3, 1852	104
Schooner Exile	outbound	Aug. 18, 1852	Dec. 8, 1852	113
Bark Hannah Brewer	inbound	Mar. 24, 1854	July 15, 1854	114
Brig Zoe*	outbound	Oct. 26, 1855	Feb. 18, 1856	116
Brig Zoe*	inbound	Dec. 19, 1856	Apr. 3, 1857	106

*Voyages of the brig *Zoe* were from New London to Heard Island and return.

The second reason for believing that Captain Rogers did not land on Heard Island before 1855 is that there would scarcely have been time for him to learn of the discovery of the island by February 1, 1854. Captain Heard had arrived in Melbourne on December 22, 1853, 27 days after sighting the island. We know that the first public announcement of his discovery was made in the Melbourne *Argus* December 24, 1853. It is most likely that Rogers learned of the discovery from a vessel he spoke while cruising for whales in the Indian Ocean. For him to have learned of the discovery in January 1854, such a vessel would have had to leave Melbourne, bound for the Cape of Good Hope, not more than a few days after Heard's arrival. It would have been possible for Rogers to have spoken such a vessel on or about January 20, 1854, but the timing of the whole sequence of fortuitous events is only barely possible. Captain Heard's letter to Maury, dated January 4, 1854, was dispatched via the bark *Auckland,* bound for San Francisco. It is not improbable that this was his first opportunity to send a message to the United States.

The third reason for believing that Rogers' landing was in January 1855 rather than 1854 is that he did not sail for home until 1856. If he had landed on Heard Island in 1854, he would have had no difficulty in getting his cargo in October and November 1854, making it possible for him to have sailed for New London early in 1855.

The fourth reason for believing that the landing was made in 1855 is a point emphasized by Lanman, who states that Perkins and Smith had no vessel available when they received Rogers' message, but that they purchased one at once.[23] If they had received Rogers' message in 1854 it would have been by their own vessel, the bark *Hannah Brewer,* which would then have been available to be dispatched to Heard Island. They purchased, and Captain Smith sailed in, the *Laurens* in 1855, the year they most likely received Rogers' message.

How Captain Rogers sent the news of his good fortune to Perkins and Smith is not now known. From Rogers' statement to Clark, it would appear that the *Corinthian* and her tenders returned to Kerguelen Island sometime in February. If, as he says, it was 1854, he could have sent word via the *Hannah Brewer,* which sailed for New London on March 24, 1854. According to a sworn statement attached to the crew list, one of his crew went home in the *Hannah Brewer.* If, on the other hand, the date was 1855, the message could have been sent via the schooner *Marcia,* which sailed for New London on March 20, 1855. Another member of Rogers' crew went home in that vessel.

Meanwhile, the *Corinthian* and her tenders took up their respective roles normally played in the annual cycle at Kerguelen. The following summer season they returned to Heard Island to complete their cargoes, the bark *Laurens* now being part of the fleet.

On June 9, 1856, the *Corinthian* arrived in New London, the first of the Perkins and Smith fleet to reach home after having been at Heard Island. Attachments to the crew list, signed April 28, 1856, show that Captain Rogers stopped at St. Helena on the homeward voyage. Four of his men had transferred to the *Laurens* on February 20 at "the Island of Desolation." The inbound cargo manifest declared by Rogers listed 2000 barrels of elephant oil, 1200 barrels of whale oil and 10,000 pounds of whalebone.

On June 14, 1856, the schooner *Atlas* arrived at New London, having been at sea 40 days since leaving St. Helena. Captain Edwards declared a cargo of 115 barrels of whale and elephant oil. The schooner *Franklin,* having left St. Helena the same day as the *Atlas,* arrived in New London on June 17, and Captain Joshua Starr declared a cargo of 130 barrels of whale oil. The *Mechanic* apparently remained at Kerguelen as tender to the *Laurens.*

THE VOYAGE OF THE *LAURENS*

When the firm of Perkins and Smith received E. D. Rogers' message about the great number of elephant seals to be had at Heard Island and his request that they send out another vessel, all of their ships were at sea. Consequently, Franklin F. Smith purchased at New York the bark *Laurens,* which he brought into New London on August 17, 1855, to be thoroughly fitted for a sealing cruise. She was registered under her new owners at New London on September 14 as a bark of 420 tons built at Kennebunk, Maine, in 1837.

Franklin F. Smith had retired in 1846 from an active life at sea as a whaling captain, to become a partner in the firm of Perkins and Smith. Although 52 years old and a man of means, he decided to take command of the *Laurens.* The bark sailed from New London on September 17, 1855, with 48 men on board. This unusually large crew was an indication that the voyage was intended to be mainly for seals rather than for whales.

Little is known of the outbound voyage of the *Laurens* or of its arrival on the sealing grounds. On October 15 the *Laurens* was spoken by Captain Richmond of the ship *Franklin* of New Bedford in 13°36′ N, 27°54′ W, in the mid-Atlantic southwest of the Cape Verde Islands.[24]

Both Rogers and Lanman[25] report that Captain Smith explored Heard Island and made a rough map of it. This map has not been located, but the names given to bays and headlands by Smith and later by other sealers have been perpetuated in the reconnaissance map made by members of the *Challenger* expedition, who received their information from the sealing boss whom they met on the island and from captains of sealing vessels encountered at Royal Sound (Baie du Morbihan) on Kerguelen Island.[26] Lanman relates how on one beach 500 elephant seals were killed. At another point 3000 barrels of oil were rolled "across a neck of the island" to a point where they could be put aboard ship. Much of this oil must have been sent home on other vessels, for on February 19, 1856, the *Laurens* had only 1200 barrels of oil in her hold.[27]

During the southern winter of 1856 the schooner *Mechanic* remained at Kerguelen as tender to the *Laurens,* and three men from the latter were transferred to the schooner. As the two vessels were sailing in company from Kerguelen to begin the next season on Heard Island, in October 1856 they were struck by a severe storm which lasted four days.[28] On October 14, while they were lying to in this storm, the *Mechanic* was struck by a great wave which washed five men overboard. Two men were rescued, but the captain and two men were lost. The remaining three still able-bodied men and a boy were unable to work the badly damaged *Mechanic* which, becoming separated from the *Laurens,* was driven eastward before the storm. The schooner drifted far to the eastward, and when the storm abated the undermanned crew found that they could not work their ship westward against the roaring winds of that latitude. Their only alternative was to try to make an Australian port to the eastward. In this distressed condition they were sighted by the streamer *Champion.* With aid of the mate and a member of the crew from the streamer, the *Mechanic* was brought into Portland, Victoria, about 200 miles west of Melbourne, on December 13.

By the time Captain Smith was ready to sail for home on January 10, 1857, Heard Island was no longer the secret preserve of Perkins and Smith vessels, for he reportedly left there, besides the *Corinthian* and the *Atlas,* the ships *Isaac Hicks* of New London and *Samuel Robertson* of Fairhaven, Massachusetts, the barks *Alert* and *Pioneer,* and the schooners *Pacific* and *E. R. Sawyer* of New London.[29] The brig *Zoe* had sailed for New London on December 19, and on that same day the 180-ton schooner *Alfred,* tender to the ship *Samuel Robertson,* was wrecked and sank when it was driven onshore at Heard Island with four anchors dragging.

The *Laurens* was at Cape Town on February 28 and at St. Helena on March 18. On May 8, 1857, she arrived at New London where Smith, according to his inbound manifest filed at the Custom House, declared a cargo of 3800 barrels of elephant oil, 50 barrels of whale oil, 300 pounds of whalebone, and 80 sealskins.

YEAR-ROUND OCCUPATION OF HEARD ISLAND

THE VOYAGE OF THE BRIG *ZOE*

The continuous occupation of Heard Island, which was to last a quarter of a century, was begun with the voyage of the brig *Zoe.* In 1856, Henry Rogers, first mate on the *Zoe,* led the first party of men to winter on the island.

Thomas Fitch, II, owned one of the New London whaling firms. In April 1855 his brig *Zoe* returned from a whaling voyage in the Pacific Ocean. In October, according to the outbound manifest filed at the New London Custom House, Fitch dispatched the brig on a voyage "bound for Desolation Is. & elsewhere whaling and elephanting." Whether it was a regular mixed voyage to Kerguelen Island in the familiar pattern of New London whalers or whether it was made with a previous knowledge of E. D. Rogers' message regarding the existence of thousands of elephant seals on Heard Island cannot be determined from the evidence at hand. There are clues to support both possibilities.

The *Zoe* was a brig of 196 tons built at Baltimore in 1847. She was commanded by Captain James H. Rogers of Montville, a cousin of Erasmus D. Rogers. Serving as first mate was the captain's younger brother, Henry Rogers. The ship's company totaled 21 men when she sailed from New London on October 26, 1855.

On November 18, 22 days from New London, the Cape Verde Islands were in sight. From the Cape Verdes Captain Rogers sailed for the waters of the south Atlantic. He was reported at Tristan da Cunha on December 22, 1855 bound for "Desolation Island." He was apparently engaged in whaling in these waters, for the *Zoe* touched at Tristan de Cunha again on December 28. Up to this point the *Zoe* had taken no whales, for in each instance she was described as "clean."[30]

On February 13, 1856, 109 days out of New London, the *Zoe* arrived at Heard Island. Five weeks were devoted to rafting "several hundred barrels of oil prepared by a previous ship to the brig."[31] On March 22, Henry Rogers moved onshore with 25 men to spend the winter on Heard Island. We know that oil prepared by a previous ship was put on board the *Zoe,* which arrived late in the season at Heard Island, and that Henry Rogers went ashore with 25 men when the entire company of the *Zoe* totaled only 21 men. These are clear indications that some cooperative arrangement was made between James H. Rogers and the captain of another ship at Heard Island. It could well have been with Captain Smith, who had reached there earlier with a crew of 42 men, or it could have been a more complex arrangement including Captain E. D. Rogers, who was still there with his tenders when the *Zoe* arrived at Heard Island. The *Corinthian* and the three tenders belonging to Perkins and Smith had been there long enough to have accumulated a greater cargo than they could carry. Although the different whaling firms were competitors, cooperation for their mutual benefit was the accepted thing. Taylor points out some examples of how they agreed on division of the beaches and how they improvised rules to govern their competition.[32]

THEIR FIRST WINTER ON HEARD ISLAND

The men who made up the first wintering party on Heard Island prepared a crude shelter for themselves by digging a square hole in the ground which they covered with boards. It was made weather tight by putting moss and snow in the cracks. After the living quarters were prepared the work of obtaining a cargo of oil was begun, for the *Zoe* sailed with its cargo for Cape Town on March 26. The *Corinthian, Atlas,* and *Franklin* left for home, and the *Laurens* and *Mechanic* sought a safer mooring for the winter at Kerguelen Island. The wintering party soon settled into a routine with a recognition, even here, of the economy of specialization. Those most expert with the lance went out to slaughter elephant seals, from three to as many as 40 being killed each day. The coopers were kept busy assembling casks. When a large number of seals were killed it was sometimes necessary for all hands to help in skinning the animals and cutting up the blubber. The blubber was cut into pieces weighing about 15 pounds each. These the men carried on their backs or dragged on crude sledges to the "try kettles" where the oil was rendered from the blubber.

From the journal kept by Henry Rogers during his stay on Heard Island, Lanman was able to describe the weather the men experienced there.[33] Apparently it was typical of what we have come to know as normal weather in that area. Gales with rain or more often snow, interrupted by less windy spells of drizzle and fog, followed one another in monotonous succession, and the men were thankful for one bright day in thirty. This was no time for leisure, and the men kept at their grim toil every day the weather permitted, Sundays included. A lighter touch, however, was provided by a one-hour celebration on July 4.

Meanwhile, the *Zoe* had reached Cape Town from where James H. Rogers wrote a letter, dated July 15, 1856, in which he reported that 225 barrels of elephant oil would be shipped home on the brig *Eutaw* of Boston.[34] He reported the *Laurens* with 1700 barrels of elephant oil at Heard Island when he left there on March 26.

When the *Zoe* again arrived at Heard Island is not known. Several weeks must have been required to raft 590 barrels of oil to the ship. This was all finished and the *Zoe* put to sea on December 19, 1856. At the time the *Zoe* sailed from

Heard Island the *Laurens* had a full cargo of oil for Perkins and Smith. Captain Erasmus D. Rogers had 500 barrels of oil on board the *Corinthian* for the same firm, Captain Church had 250 barrels of oil aboard *Alert* for Williams and Haven, and Captain Morgan had stowed the *Pioneer* with 1000 barrels of oil for E. V. Stoddard. Captain Norie had 600 barrels of oil aboard the ship *Isaac Hicks,* belonging to Lawrence and Company. On the homeward journey the *Zoe* called at Cape Town from whence she sailed on February 3, 1857. On April 3 she arrived in New London.[35]

OPERATIONS ON HEARD ISLAND

From the number of vessels at Heard Island during the 1856-57 season, it is apparent that it did not take long after its discovery for the island to become the center of an intensive sealing operation. Since the island is only about 24 miles long and 11 miles wide, with a total shoreline of roughly 65 miles, conditions must have been crowded at times. That the seals survived extinction was due only to the existence of some beaches which proved inaccessible to whaleboats. Seal oil sold then for about 55 cents a gallon, and a barrel of oil contained 40 gallons. As long as the seals withstood the slaughter, money could be made at Heard Island, and the ships continued to come. The rapid decline in arrivals is indicated in the accompanying table of ships sailing from United States ports for Heard or "Desolation Island." The data have been taken from Clark's list of American sealing voyages from 1840 to 1880.[36] Although some of the vessels reportedly sailed for "Desolation Island," most of these are known to have also been at Heard Island. As the number of seals declined and the Civil War interrupted normal activities, there were some years when no vessels sailed for Heard Island. That does not mean, however, that sealers did not occupy the island, for most voyages were of two years' duration. Moreover, men remained on the island even while the ship was on a voyage home with a cargo of oil, for it was common practice for the men to sign up for three years. The single ship that sailed in 1879 took sealskins only and apparently did not kill any elephant seals.

NUMBER OF SEALING VESSELS ANNUALLY LEAVING AMERICAN PORTS
FOR HEARD OR KERGUELEN ISLANDS, 1855 TO 1880

Year	Destination		Total Number	Year	Destination		Total Number
	Heard	Kerguelen	Number		Heard	Kerguelen	Number
1855	3	0	3	1868	0	2	2
1856	6	3	9	1869	0	2	2
1857	6	2	8	1870	2	0	2
1858	8	2	10	1871	1	1	2
1859	0	3	3	1872	2	0	2
1860	3	3	6	1873	3	0	3
1861	0	0	0	1874	1	0	1
1862	2	1	3	1875	3	0	3
1863	0	1	1	1876	0	0	0
1864	3	2	5	1877	1	1	2
1865	1	3	4	1878	0	0	0
1866	0	1	1	1879	0	1	1
1867	3	1	4	1880	1	2	3

Of all the voyages represented in the table, only 11 originated from ports other than New London. Five were from neighboring Mystic, two were from Warren, Rhode Island, three were from Fairhaven, Massachusetts, and one from Provincetown, Massachusetts. Voyages continued to be made to Heard and Kerguelen islands after 1880, but such ventures were much less frequent and at increasingly greater intervals as the 19th century came to a close.

Once operations were established at Heard Island on a year-round basis, the sealers soon found that conditions were much harsher there than they had experienced on Kerguelen. Temperatures were decidedly colder and snow was heavier and remained on the ground for much of the year. Gales with associated rain, sleet or snow might be expected at frequent intervals, even in the so-called summer season. Winter blizzards were even more frequent and wind velocities more extreme on Heard. Vegetation is much sparser on Heard Island, and many birds which frequent Kerguelen Island are not found on Heard.

After the first winter on Heard Island, the sealers' huts were made slightly more substantial with materials brought from home, but they were still cramped, dark, and lacking in normal comforts. They were heated by stoves burning coal brought in the ship and by burning scraps from the try kettles. Penguin skins, with fat clinging to them, were also used as fuel. The flickering oil lamps and the stoves made the huts both smoky and smelly. Flour, sugar, molasses, coffee, salt, and dried beans were brought from home; salt meat and sea biscuit were supplied from the ship's stores. These staples were supplemented with penguin eggs, penguins, and tongues from the elephant seals. The men became quite fond of the tongues, which were sometimes made into mince pies. In addition to living quarters, a cooper's shack and a try kettle were set up on the beaches accessible to the ships. Each of the firms engaged in the business had such establishments on the island. In addition, huts were also established on less accessible beaches as quarters for men stationed there, although try kettles were not set up.

The beaches on Heard Island where the elephant seals hauled up are separated from one another by precipitous cliffs of rock or the equally steep and more treacherous front of a glacier from which icebergs frequently are calved. Communication between men stationed on separate beaches was therefore carried on only with great danger by crossing over the crevassed glacial surfaces or by edging along the beach, beneath overhanging walls of rock or ice.

Heard Island is oriented roughly northwest-southeast, with the southwest side being the more exposed to prevailing winds and storms and having no harbors whatever. For this reason the seals were first attacked on the northeast side of the island, where landings could be made. As their numbers declined and they became more wary, the seals tended to avoid the beaches on the northeast side of the island in favor of the more exposed side, and this added to the sealers' problems. As mentioned above, blubber from seals killed on the inaccessible beaches had to be carried on the backs of men or cut into little pieces and put in casks, which were rolled over the divides to the beaches, where they could be picked up by the boats. Where this was impossible, men were stationed to drive off the seals attempting to come up on the beach in the hope that they would come up again on a more accessible spot.

There are no well-protected harbors on Heard Island, even on the northeast side, so it was found advisable for ships to winter at Kerguelen Island. Even during the warmer season, ships were never safe at Heard. Landings were made from whaleboats, often through heavy surf. While the ships remained at Corinthian Bay or were on the voyage home, the schooners coasted along the shores of the island, putting men ashore in whaleboats or rafting casks of blubber or oil from the beach to the vessel to be transferred to the ship. This was dangerous work, and while the ship might be exposed for a few weeks, the schooners were exposed for months. As a result, many schooners were wrecked.

The fate of the *Mechanic* and the wreck of the *Alfred* have already been mentioned. In February 1859 the schooner *Frank* was wrecked on the northwestern end of the island and on October 21, 1859, the schooner *Mary Powell* was driven against the glacier and sunk, south of Fairchild Beach. In 1860 the schooner *Exile* was driven ashore at Corinthian Bay and on February 1, 1863, the schooner *Pacific* was driven ashore in a gale, marooning the crew until they were picked up by another vessel the following October. The schooner *E. R. Sawyer* was lost on September 17, 1866, when she was driven ashore at Stony Beach (Rocky Beach, Gilchrist Beach). The schooners *Alfred* and *R. B. Coleman* were wrecked on a rocky reef near Spit Point. In 1880 the bark *Trinity* was driven onshore and wrecked at Spit Bay. In addition, two schooners were lost on voyages after leaving Heard Island, the *Silver Cloud* in 1862, and the *Pilot's Bride* in 1881. Such a list of wrecks is convincing testimony to the hazardous life of the sealers at Heard Island.

GEOGRAPHIC CONTRIBUTIONS OF THE SEALERS

Sealing captains were primarily interested in procuring a cargo of oil as quickly as possible. As a by-product of their operations, however, at least three maps were drawn of Heard Island, and a weather record kept by them assisted the United States Commission for the Observation of the Transit of Venus. The first map ever made of Heard Island, the rough one drawn by Captain Franklin F. Smith in 1855-56, has not been found. Another map, however, was published in 1887 by Clark in his work on American sealing.[37] It was made by Captain H. C. Chester, who spent several seasons at Heard Island. A copy of a third map is reproduced here as Plate IV. The original manuscript of this hitherto unpublished map, $10\frac{1}{2}$ x 17 inches, is on file in the National Archives among the records of the Hydrographic Office.[38] Available records of the Hydrographic Office, however, shed no light on the origin of this map.

Analysis of this manuscript map reveals a remarkable combination of professional and amateur workmanship. The geographic position of the center of the island is very accurate by present standards, although the orientation of the longer axis should be more northwest-southeast. No date is given on the map, but the location of the wreck of the schooner *Exile* is indicated, which suggests a date later than 1860. The location of other wrecks would suggest an even later date. The hachuring has a professional touch, but the misspellings indicate the work of a person with limited formal education, such as that of a sealing captain. Only a sealer would have information regarding the location of the trail along the south shore and of the several huts and try-works. Sealers normally referred to glaciers as icebergs, and the icecap of the principal peak is so designated on this map. Moreover, the sealers generally referred to the island as Hurd's Island. The map suggests, therefore, that it is either the work of a sealer who had a fine draftsman's hand or was drawn by a draftsman from a rough sketch and information provided by a sealer.

In 1872, while preparations for observation of the transit of the planet Venus were in their early stages, Mr. R. W. Chapell, junior partner of the firm of Williams and Havens, made an offer to provide meteorological data for use by the Commission for the Observation of the Transit of Venus in deciding whether or not to establish an observatory at Heard Island. In a letter of July 1, 1872, Rear Admiral B. F. Sands, Superintendent of the Naval Observatory and Secretary to the Commission, acknowledged Mr. Chapell's offer and inquired about the possibility of the company's vessels transporting one party of observers to Heard Island and another to the Crozets.[39] The report on the weather during the months of November and December at Heard Island in 1872 was received by the Commission the following summer.[40] The exact nature of the report is unknown, for it has not been located. In his letter of July 1, 1872, to Mr. Chapell, Admiral Sands asked only for a report as to whether or not the weather was clear or cloudy during each morning for the months of November and December. Whatever it contained, the report convinced the Commission that the weather would be unsatisfactory for an astronomical station on Heard Island.

THE VOYAGE OF THE U.S.S. *MARION*

The bark *Trinity*, belonging to Lawrence and Company, sailed from New London on June 1, 1880, on a sealing voyage to Heard Island. The 316-ton vessel carried a crew of 16 officers and men under the command of Captain John Williams.[41] After calling at the Cape Verdes, where 19 additional hands were signed on, and at Pot Harbor on Kerguelen Island, the *Trinity* arrived at Heard Island on October 2, 1880. Four men with supplies for four months were left at Corinthian Bay before proceeding to Spit Bay. Here, with unloading operations just begun, a northerly gale suddenly sprang up, causing the ship to drag her anchors. In spite of the crew's efforts to save the vessel, she was driven upon a steep beach on the morning of October 17, 1880. The men worked desperately for some hours rescuing all hands and the most essential supplies and provisions before the vessel was completely lost. Marooned on the island, the men sought shelter in three of the huts, living on what provisions they had salvaged and on what they could hunt on the island. Only two men were lost, being frozen to death while out searching for food, but all hands suffered from inadequate clothing which was eventually reduced to tatters. Food, too, was often scarce and sometimes absent.

When, after 18 months, the vessel did not return to New London, its fate became a matter of public concern. As a result the Navy Department ordered the U.S.S. *Marion*, commanded by Commander Silas W. Perry, to proceed from

Montevideo, where it was stationed as part of the South Atlantic Fleet, to Heard Island to investigate the matter. Calling at Cape Town, the *Marion* proceeded on December 24 for Heard Island. On January 12, 1882, the McDonald Islands were sighted and, at 4 p.m. that afternoon, Heard Island appeared out of the mists. Approaching the island from the south, the *Marion* steamed cautiously around the breakers off Spit Point and came to anchor at 9 p.m. in Spit Bay. Earlier, a party of men had been noticed on shore and now they built a fire to attract the attention of the ship. The cruise of the *Marion* had not been in vain.

On January 14 the men on the beach were taken on board, and the next day the men at Corinthian Bay were rescued. The *Marion* then steamed north to Kerguelen, where one night was spent in Greenland Harbor (Baie Greenland). From here she sailed for Cape Town, where on February 20, 1882, the crew of the *Trinity* was placed in charge of the United States Consul.

During the short stay at Heard Island, Ensign W. I. Chambers made a number of alterations on the map of Heard Island made by members of the *Challenger* Expedition. He also sketched and tinted with watercolors seven views of the island. These are now filed with his map in the Cartographic Records Division of the National Archives.[42]

The wreck of the *Trinity* did not end the sealing business on Heard Island, but changing economic conditions and the scarcity of seals resulting from the many years of wholesale slaughter were making sealing increasingly less profitable. The schooner *Charles Colgate* made a voyage from New London to the "Desolation Islands" in 1883-84, and the schooner *Francis Allyn* sailed for the Crozets and "Desolation Islands" on August 2, 1887, returning the following July 12. Other voyages followed, but with decreasing frequency.

NOTES

1. Edouard A. Stackpole, *The Sea Hunters* (Philadelphia, Lippincott, 1953), pp. 194-205. Stackpole's account of this voyage is based on the logbook of the *Asia*.

2. Kerguelen Island was discovered in February 1772 by Yves Joseph de Kerguelen-Trémarec, a French explorer. On a second voyage in 1773-74 one of his three vessels, *Oiseau*, made a landing in the bay which bears its name. Capt. James Cook anchored here on December 25, 1776, and called it Christmas Harbor. American sealers used Cook's names for parts of the island he explored and applied many of their own. The latter, however, are now practically all discarded, and current maps of Kerguelen Island carry mostly French names or French versions of English names. Impressed by the desolate character of the island, Kerguelen on his second voyage changed the name to "Land of Desolation." On his visit in 1776 Cook, too, suggested this as an appropriate name.

3. Alexander Starbuck, *History of the American Whale-fishery* (Waltham, Mass., 1878), pp. 196-197.

4. A. Howard Clark, "The Antarctic Fur-seal and Sea-elephant Industries," *The Fisheries and Fishery Industries of the United States*, U. S. Bureau of Fish and Fisheries, Sen. Misc. Doc. 124, 47th Congr., 1st Sess., 1887, Sec. V, vol. 2, p. 418.

5. *Ibid.*, pp. 454-455.

6. Frances M. Caulkins, *History of New London, Connecticut* (New London, 1895), p. 645; Barnard L. Colby, "New London Whaling Captains," *The Marine Historical Association, Inc.* (Mystic, Conn., 1936), vol. 1, No. 11, p. 188.

7. Howard Palmer, Introduction to Nathaniel W. Taylor's *Life on a Whaler* (New London, New London County Historical Society, 1929), p. iv.

8. Charles Lanman, *Recollections of Curious Characters and Pleasant Places* (Edinburgh, 1881), pp. 56-57. Also "Hunting the Sea-Elephant," *Forest and Stream & Rod and Gun*, vol. 11, No. 22, January 2, 1879, p. 437; Colby, *op. cit.*, pp. 195-196.

9. Data pertaining to the *Corinthian* and other vessels, unless otherwise indicated, were ob-

tained from ship registers of the vessel documentation series, Records of the Bureau of Marine Inspection and Navigation, Record Group 41, U. S. National Archives.

10. Taylor, *op. cit.*, p. 95.

11. *Ibid.*, p. iv.

12. Colby, *op. cit.*, pp. 203-204.

13. Unless otherwise indicated, information relating to the crews has been obtained from various Custom House documents listed in the bibliography. For the vessels dealt with in this chapter, crew lists are available for the *Corinthian* for the voyages beginning in 1851 and 1853, for the *Atlas*, the *Laurens*, and the *Zoe*. Outbound and inbound cargo manifests also give some information in terms of passengers and commanding officer, as well as ownership of the vessel.

14. Taylor, *op. cit.*, pp. 95-96, 174.

15. Inbound cargo manifest of the *Corinthian*, signed by E. D. Rogers, June 10, 1853, Records of the New London, Conn. Custom House, Federal Records Center, Waltham, Mass.

16. Taylor, *op. cit.*, pp. 51, 65, 74, 75, 79-83, 95, 131, 167-168, 170, 178.

17. Inbound cargo manifest for the *Corinthian*, June 25, 1853, Records of the New London, Conn., Custom House, Federal Records Center, Waltham, Mass.

18. Apparent from affidavits sworn to by Rogers, April 28, 1856, and by Capt. Edwards, April 29, 1856, before the American consul at St. Helena, which are attached to the respective crew lists of the two vessels now on file with the records of the New London Custom House in the Federal Records Center at Waltham, Mass.

19. Clark, *op. cit.*, pp. 419-420. Rogers' "Corinthian Harbor" is now officially named Corinthian Bay.

20. H. N. Moseley, *Notes by a Naturalist on the* "Challenger" (London, 1879), p. 229.

21. T. H. Tizard, H. N. Moseley, J. Y. Buchanan, and John Murray, *Reports on the Scientific Results of the Voyage of H. M. S. Challenger During the Years 1873-76, Narrative*, vol. 1, First Part (London, 1885), p. 376.

22. Lanman, *op. cit.*, pp. 55-66.

23. *Ibid.*, p. 59.

24. *New London Democrat*, December 8, 1855, "Marine Journal."

25. Lanman, *op. cit.*, p. 59.

26. Tizard, et al., *op. cit.*, Map Sheet 22, opposite p. 370.

27. According to a sworn statement attached to the crew list when three men were signed on and their shares indicated.

28. An account of the storm and the disaster to the *Mechanic* is contained in an article datelined December 15, Portland, New South Wales, which was published in the *New London Daily Star* March 30, 1857. In this account the *Mechanic* is said to have been sailing in company with the *Corinthian*, to which it was tender. When the *Laurens* returned to New London, according to the *Daily Star* for May 8, 1857, Capt. Smith reported that the *Mechanic* had parted company with the *Laurens* on October 14 and had not been heard from since. Either the Australian account had the ships confused or all three ships were sailing in company. The *Corinthian* had sailed from New London on July 9, 1856, and could possibly have reached Kerguelen by then.

29. *New London Daily Star*, May 8, 1857.

30. The progress of the *Zoe* was related in notes appearing in the "Marine Journal" of the *New London Democrat* for February 2, March 22, and April 12, 1856.

31. Lanman, *op. cit.*, p. 64.

32. Taylor, *op. cit.*, pp. 75-76.

33. Lanman, *op. cit.*, p. 65.

34. *New London Democrat*, September 27, 1856.

35. *New London Daily Star*, April 4, 1857.

36. Clark, *op. cit.*, pp. 454-460.

37. Clark, *op. cit.*, Sec. V, "Atlas of Plates," Plate 227.

38. Records of the Hydrographic Office, U. S. Navy, Record Group 37, Cartographic Records Division, U. S. National Archives.

39. Miscellaneous Letters Sent by the Director of the Naval Observatory, Chronological Record Book, October 13, 1870, to March 28, 1878, pp. 174-175, Record Group 78, Records of the Naval Observatory, U. S. National Archives.

40. Simon B. Newcomb, *Observation of the Transit of Venus, December 8-9, 1874*, Sen. Exec. Doc. No. 31, 46th Congr., 1st Sess., Washington, 1880, p. 13.

41. The voyage of the *Trinity* and the rescue of its crew at Heard Island by the U. S. S. *Marion* is related by W. I. Chambers, Ensign, U. S. N., in his "Rescue of the Trinity's Crew

from Heard's Island," *Proceedings of the United States Naval Institute,* vol. 9, No. 1, March, 1883, pp. 121-129.

42.   Records of the Hydrographic Office, U. S. Navy, Record Group 37, Cartographic Records Division, U. S. National Archives.

BIBLIOGRAPHY

PUBLISHED MATERIAL

Caulkins, Frances M., *History of New London, Connecticut, From the First Survey of the Coast in 1612 to 1860* (New London, H. D. Utley, 1895), xviii and 696 pp. (See pp. 638-647.)

Chambers, W. I. (Ensign, U. S. N.), "Rescue of the Trinity's Crew from Heard Island," *Proceedings of the United States Naval Institute,* vol. 9 No. 1, March 1883, pp. 121-129.

Clark A. Howard, "The Antarctic Fur-seal and Sea-elephant Industries," *The Fisheries and Fishery Industries of the United States* (George Brown Goode, ed.), 7 vols., 1884-1887, U. S. Bureau of Fish and Fisheries, Sen. Misc. Doc. 124, 47th Congr., 1st Sess., 1887. (See Sec. V, vol. 2, 1887, pp. 400-467; also "Atlas of Plates" to Sec. V.)

Colby, Barnard L., "New London Whaling Captains," *The Marine Historical Association, Inc.,* Mystic, Conn., vol. 1, No. 11, 1936, pp. 185-225.

——, a series of articles on New London whaling, *New London Day,* January 19, 1935, to April 25, 1936.

Lanman, Charles, "Hunting the Sea-Elephant," *Forest and Stream & Rod and Gun,* vol. 11, No. 22, January 2, 1879, pp. 437-438.

——, "The Desolation Islands," *New London Daily Star,* May 18, 1869. Similar to the entry just above. Also reprinted in *New London Democrat,* May 22, 1869.

——, *Recollections of Curious Characters and Pleasant Places* (Edinburgh, David Douglas, 1881), xiii and 351 pp. (Pages 55-66 carry the same story as the two Lanman entries above, the first landing on Heard Island and the account of the first winter party there.)

Moseley, H. N., *Notes by a Naturalist on the Challenger* (London, Macmillan, 1879), xvi and 620 pp. (See pp. 221, 227-229.)

New London Daily Star, January 6, 1857; March 26, March 30, April 4, May 8, 1857; June 4, June 14, July 28, August 17, August 30, 1858.

New London Democrat, April 14, August 25, September 22, September 29, November 3, December 8, 1855; February 2, March 29, April 12, June 14, July 12, July 26, August 9, September 20, September 22, September 27, November 15, November 22, December 6, 1856.

Scammon, Charles M., *The Marine Mammals of the Northwestern Coast of North America* (San Francisco and New York, John H. Carmany, and G. P. Putnam's Sons, 1874), v and 319 pp. Includes discussions of elephant sealing and fur sealing in the Antarctic. (See pp. 120-122.)

Stackpole, Edouard A., *The Sea Hunters* (Philadelphia and New York, 1853), 510 pp.

Starbuck, Alexander, *History of the American Whale Fishery, from its Earliest Inception to the Year 1876* (Waltham, Mass., privately printed, 1878), 768 pp., 6 plates. Also published as *Report of the Commissioner of Fish and Fisheries for 1875-76,* Appendix A, I, Misc. Sen. Doc. 107, 44th Congr., 1st Sess., 1878.

Taylor, Nathaniel W., *Life on a Whaler or Antarctic Adventure in the Isle of Desolation,* (New London, Conn., New London County Historical Society; 1929), vii and 208 pp.

Tizard, T. H.; H. N. Moseley, J. Y. Buchanan, and John Murray, *Report on the Scientific Results of the Voyage of H. M. S. Challenger during the Years 1873-1876,* Narrative, vol. I. First Part (London, H. M. Stationery Office, 1885), liv, 509 pp. (See pp. 376-377 and map sheet 22 opposite p. 370.)

Williams, C. A., "Early Whaling Industry of New London," *Records and Papers of the New London County Historical Society,* Part I, vol. 2, 1895, pp. 3-22.

MANUSCRIPT MATERIAL

Crew Lists for the *Corinthian,* August 19, 1851, November 15, 1853; *Atlas,* August 12, 1851; *Laurens,* September 17, 1855; and *Zoe,* October 25, 1855. New London Custom House Records, Federal Records Center, Waltham, Mass.

Inward Manifests of the *Corinthian, Franklin, Atlas, Laurens* and *Zoe.* New London Custom House Records, Federal Records Center, Waltham, Mass.

Outward Manifests of the several ships dealt with in the paper. New London Custom House Records, Federal Records Center, Waltham, Mass.

Ship Registers of New London, Conn. Vessel Documentation Series, Records of the Bureau of Marine Inspection and Navigation, Record Group 41, U. S. National Archives.

14

THE UNITED STATES TRANSIT OF VENUS
EXPEDITION TO KERGUELEN ISLAND

ORGANIZATION AND ACCOMPLISHMENTS

This expedition was one of eight specifically organized by the United States Government as its contribution to the international program for the observation of the transit of Venus in 1874. Although the primary objective of the expedition was unrelated to the Antarctic, an account of its activities is included here for two reasons. First, the biological collections of Dr. Kidder, which were a by-product of the expedition, resulted in a significant contribution to the scientific knowledge of the Antarctic. Second, Kerguelen Island (Île Kerguelen), site of the expedition's observatory, lies astride the Antarctic Convergence, the geographic boundary of the Antarctic, making the expedition strictly an Antarctic activity. If the weather had been more promising an even more poleward site would have been chosen, Heard Island especially having been considered.

In the early 1870s the scientific world was much concerned with the transit of the planet Venus across the face of the sun, which was to occur on December 9, 1874. Measurements which had been made at the previous transits in 1761 and 1769 had proven to be not sufficiently accurate, and this was looked on as an opportunity to get a more precise measurement of the distance between the sun and the earth. All of the leading nations had plans to establish parties for the observation of the transit, which was to be fully visible, weather permitting, in a belt extending from eastern Siberia across Japan, China, the East Indies, part of the western Pacific Ocean, Australia, and the Indian Ocean. Except for the great probability of bad weather, Antarctic regions were supposed to be the best place to view the transit. In a limited way the international program for observing the transit of Venus was a predecessor of the International Geophysical Year of 1957-58, with the Antarctic having a key position in the worldwide network of observations.

As part of its contribution to this international scientific undertaking, the United States sent out eight parties to observe the transit of Venus. Five of these were stationed in the southern hemisphere. One of these was scheduled to be based on the sub-Antarctic Crozet Islands (Îles Crozet) and another on Kerguelen Island (Fig. 8).

ESTABLISHMENT AND OBJECTIVES OF THE PROJECT

Upon the instigation of the National Academy of Science, the United States Congress in Section 2 of the Naval Appropriations Bill, approved March 3, 1871, provided for an appropriation of $2000 to be used for experiments preliminary to the observation of the transit of Venus. It further provided that this and other appropriations that the Congress would make for the observation of the transit of Venus should be under the control of a Commission consisting of the Superintendent of the Naval Observatory, the President of the National Academy of Sciences, the Superintendent of the Coast Survey, and two professors of mathematics attached to the Naval Observatory. The original committee consisted of the following:

Rear Admiral B. F. Sands, Superintendent of the U. S. Naval Observatory
Professor Joseph Henry, President of the National Academy of Sciences
Professor Benjamin Pierce, Superintendent of the U. S. Coast Survey
Professor Simon B. Newcomb, U. S. Naval Observatory
Professor William Harkness, U. S. Naval Observatory

On April 13, 1870, Newcomb had read a paper before the National Academy of Sciences on the observation of the transit of Venus.[1] In February 1874, Admiral Sands retired and was replaced by Rear Admiral Charles H. Davis. In the same year Professor Pierce resigned as Superintendent of the Coast Survey and was replaced by Dr. C. P. Patterson.

In 1872, Commission requests for funds resulted in Congressional appropriations of $50,000 and $100,000. The former was appropriated for the construction of instruments, mostly of American make; the latter was for actual operations. Field parties were invested with naval character and subject to naval rules, regulations, and discipline.

In view of the international nature of the undertaking, the Commission was concerned that the United States parties should make notable contributions, thereby enhancing the reputation of American science. From the beginning, the Commission sought the advice of the nation's leading astronomers. Since shortcomings in past observations had been in the human equation, it was decided that the greatest emphasis should be placed on heliometer measurements and photography, and when it was found that not enough heliometers existed in the United States, it was decided to place chief reliance on photography. There was a predisposition toward the use of photography because of the remarkable success achieved by Mr. L. M. Rutherford of New York.[2] Because photography was to be the principal method of observation, the amount of equipment required was much reduced.[3]

Officially established for the observation of the transit of Venus, the Commission in its instructions to the field parties dealt only with astronomical matters. Any other activity of a scientific nature by members of the various parties was incidental to the principal objective.

The five southern hemisphere parties were transported from New York to their respective bases on the U. S. *Swatara* under the command of Commander Ralph Chandler. The ship carried a complement of 174 men and 15 officers. The Kerguelen party was picked up by the U. S. S. *Monongahela,* commanded by Captain James S. Thornton, and transported to Cape Town, from where they reached the United States via merchant ships. The *Monongahela* carried a complement of 200 men and 21 officers. Both ships were square-rigged vessels with auxiliary steam-driven screw propellers.

Each of the eight observing parties consisted of an astronomer, who was chief of the party, an assistant astronomer, one chief photographer, and two assistant photographers. The chief photographers were working professionals; the assistants were college graduates trained in science. The entire force gathered at Washington in the spring of 1874 for several weeks of training under the direction of Dr. Henry Draper of New York. Each party was equipped with complete photographic apparatus, a transit instrument with a clock, two chronometers, a chronograph, and a five-inch equatorial telescope. All field parties had identical equipment so as to make the results as similar as possible.

The party based on Kerguelen Island consisted of the following:
Commander George P. Ryan, U.S.N., Chief Astronomer
Lieutenant Commander Charles J. Train, U.S.N., Assistant Astronomer
Mr. D. R. Holmes, Chief Photographer
Mr. G. W. Dryer, Assistant Photographer
Mr. Irvin Stanley, Assistant Photographer
Dr. Jerome H. Kidder, Passed Assistant Surgeon, U.S.N.
Joseph F. Bunker, Carpenter's Mate, U.S.N.
John Williams, Cook (shipped at Cape Town)

Since photography was to be the principal method of observation, the stations from which the observations were to be made had to be located in places where the greatest possible number of photographs could be taken during the period of the transit of the planet across the sun.

Because of the less reliable weather in the southern hemisphere, five of the eight parties were to be stationed there to insure against complete failure in that part of the world. Since weather would be the main factor affecting the success of the photographs, several American consular agents were requested through the Department of State to have meteorological observations made during November and December for both 1872 and 1873.

Astronomically, Antarctica was the ideal place from which to view the transit of Venus of 1874, but extremely unreliable weather and inaccessibility militated against establishing a base there. Kerguelen Island offered a reasonable compromise, but since it had been announced that a British party would occupy Christmas Harbor (Baie de l'Oiseau) and a German party Betsy Cove (Anse Betsy), the Commission felt an American party should occupy Heard Island. If possible, it was also proposed to land a party at Ship Bay on Possession Island (Île de la Possession) of the Crozet Islands (Îles Crozet) (Fig. 9).

Arrangements were made with the firm of Williams, Haven and Company of New London to make a record of weather at Whiskey Bay (Corinthian Bay[4]), Heard Island, for November and December 1872. This record, received in the summer of 1873, showed the weather at Heard Island to be entirely unsatisfactory.[5] The company, however, gave assurances that the weather at their base at Royal Sound (Baie du Morbihan), Kerguelen Island, was much more favorable, and suggested that an observatory be set up there. Since the British base at Christmas Harbor was to be in the northwestern part of the island and the German base at Betsy Cove was to be on the northeastern part of the island, the Commission felt that the sealers' station which was in the southeastern end of the island would be satisfactory. As a result of this decision, the five American bases in the southern hemisphere were to be located at Crozet Islands; Kerguelen Island; Hobart, Tasmania; Bluff Harbor, New Zealand; and Chatham Island. With the three northern stations they were arranged into three groups, in such a way that the combination of observations made at any two of them would give a valuable result of solar parallax.

ACCOMPLISHMENTS

The success of the United States project cannot be measured in terms of the success or failure of any one or more of the field parties, nor can the success of one national effort be considered alone. The accuracy of the final measurements of the distance between the sun and the earth would depend on the number of accurate observations obtained of solar parallax.[6] It had been agreed that each nation would compile the results for each of its stations according to a standard form and procedure, which would then be submitted to an international authority where the final calculations would be made based on the sum total of the observations. The American results were edited by Professor Simon B. Newcomb and published in 1878 as a Senate Document.[7]

In general it must be said that although the American photographic method was novel, it was remarkably successful where weather permitted. The Secretary of the Navy reported the results as follows:

At no one of these stations did the observers fail entirely, the degree of success was various at different places, the weather of course being the cause of this variation. It is gratifying to be able to say as much as this. Some parties belonging to other nations failed in consequence of bad weather.[8]

The efforts of the Kerguelen party were only partially successful. They were able to observe and photograph the ingress, but due to the weather becoming cloudy during the latter part of the transit they were not able to observe the egress. The pictures they did take, however, were successful. After viewing the photographs when he visited the American camp on December 21, Lieutenant Corbet of the British party wrote in his private journal, "... and we having all looked at their photographs of the 'Transit' which are very good...."[9]

The American party on Kerguelen included Dr. Jerome H. Kidder, Passed Assistant Surgeon of the Navy. While not a professional naturalist, Dr. Kidder was an extremely competent amateur. During his stay on Kerguelen he used every opportunity to collect specimens of plant and animal life as well as samples of the local rocks and minerals. When prepared for shipment they consisted of 19 boxes, one cask and one half-cask, according to the notation in the logbook of the *Monongahela*. The plant specimens were sent to Professor Asa Gray at Harvard. The zoological and geological specimens were sent to the Smithsonian Institution, and their value is appraised in the following statement:

The ornithological collections made by Dr. Kidder are believed to fully indicate the character of the avi-fauna of the locality, very few specimens having been overlooked. The specimens possess a high interest from the fact that they are among the rarities of American museums, while most of the eggs are new to collections, if not hitherto unknown to naturalists.[10]

Dr. Kidder discussed his collections, and the specimens were identified by experts in each field of natural science, in Bulletins of the United States National Museum.[11] His descriptions of the conditions of life on the island are excellent.

DETAILED RECORD OF OPERATIONS

VOYAGE OF THE *SWATARA*

Upon completion of the training program at Washington, the southern hemisphere parties and their equipment were transported to New York where they boarded the U.S.S. *Swatara*. The vessel, under Commander Ralph Chandler, left New York on June 7, 1874. Once at sea, steam power was used only when the wind failed. On July 10 the *Swatara* came to anchor at Bahia, Brazil, where coal, fresh meat, fresh vegetables, and bread were taken aboard. On July 14 the *Swatara* sailed for Cape Town, using steam or sails as the weather dictated.

On the afternoon of August 5 the *Swatara* anchored at Cape Town, where it remained for 16 days. While here the ship took on coal, fresh vegetables and meat, bread, flour, and other less perishable provisions for the long cruise. Coal, lumber, and other supplies were also taken on board for use of the scientific parties. A carpenter's mate for the Crozet party and a cook for the Kerguelen party were signed on.

While at Cape Town the American observing parties and the ship's officers had considerable contact with the British party which was also preparing to leave for Kerguelen in H.M.S. *Volage* and H.M.S. *Supply*. Here it was learned that the British had changed their plan as a result of a recommendation from Captain George S. Nares, Commander of the H.M.S. *Challenger,* which had visited Kerguelen in January 1874 for the specific purpose of seeking a satisfactory base for the transit of Venus party. He considered Betsy Cove the best place for an observatory, but since the Germans had signified their intention of using this position, Captain Nares recommended Molloy Point as being next best. This disturbed the Americans because the British had not been previously informed of the American plan, based on the recommendation of Williams, Haven and Company, to occupy Molloy Point. When the Commission selected this site it had been assumed that the British would carry out their announced intention of occupying Christmas Harbor. The British, at least privately, were even more disturbed, for they felt that the Americans who would reach Kerguelen first were stealing a march on them. They believed that somehow the Americans must have learned of Captain Nares' recommendation.[12]

The problem over the bases, however, was not serious enough to prevent a warm feeling of good fellowship. Lieutenant Corbet, second in command of the British party, after having met Commander Ryan and Lieutenant Commander Train, recorded the following in his private journal: "... they both seem first-rate fellows, and I think we shall agree and get on very well together down there. They are very willing to tell us everything they intend doing, and we therefore are the same to them.[13] The good feeling was also indicated by a round of dinners by and for the two groups.

The *Swatara* set sail from Cape Town on August 17. A course was set direct for the Crozet Islands. The boilers were fired and the engines started on August 28, shortly before a gale struck from the northeast. The storm moderated the next morning, but rain squalls continued with the weather remaining overcast and foggy.

On the morning of August 30 Hog Island, (Île aux Cochons) the westernmost of the Crozets, was sighted. Fog descended on the land at noon, but later the Twelve Apostle Islands (Îles des Apôtres) were sighted. From 6 to 8 p.m. the wind blew a violent gale from the southwest, accompanied by rain and hail. More or less gale conditions continued until the evening of the next day, but the ship was worked around to the side of Possession Island, and came to anchor in American Bay (Baie Américaine). At 5:30 a.m., September 1, the anchor was weighed and the ship steamed around the island to the southwest with strong winds blowing from the north and northeast. Wind prevented entering Ship Bay (Baie du Navire), where it was hoped to land the observing party. The bay was found to be dangerously small for so large a vessel, the distance between the headlands being only two cable lengths. The nearest anchorage, within a mile of the headlands, was in an exposed position with 20 fathoms of water.

The sea was very rough during the entire day, and Commander Chandler held the ship in a lee position between Possession Island and East Island (Île de l'Est) only by using the engines. Finally, at 5:30 p.m., he stood off before the wind under steam for ten miles and hove to under banked fires, expecting to try again for a better anchorage on September 2. By morning, however, he found he had been drifted 37 miles from Possession Island. Since the gale was still blowing from the northeast and north, Commander Chandler decided that the probability of being able to land a party on the Crozets was too poor to justify wasting any more time in the attempt and thereby jeopardize the establishment of one of the other bases. He therefore set a course for Kerguelen Island.

Except for a brief respite in the morning, the gale which had prevented a landing on the Crozets continued during September 2. The sea was rough, and a good deal of water was shipped. At midnight the wind shifted to the northwest, and the storm began to subside. The next three days were mostly clear, with occasional snow squalls and spells of cold cloudy weather.

High land was sighted on September 6, and the engines were started. At 6:00 p.m. the land was eight miles distant. During the night the ship steamed as slowly as the engines would turn. The next morning the ship stood in for the land under steam and sail and then moved eastward along the south coast of Kerguelen. At noon Mount Evans (Mont Evans) bore north at a distance of five miles. At 4:00 p.m. the *Swatara* entered Royal Sound and came to anchor a short time later in Three Islands Harbor (Port des Îles) in 10 fathoms. The sealing schooner *Charles Colgate* of New London was already at anchor.

September 8 began with violent wind squalls, and the sky was overcast and cloudy. Nevertheless, at 8:00 a.m. Commanders Chandler and Ryan with Lieutenant Commander Train, Professor Peters, and Lieutenant G. F. Wilkins, the navigator, left in the steam launch to examine the north side of the sound and select a landing site. They returned at 6:30 p.m., having examined several points but not being able, because of the weather and rough water, to reach the mainland. In returning, the launch had become entangled in kelp in the passage south of Hog Island (Île aux Cochons) and was assisted by the men in the boats from the sealing schooners *Charles Colgate* and *Emma Jane*. The latter had just come in and anchored at noon.

A gale prevented any movement for a day, but on the morning of September 10 the *Swatara* weighed anchor and moved across the sound and anchored in 13 fathoms about one mile off Molloy Point (Pointe Molloy). The launch and steam cutter were got out. That afternoon the landing of stores at Molloy Point was begun in fine weather and continued until 8:00 p.m., in spite of snow squalls which came up toward evening. Next day the crew of the *Emma Jane* with their boats assisted in the unloading. In one of those brief but violent squalls which spring up so quickly at Kerguelen a near-tragedy occurred when two small boats were upset in going between the ship and the shore with a party of officers and men. During the landing operations the steam cutter also became disabled. In the evening, while it was being towed through a rough sea by the *Swatara,* it was swamped and sank. This was a serious handicap to further unloading operations.

On September 12 the weather was clear and cool with, as usual, occasional snow squalls. A crew of carpenters was sent ashore to erect the house while unloading operations continued. The next day the unloading was finished at noon, and the carpenters had the building in such good shape that Commander Ryan and the astronomical party were able to establish themselves on shore. At 4:30 p.m. the *Swatara* weighed anchor and steamed out of Royal Sound on her way to Tasmania, New Zealand, and Chatham Island where the other observing parties were to be established.

ACTIVITIES AT KERGUELEN ISLAND

The house had been erected at Molloy Point when the ship departed on September 13, but much work remained to put things in proper order. Once the astronomical instruments were set up and functioning properly, the astronomers and photographers held regular practice sessions in preparation for the transit of Venus, so that when the occasion arose they would function smoothly as a team.

Dr. Kidder had begun systematic weather observations on board the *Swatara* on September 1. These were kept up all through the work of unloading and establishing the camp and were finally concluded on December 31. The weather observations were made three times daily: 8:00 a.m., 2:00 p.m., and 8:00 p.m. These observations consisted of barometric pressure, the temperature of both wet and dry bulb thermometers, wind direction and force, dew point, and precipitation. The rain gauge and tidal gauge were not, however, set up until late in October due to the urgency of other duties.

As soon as he could, Dr. Kidder began his study of the biology of the locality by observing and collecting specimens about the camp and on hikes in the vicinity. He was greatly handicapped throughout the entire period by lack of a boat for moving around. At first, biological specimens were prepared in a small tent which was wet, cold, cramped and generally unsatisfactory. As a result many specimens were spoiled. In the latter part of October a hut about ten feet square and heated by a stove was erected for the purpose.

Meanwhile the British transit party arrived at Three Islands Harbor (Port des Îles) in the *Volage,* October 8, and the *Supply,* October 10. As they expected, they found the Americans occupying Molloy Point. They were surprised, however, to find the two American schooners with the sealers' two huts on shore surrounded by piles of casks and supplies.[14] Captain Bailey of the *Emma Jane* helped them locate another site which he recommended and which proved to be equally as good as Molloy Point. While Captain Bailey was out with Captain Fairfax and Father Perry[15] locating a site for their base, Lieutenant Corbet with a crew and whaleboat from the *Emma Jane* called at Molloy Point to deliver mail. On November 3 a party from the British station steamed across the bay in the *Supply* to Molloy Point, where they visited and inspected the American base. Commander Ryan, Lieutenant Commander Train, and Dr. Kidder returned to the British base, named Observatory Bay. After spending the night aboard the *Supply* they returned to Molloy Point on November 4. During the visit arrangements were made for instantaneous gunpowder signals for the night of November 16 between the American base and the three British observation points, the latter having by then established two substations.

The transit of Venus occurred on the morning of December 9. Ingress was visible from Molloy Point and was successfully photographed. Commander Ryan and Lieutenant Commander Train disagreed on the exact time of the internal contact of ingress, but the photographic method was designed to obviate just this kind of human error so that the difference of opinion did not affect the quality of the results. As noted above, the weather became cloudy during the latter part of the transit and egress was not visible.

Voyage of the *Monongahela*

The original plan was to have the *Swatara* retrace its outbound voyage, collect each of the southern hemisphere parties, and return them to the United States. This plan was changed, however, and the *Swatara,* after picking up the observing parties on Tasmania, New Zealand, and Chatham Island, was ordered to proceed to Melbourne and then sail for San Francisco. Meanwhile, the *Monongahela,* Captain James S. Thornton in command, was dispatched from the South Atlantic Squadron at Rio de Janeiro to return the parties from Crozet and Kerguelen islands. The *Monongahela* reached Cape Town on October 29, missing a telegram that had been sent to Rio with the information that a party had not been landed on the Crozet Islands. This message was relayed to Cape Town, but did not reach there before the ship left for the Crozet Islands on November 16.

Except for one day of heavy seas and two days of overcast weather, the passage was exceptionally fine until November 28. Since instructions called for arrival at the Crozet Islands about December 1, the ship proceeded leisurely, and gunnery practice was held daily. On November 28 the typical weather of the latitude commenced. Strong winds with squalls of rain became the rule, with a gale added on November 29. Hog Island of the Crozets was sighted on the afternoon of December 2 while the ship was under sail and steam. The next morning Possession Island was sighted, and at 9:00 a.m. the ship anchored in 15 fathoms in American Bay. A whaleboat was sent ashore, but returned when no one was found there. At 11:00 a.m. anchor was weighed, and the *Monongahela* proceeded to Ship Bay. Here anchor was dropped at 1:45 p.m. after firing a 9-inch gun as a signal. The sea was perfectly smooth and a search party had no trouble getting ashore. After taking some botanical specimens, which were later given to Dr. Kidder, the party returned to the ship, which steamed out of the bay at 2:30 p.m., bound for Kerguelen.

The passage to Kerguelen was marked by overcast weather with fog and drizzle. Snow fell on December 6. During the mid-afternoon of December 7 the northwestern part of Kerguelen Island was sighted, and the ship stood in for Christmas Harbor (Baie de l'Oiseau) where anchor was dropped at 7:40. The next day Lieutenant Commander Nicoll Ludlow went ashore in search of the transit party, and the launch was made ready for watering the ship. Ludlow discovered the cairn left by the *Challenger* in January of that year. He opened the outer tin and inserted a message concerning the nature of his visit. From this excursion Mr. R. P. Maynard brought back some geological specimens, including pieces of coal, which he later turned over to Dr. Kidder.

On December 9, the ship steamed out of Christmas Harbor, observing en route the ingress of the transit of Venus between 6:15 and 7:15. At 8:20 she spoke the American schooner *Roswell King* of New London and learned the whereabouts of the American observers. From 9:00 to 11:00 a.m. the egress of the transit of Venus was observed. That evening the *Monongahela* entered Royal Sound (Baie du Morbihan), coming to anchor off Molloy Point and sending a boat on shore. The next day Lieutenant Commander Ludlow and Mr. Maynard went ashore with dispatches and mail, and the officers of the *Volage* were received on board.

During the ensuing weeks the *Monongahela* occupied several anchorages in Royal Sound, but she lay mostly at Three Islands Harbor waiting for the astronomers to finish their work. A few days were spent along the northwest shore at the head of the sound, where a supply of good water was used to fill the ship's tanks. Meanwhile part of the crew was employed at tarring and painting the vessel. British and American astronomers compared chronometers on December 18 in anticipation of an occulation of the moon which was observed on December 20. Chronometers were compared again on December 21. Since precise longitude was important in the astronomical calculations, such chronometer checks were carefully made as often as possible.

Various forms of geographical reconnaissance also were engaged in. On December 29 the navigator from the *Mononghela* went out in the launch to take soundings and do some surveying. On January 2, 1875, the steam cutter was sent to Molloy Point. After picking up Dr. Kidder, the party cruised southeastward along the shore of the low isthmus connecting the Prince of Wales Foreland (Presqu'île Prince de Galles) to the mainland. Soundings were made and samples dredged from the bottom. On January 5 Lieutenant Commander Gridley took the launch to reconnoiter various parts of the sound.

On January 6, 1875, the dismantling of the base at Molloy Point was begun. Progress was hindered much of the time, and was completely stopped during one day by high winds and snow squalls. By January 10, however, the entire transit party came on board, and the next day the *Monongahela* steamed over to the British base for a final check of chronometers and to pick up mail.

It is interesting to note that the American party felt that, due to the change in plans, they were leaving too soon. On the other hand, many of the British party, especially the men on the ships, were tired of Kerguelen and angry with Father Perry for holding them there so long. He insisted on fulfilling his instructions to the letter with regard to obtaining the specified lunar observations. Consequently the British did not leave until February 27.

Dr. Kidder expressed his disappointment about leaving ahead of schedule thus:

On the 9th of December, the day of the transit, and fully three months before the Swatara could reasonably be looked for back again, the Monongahela arrived most unexpectedly, having been ordered to take the party off. Fortunately for the natural history work, the astronomers detained the ship until January 11; but it is greatly to be regretted that the original programme was not carried out, and that the months of January and February were lost in so interesting a locality.[16]

Describing the American leave-taking, Lieutenant Corbet recorded the following in his journal: "Of course we all envied these Americans, going home and leaving us here for another six weeks, but there is no help for it, I suppose."[17]

Early on January 12 the *Monongahela* steamed out of Three Islands Harbor and down Royal Sound. At 8:30 she left the sound and sailed northeastward around the eastern end of Kerguelen. The weather was good for the entire passage to Cape Town, and the ship made good progress, first sailing north to about 42° S, 72°22′ E and thence northwest to about 33°30′ S, 58°30′ E, after which a westerly course was set. Captain Thornton was seriously hurt in an accident aboard ship on January 14, and Lieutenant Commander Nicoll Ludlow assumed command. A medical board of inquiry, which included Dr. Kidder, met and decided that because of his injury Captain Thornton should be sent home from Cape Town.

At 11:20 a.m. on February 6 the *Monongahela* anchored at Cape Town. From here the equipment and personal belongings of the Kerguelen transit party, along with Dr. Kidder's collections, were sent to the United States on the schooners *Roswell King* and *Charles Colgate*. Some of the remaining material was sent via the German bark *Emily*. Captain Thornton and the transit party, except for John Williams, the cook, and James Bunker, the carpenter's mate, who were discharged at Cape Town, went home via London in the British mail steamer *Roman* which left Cape Town February 16, 1875. On the following May 14 Captain Thornton died.

NOTES

1. Frederick W. True (ed.), *A History of the First Half Century of the National Academy of Sciences, 1863-1913* (Washington, 1913), p. 256; Simon B. Newcomb, "On the Mode of Observing the Coming Transit of Venus," *American Journal of Science*, Serial 2, vol. 50, 1870, pp. 74-83.

2. Simon B. Newcomb (ed.), *Observations of the Transit of Venus, December 8-9, 1874*, Sen. Exec. Doc. 31, 46th Congr., 1st Sess., Washington, 1880, p. 11.

3. The American party on Kerguelen Island had approximately 30 tons of supplies and equipment in contrast to 250 tons for the British party, as was noted by Lt. Cyril Corbet in his published journal, *"Venus" at the Isle of Desolation* (Southampton, 1875), p. 29.

4. Names in use in 1874, some of them given by Capt. James Cook, some by American sealers, have subsequently been changed in form or have been dropped in favor of other names. The name appearing on current maps for those features for which names have been changed is shown in parentheses in this chapter.

5. Newcomb, *Observations . . ., op. cit.*, pp. 12-13. Correspondence concerning this report is filed in the chronological record book, October 13, 1870-March 28, 1878, of miscellaneous letters sent by the Director of the Naval Observatory. Records of the Naval Observatory, Record Group 78, U. S. National Archives, but the weather report itself has not been found.

6. Once thought to be the best method for determining the distance between the earth and the sun, this method has now been superseded by other methods which give more certain results.

7. Newcomb, *Observations . . ., op. cit.*

8. George M. Robeson, Secretary of the Navy, *Annual Report of the Secretary of the Navy for the Year 1875*, Washington, 1876, p. 12.

9. Corbet, *op. cit.*, p. 97.

10. Joseph Henry, "Report of the Secretary," *Annual Report of the Board of Regents of the Smithsonian Institution, 1875* (Washington, 1876), p. 17.

11. J. H. Kidder, "Contributions to the Natural History of Kerguelen Island, I, Ornithology" (edited by Dr. Elliott Coues), *Bulletin of the United States National Museum*, No. 2 (Washington, 1875), 47 pp.; J. H. Kidder "Contributions to the Natural History of Kerguelen Island, II," *Bulletin of the United States National Museum*, No. 3 (Washington, 1876), 116 pp. Both papers were reprinted in the *Smithsonian Miscellaneous Collections*, vol. 13 (Washington, 1878); J. H. Kidder, "Summary Report on the Natural History of Kerguelen Island," *Annual Report of the Bureau of Medicine and Surgery* (Washington, 1876), pp. 727-743.

12. Corbet, *op. cit.*, p. 32.

13. *Ibid.*

14. *Ibid.*, p. 53.

15. The Rev. Stephen J. Perry, S. J., was leader of the British expedition and Capt. Fairfax was in command of the H. M. S. *Volage*.

16. Kidder, "Contributions . . . I, . . .," *op. cit.*, p. ix.

17. Corbet, *op. cit.*, p. 105.

BIBLIOGRAPHY

PUBLISHED MATERIAL

Anonymous, "The Coming Transit of Venus," *Harper's Magazine*, vol. 50, December, 1874, pp. 25-35.

Airy, Sir George Biddle (ed.), *Account of Observations of Venus 1874, December 8, Made Under the Authority of the British Government, and of the Reduction of the Observations* (London, Her Majesty's Stationery Office, 1881), viii and 512 pp.

Corbet, Cyril, Lt. R. N., *"Venus" at the Isle of Desolation, My Private Journal During the "Transit of Venus," Expedition in 1874* (Southampton, A. Randle, 1875), 135 pp.

Hamersly, Lewis R., *The Records of Living Officers of the U. S. Navy and Marine Corps*, 4th ed. (Philadelphia, L. R. Hamersly & Co., 1890), 1750 pp.

Henry, Joseph, "Report of the Secretary," *Annual Report of the Board of Regents of the Smithsonian Institution, 1875*, Government Printing Office (Washington, 1876), pp. 7-57. (See pp. 17, 49.)

————, "Report of the Secretary," *Annual Report of the Board of Regents of the Smithsonian Institution, 1877*, Government Printing Office (Washington, 1878), pp. 7-54. (See p. 45.)

Kidder, J. H., "Contributions to the Natural History of Kerguelen Island, I, Ornithology" (ed. by Dr. Elliott Coues), *Bulletin of the United States National Museum*, No. 2, Government Printing Office, (Washington, 1875), 47 pp. and index. Reprinted in *Smithsonian Miscellaneous Collections*, vol. 13 (Washington, 1878).

——, "Contributions to the Natural History of Kerguelen Island, II," *Bulletin of the United States National Museum*, No. 3, Government Printing Office (Washington, 1876), 116 pp. and index. Identification of the several specimens by various specialists. Includes an appendix containing descriptions of collections by Surgeon E. Kershner, U. S. N., in Chatham and Auckland islands and in New Zealand, and Mr. I. Russell in New Zealand, Reprinted in *Smithsonian Miscellaneous Collections*, vol. 13 (Washington, 1878).

——, "Summary Report on the Natural History of Kerguelen Island," Report of Jerome H. Kidder, Passed Assistant Surgeon of U. S. Navy, to Surgeon General J. Beale, U. S. Navy, Navy Yard, New York, June 12, 1875. *Annual Report of the Bureau of Medicine and Surgery* (Washington, 1876), pp. 727-743. A reprint of this report is on file in the Library of the United States Museum.

Newcomb, Simon B., "On the Mode of Observing the Coming Transit of Venus," *American Journal of Science*, Series 2, vol. 50, 1870, pp. 74-83.

——, (ed.), *Observations of the Transit of Venus, December 8-9, 1874*, Made & Reduced Under the Direction of the Commission Created by Congress, Published by Authority of the Hon, Sec. of the Navy. Sen. Exec. Doc. 31, 46th Congr., 1st Sess., 1880, 157 pp, 2 plates.

——, *Astronomy for Everybody* (revised by Robert H. Baker) (New York, New Home Library, 1942), xix and 334 pp. (See pp. 147-149.)

Perry, Rev. Stephen J., S. J., F. R. S., *Notes of a Voyage to Kerguelen Island to Observe the Transit of Venus, December 8, 1874* (Roehampton, Manresa Press, 1876), 48 pp. Reprinted from the *Month and Catholic Review*.

Robeson, George M., Secretary of the Navy, *Annual Report of the Secretary of the Navy for the Year 1873*, Government Printing Office (Washington, 1873), p. 628. (See p. 17.)

——, *Annual Report of the Secretary of the Navy for the Year 1874*, Government Printing Office (Washington, 1875), 225 pp. (See p. 16.)

——, *Annual Report of the Secretary of the Navy for the Year 1875*, Government Printing Office (Washington, 1876), 311 pp. (See p. 12.)

True, Frederick W. (ed.), *A History of the First Half Century of the National Academy of Sciences, 1863-1913* (Washington, 1913), xiv and 398 pp. (See pp. 256-261.)

U. S. Commission on the Transit of Venus, *Papers Relating to the Transit of Venus in 1874*. Prepared under the direction of the Commission Authorized by Congress and Published by Authority of the Honorable Secretary of the Navy. Government Printing Office (Washington, 1872), Part 1, 25 pp.; Part II, 48 pp., 4 charts.

U. S. Commission on the Transit of Venus, 1874, *Instructions for Observing the Transit of Venus, December 8-9, 1874*. Prepared by the Commission Authorized by Congress and Printed for the Use of the Observing Parties by Authority of the Honorable Secretary of the Navy. Government Printing Office (Washington, 1874), 28 pp.

MANUSCRIPT MATERIAL

Correspondence relating to the Transit of Venus Expedition by the Superintendent of the Naval Observatory. Letter File of the Director of the U. S. Naval Observatory for 1872-74, Records of the U. S. Naval Observatory, Record Group 78, U. S. National Archives.

Correspondence relating to the Transit of Venus Expedition, Letter File of the South Atlantic Squadron for 1874-75, Naval Records Collection of the Office of Naval Records and Library, Record Group 45, U. S. National Archives.

Logbook of the U. S. S. *Monongahela*, Capt. James S. Thornton, succeeded by Lt. Comdr. Nicoll Ludlow, 1874-75, Records of the Bureau of Naval Personnel, Records Group 24, U. S. National Archives.

Logbook of the U. S. S. *Swatara*, Comdr. Ralph Chandler, 1874-75, Records of the Bureau of Naval Personnel, Record Group 24, U. S. National Archives.

15

ROBERT CUSHMAN MURPHY'S VOYAGE
IN THE BRIG *DAISY*

SIGNIFICANCE AND ACCOMPLISHMENTS OF THE VOYAGE

Following the heyday of the industry, American sealers continued to make sporadic voyages into the Antarctic in search of both fur seals and elephant seals, even into the early 20th century. One of the last of these latter-day voyages was that of the brig *Daisy*, on a mixed voyage, whaling in the Atlantic and sealing at South Georgia. This voyage of 1912-13 differed from the others of its kind in that the ship's company included a young scientist, Robert Cushman Murphy.[1] Murphy's scientific papers, reporting his observations, launched a professional career that gave the United States, at a time when American Antarctic specialists were rare, an authority of international renown on Antarctic fauna.

The closing days of the 19th century were marked by a renewed interest in the South Polar regions which resulted in numerous national expeditions entering the field just before and during the decade following the turn of the century. These made little impact, however, in America, then preoccupied with Admiral Robert E. Peary's attempts at and attainment of the North Pole. The work of Murphy was at this time a lone, though nonetheless significant, American contribution to the scientific knowledge of Antarctica.

The project began to take form late in 1911 when Dr. Frederic A. Lucas, Director of the American Museum of Natural History, proposed to send a naturalist on a whaler which would spend several weeks in sub-Antarctic and Antarctic waters. To this end the Museum contracted with the owners of a New Bedford whaler bound on a whaling and elephant sealing voyage to South Georgia. By this agreement, Robert Cushman Murphy, of the staff of the Museum of the Brooklyn Institute of Arts and Sciences, a joint sponsor of the project, was to become a member of the crew of the brig *Daisy* during its cruise to and from South Georgia, where he was to be given the opportunity of spending three or four months ashore. En route, Murphy was to be permitted to catch oceanic birds whenever opportunities were favorable.

The principal objective of the voyage, insofar as Murphy and his sponsors were concerned, was the collection of natural history specimens for the museums and the accumulation of data relative to marine fauna and avifauna of the sub-Antarctic waters of the South Atlantic. Regarding the latter, there was then a minimum of systematic information due to the wide gaps in existing collections.

While at South Georgia Murphy made a survey of the vicinity of the Bay of Isles which resulted in the first detailed map of that part of the island. From his observations and investigations on the voyage and at South Georgia, he subsequently published 67 different articles.[2] Many of those of a scientific nature and two that are somewhat popular are included in the accompanying bibliography.

267

The masterpiece of Robert Cushman Murphy's professional career is his monumental two-volume work, *Oceanic Birds of South America*.[3] A part of this includes the results of his work on the *Daisy* and at South Georgia. A less tangible but no less real accomplishment of the voyage was the basis it afforded for the development of his career.

The brig *Daisy* of New Bedford, Massachusetts, was a vessel of 383 tons, built at Brookhaven, New York, in 1872. Master of the vessel and her company of 34 men was the veteran whaler Captain Benjamin D. Cleveland, also of New Bedford, who passed his 69th birthday during the voyage. Murphy, then 25 years old and recently graduated with the degree of Bachelor of Arts from Brown University, was just launching his professional career. The first mate, John da Lomba from the island of Brava in the Cape Verdes, was a scarcely literate though very skillful seaman and whaleman. Only the captain and Murphy were natives of the United States, although the first mate and the cooper, José G. Correia, were residents of New Bedford. The others were mostly from the Cape Verde Islands or from the West Indies. One man was from the Azores, and the second mate was from the Philippines. The composition of the ship's company was an indication that old-time Yankee whaling was coming to a close.

Murphy shared the captain's quarters on board ship. For his work, he was equipped with firearms, various scientific equipment, and supplies for making observations and taking and preserving specimens. He also had photographic equipment, including the means for developing and printing pictures, and he had a dory for his own use. This dory is now a prized exhibit at the Whaling Museum, Cold Spring Harbor, New York.

DETAILS OF THE VOYAGE

THE OUTBOUND VOYAGE

Murphy and Captain Cleveland left New York on May 25, 1912, joining the *Daisy* at Barbados, where she lay after returning from a previous whaling voyage in command of a Captain Reed. After cruising among the Lesser Antilles for a month, the *Daisy* headed north on July 31, on a whaling cruise into the Atlantic. At roughly the 32nd parallel the brig crossed the mid-Atlantic and then sailed southward toward the Cape Verdes. On September 17 the *Daisy* came to anchor at Porto Grande, on São Vicente Island where, while fresh provisions were being taken aboard, Murphy spent a day collecting specimens of the fauna and flora. From Porto Grande the whaling cruise continued slowly to the southward, with many days of calm or light winds. On October 16 a call was made at the island of Fernando Noronha, off the "hump" of Brazil, where fresh provisions were again taken aboard and Murphy had another day of collecting.

During the cruise through tropical seas Murphy was able occasionally to go out in his dory to collect specimens of marine life. Some collecting was also made from the deck of the brig, members of the crew being cooperative in calling to his attention the appearance of any new fish, bird, or mammal.

On the way southward from Fernando Noronha a lookout was kept for whales, but only one was taken, and as progressively higher southern latitudes were reached sperm whales became increasingly scarce. The weather, too, became increasingly unfavorable and the seas more boisterous. The abundant bird life of the South Atlantic afforded great opportunity for observation, and some

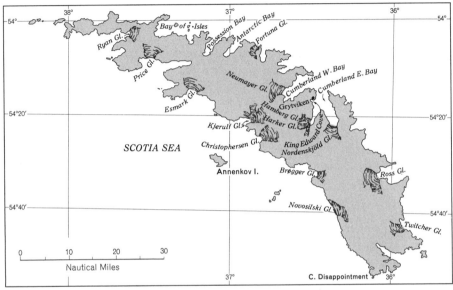

FIGURE 10. South Georgia.

collecting was done from the deck. On one occasion conditions were such that the dory could be used.

CUMBERLAND BAY, SOUTH GEORGIA

On November 23, 1912, the gray, mountainous coast of South Georgia was seen through the mist. The landfall was made in the vicinity of Possession Bay. Captain Cleveland then coasted the island to the eastward toward Cumberland Bay, keeping a distance offshore because of a snow squall. On November 24 the *Daisy* entered Cumberland East Bay as the wind died away. The first mate, Murphy, and a boat crew rowed in to the government post at the entrance to King Edward Cove, and the brig was subsequently taken in tow by the whale catcher *Fortuna*. The business of port charges and a sealing permit, very annoying to Captain Cleveland — who remembered South Georgia as a one-time no-man's land where each sealing captain was a law unto himself — was quickly concluded. Murphy and the captain were also welcomed by a dinner given by Captain C. A. Larsen, chief of the whaling station at Grytviken at the head of King Edward Cove.[4] Captain Cleveland being desirous to wait until the arrival of the *Harpon* from Buenos Aires with mail, the *Daisy* remained at anchor in King Edward Cove until December 13. Meanwhile the crew took a few elephant seals, and the ship's supplies were replenished, partly from the resources of the island and partly from the stores of the Norwegian whaling station (Fig. 10).

The stay at King Edward Cove afforded Murphy an opportunity for observation and collecting. He accompanied the whale catcher *Fortuna* on one of her cruises; at other times he hiked about the area or traveled by whaleboat or dory. The result was more than a hundred bird skins, various rock samples, some seal skulls and whale embryos, various invertebrates and fishes, and a representative collection of South Georgian plants.[5]

On December 13 the *Daisy* was towed out into Cumberland East Bay by one of the whale catchers, but the wind died away before the brig got out of the bay. Three whaleboats with full crews were then put out to tow the vessel from beyond the sheltering headlands into the open sea. Here there was just enough breeze to swell the sails and move the brig, but that night boats had to be put out again to prevent her from being carried onshore by the swell during a calm. Finally the vessel got under way. This was one of those brief spells of calm which can endanger a sailing vessel entering or leaving a harbor in the various Antarctic islands, areas where boisterous, gusty, and shifting winds, interspersed with violent gales are the rule.

AT THE BAY OF ISLES

Early in the afternoon of December 15 the *Daisy* came to anchor in the Bay of Isles between two small islets, Shag Island and Tern Island, just to the east of Start Point. No time was lost in getting down to business, and that same afternoon Murphy visited Albatross Island with a sealing crew. The next day, while out in his dory, he located a small, well-protected cove just east of Start Point and very near the *Daisy*'s anchorage, which he called Boat Cove. Here he set up his tent on a platform which he and three crewmen built of turf and stones from the beach. Equipped with a stove, a chair, and a table, this tent was Murphy's workshop ashore although he continued to return to the brig each night. While the boat crews ranged along the shores bordering the Bay of Isles, hunting elephant seals, he carried on a great variety of scientific work (Fig. 11).

At South Georgia the activities of the men aboard the *Daisy* were subject to the caprice of the ever-changing but mostly inclement weather. Occasionally they were shipbound for a day or more by a severe storm, but Murphy's shore base was near enough to the *Daisy* to permit him to go ashore whenever it was possible to lower a boat, even on days when poor visibility kept the sealers inactive. He soon became acclimated to the cold and disagreeable weather that prevails so much of the time and often worked at low temperatures or when it seemed that the wind would blow his tent away with the next gust. The tent, too light for the strong and gusty winds of South Georgia, was in fact blown down on more than one occasion, and much of the time it was too drafty to keep the oil stove burning. Often he was caught in the field by rain, sleet, or snow, for squalls were frequent.

Murphy visited, observed, photographed, and collected from a number of colonies of nesting birds. Several visits were made to the colony of wandering albatross on Albatross Island. Behind and uphill from his tent was a small colony of wandering albatross and giant fulmars. A king penguin rookery and a gentoo penguin rookery were not far away. On Shag Island, next to where the *Daisy* was moored, Murphy found a colony of blue-eyed shags. Sometimes he went along with the sealers to more distant positions; at other times he made

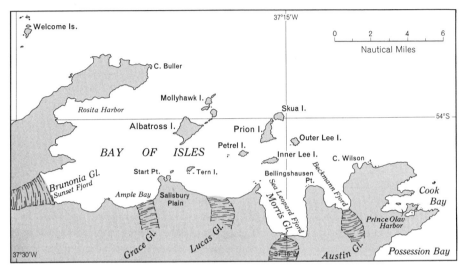

FIGURE 11. Bay of Isles and Vicinity.

inland excursions to visit colonies of nesting birds, to collect geological specimens, or to observe natural phenomena in general. Overland hikes were limited by the fact that he was alone and therefore dared not travel too far nor over the more treacherous crevassed areas of the neighboring glaciers. When for some reason a lull occurred in sealing operations, da Lomba or Correia accompanied Murphy on shore, but the skipper never afforded Murphy an opportunity for organizing a long hike.

On the rare days of clear weather and good distant visibility, Murphy took bearings and cross bearings to and from various landmarks as a basis for a map which he drew of the Bay of Isles. This map, published in *Petermanns Geographische Mitteilungen*[6] and the *National Geographic Magazine*,[7] was the first detailed chart of the Bay of Isles, and until November and December, 1929, when a survey party of the Discovery Committee worked in the area, Murphy's was the only survey.[8] The few differences between the chart resulting from this professional survey and Murphy's chart, produced with much less refined methods, testify to the careful work of the young ornithologist.

Although Robert Cushman Murphy subsequently became famous as an ornithologist, his early work at South Georgia was quite diversified. He kept a record of daily weather conditions, collected rock specimens, and made geological observations. He processed fresh tissue from the various organs of the ele-

phant seals in preparation for a series of stained microscopic sections. He collected a graded series of albatross embryos and a series of elephant seal skulls
showing growth stages of both sexes from the young pups to the largest bulls.
The stomachs of many seals were opened to determine their feed. Only one of
these contained fish; in the others were mostly the horny beaks of squids, the
residues of the process of digestion.[9] Two elephant seal skeletons were prepared for museums, and an entire leopard seal was prepared for mounting.
Great numbers of bird skins of all available species were taken, as were collections of eggs. Many of the migratory birds were banded. Collections representing all of the 19 vascular plants on the island and some of the mosses and lichens
were made. Not all of these, however, were collected at the Bay of Isles, because
this more exposed locality did not afford a habitat for some of the plants growing in more sheltered locations such as King Edward Cove, where Murphy began his work. Insects, crustaceans, and fish also came under his scrutiny and
were part of his collections.

At Possession Bay

On February 24, Captain Cleveland announced that the brig would move its
mooring as soon as practicable. Murphy broke camp and moved his equipment
on board the *Daisy*. At 4 p. m. that day the anchor was hauled, and the brig
sailed for Possession Bay. As they left the Bay of Isles the weather was clear, and
Murphy was able to take final bearings on the easternmost islets on his map.
Sailing south into Possession Bay, the *Daisy* crossed the mouth of Cook Bay on
the west, and looking in, the men could see the British whaling station located
on Prince Olav Harbor, one of the two inner arms of the bay. Late in the day
the *Daisy* came to anchor at the head of Possession Bay, a narrow fjord just east
of the Bay of Isles.

After exploring the shoreline at the head of Possession Bay in his dory, Murphy selected a protected site for his tent at the foot of a cliff on the west side of
the fjord. Possession Bay, confined by steep mountain walls, was to the men on
the *Daisy* even more desolate than the Bay of Isles. Here Murphy collected two
new plants and found a colony of diving petrels.

On Sunday, March 2, Captain Cleveland, Murphy, and two whaleboat crews
paid a visit to the British whaling station in Prince Olav Harbor. Here they
mailed letters, bought provisions for the ship, were entertained, and heard
news of the outside world. The big news at the time was the discovery that Captain Robert F. Scott's party had perished on the return from the South Pole. In
walking about the whaling station Murphy found a number of graves of crewmen of the American schooner *Elizabeth Jane* of New York who died there
in 1835.

The men in the whaleboats were finding few seals and, it being late in the
season, these had lost most of their blubber during the long fast on land. Consequently, Captain Cleveland asked da Lomba and Murphy to trek over the
divide to Antarctic Bay, the fjord immediately to the east of Possession Bay.
This was accomplished on March 3. At Antarctic Bay Murphy made his first

discovery of the ringed penguin, but the prospects for sealing were poor. Only eight small elephant seals were found, and the head of the bay was filled with floating ice.

Storms were becoming more frequent, and because all evidence indicated the end of the sealing for the 1912-13 season, Captain Cleveland decided to sail north for the sperm whaling ground in tropical waters. On March 9 and 10 the men filled the water casks of the *Daisy,* and Murphy brought his tent and equipment back on board. While a few elephant seals were killed in the intervals between storms on these last days, preparations were being made to leave. On March 15, 1913, the *Daisy* made sail toward the mouth of Possession Bay, where she came to for a few hours while a whaleboat went in to the whaling station with and for mail. That night the brig set out into the open sea on a northerly course.

As the *Daisy* sailed northward with favorable winds, the weather steadily improved. On March 24 from the deck and on March 26 from the dory Murphy was able to add to his collection of south Atlantic birds. On April 8 they made Trinidade Island, about 600 miles from the coast of Brazil at 20° 30′ S. A landing proved impossible, but Murphy shot some birds for his collection and a number of fish were also caught for the same purpose. Although lookouts were kept at the masthead during the passage through the lower latitudes, only one day, when six sperm whales were taken, yielded any results. Two men died on the voyage home, partly as a result of neglect and partly as a result of the hard life they had experienced on the voyage. On May 8, 1913, the *Daisy* arrived at Barbados.

From Barbados part of Murphy's collections was sent home to New Bedford on the *Daisy,* and part was sent home on the steamer *Guayana.* On May 13 Murphy took passage for New York on the steamer *Vestris.*

CORREIA'S RETURN TO SOUTH GEORGIA

José G. Correia, cooper on the *Daisy,* took special interest in Murphy's work and was especially helpful in many ways. Murphy in turn taught him the technique of collecting and preparing birds. While the *Daisy* lay at anchor in King Edward Cove, Correia made arrangements with C. A. Larsen to return there as a workman at the close of the *Daisy's* current voyage. Traveling by steamer to Buenos Aires and from there on one of the vessels carrying oil, he returned to South Georgia late in 1913. Using all his free time for several months at Grytviken, Correia was able to collect series of specimens which Murphy had been unable to obtain, or to fill gaps in Murphy's collections. These were turned over to Murphy and to the American Museum of Natural History.

NOTES

1. A similar voyage on the Norwegian whaler *Fridtjof Nansen* was made to South Georgia in 1907 by Dr. A. Szielasko, an ornithologist. See A. Szielasko, "Die Cumberland-Bai in Südgeorgien," *Petermanns Geographische Mitteilungen,* Bd. 53, 1907, pp. 278-280.

2. Robert Cushman Murphy, *Logbook for Grace; Whaling Brig Daisy, 1912-1913* (New York, 1947), p. viii.

3. Robert Cushman Murphy, *Oceanic Birds of South America* (New York, Macmillan, 1936).

4. Larsen was by then a famous polar explorer and a pioneer in Antarctic whaling. He had served with Nansen in the Arctic. He had been captain of the *Jason,* an Antarctic whaling, sealing and exploring vessel, in 1892-93 and in 1893-94. He had been captain of Nordenskjöld's ill-fated ship, the *Antarctic,* in 1901-03. He headed the company which established the first modern whaling station on South Georgia, at Grytviken, in 1904.

5. Murphy, *Logbook . . ., op. cit.,* p. 165.

6. Robert Cushman Murphy, "Die 'Bay of Isles' in Südgeorgien," *Petermanns Geographische Mitteilungen,* Bd. 60, May 1914, pp. 279-280.

7. Robert Cushman Murphy, "South Georgia; An Outpost of the Antarctic," *National Geographic Magazine,* vol. 41, No. 5, May, 1922, p. 412.

8. Lt. Comdr. J. M. Chaplin, "Narrative of Hydrographic Survey Operations in South Georgia and the South Shetland Islands, 1926-1930," *Discovery Reports,* Discovery Committee, Colonial Office, London, vol. 3, 1932, pp. 322-326, and Chart 3.

9. Murphy, *Logbook . . ., op. cit.,* p. 227.

BIBLIOGRAPHY

PUBLISHED MATERIAL

Murphy, Robert Cushman, "A Desolate Island of the Antarctic," *American Museum Journal,* vol. 13, No. 6, October, 1913, pp. 242-259.

——, "Report on the South Georgia Expedition," *Museum of the Brooklyn Institute of Arts and Sciences, Science Bulletin,* vol. 2, 1914, pp. 41-102, plates 14-18.

——, "A Sub-Antarctic Island," *Harper's Magazine,* vol. 128, January, 1914, pp. 165-176, illus.

——, "Observations on Birds of the South Atlantic," *Auk,* vol. 31, 1914, pp. 439-457, plates 35-39.

——, "A Flock of Tubinares," *Ibis,* 10th series, vol. 2, 1914, pp. 317-319.

——, "Die 'Bay of Isles' in Südgeorgien," *Petermanns Geographische Mitteilungen,* Bd. 60, May, 1914, pp. 279-280, map.

——, "The Penguins of South Georgia," *Museum of the Brooklyn Institute of Arts and Science Bulletin,* vol. 2, No. 5, 1915, pp. 103-133, plates 19-43.

——, "The Anatidae of South Georgia," *Auk,* vol. 33, 1916, pp. 270-277, plate 14.

——, "At Home with the Blue-eyed Shags," *Museum of the Brooklyn Institute of Arts and Sciences, Quarterly,* vol. 3, 1916, pp. 21-28.

——, "Notes on American Subantarctic Cormorants," *Bulletin, American Museum of Natural History,* vol. 35, 1916, pp. 31-48, illus.

——, "Faunal Conditions in South Georgia," *Science,* new series, vol. 46, 1917, pp. 112-113.

——, "A Study of the Atlantic Oceanites," *Bulletin, American Museum of Natural History,* vol. 38, 1918, pp. 117-146, plates 1-3.

——, "Bird Life at South Georgia," *American Museum Journal,* vol. 18, 1918, pp. 463-472, illus.

——, "A Review of the Diving Petrels," *Bulletin, American Museum of Natural History,* vol. 44, 1921, pp. 495-554.

——, "South Georgia: an Outpost of the Antarctic," *National Geographic Magazine,* vol. 41, No. 5, May, 1922, pp. 409-444, map, illus.

——, "Notes Sur Anthus Antarcticus," *El Hornero,* vol. 3, 1923, pp. 56-59.

——, "Antarctic Zoögeography and Some of its Problems," *Problems of Polar Research,* Special Publication No. 7, American Geographical Society, New York, 1928, pp. 355-379.

——, *Oceanic Birds of South America* (New York, Macmillan and American Museum of Natural History, 1936), 2 vols., xx and vii and 1243 pp., 72 plates, illus.

——, *Logbook for Grace; Whaling Brig Daisy, 1912-1913* (New York, Macmillan, 1947), 290 pp.; (New York, Time, Inc., 1965), 371 pp.

MANUSCRIPT MATERIAL

Register of the brig *Daisy,* Permanent Register No. 13, May 12, 1908, Ship Registers, Port of New Bedford, Vessel Documentation Series, Records of the Bureau of Marine Inspection and Navigation, Record Group 41, U. S. National Archives.

16

THE BEGINNING OF THE MECHANICAL AGE
IN ANTARCTIC EXPLORATION

CHARACTERISTICS OF THE MECHANICAL AGE

A New Technology

The second quarter of the 20th century ushered in a new era for Antarctica, an era in which the airplane, the aerial camera, radio, and motorized transport revolutionized exploration. The perfection of these devices to the point where they were of practical use at this time in Antarctica was largely an outgrowth of the accelerated and widespread technological development brought about by the urgent demands of World War I.

For this new era in Antarctica, J. Gordon Hayes has suggested the term *mechanical* in contradistinction to what he called the *heroic* era that preceded it.[1] Hayes, of course, did not mean that the men who have explored in the modern period are any less heroic or courageous than their predecessors, for they have had to face new dangers and risk death in other ways. Conversely, in view of the ever-increasing range of scientific investigation carried on by modern expeditions and the manner in which applied science is now utilized in exploration, the present period might also be called the *scientific* era without disparaging the science of what Hayes called the *heroic* era.

Before the introduction of the airplane, the radio, and other mechanical devices, Antarctic exploration was essentially a matter of human muscle and courage against the elements. The explorer of an earlier day, once he left his ship, was mainly dependent on his own physical resources. Wherever he traveled, he had to carry with him his camping equipment, scientific gear, and food supply for the entire journey. Even though he used sledge dogs or Siberian ponies as transport animals, the explorer mostly traveled on foot. Without the use of these animals, it was a matter of man-hauling the sledges. Before the introduction of vessels with auxiliary steam power, the explorer, even on his ship, was entirely at the mercy of the elements.

Unlike his predecessors, the explorer of the mechanical age has been greatly aided by the mechanical developments of our time in the task of facing up to the severe test that the Antarctic elements impose. By means of these devices he has been able to accomplish infinitely more in a given period of time. From the experience of his predecessors, the modern explorer is more fully aware of the conditions for which he must prepare. He has the benefit of a trail diet whose calorific adequacy is scientifically determined. His clothing has been designed as a result of practical experience and laboratory experiments in physiological climatology. By means of radio the base camp is in constant touch with the outside world, and field parties are in turn able to contact the base. Weather permitting, speedy relief is possible to field parties by means of aircraft which can also deliver supplies to men on the trail. It should, of course, be realized that not all of these things were fully perfected at the beginning of the modern era, but have since been developed and improved. Although the life of the explorer has been greatly changed for the better by the mechanical age, it is still far from easy. Accidents and mechanical failures can result in hardship, injury, and death. Operating machines and making field surveys in subzero temperatures is difficult at best. Sledging behind a dog team or driving a motor toboggan, loading and unloading supplies, building camps, and laying depots is exhausting labor even in the mechanical age. Guiding tracked vehicles through a crevasse field and, if necessary, extricating a vehicle or sled from a crevasse is exhausting both nervously and physically. The meteorologist who daily risks frostbitten fingers in the monotonous task of sending up pilot balloons requires heroic devotion to his science, for while he risks little compared to the mariner skirting the edge of the pack ice in a sailing vessel in search of open leads, he is denied the thrill of discovering an unknown coast. Exploration today is not less heroic; it requires a different kind of heroism.

It should be recognized that the introduction of the new did not eliminate all aspects of the old in methods of exploration. For example, aerial photography has not eliminated the need for ground surveys; in fact, the latter are necessary fully to utilize the former. The aerial camera has just simplified the task of the surveyor. Dog team and sledge is still a practical means of traveling in the Antarctic and as of 1970, dogs were still being used by some expeditions to obtain ground surveys and for possible rescue missions in the event of an airplane crash. It should also be pointed out that automotive transport and radio were both used in the Antarctic with limited success before World War I, but the developments stimulated by military requirements greatly increased the range and usefulness of this equipment. In fact, it was not until the second Byrd Expedition, 1933-35, that motorized land transport proved to be practical in the Antarctic.

The Use of the Airplane

Its development having been hastened by its prior military use both for scouting and attack, the introduction of the airplane in 1928 brought about a truly revolutionary change in Antarctic exploration. Post World War I activities such as transatlantic flights, aerial exploration in the Arctic, flights to establish endurance records, and early commercial flying also contributed to the development of planes with a ceiling of thousands of feet capable of carrying thousands of pounds hundreds of miles. In all of this development Americans played a prominent part.

The first airplane flight in Antarctic history was made by Sir Hubert Wilkins on November 16, 1928, in the vicinity of Deception Island. The major exploratory flight of this expedition was made on December 20 along the east coast of the Antarctic Peninsula. By the end of 1929, less than 14 months after the first flight, three additional expeditions had begun programs of aerial exploration in the Antarctic. The first flights by then-Commander Richard E. Byrd were made on January 15, 1929, in the vicinity of Little America. Several flights were made in early November by Commander Finn Lützow-Holm in the vicinity of Bouvet Island at the beginning of the Norwegian Expedition in the *Norvegia* under Captain Hjalmar Riiser-Larsen. The first flight from the *Discovery* of the British-Australian-New Zealand Antarctic Research Expedition was made over Mac.Robertson Land on December 31, 1929, by Flight Lieutenant S. Campbell and Air Pilot E. Douglas. It is worthy of note that most of the aviators attached to these four expeditions had had previous military or naval experience as pilots, and most of them had also previously flown in the Arctic. Three of the expeditions used American-built aircraft.

Given a base, such as Little America or McMurdo Sound, from which an airplane can take off and land at a point accessible to a ship, the explorer's range is limited only by the range of his airplane. Although he has to wait for good weather, the aerial explorer can in a matter of hours fly over territory it would take men with dog teams weeks to traverse. Moreover, the plane can fly over mountains and crevassed ice fields that are inaccessible to man on the ground. Due to his greater altitude the aerial observer has the additional advantage of a tremendously increased range of vision. Assuming satisfactory atmospheric conditions, the range of visibility of a man on foot is limited to a few miles. At six feet, approximately eye level, the horizon line is 2.8 nautical and 3.2 statute miles distant. From a plane at 2000 feet the horizon line is 51.2 nautical miles and 59.0 statute miles distant. At an elevation of 5000 feet this distance is increased to 81.0 miles and 93.3 statute miles. At 10,000 feet the figures are 114.6 and 132.0, respectively.[2] Objects rising above the horizon line are, of course, visible at greater distances in proportion to their elevation. Since exploratory flights are made only in good weather, unless conditions change before the flight is completed the aerial observer generally has clear visibility. By contrast, the man on the trail, because of the short field season, is often compelled to travel in thick weather with limited visibility.

Small planes equipped with pontoons and small flying boats have also been used in connection with exploring ships working along the coast at the edge of the pack ice. In this case they are used to scout for open leads in the pack and for short sorties over the land where the ship cannot get in for a landing. This type of operation is limited to times when the weather is satisfactory for flying. Also, the water must be smooth enough for the plane to be launched safely and to permit it to land. Such planes have generally been of small size and, therefore, of limited range. The German Expedition of 1938-39 to Queen Maud Land used a ship with a catapult for launching the two flying boats used for aerial exploration. In 1946-47 the U.S. Navy Task Force 68 ("Operation Highjump") used long-range flying boats, operated from seaplane tenders, to photograph about half of the coastal perimeter of Antarctica.

With the improvement and development of aircraft the range of flight has been increased to the point where it is now feasible to have direct connection between Antarctica and the other land areas of the Southern Hemisphere. On December 13, 1947, a land-based plane belonging to the Argentine Navy is reported to have been flown by Almirante Gregorio Portillo from Piedrabuena in Patagonia as far south as Adelaide Island. The plane did not land in the 15½ hour round-trip flight, but mail was dropped to Argentine parties on Deception Island and on Gamma Island.

On December 20, 1955, as part of the preparations for the U. S. participation in the International Geophysical Year, 1957-58, four airplanes attached to the U. S. Navy Task Force 43, two four-engined (R-5 D4) Skymaster transport planes, and two two-engined Neptune PV-2 patrol bombers flew from Harewood Field, Christchurch, New Zealand, to McMurdo Sound in a 2400-mile nonstop flight of 14 hours. They landed on a landing strip which had been previously marked out on the bay ice, from which they subsequently carried on long-distance exploratory flights across the continent. On January 18, 1956, the four planes made the return flight to New Zealand.

Since 1956, although there have been a few unfortunate accidents, flights by U. S. Navy R7V Super Constellations, U. S. Air Force C-124 Globemasters, and U. S. Navy C-130 Hercules between Christchurch and McMurdo Sound have become almost routine from mid-October to mid-December and during February. The Hercules, a four-engine prop-jet plane, is the largest aircraft ever equipped with skis. Used to transport cargo from McMurdo to other U. S. stations in Antarctica, it is capable of landing and taking off at the South Pole station at an elevation of 9100 feet. In 1963-64, resupply of U. S. Antarctic inland stations was carried out exclusively by aircraft.

Another milestone in Antarctic aviation was marked on September 30, 1963, when two LC-130Fs took off from Cape Town, South Africa, and flew across the South Pole to McMurdo Sound in 14 hours and 26 minutes. Admiral James R. Reedy, USN, Commander of U. S. Naval Support Force, Antarctica, was aboard one of the planes. Special tanks were installed in the cargo area to enable each plane to carry 9600 gallons of fuel for the 4700-mile flight.

The first mid-winter flight to Antarctica was made from Christchurch to McMurdo Sound and return on June 26-27, 1964, to evacuate a critically injured Seabee. The Hercules C-130 which made the landing at McMurdo was piloted by Lieutenant Commander Robert D. Mayer. A second C-130 accompanied the rescue plane but did not land. Both planes had flown from Quonset Point, Rhode Island.

Vertical take-off aircraft were introduced in Antarctica by the Second Byrd Antarctic Expedition, 1933-35, in the form of a Kellett autogyro. Helicopters were used in U.S. Navy "Operation Highjump," 1946-47, and they had an important role in "Operation Windmill" the following year. American support forces in the various Deep Freeze operations made considerable use of helicopters. An historic event was the introduction of Army UH-1B turbine helicopters in 1961-62 to transport and support a ground control survey party. Surveyors using a tellurometer, an electronic distance-measuring device, and a theodolite were landed on 68 mountain peaks in Victoria Land in a zigzag traverse of 1500 miles. Two of these large and powerful helicopters and the tellurometer enabled three surveyors to obtain ground control for almost 100,000 square miles of mountainous terrain in 57 days, a revolutionary innovation in Antarctic mapping.

THE USE OF THE AERIAL CAMERA

When equipped with an aerial camera, which was also an outgrowth of military requirements of World War I, the airplane became an unexcelled exploring mechanism. The aerial camera has enabled the explorer to record on film every minute detail within the range of the lens. Although all but the broader aspects of the scene may soon become blurred in the observer's memory, the film, when properly developed and printed, remains a permanent record of the most minute detail to be studied as long and so often as necessary to obtain available data. Such data may often have been of no interest at the time the pictures were taken, but have subsequently become valuable. When taken in overlapping series, aerial pictures provide a continuous strip of stereographic pairs affording three-dimensional views from which relative elevations may be determined. No quickly written description in the field notebook, no panoramic sketch or penciled form lines by the man on the trail, can equal the aerial photograph as a representation of terrain. Moreover, the time required for extensive sketching is prohibitive.

On the first expedition of Captain Robert F. Scott, 1901-04, photographs were taken from a captive balloon at McMurdo Sound by Shackleton[3] on February 4, 1902. Drygalski, leader of the German Expedition of 1901-03, on March 29, 1902, also took photographs from a captive balloon sent aloft off Wilhelm II Coast where his ship, the *Gauss,* was icebound.[4] Strictly speaking, these are aerial photographs, the first taken in Antarctica, but they are hardly in a class with those taken more than a quarter of a century later from free-flying planes. On his initial Antarctic flight over the Antarctic Peninsula on December 20, 1928, Sir Hubert Wilkins used a hand-held Kodak 3A camera and two movie cameras to photograph portions of the area over which he flew.

Colonel Ashley C. McKinley, then a captain in the U.S. Army Air Corps, as photographer for the first Byrd Expedition, 1928-30, was the first to use an aerial mapping camera in the Antarctic. The Rockefeller Mountains were photographed in the first photographic flight on February 18, 1929. The camera on all photographic flights was pointed obliquely out of the side of the plane to include the distant horizon, and a continuous strip of pictures was taken with a 60 percent overlap. For each exposure McKinley manually recorded its number, the exact time, and the latitude of the plane. The following season Wilkins continued his exploration of the area west of the Antarctic Peninsula and again made aerial photographs. In addition to Byrd's Expedition operating out of Little America and Wilkins', west of the Antarctic Peninsula, two other expeditions were using aerial photography in Antarctica in the 1929-30 season. Captain Hjalmar Riiser-Larsen explored Bouvet Island and the Queen Maud coast in the *Norvegia,* from which photographic flights were made in a seaplane. Sir Douglas Mawson used a small plane on pontoons in flights from the *Discovery* to aid his exploration of the area from Wilhelm II Coast to Prince Olav Coast.

Trimetrogon cameras were first used by the U. S. Naval Task Force 68 ("Operation Highjump") in 1946-47, and by the Ronne Antarctic Research Expedition in 1947-48. These cameras at regular, predetermined intervals simultaneously take three pictures, one obliquely to the left-hand horizon, another obliquely to the right-hand horizon, and a third vertically directly beneath the plane. All have a 60 percent overlap to provide for stereoscopic use. These cameras are also equipped with "gremlin" cameras whose operation is synchronized with the main camera so as to make for each exposure a photographic record of dials indicating the time, altitude above the surface, and other pertinent data.

Aerial photographs can be used to construct large-scale relief maps or small-scale reconnaissance maps, depending on the nature of the photography and the available supplementary data. Such data include the pilot's flight log and the navigator's chart for the flight on which the pictures were taken. The time each photograph was taken, the direction the plane was flying, its height above the surface, and the indication of tilt, if any, are all important data in the proper use of the photograph. Perhaps of greatest importance is a minimum of ground control by which the photographs can be tied to actual locations on the earth. Even where ground control was entirely lacking, however, W. L. G. Joerg and O. M. Miller succeeded in making a useful map for a portion of the Bowman Coast.[5] Adequate ground control generally requires a ground survey in which geographical fixes are obtained by celestial observation for features identifiable in the pictures and for which bearings to prominent landmarks are obtained. Normally, the accuracy of the resultant map is in direct proportion to the number of such fixes available along a photographic flight line. Satisfactory reconnaissance maps have been made from only a few fixes, scores to over a hundred miles apart.

From the foregoing it is obvious that the airplane and the aerial camera have not eliminated field journeys. In fact, the requisite ground control for aerial photography is most easily obtained by ground surveys. When no alternative is possible, geographical fixes have been obtained by planes landing in the field at stages or at turning points on the photographic flights, but so few fixes provide only the barest minimum of control. Moreover, such landings are not always possible.

Although photographic interpretation can supply information on geology, field work is still necessary to obtain detailed structural information, petrographic samples, and paleontological specimens. Botanical and zoological studies also require field observation and collecting. Photographic analysis is especially fruitful in glaciological studies dealing with the direction of ice movement and the comparative advance or retreat of ice fronts. In all field work, however, the photographs are valuable for planning the places that should be visited and the route by which they can most easily be reached. In fact, photographs taken by previous expeditions can be invaluable in planning an entire future expedition, from the selection of the base to laying out a field program. While the airplane has not eliminated the need for field journeys, it has greatly simplified the work of field parties. In cases where planes have been used to drop supplies or to make field caches, the sledging loads have been greatly lightened.

At the same time, field parties are able to supply meteorological data to aid in flight operations, and they are always available as advance rescue parties in case of a plane crash.

THE USE OF RADIO

During his expedition of 1911-14, before the advent of the mechanical age, Sir Douglas Mawson established a radio station at his main base at Commonwealth Bay, the first such station in Antarctica. However, at this stage in the development of radio, contact with Australia, Macquarie Island, and with ships at sea was possible only under favorable conditions.[6] There was then no means by which field parties could send or receive messages. During and following World War I radio was greatly perfected. Sir Ernest Shackleton, on his last expedition, 1921-22, had two wireless transmitting and receiving sets aboard the *Quest*. The smaller one, the only one that proved serviceable, had a transmitting range of 250 miles but was normally able to receive time signals from as far as 3000 miles distant. In certain instances, time signals were received from 8000 and 9000 miles away. A radio functioned for a distance of 100 miles off Rio de Janeiro.[7] Whalers were also equipped with wireless telegraph sets and radio, and the ships of all the expeditions in Antarctica in 1929 were so equipped.

By the time of Admiral Byrd's First Expedition, 1928-30, radio had been developed to the point where Byrd could make it a most useful tool. His radio operators at Little America were able to maintain regular contact with New York and other large cities in other parts of the world. Messages were even exchanged with the University of Michigan camp in Greenland and with a Russian polar expedition on Franz Joseph Land.[8] Although there were occasional failures, trail parties and flight personnel were able to maintain regular contact with Little America. In the case of the latter, the base was constantly tuned in to the plane's radio so as to be informed immediately of any emergency. In this way the needs of the flight parties and the conditions under which they operated were known at the base, and 'Admiral Byrd could modify orders to suit the situation. Of special help on Byrd's flight to the pole were the weather reports radioed in by the geological party. This was the first complete radio communication system used in Antarctic exploration, and it set the pattern for future expeditions.

THE USE OF MOTORIZED TRANSPORT

More time was required to develop and adapt motorized transport to the point of practical usefulness than any of the other devices which characterize the mechanical age in Antarctic exploration. Shackleton experimented with the use of a specially equipped automobile in 1908, but it was not until 1934 that Admiral Byrd, by his use of crawler-type tractors, demonstrated that motorized transport could be practical in the severe Antarctic conditions. On his first expedition of 1908-09, based at McMurdo Sound, Sir Ernest Shackleton experimented with an automobile with an air-cooled engine.[9] The front wheels were placed on skis, and other modifications were made to the motor to counteract the low temperatures. In spite of its low power, it worked fairly well pulling loaded sledges on hard surfaces in the vicinity of the camp. It required a great deal of maintenance, however, and could not cope with soft snow surfaces. Later in 1908, Dr. Jean-B. Charcot was supplied with three De Dion-Bouton motor sledges which resembled light weight crawler-type tractors, but in the rugged terrain along the west coast of the Antarctic Peninsula he never found conditions where he felt he could put them to use.[10] On his last expedition, 1910-13, Captain Robert F. Scott also tried so-called motor sledges which were actually small, low, lightweight, crawler-type tractors. They were used with fair success in the unloading operations and around the base to draw loaded sledges. They were very slow, had difficulty on icy surfaces, and were in constant need of maintenance.[11] In 1911-12 Mawson found a propeller-driven sled converted from an airplane fuselage to be impractical.[12] On his first expedition Admiral Byrd tried a Ford snowmobile. The front wheels were replaced by skis, and the rear wheels were fitted with a crawler-type tread. This was much faster and far more efficient than any previous type of automotive transport used in the Antarctic, but it had difficulty in soft snow if it was deep. The snowmobile finally broke down, mired in deep snow 75 miles south of Little America, while pulling three sledges loaded with food.

On his second expedition Byrd used a heavy Cletrac crawler-type tractor, three Citroën tractors, and two Ford snowmobiles. The Citroëns were a combination light tractor and light motor truck with the front wheels resting on skis. The traction was obtained by crawler tracks under the rear of the machine. After initial difficulties were ironed out, the tractors proved extremely valuable in hauling heavily loaded sledges from the ships to the base during unloading operations. Later they were used to lay depots and to establish the advanced weather station 100 nautical miles south of Little America. On this operation the Cletrac pulled four sledges and the Citroëns three each. The following field season the machines were used on regular field journeys. In all this work they proved satisfactory in spite of difficulty in crossing crevasses.

This marked the beginning of motorized transport on an independent basis in Antarctica, and increased use of this kind of transport was made by the U. S. Antarctic Service Expedition, 1939-41. Various types of motorized transport were tested by the central group of U. S. Navy Task Force 68 (Operation Highjump) based on Little America. The Ronne Antarctic Research Expedition, 1947-48, had two "Weasels," amphibious crawler vehicles developed by the U. S. Army and the Studebaker Corporation, but because of the mountainous terrain surrounding Marguerite Bay, they were used only in the vicinity of the base. Weasels were extensively used by the Norwegian-British-Swedish Expedition, 1949-52. They were used on depot-laying journeys of from 90 to 360 miles, round trip, covering scores of miles per day. One journey with seismic equipment up onto the inland ice plateau of Queen Maud Land covered over 800 miles.[13]

Mechanized overland transport came into its own in Antarctica during the IGY and the preparation for it. United States Navy Antarctic Support Forces used crawler-type tractors to pull trains of heavily loaded sleds long distances to erect bases and lay caches of gasoline and supplies. The Commonwealth Trans-Antarctic Expedition, under the leadership of Dr. Vivian Fuchs, with three Sno-Cats, two Weasels, and a Muskeg tractor traveled across Antarctica via the South Pole from Shackleton Station on the Filchner Ice Shelf to Scott Base on Ross Island, a distance of 2158 statute miles, from November 24, 1957, to March 2, 1958. As part of the United States Antarctic Research Program under the auspices of the National Science Foundation during and since the IGY, several long-distance traverses have been made over the snow surfaces with tractors, Weasels, Sno-Cats, and Nodwells for distances ranging from several hundred to over 1500 miles. An important aspect of improved surface travel is an electronic device suspended in front of the lead vehicle for the detection of crevasses.

Field work has been greatly facilitated by the successful introduction of motor toboggans capable of traveling hundreds of miles. These small machines can travel over rough surfaces and up fairly steep slopes of mountain glaciers. They have pulled sledge loads of from 1500 to 2000 pounds over long distances without breakdown and are thus capable of long-distance unsupported travel if necessary.[14] The success of mechanized surface transport is indicated by the fact that dog teams are no longer used by any activity under U. S. auspices in Antarctica. Dr. Henry M. Dater has calculated that a total of 9090 miles were traveled on U. S. logistic traverses in Antarctica from 1956 to 1964. In the same period, 18,610 miles were logged on U. S. scientific traverses.

RENEWAL OF AMERICAN INTEREST

AMERICAN ACTIVITY FROM 1842 TO 1928

The opening of the mechanical age of Antarctic exploration marked the beginning of renewed American activity in the far south. The four ships under Lieutenant Wilkes' command left the icebound coasts of Antarctica early in 1840. The Wilkins-Hearst Antarctic Expedition of 1928-29 landed at Deception Island on November 6, 1928. Although this expedition was led by Sir Hubert Wilkins, an Australian, it was sponsored by the American Geographical Society and a large part of the support was contributed by Americans. The first Byrd Antarctic Expedition, 1928-30, the first full-fledged American expedition to the south polar regions since Wilkes', entered the Ross Sea in December 1928. In the 89 years that intervened between Wilkes and Byrd, American interest in the Antarctic had been limited.

Sealing, the activity that first aroused American interests was (except at Heard Island in the 1850s) reduced to insignificance. Yet sealers such as William H. Smyley in the South Shetlands in the 1840s and E. D. Rogers, Henry Rodgers, and Franklin F. Smith and their New London compatriots at Heard Island at mid-century made indirect contributions to geographic knowledge of the Antarctic. Matthew Fontaine Maury contributed to and stimulated interest in the meteorology of the high southern latitudes. Dr. Jerome H. Kidder with the American party at Kerguelen observing the transit of Venus in December 1874, Dr. Frederick A. Cook with the Belgian expedition of 1898-99, and Robert Cushman Murphy at South Georgia in 1912-13 individually made contributions to scientific knowledge of Antarctica.

An American Antarctic activity of a scientific nature in the interval between 1840 and 1928 was the sub-Antarctic circumnavigation of the *Carnegie* in 1915-16. This cruise, which is rarely mentioned in accounts of Antarctic exploration, was a part of worldwide magnetic investigations begun in 1905 by the Department of Terrestrial Magnetism of the Carnegie Institution of Washington. The cruise on which the sub-Antarctic circumnavigation was made began at New York in March 1915 and ended at Buenos Aires in April 1917. With W. J. Peters in command, the magnetic research vessel entered the Pacific via the Panama Canal, worked north to Alaska and then south to New Zealand. From here it was proposed to complete a sub-Antarctic circumnavigation in one season, something which had not been done before.

The *Carnegie* sailed from Lyttelton, New Zealand, on December 6, 1915. Crossing the south Pacific, she dipped south of the 60th parallel between 150° W and 135° W, and at 125° W. The remainder of the circumnavigation was north of 60° S. Ross' course in the Pacific was followed or intersected for 200 miles to determine changes in magnetism since 1842. The *Carnegie* took on fresh water and provisions at South Georgia, but because of stormy weather and ice did not sight Bouvet Island nor make the planned stop at Kerguelen Island. On April 1, 1916, the *Carnegie* was back at Lyttelton after covering 17,084 miles in 118 days at sea, having recorded during this time some form of precipitation on 100 days, and gales, half of which reached hurricane force, on 52 days.[15]

THE AIRPLANE AS A FACTOR IN RENEWED AMERICAN INTEREST

Aviation had been given a tremendous stimulus during World War I, and this momentum carried forward into the 1920s in several forms. Aviation enthusiasts, including pilots who had been trained during the war, were looking for new peacetime uses for the airplane. The aircraft manufacturers were vitally interested in maintaining their markets by encouraging the development of commercial aviation, and designers were striving to meet the anticipated needs. Confident in their product and in their cause, these enthusiasts sought to demonstrate the practicability of aircraft and to arouse public interest in aviation through the performance of spectacular feats. Such feats took the form of aerial races, races against time, endurance flights, transcontinental and transatlantic flights. Not the least of these were Arctic flights, including flights to the North Pole. It is not surprising that such activity should have been especially popular in the United States, a country of great distances where people were becoming accustomed to an ever-increasing mechanization of all aspects of life and a land where practical flights by heavier-than-air craft had first been demonstrated. Thus in the United States in 1928 two expeditions were in preparation to begin aerial exploration in the Antarctic. Sir Hubert Wilkins, who had flown with Carl Ben Eielson from Point Barrow, Alaska, to Svalbard (Spitsbergen), now proposed to make a transantarctic flight from the Weddell Sea to the Ross Ice Shelf. Commander Richard E. Byrd, who with Floyd Bennett on May 9, 1926, had been the first to fly to the North Pole, now proposed to lead a large expedition of which one objective would be to fly to the South Pole.

THE WILKINS-HEARST ANTARCTIC EXPEDITION, 1928-1929

Strictly speaking, the Wilkins-Hearst Expedition was an international undertaking, and its inclusion in this account of American exploration in the Antarctic is, as we have mentioned, justified only by the fact that it was organized in the United States, was sponsored by the American Geographical Society, and was to a large extent financed by Americans. Sir Hubert Wilkins, who had been a captain in the Australian Flying Corps in France during World War I and who prior to that had served in the Arctic with Vilhjalmar Stefansson, was organizer and leader of the expedition. Wilkins had also served in Sir Ernest Shackleton's last Antarctic expedition in the *Quest,* 1921-22. William Randolph Hearst, prominent American newspaper publisher, made a major financial contribution to the expedition by purchasing exclusive news rights to its operations for his Universal News Service. The Detroit Aviation Society was also a supporter. The Vacuum Oil Company of Australia gave $10,000 and the gasoline used by the expedition. The two Lockheed Vega monoplanes with Wright Whirlwind engines were of American manufacture. One of the planes had been used by Wilkins in his Arctic flight. The other, with accessories, was given to the expedition by the Lockheed Aircraft Company. Other contributions of money, supplies, and equipment were received from numerous individuals and companies in the United States, Australia, the United Kingdom, and Norway. Transportation was provided at reduced rates from New York to Montevideo by the Munson Line, and from Montevideo to Deception Island the expedition was carried on board the S. S. *Hektoria* by courtesy of the N. Bugge Hektor Whaling Company of Tönsberg, Norway. The return to Montevideo was made on board H.M.S. *Flerus.*[16] In addition to Wilkins, the expedition personnel consisted of two American pilots, Lieutenant Carl Ben Eielson and Joe Crosson, and American engineer Orval Porter, and a Norwegian radio operator, Victor Olsen.

With his Arctic experience behind him, Wilkins now proposed to make a transantarctic flight by establishing a base at Deception Island from which it was planned that planes, equipped with skis, might take off from the bay ice which usually remained firm until the latter part of December. Two planes were taken along with the intention that a preliminary flight should be made along the east side of the Antarctic Peninsula in search of a spot 500 or 600 miles south where the planes might land in the field. Before December 20 it was planned to fly both planes to this advanced landing spot; one plane, after transferring gasoline to the second, would return to Deception Island while the other would fly westward along the coast to the Ross Ice Shelf.[17]

When the expedition arrived at Deception Island on November 6, 1928, it was discovered that the season was unusually advanced, and that the bay ice inside the harbor was unsafe for the planes. Continued warm weather and rain soon melted the snow on the low-lying land that might have been used for taking off and landing the planes equipped with skis (Fig. 3).

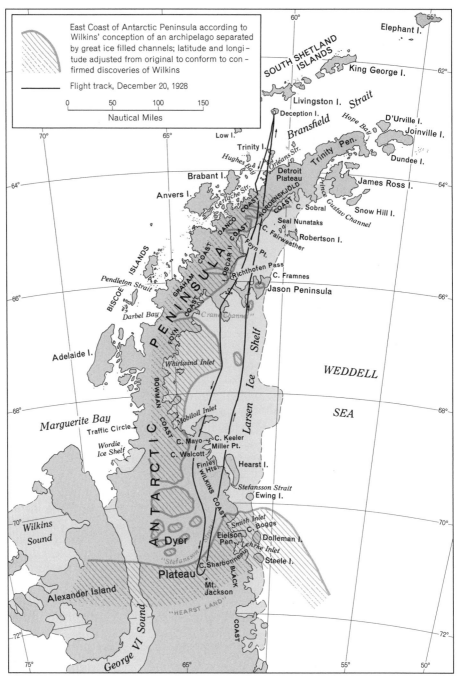

FIGURE 12. Track of the Pioneer Antarctic Flight by Sir Hubert Wilkins, December 20, 1928.

It was now necessary to smooth off a runway on the sloping surface of volcanic ash on the low-lying peninsula at the entrance to the whalers' harbor, and the planes were fitted with wheels. On November 16, 1929, in spite of cloudy weather, a short flight was made about Deception Island, the first in Antarctic history. On November 26 both planes, in a reconnaissance of the western part of the South Shetland Islands, failed to find a place where the planes could take off and land on skis. After all other possibilities were tried in vain, it was finally decided to enlarge the runway to accommodate a heavily loaded plane which would take off with wheels on the landing gear. This meant that a landing in the field was now impossible, and the idea of one plane supporting the other on a long transantarctic flight had to be abandoned. Moreover, the risk involved was greatly increased, for a forced landing anywhere on the flight would probably mean disaster.

On the morning of December 20 conditions were excellent for flying. Sir Hubert Wilkins and Lieutenant Eielson took off at 8:20 a. m. and headed south over the Antarctic Peninsula. Rising to 8200 feet as they flew across the inner portion of Hughes Bay, they crossed the plateau-like summit of the Antarctic Peninsula and proceeded south over the Larsen Ice Shelf. Sir Hubert noted that great glacier-filled valleys opened into the Weddell Sea. One of these, Crane Glacier, he thought was a great channel actually cutting the peninsula in two between 66° S and 67° S. Still farther south he saw that the peninsula became much narrower and that it was cut by several broad transverse glaciers. They were now flying across a great bight in the east coast which Sir Hubert named Mobiloil Bay, and as they did so they dropped down to an elevation of 2000 feet to observe the snow surface on the ice shelf. This must have given him an erroneous perspective, for Sir Hubert thought that three great channels cut completely across the Antarctic Peninsula, separating it from the mainland and making it in truth an archipelago. The largest and southernmost of these channels, the one that separated the archipelago from the mainland, he called Stefansson Strait, and that portion of the continent which bordered the strait he named Hearst Land[18] (Fig. 12).

When they had reached what Sir Hubert reckoned to be 71°20' S, 64°15'. W, a point somewhere in Stefansson Strait, half of the gasoline supply had been used up. Storm clouds gathering in the north threatened to cut them off from their base. Consequently, they decided to return immediately to Deception Island where, as they approached at an elevation of 5000 feet, they were fortunate enough to see their landing field through a break in the clouds.

A second long flight 250 miles to the southward, over almost the same course as the first flight, was made on January 10, and Sir Hubert felt that he had now confirmed the results of December 20. Since conditions were not likely to permit the completion of the originally planned transantarctic flight during the remainder of the season, the planes and supplies were stored in the whaling company warehouse, and Sir Hubert proposed to try again in 1929-30. In this later attempt he had the assistance of the R. R. S. *William Scoresby* of the Discovery Committee of the British Colonial Office and again failed to achieve his goal.

Many of Wilkins' landmarks have been identified, but the general outline of the coast has been greatly changed as a result of the work of subsequent expeditions. From the results of Lincoln Ellsworth's flights in 1935 and the surveys of the British Graham Land Expedition, 1934-37, it was obvious that the great transverse straits reported by Wilkins did not exist. As late as 1947, as a result of a thorough study of aerial photographs taken by Wilkins, Ellsworth, and the members of the East Base of the U. S. Antarctic Service, the Advisory Committee on Antarctic Names of the U. S. Board on Geographic Names was able to match a sufficient number of critical landmarks to prove that Stefansson Strait was actually the strait, about 40 miles long and filled with shelf ice, separating Hearst Island from the Peninsula.[19]

ADMIRAL BYRD AND THE RENEWAL OF AMERICAN INTEREST

History shows that in each nation each period of popular interest in polar exploration has generally been aroused and sustained by one man who possessed those qualities which stir the public fancy. Such a man was Jeremiah N. Reynolds, whose efforts had a great deal to do with the eventual establishment of the U. S. Exploring Expedition under Lieutenant Wilkes, 1839-42. No man has been more important in American Antarctic exploration than Captain Edmund Fanning. Until his book, *Voyages Round the World*,[20] was first published in 1833, however, he was not widely known outside of maritime circles although he was a man of considerable influence. Robert E. Peary was another man who could capture the public fancy. From 1925 to 1956, this role was played by Admiral Richard E. Byrd.

Much credit must be given Byrd for the present American interest in south polar regions, for by his deeds and by his popular appeal he succeeded in stirring the fancy of the people to the point where in the popular mind his name was synonymous with Antarctica. His exploits as a naval aviator and transatlantic flier, and his achievement on being the first to fly to the North Pole instilled in the public sufficient confidence in him to make them willing to support his first two Antarctic expeditions. From Byrd's First Expedition in 1928-30 until 1955, 11 expeditions, not counting the Wilkins-Hearst Expeditions, left the United States for the Antarctic. Byrd had a prominent position in six of these, four of them being government-supported expeditions. The success of his polar flights undoubtedly lay in the successful planning which he learned by experimentation as a naval pilot during World War I. In this service he pioneered in flying over water out of sight of land. Navigation of these early seaplanes without the usual landmarks as an aid caused him to experiment with compasses suitable for aerial navigation, drift indicators, and bubble sextants.[21] His reputation from this work was responsible for his appointment to plan the flight navigation for the transatlantic flight in 1919 of the United States Navy Flying Boats NC1, NC3, and NC4. The NC4 succeeded in crossing the Atlantic via Newfoundland and the Azores in May 1919, the first plane to do so. With this background and experience in aerial navigation and organizing expeditions, Richard E. Byrd began the modern American assault on the icy ramparts of Antarctica.

NOTES

1. J. Gordon Hayes, *The Conquest of the South Pole* (London, 1930), pp. 29-31.

2. *American Practical Navigator*, "An Epitome of Navigation and Nautical Astronomy," originally by Nathaniel Bowditch, U. S. Hydrographic Office, No. 9, (Washington, 1943), Part 2, Table 8, p. 130.

3. Capt. Robert F. Scott, *The Voyage of the "Discovery"* (London, 1907), vol. 1, pp. 145-148.

4. Erich von Drygalski, *Zum Kontinent des eisigen Südens* (Berlin, 1904), pp. 271-273.

5. W. L. G. Joerg, "The Cartographical Results of Ellsworth's Trans-Antarctic Flight," *Geographical Review*, vol. 27, No. 3, July, 1937, pp. 430-444 and Plate III.

6. Sir Douglas Mawson, *The Home of the Blizzard* (London and Philadelphia, 1915), vol. 2, pp. 32, 134-137.

7. Frank Wild, *Shackleton's Last Voyage* (New York, n. d.), pp. 10-11, 345.

8. Richard E. Byrd, *Little America* (New York, 1930), p. 269.

9. E. H. Shackleton, *The Heart of the Antarctic* (London, 1909), vol. 1, pp. 22-23, and 238-240.

10. Dr. Jean Charcot, *The Voyage of the "Why Not?" in the Antarctic* (London, 1911), pp. 17 and 111.

11. Robert F. Scott, *Scott's Last Expedition* (London, 1913), vol. 1, pp. 438-451.

12. Mawson, *op. cit.*, vol. 1, p. 24; vol. 2, p. 6.

13. Charles Swinthinbank, "Mechanical Transport of the Norwegian-British-Swedish Antarctic Expedition, 1949-52," *Polar Record*, vol. 6, No. 46, July, 1953, pp. 766-767.

14. Charles Swinthinbank, "Motor Sledges in the Antarctic," *Polar Record*, vol. 11, No. 72, September, 1962, pp. 265-269.

15. J. P. Ault, "Sailing the Seven Seas in the Interest of Science," *National Geographic Magazine*, vol. 42, No. 6, December, 1922, p. 649.

16. Capt. Sir Hubert Wilkins, "The Wilkins-Hearst Antarctic Expedition, 1928-1929," *Geographical Review*, vol. 19, No. 3, July, 1929, p. 375.

17. *Ibid.*, p. 357.

18. *Ibid.*, pp. 366-368.

19. K. J. Bertrand, W. L. G. Joerg, and H. E. Saunders, "The True Location of Stefansson Strait and Hearst Land, Antarctica," *Geographical Review*, vol. 38, No. 3, July 1948, pp. 475-486. This article gives a critical summary of the manner in which Wilkins' landmarks have been substantiated or corrected by subsequent expeditions.

20. Capt. Edmund Fanning, *Voyages Round the World* (New York, Collins and Hannay, 1833).

21. Charles J. V. Murphy, *Struggle; the Life and Exploits of Commander R. E. Byrd* (New York, 1928), pp. 59-60.

17

THE FIRST BYRD ANTARCTIC EXPEDITION, 1928-1930

GENERAL FEATURES OF THE EXPEDITION

SIGNIFICANCE

The Antarctic exploring expedition organized and led by then-Commander Richard E. Byrd (USN, retired) during the years 1928 to 1930, insofar as it coordinated in its program the use of the airplane, the aerial camera, the radio, and the snowmobile, may be considered the first full realization of the mechanical age of exploration in Antarctica.

Although Sir Hubert Wilkins on November 6, 1928, succeeded in making the first airplane flight in the Antarctic, he preceded Byrd, who made his first flight on January 15, 1929, by only 10 weeks. Byrd's flights, made with three planes, were more extensive and were all made in a much higher latitude. From the standpoint of exploration, they were more successful because they were tied in with ground surveys. Sir Douglas Mawson (1911-14) was the first to use radio in the Antarctic, and the whalers, the R.R.S. *Discovery,* the Norwegian exploring ship *Norvegia,* and Wilkins had all been using radio in the Antarctic at the time the Byrd Expedition entered the field. Byrd, however, made a much more extensive use of wireless communication, for not only did the base camp at Little America keep in regular communication with the outside world but all flights and field parties were likewise in regular contact by radio with the base. Wilkins took photographs from his plane while in flight, but they were taken with hand-held cameras. Captain Ashley C. McKinley of the Byrd expedition was the first to use an aerial mapping camera in the Antarctic — a Fairchild K-3. It was the best in its day for the purpose and by present-day standards is still a satisfactory machine as far as results are concerned. Sir Ernest Henry Shackleton, Captain Robert Falcon Scott, and Mawson had tried with mixed success to use automotive vehicles for land transport. Shackleton's trial of a specially equipped automobile in 1908-09 and Scott's use of light crawler-type tractors resulted in moderate success for drawing sledges in the vicinity of the base camp. Mawson found a propeller-driven sled converted from an airplane fuselage to be impractical. Byrd had more success with a Ford snowmobile, but it too broke down 75 miles from the base while hauling supplies.

From the American point of view the first Byrd expedition had additional significance, for it was the first American expedition to explore Antarctica since the U. S. Exploring Expedition under Lieutenant Charles Wilkes had left its icebound coast in February 1840. The Byrd expedition marked a revival of American interest in the Antarctic, an area which had been so much in the public mind during the first half of the 19th century. Following the first Byrd expedition and prior to preparations for the International Geophysical Year, 1957-58, ten American expeditions entered Antarctic regions. Four of them were government-sponsored.

ESTABLISHMENT AND COMPOSITION

After having made the first successful airplane flight to the North Pole on May 9, 1926, and having completed a transatlantic flight from New York to Paris in June 1927, Richard E. Byrd turned his attention to the Antarctic and the South Pole in search of new fields to conquer. From experience gained in the north he was confident that he could successfully explore by airplane in the Antarctic, the one part of the world still having vast areas unvisited by man. For much of this area the airplane offered the easiest means of access. A flight to the South Pole, however, required a much larger, more elaborate, and more costly expedition than did that which launched the North Pole flight from Kings Bay, Spitsbergen (Svalbard).

To this problem Byrd applied his promotional ability and his organizing skill. Early in 1928 an office was set up in New York City to serve as headquarters for the proposed expedition. The principal backers were Edsel Ford and John D. Rockefeller, Jr. Additional support in the form of monetary contributions, both large and small, and donations of supplies and equipment came from many sources. These included the National Geographic Society, the American Geographical Society, the *New York Times,* Fisher Brothers, the Todd Shipbuilding Company, the Tidewater Oil Company, and a host of private individuals. A hectic nine months were devoted to raising money, buying and begging supplies and equipment, procuring ships and airplanes, and recruiting members of the expedition.

The principal expedition ship was a wooden 515-ton Norwegian sealing vessel, *Samson,* purchased in Tromsoe at the recommendation of Amundsen. The ship, built in 1882, was 170 feet in length and had a beam of 31 feet. She was rigged as a barkentine and had an auxiliary engine rated at 200 horsepower. She was reconditioned at the yard of the Todd Shipbuilding Company, rerigged as a bark, and rechristened the *City of New York.*[1] The second ship was an 800-ton steel cargo vessel with a speed of only 9 knots, yet considerably faster than the *City of New York.* After reconditioning, she was renamed the *Eleanor Bolling.*[2] In addition to the two regular expedition ships, two whalers, the *James Clark Ross* and the *C. A. Larsen,* assisted by transporting part of the expedition equipment and personnel to the Antarctic.[3]

Three airplanes were taken to Antarctica by the expedition. The largest was a Ford — a trimotored, all-metal monoplane considered to be the best plane of this size then available. It was powered by three 225-horsepower Wright Whirlwind engines, but the nose engine was replaced by a Wright Cyclone engine with a rating of 525 horsepower, giving the plane a total of 975 horsepower with a top speed of 122 miles per hour and a load capacity of 15,000 pounds. In its construction the aircraft, a factory transport plane, had been carefully redesigned to reduce weight so as to permit the maximum lift in getting over the passes of the Queen Maud Mountains.[4] The second plane was a Fokker Universal monoplane powered by a 425-horsepower Pratt and Whitney Wasp engine. The third and smallest plane was a Fairchild folding wing monoplane also powered by a 425-horsepower Pratt and Whitney Wasp engine. The Ford was named the *Floyd*

Bennett, the Fokker was called the *Virginia,* and the Fairchild was christened the *Stars and Stripes.*

Organizer and leader of the expedition which bore his name was then-Commander Richard E. Byrd. Early in 1930, while the expedition was still at Little America, he was raised to the rank of Rear Admiral by special act of Congress. Second in command was Dr. Laurence McKinley Gould, then assistant professor of geology at the University of Michigan, geologist on the expedition. Third in command was then-Captain Ashley C. McKinley (AAC), aerial surveyor on the expedition. The wintering party at Little America consisted of 42 men including four airplane pilots in addition to Commander Byrd, five scientists, and a physician.

The *City of New York* carried a crew of 20 with Captain Frederick C. Melville in command. Bendik Johansen was first mate and ice pilot. The same number of men manned the *Eleanor Bolling* under the command of Captain Gustav L. Brown, with Charles J. McGuinness as first mate. On the return voyage to Little America in 1930, the crew of the *City of New York* was increased by eight and that of the *Eleanor Bolling* by three.

Objectives and Accomplishments

The principal objectives of the First Byrd Antarctic Expedition were geographical exploration and the distinction of being the first to reach the South Pole by air. These two goals determined a number of subordinate but no less important objectives. The first of these was the establishment of a base camp in which the Expedition could spend the winter at the Bay of Whales. This indentation in the perpendicular and cliff-like front of the Ross Ice Shelf was chosen as the site for the base of operations for several reasons. The Ross Sea was known to be one of the few places where ships can regularly push through the pack ice to the edge of the continental land area during the latter part of the Antarctic summer. This inlet in about 164° W longitude afforded a satisfactory harbor where ships could be moored alongside bay ice to unload supplies. It had been used by Amundsen, who established his base here for his successful dash to the South Pole in 1911-12, thus proving the ice shelf to be sufficiently stable to safely support a winter camp. The snow-covered surface of the ice shelf in the vicinity of the Bay of Whales was considered to offer a satisfactory surface for a landing field for planes equipped with skis, and from Roald Amundsen's observations the wind conditions were not considered prohibitive for flying. Moreover, this is the nearest point to which a ship can approach the South Pole and therefore the nearest point at which the construction of a base camp was feasible. In view of Byrd's intention to carry on geographical exploration, the Bay of Whales was an excellent site for a base because vast areas of unexplored territory existed a relatively short distance to the northeast, east, and southeast. It was proposed that these areas should be investigated.

Not only was it necessary to select a site for the base with a view to its suitability for the operation of aircraft, but it was also proposed to maintain a continuous series of daily meteorological observations at the base as a means of predicting favorable weather for flying. That these weather records would in themselves prove a valuable addition to the knowledge of the Antarctic was recognized. In addition to the weather observations, the proposal to carry on geological investigations in the Queen Maud Mountains was tied in with the polar flight, but at the same time it had genuine scientific merit of its own. While in the field the geological party, traveling by dog sled, would be able to radio back to camp reports on the weather conditions in the Queen Maud Mountains. The geographical fixes obtained by the geological party would serve as control points for the map to be made from aerial photographs taken on the polar flight. Moreover, should the plane crash or be forced down on the polar flight, the geological party would serve as an advance rescue team. Not only were the radio operators responsible for communications between the base and the outside world and between the base and the various field parties, but they were also expected to carry on experiments in atmospheric conditions affecting radio in the Antarctic.

Two remaining objectives had no relation to flying operations. It was proposed that the two physicists should make daily observations of terrestrial magnetism and auroral activity as soon as an observatory could be completed. Instruments for photographic recording of the declination, horizontal intensity, and vertical intensity of the earth's magnetic field were to be installed. It was also planned to continue experiments on the determination of condensation nuclei. This study was begun on the voyage across the Pacific.

The second objective not directly connected with flying operations pertained to the detailed mapping of the Bay of Whales. Since it was known from surveys of previous expeditions that the seaward face of the Ross Ice Shelf was slowly changing as the great tabular icebergs broke off and floated northward, it was felt that a detailed survey, when compared with that made by Amundsen's expedition, might reveal some principle affecting the movement of the ice.

The First Byrd Antarctic Expedition succeeded in accomplishing all of its objectives:

(1) Byrd and three companions on November 29, 1929, became the first men to fly over the South Pole (Fig. 13).

(2) On a flight eastward from the Bay of Whales to what was then known as Edward VII Land on January 27, 1929, the Rockefeller Mountains were discovered.

(3) On a flight to the northeast on December 5, 1929, the coastline of the Ross Sea eastward to longitude 145° W was roughly delineated.

(4) On this same flight a great new chain of mountains, the then-named Edsel Ford Mountains, were discovered, and the land east of the 150th meridian W longitude was named Marie Byrd Land by the Commander in honor of his wife.

(5) In these and other flights 1600 aerial photographs were taken covering an area of approximately 150,000 square miles. There was a 60-percent overlap on all pictures, and the time, number, and altitude of the plane at the time of exposure were recorded for each picture.

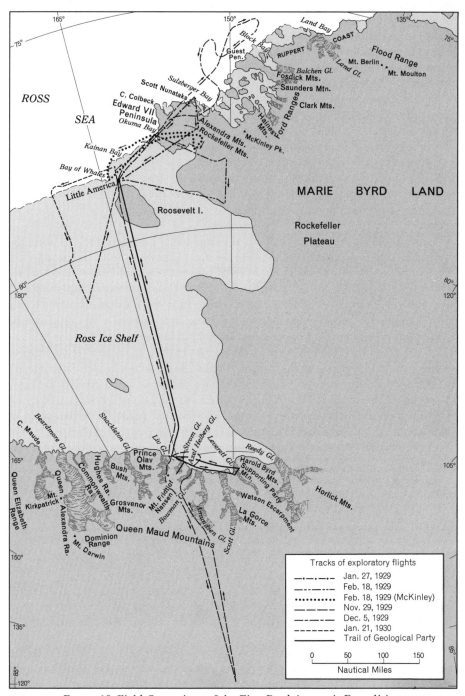

FIGURE 13. Field Operations of the First Byrd Antarctic Expedition.

(6) The geology of the Queen Maud Mountains was investigated, and its true geographical alinement to the eastward was determined. The range was found to be a structural continuation of the mountains of Victoria Land.

(7) Observations of the geological party on the surface and of the flight personnel from the air failed to verify Carmen Land as described and placed on the map by Amundsen.

(8) Meteorological observations were made three times daily on board ship, both going to and returning from the Bay of Whales. After the instruments were set up, the observations were continued at Little America for almost 13 months. In addition to the regular observations of atmospheric conditions at the surface of the earth, a large number of pilot balloon soundings were made of the upper atmosphere at Little America.

(9) The magnetic observatory was in operation at Little America from May 1929 to February 1930, during which time 240 daily records were obtained.

(10) A ground survey was made of the outline of the Bay of Whales. A sounding made through a hole in the bay ice by Siple and Czegka gave a depth of 1600 feet for the Ross Sea at that point.

(11) By the several flights made from Little America, it was clearly demonstrated that planes could be flown successfully in Antarctica, that they could land in the field to lay a depot, to refuel, or to obtain a geographical fix. Vast areas of rugged terrain were photographed by the aerial camera, thus permitting a correlation of the work of the expedition with that of earlier expeditions as well as with the work of those that were to follow.

(12) A considerable number of zoological specimens were obtained for the American Museum of Natural History of New York.

DETAILED RECORD OF OPERATIONS

DEPARTURE

Due to her slow speed the *City of New York* departed first, leaving Hoboken, N.J., on August 25, 1928, en route to Dunedin, New Zealand, via the Panama Canal. She carried 200 tons of material and 33 people. The *Eleanor Bolling* left Norfolk, Va., with 300 tons of supplies and 28 men, including Gould, Haines, and McKinley, on September 25. The dog drivers and 94 dogs with 40 tons of dog biscuit were taken aboard the *James Clark Ross* at Norfolk, Va. The greater speed of this whale ship would mean less danger to the huskies while crossing the tropics. The aircraft, the aviation personnel, gasoline, oil, and 100 tons of supplies were also shipped out of Norfolk on the whaler *C. A. Larsen*. Commander Byrd boarded the *Larsen* at San Pedro, Calif., from whence she departed on October 10.

The *James Clark Ross* arrived in New Zealand ahead of the rest of the expedition. The *Larsen* arrived in Wellington on November 5, disembarking the expedition members and material, and then in company with her catchers put out on a whaling cruise. The *Eleanor Bolling* arrived at Dunedin on November 18 and was soon sent to Wellington for the cargo left there by the *Larsen*. The *New*

York did not arrive at Dunedin until November 26, after being at sea three months. The cargo was restowed at Dunedin so that if only the *New York* succeeded in getting through the pack of ice to the Bay of Whales she would afford adequate supplies for the men for a year on the ice and permit a limited program of exploration and scientific investigation. The Fairchild airplane was lashed on the deck of the *New York*.

Approaching the Antarctic

Heavily laden, the *Eleanor Bolling* and the *New York* left Dunedin for the Antarctic at 6 a.m. December 2, 1928. Twenty-nine men were aboard the *New York* and 54 on the *Bolling*. At first the expedition was blessed with fine weather. When the wind was right the *New York* progressed under both sail and steam. When the wind failed she was taken in tow by the *Bolling*. The first gale struck on the evening of December 6 and continued through the next day with peril to the deck cargo from the high seas. During the day the towline broke and a sail on the *New York* was ripped, but no more serious damage occurred before the storm blew itself out. A period of thick weather followed, making for difficult navigation, especially since the two ships were hoping to rendezvous with the *Larsen* before the whaler entered the pack ice.

The first iceberg was sighted Sunday, December 9. Many more followed on this and the next day. December 10 was marked by fitful weather, with moments of sunshine followed by snow squalls or thick foggy weather. On this day Scott Island was sighted, after which the course was set due south and they soon reached the edge of the pack ice. On the next day, still December 10, but east of the international date line, the *Larsen* was sighted. With considerable difficulty caused by the rough sea, 90 tons of coal were transferred in sacks from the *Bolling* to the *New York* by 11 a.m. the next morning. The *Bolling* then steamed back to Dunedin while the *New York* hove to, waiting to be taken in tow by the *Larsen*. On December 15 the leads opened sufficiently for Captain Nilsen to enter the pack ice in about 178° E. Finally, after a constant struggle with the pack, the *Larsen* broke through into the open water of the Ross Sea on December 23. At 2 p.m. she cast off the towline, and from this point the *New York* was on its own. The edge of the Ross Ice Shelf was reached in about 177° W on December 25. The ice cliff rose from 40 to 90 feet above the water, and soundings three miles out from the front showed the bottom of the Ross Sea to be 250 to 300 fathoms deep. As the ship worked eastward along the ice front, a stop was made at Discovery Inlet, but since no satisfactory landing field was found, the *New York* continued toward the Bay of Whales, which was reached on December 28.

Establishment of the Base

The Bay of Whales was found to be almost completely blocked with bay ice. The *New York* was moored to the edge of this ice and a party consisting of Byrd, Balchen, Braathen, Petersen, Vaughan, and Walden with two dog teams prepared to go ashore. After several days' reconnoitering and short trips of exploration in the vicinity of the Bay of Whales, a site for the base camp was selected on top of the Ross Ice Shelf on the east side of the bay, about eight miles from the point where the ship was moored. This was four miles north of the position where Amundsen had located his base, Framheim. No trace, however, was seen of Framheim either in this preliminary exploration or later. The new American base was named Little America. Unloading began on January 2, with great piles of supplies being stacked on the bay ice, from where it was hauled by dog team to Little America along a trail marked by orange flags. Gould was in charge of the construction at Little America while McKinley had charge of supplies on the bay ice. The dog teams traveled in pairs and their departure and arrival were noted by radio. On good days each team made two trips, totaling 30 miles. In this manner a total of 650 tons were transported to Little America. The *New York* had transported 1 airplane, 1200 gallons of gasoline, 75 tons of coal, 54 men, 80 dogs, and food enough for 54 men for 15 months. On January 15 the Fairchild airplane was put ashore. By next day it was assembled and made its first test flight successfully.

The base at Little America consisted of two main buildings and several smaller special-purpose buildings, mostly of prefabricated design for use in the Antarctic. The executive building contained the library, the hospital room, the radio laboratory, and quarters for the physician, geologist, meteorologist, and physicist. A second building served as mess hall, bunk house, and photographic laboratory. A third building served as a machine shop. A magnetic observatory and a weather station were also constructed. All buildings were separated by some distance as a precaution against fire and were connected by snow tunnels as passageways during the long winter. The machine shop, the radio storeroom, and the aviation workshop were built from boxes and crates. Other rooms were carved out of the snow and roofed with tarpaulins which were soon covered with snow.

Unloading continued as construction went on. After leaving the *New York* at the edge of the pack ice on December 11, 1928, the *Bolling* had reached Dunedin on December 20. Taking on a second cargo, she departed for the Antarctic on January 14. After weathering a bad storm in the Pacific, she passed through the pack ice of the Ross Sea with little difficulty, arriving at the Bay of Whales on January 27 with the other two airplanes, additional dogs, and 7500 gallons of gasoline. Breaking up of the bay ice added to the hazards of unloading and forced the *New York* to be moved on January 22. On January 29 both ships were forced to move again, and were now moored only five miles from Little America. On January 31 a piece of shelf ice broke off, almost capsizing the *Bolling*. The *Bolling* was unloaded in 5½ days, and on February 2 departed for New Zealand, encountering severe storms before reaching Dunedin on February 16.

On February 6 the *New York* had to be moved to avoid an iceberg, and a storm 24 hours later forced the ship into the Ross Sea where she battled floating ice during the night. On February 11 and 12 the ship was again forced to leave her moorings, and when she could not tie up on February 13, Byrd decided to cruise to the eastward to explore the area in the vicinity of the land then known as Edward VII Land, but they were stopped by pack ice the next morning. Another attempt was made on February 18, but it too was abandoned the next day. On February 22 the *New York* sailed for New Zealand. She finally worked through the pack ice with much difficulty, as new ice was freezing in the leads. Captain Nilsen of the *Larsen* dispatched two whale chasers to find a lead for the *New York* to the westward. Succeeding in this, Captain Nilsen then met the expedition ship and on February 28 transferred 90 tons of coal to her from the *Larsen*. Due to the bad ice conditions Byrd ordered the *Bolling*, which was then on its way with another cargo for Little America, to wait for the *New York* at the edge of the pack ice and then return to New Zealand.

PRELIMINARY EXPLORATORY FLIGHTS

Aerial operations began as soon as the Fairchild airplane was unloaded on January 14, long before unloading operations were completed or the construction of the base camp was finished. Seven short flights were made to the west and southwest of Little America on January 15. On January 27 Byrd, with Bernt Balchen as pilot and Harold June as radioman, took off to the eastward on a flight to the Alexandra Mountains, which had been discovered by Captain Robert F. Scott in 1902 while on an exploring cruise in the *Discovery* along the front of the Ross Ice Shelf.[5] Flying in fine weather which Haines, the meteorologist, had predicted, they first noted the two inlets in the Ross Ice Shelf to the east of the Bay of Whales, Kainan Bay, and Okuma Bay, named by the Japanese Expedition of 1911-12.[6] They continued northeast until they sighted first Scott Nunataks, and then the Alexandra Mountains. At this point snow squalls to the eastward caused them to turn south, when suddenly from an altitude of about 4000 feet they saw a new range of mountains which Byrd named the Rockefeller Mountains. Further exploration was curbed by a dwindling fuel supply, and they returned to Little America after having been in the air for five hours.

With a favorable weather forecast and with temperatures between 7° F and −9° F, on February 18 Byrd and Bernt Balchen took off in the Fokker, while Harold June and Alton Parker flew in the Fairchild on another exploratory flight to the eastward. Byrd's course was first set northeastward along the edge of the ice shelf to Okuma Bay and then east to the Rockefeller Mountains. Here a very prominent peak was seen beyond the Rockefeller Mountains, but Byrd decided to wait for clearer weather before exploring further to the east. The course was then set to the southward, going about 100 miles farther south than on the previous flight. Only uncertain appearances of high land could be seen beyond the turning point, as the planes headed back to Little America. As soon as the planes returned to the base, McKinley was given permission to make a photographic flight in which he went northeastward along the coast to the Rockefeller Mountains which he included in a photographic strip map. He too saw the impressive peak and other mountains to the east of the Rockefeller Mountains. This new land beyond the discoveries of his predecessors Byrd named Marie Byrd Land in honor of his wife.

In the mid-afternoon of March 7 Gould, Balchen, and June took off in the

Fokker on a flight to the Rockefeller Mountains. After 2 hours and 10 minutes in the air, they landed near the southern extremity of the mountains on a surface that turned out to be solid blue ice thinly covered with snow, apparently the frozen surface of a melt-water lake. The next morning they began measuring a base line for a triangulation of the mountain peaks. By noon the wind had increased to such an extent that the survey work was halted. In the late afternoon they were able to ascend one of the peaks, but high winds on the following three days made work extremely difficult. On March 13 they were able to complete a triangulation and collect geological specimens. The next day the winds were stronger than ever, and the men worked desperately to save the plane. A sudden gust of wind in the evening, however, tore the plane from its light moorings, carried it tail first over a half mile, and smashed it on the ice. On March 18 the weather improved enough so that Byrd, Dean Smith, and Malcolm Hanson were able to fly over in the Fairchild to find out what had happened, since the field party had not been able to send a radio message to Little America. In the meantime a dog team, sent out as a rescue mission when the bad weather persisted, reached 43 miles east of Little America before it was ordered to return. Balchen and June returned in the plane with Smith, while Byrd and Hanson remained with Gould until a second flight could be made on March 22 to return them to Little America. The Rockefeller Mountains had been found to be old subdued erosion remnants consisting of a pinkish, coarse-grained granite into which pegmatite dikes and younger gray and pink granite had intruded. The scattered peaks rise to elevations of 500 to 2000 feet above sea level and are almost entirely covered with snow. The surrounding ice surface to the southward was of such low elevation that Gould thought at that time that, if it were melted away, the Rockefeller Mountains area might possibly become an archipelago.[7]

WINTER AT LITTLE AMERICA

After the geological party had been rescued from the Rockefeller Mountains, the remaining two planes were put for the winter in hangars built of snow blocks. While the geological party had been investigating the Rockefeller Mountains, four dog teams had been sent south on March 7 to lay depots of supplies and gain trail experience. The first part of the trail through pressure ridges and crevasses had been marked by flags placed by Balchen and Braathen on skis. The teams returned to Little America on March 13 after having deposited 1350 pounds of supplies in three depots marked by flags and snow cairns. The first was laid at a point 20 miles out, the second at 40 miles, and the third at 44 miles from Little America. This was a start on more complete depot laying the following spring. The 42 men now settled down for winter in camp. On April 19 the sun set and was not seen again until spring. Meanwhile Little America was a place of great activity. The machine shop was a busy place, improvising and preparing equipment for the summer flights and trail journeys. Tents, clothing, footwear, and trail rations had to be prepared. Frank T. Davies made daily magnetic observations, and the radio operators kept a regular schedule of communications with the outside world.

Daily meteorological observations were made by William C. Haines and Henry T. Harrison at 8 a. m., 2 p. m., and 8 p. m., 180° meridian time.[8] Meteorological observations had been made regularly on the two Expedition ships in the voyages from Dunedin to the Bay of Whales. Because the ice conditions prolonged the unloading operations and delayed the completion of the base, the meteorological observations were continued aboard ship in the Bay of Whales from December 28 until February 16, when they were begun at Little America. By this time the base was sufficiently completed to move the instruments to Little America. The first pilot balloon was sent aloft on January 16 to obtain meteorological data in the upper atmosphere. It had been planned to take balloon observations every 12 hours, but this schedule could not be adhered to, due to the frequency of low hanging clouds and drifting snow. Nevertheless, between January 16, 1929, and February 5, 1930, when the last balloon was sent aloft before crating the equipment for shipment home, 414 pilot balloon observations were made in 385 days.[9] During the winter darkness a small paper lantern lighted by a tallow candle was attached to the balloon so that its ascent could be followed with the theodolite. Due to the cold it was necessary to heat the candle before placing it in the lantern or the tallow would not contine to burn.[10] Also, it was frequently necessary to scrape frost from the lenses of the theodolite during the observation. Sending kites aloft was seriously delayed by the fact that a crate of essential parts was lost when it was buried by drifting snow during a March blizzard. The first kite ascent was made in September, but several men suffered severe frostbite on the hands and face in the process. Consequently, further kite flying was postponed until more favorable weather.

The lowest temperature recorded at Little America was −72.2° F on July 28.[11] Yet, according to Harrison, ". . . a far more severe condition than this prevailed in July when a combination of a 25-mile wind and a temperature of −64° was experienced."[12] This is equivalent to a wind-chill factor of approximately 2800.[13] Subzero temperatures were recorded in every month that the expedition remained at Little America, and the mean temperature for each month from March through October was below zero.[14] From April 1 through October 31 the highest temperature recorded was 17° F on August 19. The sun shone above the horizon again for the first time on August 23, 1929, but the mean temperature for September was −44.2° F, almost as cold as −45.8° F, the mean for July.[15] Moreover, the highest temperature recorded during September was −2° F, and the lowest was −67.5° F.

BEGINNING OF SPRING SLEDGING

One phase of the scientific program of the expedition entailed the geological investigation of the Queen Maud Mountains. This involved a long sledge journey from Little America across the Ross Ice Shelf, and it could be accomplished only by laying a series of depots along the first part of the trail. After careful planning and some preliminary tryouts, five teams started south shortly after noon on Sunday, October 13. Each team pulled two sledges, one loaded with 400 pounds of material and one empty. This was more or less of a staging as well as an experimental effort, and the loaded sledges were to be left in the field where they would be picked up later by the sledgers on the southern journey. Four hours and seven miles from Little America, it was decided that the temperature was too low for proper sledging. The dogs were tiring due to the cold, and the dry snow was creating too much friction on the sledge runners. The loaded sledges were left at this point, and the entire party returned to Little America to await better conditions. Temperatures lower than —20° F were considered unsatisfactory for sledging.[16]

On October 15, with the temperature at − 10° F, the supporting party, consisting of Arthur Walden (leader), de Ganahl, Bursey, and Braathen, started on the southern journey. They were accompanied by the geological party and by Petersen, who went along to test radio equipment. After picking up the loaded sledges that had been left on the trail, the combined parties reached the 20-mile depot on October 16. At this point the geological party cached their loads and with Petersen returned to Little America. The supporting party continued southward, with two sledges being pulled by each team and carrying a total of 800 pounds. The men traveled from 6 a. m. to 9 p. m. unless held in camp by bad weather. They marked the trail with orange flags each half mile and with snow cairns which they built each noon and night. This would help the geological party on the first half of its journey and would aid in navigation on the flights southward. Depots of food and supplies were laid down every 50 miles. After experiencing blinding snow and wind during several days, the men reached, on October 29, the heavily crevassed area reported by Amundsen at about 81° S. On November 1, depot No. 4 was reached at 81°45′ S. This was 220 miles (199 geographical miles) from Little America. The last of the supplies were cached here, and the supporting party began the return journey to Little America where they arrived on November 8.

After returning from the 20-mile depot, the geological party on Sunday, October 20, started again hauling supplies to the trail depots. By October 25 they had reached the 100-mile depot from where, after caching their loads, they returned again to Little America which was reached on the evening of the 29th. On October 25 Strom, with Black and Feury, set off in the Ford snowmobile, pulling three sledges loaded with supplies. After following the trail to the south for about 75 miles, the machine broke down while bogged down in soft snow. The men abandoned the vehicle and hiked back to Little America, reaching the base on November 5.

The geological party had gained considerable sledging experience, and when they finally departed for the Queen Maud Mountains on November 4, the sledge loads were consequently considerably lighter and organized differently from what had been originally planned. The extra depot laying had made this new arrangement possible. The geological party consisted of Gould (the leader), Vaughan, Crockett, Thorne, Goodale, and O'Brien, with five dog teams each pulling two sledges.

LAYING A BASE AT THE QUEEN MAUD MOUNTAINS

While the trail parties had been busy laying depots, the aviation group, with the aid of all hands at Little America, had been digging out the planes from their snow hangars and getting the machines ready for the big program of aerial exploration. Excellent weather was the forecast on November 18, 1929. With Dean Smith as pilot, Commander Byrd, Harold June, and Captain McKinley took off in the trimotor Ford, the *Floyd Bennett,* on a base-laying flight to the foot of the Queen Maud Mountains, 440 miles away. About 200 miles out the geological party was spotted struggling along the trail under heavy loads which they had just taken on at depot No. 4. The plane swooped low to drop mail and miscellaneous equipment. Approaching the Queen Maud Mountains, some difficulty was experienced in identifying from the air features shown on copies of Amundsen's charts and on pictures taken by Amundsen from the ground in 1911. Finally, they landed at the foot of Liv Glacier, where, without stopping the engines, they deposited a supply of gasoline, oil, and 350 pounds of food along with a pressure cooker and other trail equipment. McKinley had taken photographs of the mountains with the aerial mapping camera, and while they were on ice, Byrd took some astronomical sights and some bearings to fix their position. The party took off immediately, making a brief photographic flight to the east along the foot of the mountains before returning to Little America.

The gas supply was low due to a leak that had developed, and about 100 miles south of Little America, on the edge of the worst crevassed area, they were forced to land the plane for lack of fuel. Although they failed to reach Little America with the emergency trail radio, Haines suspected trouble when the plane's transmitter stopped. Consequently, Balchen and Petersen flew out in the Fairchild to investigate, taking 100 gallons of gasoline along on the suspicion that the Ford was out of fuel. Since both planes flew close to the sledge trail, Balchen had little difficulty in finding the downed plane about 11 p. m. After the Fairchild took off, the Ford crew failed to start the engines because of the cold, and since the 100 gallons of gasoline was not enough to get them to Little America if the heavy consumption continued, they waited until more gasoline and assistance could be brought out. This arrived at 7 p. m. the next day. This time the men were successful in starting the Ford's engines with the aid of the booster from the Fairchild. That night, about midnight, they reached Little America. The base-laying flight had been a good preliminary to the polar flight.

THE POLAR FLIGHT

William C. Haines, the expedition meteorologist, operated on the assumption, which experience proved to be correct, that good flying weather could be expected when both the surface and upper winds at Little America were of a low velocity and from the same direction, coming from the south and southeast.[17] Although the weather was hazy at Little America on November 28, 1929, flying conditions appeared to be favorable according to Haines' ideas. This was confirmed at noon by a radio message from Gould that visibility 100 miles from the Queen Maud Mountains was perfect.[18] It was decided that the flight to the Pole should be attempted. Prearranged work plans were immediately put into effect in preparation for the flight. At 3:29 p. m. the *Floyd Bennett* took to the air with Balchen at the controls, Byrd as navigator, Harold June as copilot and

PLATE V-A. Ford snowmobile pulling a sledge on the ice in the Bay of Whales, with pressure ridge in background. U. S. Information Agency Photo No. 306-NT-548-14 in the National Archives.

PLATE V-B. Little America under construction. U. S. Information Agency Photo No. 306-NT-547-1 in the National Archives.

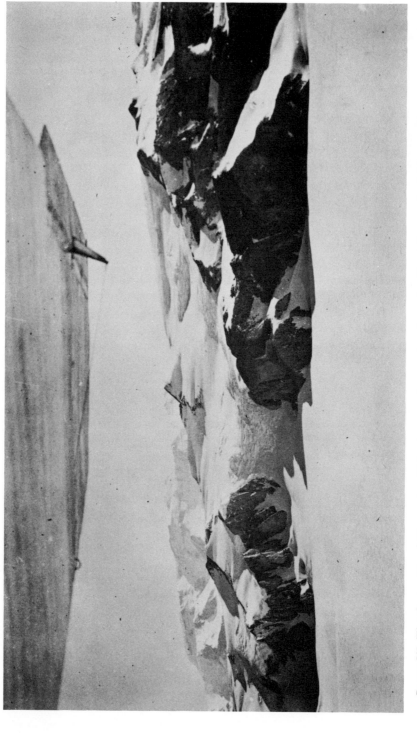

PLATE VI. The Queen Maud Mountains. This photograph was taken from the *Floyd Bennett* by Ashley McKinley as he flew down Axel Heiberg Glacier on the return from the Pole. U. S. Information Agency Photo No. 306-NT-548-15 in the National Archives.

radio operator, and McKinley as aerial photographer. The plane was heavily loaded with gasoline, food, and emergency equipment, yet all excess weight had been eliminated to enable the plane to climb through the passes of the Queen Maud Mountains to the Polar plateau.

For purposes of navigation, reliance had to be placed on the sun compass, for in an area so close to the south magnetic pole the magnetic compass is useless. Therefore, the hour of takeoff was chosen when the sun would be on the beam both going and returning, to facilitate reading the sun compass from the side windows of the plane.[19] "When approaching the South Pole, the sun would be about south, and the line of position from solar observations would run east and west, an advantageous direction for determining the latitude."[20] Balchen flew south on the meridian of 163°45′ W. When they had reached 85° they scanned the eastern horizon in vain for a sign of land in the position of Amundsen's Carmen Land. At 8:15 p. m. the geological party was sighted about 325 nautical miles south of Little America and 100 miles from the base of the Queen Maud Mountains. A bag containing messages and aerial photographs of the Queen Maud Mountains taken by McKinley on the base-laying flight was dropped by parachute. The geological party radioed their position, from which Byrd could check his navigation.

From this point the plane began to gain altitude for the approach to the glacier-filled passes of the Queen Maud Mountains. Originally it had been planned to ascend to the plateau via Axel Heiberg Glacier, which Amundsen had used in his journey to the Pole, but on the base-laying flight Byrd and his companions had been impressed by the much greater width of the Liv Glacier to the west of Mount Fridtjof Nansen. It was now decided to try the Liv Glacier, and the course was set slightly to the west of south. At 9:15 p. m. they climbed to 9000 feet, but this was 2000 feet less than required. Gasoline that had been brought along in tins was emptied into the regular tanks which now were no longer full, and the tins were thrown out to reduce weight. As the plane ascended Liv Glacier, a 30-minute nerve-tingling struggle began against the forces of gravity and the treacherous wind currents sweeping across and down the glacier. In order to gain sufficient altitude to clear the 11,000-foot pass between Mount Fridtjof Nansen and Mount Fisher at the head of Liv Glacier, it was necessary to jettison 300 pounds of food. Fortunately, this enabled the plane to gain the level of the polar plateau with a few hundred yards to spare, making it unnecessary to sacrifice any more of the 500 pounds of food remaining.

On the flight to the Pole, Byrd and his companions were flying over territory that had been traversed by Amundsen and, near the Pole, also by Scott. Because of their greater range of visibility due to the elevation of the plane, they were, however, able to see a great deal more territory than the men of the other two parties. For instance, as the plane approached the Queen Maud Mountains it was flying at an elevation of 9000 feet, which would place the horizon line of the aerial observers approximately 125 statute miles distant over the Ross Ice Shelf. Once through the pass over the Queen Maud Mountains, the plane flew at an elevation of about 2000 feet above the surface of the Polar plateau. In the clear weather in which they were flying, Byrd and his companions therefore could see a distance of approximately 59 statute miles. Consequently, they were able to discover new features not seen by their predecessors whose horizon line from the surface of the ground was about 3 statute miles distant.

As they flew out over the Polar plateau, Byrd and his companions saw to the west and southwest a new mountain range, the Grosvenor Mountains. Looking back on the Queen Maud Mountains, they could identify the Mount Thorvald Nilsen massif, now called Nilsen Plateau. In a short time they saw low, ice-covered hills to the east which lie west of the head of Scott Glacier.

On the Polar plateau the course was set at 12° to the left to compensate for wind drift. They passed over the heavily crevassed area named by Amundsen the Devil's Ballroom. Observations with the sextant at 12:30 a.m. showed the plane to be about 50 miles from the South Pole. When a careful check of the navigation showed that they had arrived at the Pole, Byrd dropped an American flag. The plane was flying 2000 feet above the smooth, snow-covered surface. They flew a few miles beyond the Pole and then to the right and to the left to compensate for possible errors in calculation. At 1:25 a. m. on November 29, 1929, Byrd directed that the plane be headed for Little America, and a course was set on the meridian 2° to the right of the outward flight.

On the way to the Pole, McKinley had made a continuous strip of overlapping aerial photographs from the left side of the plane to the eastern horizon. On the return to Little America he now began a similar strip to the west. As each exposure was made, he recorded its number, the clock time, and the elevation of the plane above the surface.

Descending from the Polar plateau, the plane flew down Axel Heiberg Glacier on the east side of Mount Fridtjof Nansen. At the foot of the glacier they flew a few miles to the east along the front of the Queen Maud Mountains to the base of Amundsen Glacier. From here they could detect only the Queen Maud Mountains trending to the southeast as far as the eye could see. A dwindling fuel supply forced them to turn westward at this point to locate the cache laid down at the foot of Liv Glacier on November 18. Landing beside the cache, they took on 200 gallons of gasoline and left 350 pounds of food for the geological party. In an hour they took off again. At 10:10 a. m. on November 29 they landed at Little America after an absence of 18 hours and 41 minutes. One night later, McKinley developed the film record of the flight and found that his efforts had been successful.

GEOLOGICAL INVESTIGATION OF THE QUEEN MAUD MOUNTAINS

At the conclusion of the polar flight the geological party was still some distance away from the Queen Maud Mountains. After a 35-mile trek on November 30 they were able to camp at the foot of Liv Glacier. For the first 200 miles south of Little America they had had the benefit of a trail marked by the supporting party. This had been particularly helpful in crossing the heavily crevassed area of the Ross Ice Shelf between 81° 10′ S and 81° 17′ S. Although they experienced difficulty here, it was not as serious as that faced by the supporting party in blazing the trail.

Twenty-five miles south of Little America, Gould and his companions became aware of a fairly gentle slope in the surface rising from about 200 feet to about 895 feet above sea level. This was subsequently found to be due to the fact that the trail passed diagonally over the northwestern end of a great bulge in the ice shelf.[21] This bulge, centered about 45 miles south of Little America, was described by Gould as, ". . . a large, elongated, dome-shaped mass, with nearly east-west axis. This is undoubtedly an ice-covered island for it rises to 1,000 feet where we crossed it and appeared to be even higher farther east."[22] In the paper just quoted, read before the Geological Society of America December 27, 1934, Gould named the ice-covered island for Lieutenant K. Prestrud of Amundsen's Expedition. The island was further investigated, however, by the Second Byrd Antarctic Expedition in 1934 and named Roosevelt Island. This latter name has been recognized as the official name.[23] Gould found, in descending the great ice dome on the south, that the shelf ice was not greatly disturbed and he assumed that the ice was moving around rather than over the ice-drowned island.[24] This undoubtedly helps to explain the persistent existence of the Bay of Whales as an ever-changing inlet in the edge of the ice shelf.

The crevassed area between 81° S and 82° S revealed interesting snow-covered, cone-like domes which Gould called "haycocks."[25] Investigation showed them to be vaulted pressure domes. They apparently collapse to form the circular, sinkhole-like depressions found in the old crevassed area to the north of them. Aerial photographs showed the crevassed area to be 75 miles in length, with movement from the southeast.[26]

As the geological party approached the Queen Maud Mountains, the surface of the shelf ice was observed to form great undulations, ". . . 15 to 20 feet high and from one half to three quarters of a mile apart".[27] Apparently caused by the pressure of the entering ice tongues, the folds were found to increase in height and the crests to be closer together nearer to the mountains.[28]

From some distance out on the Ross Ice Shelf, Gould could discern a lower foothill zone of ragged and irregular peaks in front of very high, massive, flat-topped mountains rising to elevations of over 12,000 feet. Late in the evening of November 30, the geological party camped at the foot of Liv Glacier. Thwarted by a series of coarsely crevassed folds in the ice in their attempt to reach the flanks of Mount Fridtjof Nansen via Liv Glacier, they succeeded in ascending the smaller glacier on the north flank of the mountain. In this climb Gould found that the low ragged mountains are composed of ". . . an extensive complex of ancient gneisses, schists, and granites which later investigation have shown to be pre-Cambrian."[29] Above and resting upon this basement complex, Gould found a series of sedimentary rocks 7000 feet thick, mostly arkoses and shaly arkoses which underlay the lofty peaks in the background. Both the ancient crystalline rocks and the overlying sedimentaries were shot through with diabase intrusions. The nearly horizontal stratification of the light yellow to buff colored sedimentary rocks was accentuated by the dark colored diabase sills intruded between the beds. Where the diabase outcrops on the mountain sides, cliffs occur.[30] Although he found no fossils, Gould was of the opinion that the sedimentary rocks of the Queen Maud Mountains are equivalent to the Beacon sandstone of Victoria Land farther north on the west side of the Ross Sea. This conviction was substantiated by later petrographic analysis.[31]

Considering their topographic relationship with the Polar plateau, Gould concluded from his field observations and an analysis of McKinley's photographs that the Queen Maud Mountains are a great horst elevated along almost vertical fault planes between the Polar plateau and the depressed segment of the Ross Sea. At right angles to these major lines of displacement is another series of faults responsible for the broad troughs occupied by the great outlet glaciers of which Liv and Axel Heiberg are examples.[32]

After descending the glacier from the flank of Mount Fridtjof Nansen to the Ross Ice Shelf, the geological party began on December 13 an eastward trek along the base of the Queen Maud Mountains, crossing the lower ends of the great outlet glaciers. Astronomical sights were made for geographical fixes, and Thorne and O'Brien took bearings on the various peaks in mapping the mountains and the great glaciers. As they journeyed eastward over ice much crevassed by the thrust of these glaciers, the mountains appeared to be lower in that direction, dropping to an elevation of about 6000 feet or lower, east of 150° W. The sedimentary cap retreats southward and is missing from many of the mountains. Peaks now 800 feet above the ice were found to be polished by glacial action, indicating a greater thickness of ice in the past.

On December 20 the geological party reached the mouth of a great westward-flowing outlet glacier which Gould named Leverett Glacier. Their easternmost camp was located on December 20 at 85°25'17" S, 147°55' W at the base of a small mountain, named Supporting Party Mountain, on the north side of the foot of this glacier. On December 21 the party built a cairn on top of the mountain in which they deposited a record of their having visited the spot and, in the name of Commander Byrd, claimed all the land east of 150° W as a part of Marie Byrd Land and territory of the United States.[33] From Supporting Party Mountain they could see the Queen Maud Mountains extending away to the southeast for 35 to 40 miles. "The mountains appeared to be progressively lower. To the southeast of us the tabular mountains — the structural equivalents of Mount Fridtjof Nansen — were not more than 8,000 feet high."[34]

The geological party had now mapped 175 miles of the front of the Queen Maud Mountains and had been the first men to set foot on Marie Byrd Land. On December 21 they began the return to the westward. From the pattern of crevasses observed as they traveled eastward and back across the ice, Gould concluded that the major flow of ice was from Leverett Glacier westward, a flow strong enough to deflect the northward flow of the great outlet glaciers such as Scott, Amundsen, Axel Heiberg, and Liv.[35]

While breaking camp on Christmas Day, the cairn built by Amundsen was discovered. In it Gould found a small tin can containing a page from Amundsen's notebook on which he had written a brief account of his attainment of the South Pole. This they took with them to Little America. From December 26 to 30 they remained at Strom Camp in front of Mount Fridtjof Nansen, preparing for the return to Little America. Leaving December 30, they traveled as lightly as possible, sledging at night and camping by day to get better snow surfaces and to keep the sun on their backs. Because of foggy weather, they had difficulty in crossing the crevassed area south of Little America, but they reached the base without serious incident on January 19, 1930, after sledging 1500 miles in 2½ months.

THE FLIGHT TO MARIE BYRD LAND

Shortly after the polar flight, weather conditions proved favorable for the second major flight of discovery, this time to the northeastward beyond the area which Scott in January 1902 had called Edward VII Land. On December 5, the meteorologists reported slight winds from the south and southwest up to 10,000 feet. With favorable flying conditions indicated, Byrd, with Alton Parker, Harold June, and McKinley took off at 10:50 a. m. in the *Floyd Bennett*. A course was laid to the northeast to pass about five miles north of Scott Nunataks. They flew along the edge of the Ross Ice Shelf to Okuma Bay, which they passed over at an elevation of 4300 feet at 11:40 a. m. Except for distant scattered pack and icebergs, the Ross Sea was free of ice.[36] The subdued peaks of the Alexandra Mountains and the Rockefeller Mountains appeared to be connected by a low but undulating surface. Only La Gorce Mountain rose as a conspicuous peak in the Alexandra Mountains.[37]

After passing over Scott Nunataks, Byrd could see open water in a great southeastward extension of what he interpreted as Scott's Biscoe Bay. This he named Sulzberger Bay. One hundred miles away to the eastward they saw a great mountain range. They flew northeast across 35 miles of open water in Sulzberger Bay, which was filled with shelf ice. At 1:13 p. m. the course was changed to east of north in an attempt to follow what appeared to be the coastline fringed by shelf ice. At 1:48 p. m. they were opposite the mouth of a large bay which extended far back into the land. Byrd named this Paul Block Bay, now known as Block Bay, and named for Balchen the large glacier which entered the head of the bay from a great valley in the newly discovered mountain range, which he named the Edsel Ford Range. This is now officially the Ford Ranges. At this point the course was changed again to the northeast. At 2:10 p. m. they turned south to fly in a great loop across the mouth of Block Bay. They were now east of 150° W, the eastern limit of possible discoveries of their predecessors. This newly discovered land, including the Ford Ranges, the Commander named Marie Byrd Land.

On the return to Little America, they made a loop to the north of Sulzberger Bay to investigate the great ice island that appeared to be aground and surrounded by old sea ice. At about 3:10 p. m. they turned south and flew across the open water of Sulzberger Bay and a large grounded ice island. It was now apparent from the air that what Scott had named Edward VII Land was a peninsula between Sulzberger Bay and the Ross Sea. The course was now set southwestward so as to pass close to La Gorce Mountain, the prominent peak that had been first seen on January 27, 1929, at the southern end of the Alexandra Mountains. At 6:42 p. m. the plane landed at Little America after a flight of nearly eight hours in which a new mountain range had been discovered and many miles of coastline had been seen and photographed for the first time.

CLOSING LITTLE AMERICA

With the beginning of 1930, arrangements began for concluding the Expedition program, and preparations were made for departure from Little America. On January 19 the geological party returned. Dr. Coman and Quin Blackburn had been making a ground survey of the Bay of Whales so as to show changes that had occurred in the shape of the bay since Amundsen's men had mapped it 18 years before. With the aid of Captain McKinley, this job was finished on January 20. The next day the last flight was made. Byrd, Smith, Petersen, June, and McKinley took off in the *Floyd Bennett* and flew 100 miles west to Discovery Inlet and thence south for 140 miles across the center of the Ross Ice Shelf before returning to Little America.

Radio reports from the whalers indicated that the pack ice blocking the entrance to the Ross Sea was especially solid, and Byrd was concerned about the possibility of the ships reaching Little America. The *City of New York* had left Dunedin for Little America on January 6, 1930. After being hit by a storm the first day out, she progressed under sail and steam without serious incident, reaching the whaler *Kosmos,* lying north of the pack, on January 20. The whalers advised against sending the *Eleanor Bolling* into the pack at all and suggested that the *New York* should await more favorable conditions which were expected later in the season. The *Bolling* left Dunedin on January 20, reaching the *New York* at the edge of the pack on January 29. Commander Byrd on January 31 ordered her to return for more coal because much of the supply of the *New York* had been used in steaming off the edge of the pack ice.

Meanwhile, Byrd had ordered the men at Little America to pack their equipment and supplies in three different classes, each with a lower priority, in the event that there would not be room for all. McKinley was ordered to take charge of transporting the material to a site at the edge of the Bay of Whales where the expedition ship would be able to load. A camp was established there with the intention of being able to load the ship in the quickest possible time. The airplanes were securely moored on a point where the wind swept the snow away, for it would be impossible to take the planes along if only one ship got through the pack ice.

On February 6 the *New York* took on 50 tons of coal from the whaler *Southern Princess* and started through the pack ice, which had now begun to open up. By the evening of February 7 the ship had forced her way through the pack, but on the next day a southerly gale struck with great force. Lasting for 24 hours, it forced the *New York* back into the ice. On February 10 another gale struck. For four days the ship was in great peril of foundering due to a heavy coating of ice which formed faster than the men could chop it off. In the meantime she was driven 300 miles off her course, being off Ross Island when the gale subsided. At 6:45 p.m., February 18, the *New York* reached the Bay of Whales. Everything and all hands were ready. She was loaded that night and cast off at 9:30 a.m. on

February 19. By February 26 she had cleared the pack of the Ross Sea and came to alongside the *Kosmos*. Howard F. Mason, radio operator, who had been suffering from a case of appendicitis, and Dr. Haldor Barnes, medical officer on the *Bolling*, were transferred to the whaler. The dogs were also transferred to the larger and much faster ship. The *Bolling* had returned to Dunedin on February 9. Two days later she left with a cargo of coal and now was standing by the *Kosmos* ready to coal the *New York*. The two ships then sailed in company for Dunedin where they arrived on March 10, 1930. The expedition reached New York on June 18, 1930.

NOTES

1. Richard E. Byrd, *Little America* (New York, 1930), pp. 26-28.

2. *Ibid.*, p. 28.

3. *Ibid.*, pp. 37-38.

4. *Ibid.*, pp. 32-33; also, Bernt Balchen, *Come North With Me* (New York, 1958), pp. 134-138, 144.

5. Capt. Robert F. Scott, *The Voyage of the "Discovery"* (London, 1907), vol. 1, pp. 141-142.

6. Richard E. Byrd and Harold E. Saunders, "The Flight to Marie Byrd Land, with a Description of the Map," *Geographical Review*, vol. 23, 1933, p. 188, footnote.

7. Laurence M. Gould, "Some Geographical Results of the Byrd Antarctic Expedition," *Geographical Review*, vol. 21, 1931, pp. 178-180. Seismic soundings on post-IGY oversnow traverses up to 1969 have not passed near enough to the base of the Edward VII Peninsula to provide conclusive evidence, but they suggest that the peninsula might well be a large island.

8. George Grimminger and William C. Haines, "Meteorological Results of the Byrd Antarctic Expeditions, 1928-30, 1933-35: Tables," U. S. Department of Agriculture Weather Bureau, *Monthly Weather Review*, supp. No. 41, October, 1939, p. 1.

9. *Ibid.*, p. 3.

10. Henry T. Harrison, "Antarctic Meteorology," U. S. Department of Agriculture Weather Bureau, *Monthly Weather Review*, vol. 59, No. 2, February, 1931, p. 71.

11. George Grimminger, "Meteorological Results of the Byrd Antarctic Expeditions, 1928-30, 1933-35: Summaries of Data," U. S. Department of Agriculture Weather Bureau, *Monthly Weather Review*, supp. No. 42, Table 30, p. 71, 1941.

12. Harrison, *op. cit.*, p. 72.

13. Paul A. Siple and Charles F. Passel, "Measurements of Dry Atmospheric Cooling in Subfreezing Temperatures," *Proceedings of the American Philosophical Society*, vol. 89, No. 1, April 30, 1945, pp. 182-183, 186-187.

14. Grimminger, *op. cit.*, Table 23, p. 68, and Table 30, p. 71.

15. *Ibid.*

16. Byrd, *Little America, op. cit.*, pp. 281-284.

17. Harold E. Saunders, "The Flight of Admiral Byrd to the South Pole and the Exploration of Marie Byrd Land," *Proceedings of the American Philosophical Society*, vol. 82, No. 5, June, 1940, p. 802.

18. Byrd, *Little America, op. cit.*, p. 326.

19. Saunders, *op. cit.*, p. 803.

20. *Ibid.*

21. Laurence M. Gould, "Some Geographical Results of the Byrd Antarctic Expedition," *Geographical Review*, vol. 21, 1931, p. 182.

22. Laurence M. Gould, "The Ross Shelf Ice," *Bulletin of the Geological Society of America*, September, 1935, vol. 46, No. 9, pp. 1374-1375.

23. *Geographical Names of Antarctica*, U. S. Board on Geographic Names, Special Publication No. 86, 1947, p. 222.

24. Gould, "The Ross Shelf Ice," *op. cit.*, p. 1375.

25. Gould, "Some Geographical Results . . .," *op. cit.*, p. 183.

26. *Ibid.*, p. 185.

27. Gould, "The Ross Shelf Ice," *op. cit.*, p. 1372.

28. *Ibid.*

29. Laurence M. Gould, "Structure of the Queen Maud Mountains, Antarctica," *Bulletin of the Geological Society of America*, vol. 46, No. 6, June, 1935, p. 974.

30. *Ibid.*, p. 967.

31. Duncan Stewart, "The Petrography of the Beacon Sandstone of South Victoria Land," *American Mineralogist*, vol. 19, 1934, pp. 351-359.

32. Gould, "Structure of the Queen Maud Mountains . . .," *op. cit.*, pp. 977-978.

33. The cairn contained the following proclamation [Richard E. Byrd, *Little America* (New York, 1930), pp. 407-408.]:

"Dec. 21st, 1929
Camp Francis Dana Coman
85°25'17" S
147°55' W   Marie Byrd Land, Antarctica
     This note [sic] the farthest east point reached by the Geological Party of the Byrd Antarctic Expedition. We are beyond or east of the 150th meridian, and therefore in the name of Commander Richard Evelyn Byrd claim this land as a part of Marie Byrd Land, a dependency or possession of the United States of America. We are not only the first Americans but the first individuals of any nationality to set foot on American soil in the Antarctic. This extended sledge journey from little [sic] America has been made possible by the cooperative work of the Supporting Party, composed of Arthur Walden, leader; Christopher Braathen; Jack Bursey; and Joe de Ganahl. Our Geological Party is composed of:
     L. M. Gould, leader and geologist
     N. D. Vaughan, dog driver
     G. A. Thorne, topographer
     E. E. Goodale, dog driver
     F. E. Crockett, dog driver and radio operator
     J. S. O'Brien, civil engineer."

34. Gould, "Some Geographical Results . . .," *op. cit.*, p. 193.

35. Gould, "The Ross Shelf Ice," *op. cit.*, p. 1382.

36. Byrd and Saunders, "The Flight . . ." *op. cit.*, pp. 180-181.

37. *Ibid.*, p. 184. On Plate II, opposite p. 208, and Fig. 2, p. 178, this mountain is named LaGorce Mountain. It was later officially named LaGorce Peak to distinguish it from the LaGorce Mountains beside Scott Glacier in the Queen Maud Mountains. See *Geographical Names of Antarctica, op. cit.*, p. 189. In *Little America, op. cit.*, pp. 141-142, 144, 349, and 354-356, Byrd refers to the Peak as "the matterhorn."

BIBLIOGRAPHY

Adams, Harry, *Beyond the Barrier With Byrd* (Chicago and New York, M. A. Donohue & Co., 1932), xviii, 253 pp. This is a personal account of the voyage of the *Eleanor Bolling*, on which the author was second mate, from New York to Dunedin, and from Dunedin to the edge of the pack. From that point it pertains to the *City of New York*, to which the author transferred as second mate. It deals much with personalities and personal incidents. It closes with a biographical sketch of most of the members of the expedition.

Balchen, Bernt, *Come North With Me* (New York, E. P. Dutton & Co., Inc., 1958), 318 pp., illus. An autobiography, pp. 134-195.

Bursey, Lt. Cmdr. Jack, USCGR. *Antarctic Night* (New York, Rand McNally & Co., 1957), 255 pp., illus., map. pp. 27-99.

Byrd, Richard E., "The Conquest of Antarctica by Air," *National Geographic Magazine*, vol. 58, No. 2, August, 1930, pp. 127-227, 89 illus. A preliminary narrative account of the expedition. Some dates and figures differ from those in the official narrative.

——, *Exploring With Byrd* (New York, G. P. Putnam's Sons, 1937), viii, 241 pp., end paper maps. An autobiography in terms of Byrd's exploring expeditions.

——, *Little America* (New York and London, G. P. Putnam's Sons, 1930), xvi, 422 pp. 4 maps. The official narrative of the expedition. The last chapter is a journal account by Gould of the geological party's sledge journey.

——, and Harold E. Saunders, "The Flight to Marie Byrd Land, With a Description of the Map," *Geographical Review*, vol. 23, No. 2, April, 1933, pp. 177-209. Map, scale 1:500,000, based on aerial photography.

Dater, Henry M., "First Flight Over the South Pole," *Antarctic Journal of the United States,* vol. 4, No. 6, November-December, 1969, pp. 285-288.

Davies, Frank T., "Observations of the Aurora Australis on the Byrd Antarctic Expedition 1929," *Terrestial Magnetism and Atmospheric Electricity,* vol. 36, No. 3, September 1931, pp. 199-230.

Ennis, C. C., "Correlations of Auroral and Magnetic Activity at Little America, First Byrd Antarctic Expedition," *Transactions of Amer. Geophysical Union,* 16th Annual Meeting, Part 1, April, 1935, pp. 165-168.

——, "Relationship Between Auroral and Magnetic Activities at Little America, First Byrd Antarctic Expedition, 1928-30," *Terrestial Magnetism and Atmospheric Electricity,* vol. 41, No. 1, March, 1936, pp. 45-55.

Gould, Laurence M., *Cold* (New York, Brewer, Warren and Putnam, 1931), x, 275 pp. A narrative of the geological flight to the Rockefeller Mountains and of the sledge journey of the geological party to the Queen Maud Mountains.

Gould, Laurence M., "Geomorphology of the Queen Maud Mountains," *Annals of the Association of American Geographers,* vol. 27, No. 2, June, 1937, p. 106. Abstract of a paper read before the Association at Syracuse, December, 1936.

——, "The Ross Shelf Ice," *Bulletin of the Geological Society of America,* vol. 46, No. 9, September, 1935, pp. 1367-1393. Read before the Society, December 27, 1934.

——, "Some Geographical Results of the Byrd Antarctic Expedition," *Annual Report of the Smithsonian Institution,* 1932 (Washington, 1933), pp. 235-250. Reprint of an article of similar title in the *Geographical Review.*

——, "Some Geographical Results of the Byrd Antarctic Expedition," *Geographical Review,* vol. 21, No. 2, April, 1931, pp. 177-200 and map. Results of the flight to Rockefeller Mountains and the sledge journey by the geological party to Queen Maud Mountains. Topographic map of Queen Maud Mountains based on aerial photography, scale 1:500,000.

——, "Structure of the Queen Maud Mountains, Antarctica," *Bulletin of the Geological Society of America,* vol. 46, No. 6, June, 1935, pp. 973-983. Read before the Society, December 28, 1933.

Grimminger, George, "Meteorological Results of the Byrd Antarctic Expeditions, 1928-30, 1933-35: Summaries of Data," Weather Bureau, U. S. Department of Agriculture, *Monthly Weather Review,* supp. 42, February 1941. viii, 106 pp.

——, and William C. Haines, "Meteorological Results of the Byrd Antarctic Expeditions, 1928-30, 1933-35: Tables," Weather Bureau, U. S. Department of Agriculture, *Monthly Weather Review,* supp. 41, October, 1939, iv, 377 pp. Introduction by Haines relative to instruments and methodology. Includes the record of the meteorological observations made aboard the *Eleanor Bolling* and the *City of New York* on all voyages, except the final departure of the latter, between Little America and Dunedin, New Zealand. These daily records, containing noon positions and remarks, serve as excellent abstract logs for these voyages.

Haines, William C., "The Green Flash Observed October 16, 1929, at Little America by Members of the Byrd Antarctic Expedition," Weather Bureau, U. S. Department of Agriculture, *Monthly Weather Review,* vol. 59, No. 3, March, 1931, 117-118.

——, "Meteorological Observations in the Antarctic," *Bulletin of the American Meteorological Society,* vol. 12, 1931, pp. 169-172.

——, "Winds of the Antarctic," *Transactions of the American Geophysical Union,* 13th Annual Meeting, June, 1932, pp. 124-128.

Hanson, Malcolm P., and E. O. Hulburt, "On Some Solar and Lunar Spectra Taken in Little America, Antarctica," *Physical Review,* vol. 37, 1931, pp. 477-480.

Harrison, Henry T., "Antarctic Meteorology," Weather Bureau, U. S. Department of Agriculture, *Monthly Weather Review,* vol. 59, No. 2, February, 1931, pp. 70-73. A narrative of the meteorological observations during the expedition.

Hoyt, Edwin P., *The Last Explorer* (New York, The John Day Co., 1968), 380 pp., illus.

Joerg, W. L. G., *The Work of the Byrd Antarctic Expedition 1928-1930,* American Geographical Society, New York, 1930. 71 pp. Narrative account based on newspaper dispatches.

McKinley, Capt. Ashley C., "Mapping the Antarctic from the Air," *National Geographic Magazine,* vol. 62, No. 4, October, 1932, pp. 471-485. An account of the aerial photographic work on the expedition, particularly on the polar flight.

O'Brien, J. S., *By Dog Sled for Byrd* (Chicago, Thomas S. Rockwell Co., 1931), 192 pp., illus.

Saunders, Harold E., "The Flight of Admiral Byrd to the South Pole and the Exploration of Marie Byrd Land," *Proceedings of the American Philosophical Society,* vol. 82, No. 5, June, 1940, pp. 801-820. Map of Marie Byrd Land based on ground control of 1933-35 expedition shows considerable shortening of longitude from the map in the *Geographical Review,* April, 1933, and the flight line is therefore more accurately plotted.

Siple, Paul, *A Boy Scout With Byrd* (New York, G. P. Putnam's Sons, 1931), viii, 165 pp.

Steward, Duncan, "Contributions to Antarctic Petrography," *Journal of Geology,* vol. 42, No. 5, July-August, 1934, pp. 546-550.

——, "The Petrography of the Beacon Sandstone of South Victoria Land," *American Mineralogist,* vol. 19, 1934, pp. 351-359.

18

THE SECOND BYRD ANTARCTIC
EXPEDITION, 1933-1935

ORGANIZATION AND ACCOMPLISHMENTS

SIGNIFICANCE

At the close of his first Antarctic expedition, Admiral Byrd was aware of numerous questions left unanswered and of new problems that had been raised which only a second expedition could hope to solve. This second expedition he proposed to organize as soon as possible after the first, to take advantage of the experienced personnel and the popular interest that the expedition of 1928-30 had developed.

The Second Byrd Antarctic Expedition, 1933-35, was a positive indication of continued modern American interest in south polar regions. After having been on the wane for decades, popular interest in the Antarctic had been greatly revived between 1928 and 1930 by the First Byrd Expedition and by the Wilkins-Hearst Expedition. When it is realized that Admiral Byrd was able to win support for his second expedition from a wide variety of sources at a time when the country was in the depths of the great economic depression of the early 1930s, the vigor of this renascent interest in the Antarctic is manifest.

The almost daily newspaper accounts of events, based on radio messages from Little America, regarding Byrd's flight to the South Pole and of the discovery of Marie Byrd Land made the Antarctic, during Byrd's First Expedition, a topic of conversation in the United States. This new interest, which might otherwise have been dissipated, was given added vigor by the Second Byrd Antarctic Expedition. The second expedition was not only covered as thoroughly as the first by newspaper accounts, but radio programs also brought the voices of the men from Little America into the living rooms of the United States. As a result, Marie Byrd Land became, in the popular mind, peculiarly American. This attitude undoubtedly encouraged and sustained American activity in the Antarctic which has placed the United States during the last four decades, in a position of prominence in south polar affairs.

To the Second Byrd Antarctic Expedition goes the honor of having achieved many "firsts" in the history of Antarctic exploration. It was the first Antarctic expedition on which long-distance automotive land transport proved to be of practical use. It was the first to make seismic investigations in Antarctica, and the results of this work were the first, and for years the only, quantitative evidence as to the extent to which the Ross Ice Shelf is aground or afloat. The sound of the human voice was broadcast from Antarctica to the rest of the world for the first time on February 1, 1934, and later weekly programs from Antarctica were broadcast in the United States by the Columbia Broadcasting System.

The expedition also marked the first time that cosmic ray investigation and meteor observation were conducted at such a high southern latitude.

While the First Byrd Antarctic Expedition introduced the mechanical age to Antarctica, the Second Byrd Expedition was even more thoroughly mechanized. The base camp at Little America was provided with electric power by motor-driven generating plants. This made possible the use of power tools for the great amount of mechanical improvising that had to be done at Little America in preparation for the field campaigns. The extensive adaptation of mechanical devices of all kinds to meet the rigorous demands of polar conditions was in itself a significant if not a revolutionary achievement.

ESTABLISHMENT AND COMPOSITION

The Second Byrd Antarctic Expedition, like the first, was organized and financed by Rear Admiral Richard E. Byrd (USN, retired) with the aid of contributions of money, equipment, supplies, and services from a great number of private individuals, business concerns, industrial firms, research institutes, and government agencies. The expedition, originally scheduled to leave in the fall of 1932, had to wait until 1933 for sufficient money and supplies.

In the depth of a great economic depression, money was difficult to raise, and the $150,000 contributed in cash came mostly in small amounts from thousands of donors, with larger contributions from Edsel Ford, William Horlick, Thomas J. Watson, Col. Jacob Ruppert, and the National Geographic Society. This amount, however, provided for only a small part of the requirements of the expedition. Additional funds were realized from the sale of newspaper rights, photographic privileges, and especially from the weekly radio broadcasts from Little America. Commercial firms and manufacturers contributed all of the fuel oil and gasoline, much of the supplies, and a great deal of the equipment used by the expedition. Nearly $100,000 worth of scientific instruments were borrowed from government agencies, universities, and scientific institutions.

The flagship of the expedition was leased from the U. S. Shipping Board for $1 a year. This 8257-ton steel cargo vessel, the *Pacific Fir,* had been in the west coast lumber trade, but was then laid up at Staten Island with other surplus ships of World War I. The rusty old oil burner was thoroughly reconditioned at Boston and rechristened the *Jacob Ruppert.*

For use in ramming through the pack ice, Admiral Byrd acquired for a nominal sum from the city of Oakland, Calif., an old wooden ice ship, the barkentine *Bear,* built in Greenock, Scotland, in 1874. After 10 years as a whaler, the *Bear* had been purchased by the U. S. Coast Guard for use in the rescue of the U. S. Arctic Expedition led by Lieutenant A. W. Greely. In 1928 the vessel had become the property of the city of Oakland. Admiral Byrd had it rechristened the *Bear of Oakland* after it had been reconditioned at Boston. The 703-ton *Bear* was 200 feet long, had a beam of 32 feet, and a draft of 17 feet, 2 inches. Under auxiliary steam power she once was capable of nine knots.

Since it was not known whether the two planes left at Little America in 1930 would be operable, a new Curtiss-Wright Condor was acquired. This long-distance, twin-engined biplane, named the *William Horlick,* was equipped with both skis and floats and powered by two supercharged Wright Cyclone engines, each rated at 725 horsepower. With special fuel tanks, the plane had a range of approximately 1300 miles with a full load of 19,000 pounds.[1] Two smaller single-engined monoplanes, a Fokker and a Pilgrim, which had already seen hard service, were lent to the expedition. A Kellett autogyro was also lent for use in short-range reconnaissance and high-altitude aerological flights.

The Second Byrd Antarctic Expedition was the first to use motorized transport successfully for long-distance overland journeys. The equipment included a Cletrac tractor, two Ford snowmobiles and three Citroën vehicles originally designed for desert travel. The Citroëns were light trucks on which a "crawler" type tread replaced the rear wheels. For use in the Antarctic the front wheels were placed on skis. The performance of these 40-horsepower vehicles has been described by Demas.[2] Since motorized transport up until then had not proved practical in the Antarctic, 153 sledge dogs of various breeds and crossbreeds, collected from Alaska to Labrador, were taken to Antarctica.[3]

Admiral Byrd, organizer and leader of the expedition, appointed Dr. Thomas C. Poulter, physicist, as chief of the scientific staff and second in command of the expedition as a whole. William C. Haines, chief meteorologist, was third in command, Harold I. June, chief pilot, was chief of staff, and George O. Noville was executive officer. The 1934 wintering party of 56 men included five pilots, three physicists, two geologists, a geophysicist, two meteorologists, three biologists, four radio operators, two navigators, an aerial photographer, a surveyor, a physician, two carpenters, an artist, a newspaper correspondent, and two Paramount News cameramen. Most of the others were dog drivers, mechanics and tractor drivers, the last named being, of necessity, mechanics in fact if not in name.

Officers and crew of the *Jacob Ruppert* numbered 45 men on the outgoing voyage in 1933 and 33 on the homeward voyage in 1935. On both voyages the ship was under the direction of Commodore Hjalmar Fridtjof Gjertsen, considered one of the ablest ice pilots in the Norwegian Navy. On the outward voyage, the master of the *Ruppert* was Lieutenant (jg) W. F. Verleger, USNR. He was replaced on the homeward voyage by S. D. Rose, who had served as first officer on the *Bear of Oakland*.

The *Bear* was commanded by Lieutenant (jg) Robert A. J. English, USN, with Bendik Johansen as sailing master and ice pilot. The ship's company numbered 26 officers and men, including S. Edward Roos, oceanographer.

Of the total number of men engaged in the expedition, 18 were veterans of the First Byrd Antarctic Expedition.

OBJECTIVES AND ACCOMPLISHMENTS

On his second expedition Byrd proposed to reoccupy his old base camp at Little America, from where the exploration of newly discovered Marie Byrd Land would be carried on by airplane, dog team, and tractor. The ships, too, were to be employed in actual exploration. The scientific program was considerably expanded beyond that of the first expedition.

Geographical exploration included four major objectives: (a) the delineation of as much as possible of the coastline of Marie Byrd Land, (b) a more extensive exploration of the Ford Ranges, (c) the determination of the probable existence of an ice-filled strait connecting the Ross Sea with the Weddell Sea, and (d) the determination of the eastward trend of the Queen Maud Mountains beyond the Ross Ice Shelf. It was proposed to accomplish the first objective by means of aerial reconnaissance and by cruising along the coast in the *Bear of Oakland*. The other objectives were to be carried out by means of aerial exploration and photography and by trail parties on the ground.

As in the case of Byrd's First Antarctic Expedition, meteorological observation was a major part of the scientific program of the second. This was of immediate practical importance, for aerial exploration depended upon adequate weather forecasting. In addition to the base at Little America, Byrd proposed to establish — as far inland as possible, perhaps on the Polar plateau — a weather station which would be occupied during the long winter night.

A major feature of the scientific program was the proposal to determine the thickness of the Ross Ice Shelf and of the glacial ice cap on the Polar plateau by applying the seismic techniques developed for the discovery of petroleum.

As a link in two worldwide chains of observatories, the expedition was prepared to gather data in Antarctica on meteors and cosmic rays. The expedition was also equipped with continuous recording instruments for Little America and with field instruments for trail parties to observe conditions of terrestrial magnetism in Antarctica. It was also proposed to observe, record, and photograph conditions pertaining to displays of aurora australis.

The scientific program called for an extensive biological investigation ranging from the collection of bacteria in isolated field locations to the study of seals in the Bay of Whales. Plankton and invertebrate life were to be studied at sea and in the Bay of Whales.

The *Bear of Oakland* was equipped with a sonic sounding unit by which it was proposed to make a bathymetric profile across the Pacific and on all voyages through the Ross Sea. More complete oceanographic observations were planned at intervals during the voyage. The program also called for a survey of the position of the front of the Ross Ice Shelf to determine what changes had taken place since the last survey had been made from the *Terra Nova* in 1911.

Most of the objectives of this extensive program were accomplished. Some were exceeded; others were fulfilled in modified form. The major accomplishments of the expedition may be briefly enumerated as follows:

(1) The Rockefeller Plateau was discovered east of the Ross Ice Shelf and south of the Ford Ranges.

(2) The western mountains of the Ford Ranges, discovered from the air in 1929, were found to be about 37 miles westward of the position originally assigned to them at the time of their discovery.

(3) It was established that the Ford Ranges had a roughly east-west axis and that they were petrographically and structurally related to the mountains of the Antarctic Peninsula.

(4) The eastern edge of the Ross Ice Shelf was tentatively delineated.

(5) Insofar as surface topography indicated, the existence of a strait between the Ross Sea and the Weddell Sea was shown to be highly improbable.

(6) The existence of Roosevelt Island under the Ross Ice Shelf south of Little America, and the fact that part of the ice shelf was aground below sea level was established.

(7) The ice cover on the Rockefeller Plateau was found to be from 1000 to 2000 feet thick.

(8) Many new peaks of the Queen Maud Mountains were discovered and mapped.

(9) Lichens were found on rocks halfway up Scott Glacier, the most southerly plants yet known. Coal-bearing formations on Mount Weaver, at the head of Scott Glacier, yielded the southernmost known fossils.

(10) A geological reconnaissance was made of the Rockefeller Mountains, and the individual peaks were triangulated.

(11) The meteorological station at Little America carried on surface and upper air observations over a period of 360 days.

(12) A continuous meteorological record from March 27, 1934, to October 11, 1934, was obtained at Bolling Advance Base on the Ross Ice Shelf, 100 miles south of Little America. This was the first instance of observations from an interior location during the winter.

(13) Relative and absolute variations in the intensity and direction of the earth's magnetic field were recorded for almost a year at Little America and by field parties.

(14) Observations of the intensity of cosmic rays, begun on the voyage to Antarctica, were continued at Little America for nearly a year.

(15) Approximately 7000 meteors were observed and recorded during the winter of 1934 at Little America. About 250 photographs were made of typical aurora forms.

(16) A study of the life history of the Weddell seal was conducted on the herd that wintered at the Bay of Whales. Less complete observations were made on the crab-eater seals.

(17) Extensive studies were made of bird life at sea, at the Bay of Whales, and in the field. The known southerly range of at least four species was extended.

(18) Five species of moss and 89 species of lichens were collected from 215 localities in Marie Byrd Land, while at least eight different species of lichens were collected in the Queen Maud Mountains.

(19) Many bacteria and molds were identified in aseptically collected samples of snow, stagnant water, mud, and rock. Algae, infusoria, and rotifers were found in samples of mud and water collected in the field.

(20) Photomicrographic and cinemicrographic records were made of all materials collected in numerous dredge hauls of plankton from the ship and at the Bay of Whales.

(21) The *Bear of Oakland* made bathymetric profiles across the Pacific, be-

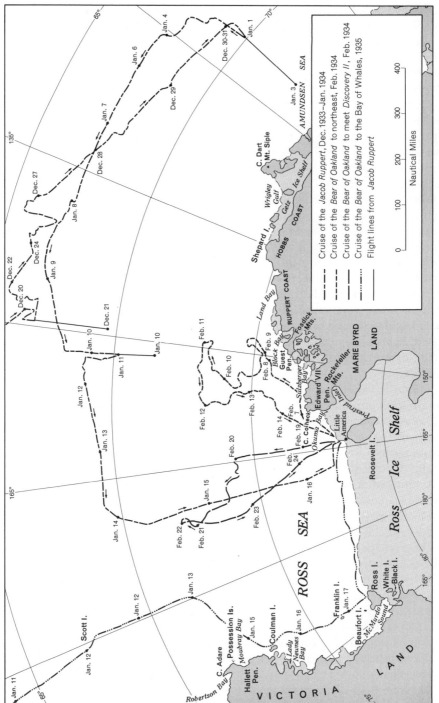

FIGURE 14. Exploratory Cruises by Ships of the Second Byrd Antarctic Expedition, 1933-35.

tween New Zealand and Antarctica, and on several cruises in the Ross Sea. About 200 miles south of Scott Island, Iselin Bank was discovered. A submarine ridge was found connecting Cape Colbeck with Pennell Bank.

DETAILED RECORD OF OPERATIONS

Outward Voyages

The *Bear of Oakland,* being slower than the *Jacob Ruppert,* left Boston on September 25, 1933, but was damaged by a hurricane off the North Carolina coast, and was forced to go into dry dock at Newport News. The *Ruppert* left Boston on October 11, put in at Newport News, and sailed again on October 22. The *Bear* sailed from Newport News on November 1.

After passing through the Panama Canal, the *Ruppert* proceeded south with the intention of penetrating the Antarctic pack ice in the vicinity of Peter I Island. From this point, Admiral Byrd hoped to launch the *William Horlick,* fly across the pack to the hitherto unseen coastline, and follow it westward to the Bay of Whales. For this purpose the plane was equipped with variable-pitch propellers, an innovation then being tested by the War Department. Learning by radio that these tests revealed structural weaknesses, Byrd decided that the proposed flight could not be risked, and on November 8, 1933, when the ship was 500 miles west of Callao, off the coast of South America, the course was changed for Wellington, New Zealand.[4]

After crossing the equator, the physicists began cosmic ray observations. The *Ruppert* proceeded on a west-southwest course across the South Pacific at about nine to ten knots. This part of the ocean was found to contain surprisingly little plankton and few birds.

On November 16 the ship called at Easter Island and left the next day. Wellington was reached on December 5. Here the ship's engines were overhauled and the bunkers filled with oil. The *William Horlick* was swung ashore and readied for flight, including the installation of standard propellers. It was then secured on the deck on a specially built pedestal. The crew was increased by 18 men signed on to help unload the ship at the Bay of Whales, and three stowaways were discovered after the ship had put to sea on December 12, 1934.

A course was set to cross the Antarctic Circle at 150° W, from where it was hoped to reconnoiter along the edge of the pack ice seeking an opportunity to fly south to the coast of Antarctica. Progress was slowed by a severe gale on December 17. At 6:30 a. m., December 20, 1934, the ship reached the edge of the pack ice at 65°55′ S, 151°10′ W (Fig. 14).

From this point the first phase of the aerial exploration was begun. For the next three weeks the *Ruppert* cruised along the edge of the pack ice, seeking open leads through which the ship might be maneuvered to an area of quiet water from which the plane might take off for a flight southward. Often Commodore Gjertsen piloted the *Ruppert* through ice dangerously heavy for her thin plates, as on each penetration he tried to steam as far south as possible before launching the plane.

The first penetration was made on December 20 when the ship was stopped by ice at about 67°09' S, 148°00' W. There was very little open water here, however, and it was necessary to retreat northward about 28 miles before a place suitable for takeoff was found. At 10:53 a. m., December 21, Admiral Byrd, Harold I. June (pilot), William H. Bowlin (copilot), Carl O. Petersen (radio operator, and Joseph A. Pelter (aerial photographer) took off in the *William Horlick*. Preliminary test flights were made about the ship; then, at 11:40 a. m., they headed south along the 150th meridian. After flying over loose pack ice for two hours half of the gasoline supply had been consumed. At 1:40 p. m., at about 69°51' S, 149°45' W, the plane was headed back toward the ship. At no time during the flight, which was made in clear weather at an elevation of 2000 feet, was land seen, although from a distance a row of icebergs was temporarily mistaken as an indication of land.

With the big plane once more on deck, the ship began a retreat northward, reaching the open sea late on December 22. From about 65°51' S, 147°20' W, the *Ruppert* was set on an easterly course along the edge of the pack ice, but foul weather delayed the second flight until January 3. For several days the vessel, surrounded by thousands of icebergs, drifted on a heaving sea filled with growlers, with visibility blotted out by a succession of snowstorms and fog. Only during short intervals of improved visibility was the easting continued. Thus surrounded by great bergs, the vessel miraculously survived a northwest gale on December 26. In about 24 hours the ship was blown 60 miles to the east in spite of having been headed into the wind with engines running.

As the gale subsided, the *Ruppert* continued through open water to the eastward. East of the 140th meridian the number of icebergs greatly decreased. Not until December 30, however, was a place suitable for take off discovered in about 69°12' S, 116°42' W, but the weather was unsatisfactory. When the bad weather continued, Admiral Byrd held the ship in the vicinity for several days in the hope of being able to make a flight, for if the ship were to arrive at the Bay of Whales in mid-January, no further easting could be attempted. Finally, on January 3, 1934, he decided the flight would have to be made under adverse conditions. The ship was then at 69°57' S, 116°35' W. The plane took off at 11:22 a. m. Snow was falling and visibility was limited to 10 miles or less, and the ceiling was less than 1000 feet. In constant radio contact with the ship, the plane flew south over compact pack ice at an altitude of 400 feet. At latitude 72°30' S, the southern horizon being black with snow squalls, the plane was headed back to the ship, where it landed at 2:31 p. m. No land had been seen. After waiting in vain for 24 hours for clearing weather, Byrd ordered the *Ruppert* withdrawn from the pack.

Early January 6, 1934, the *Ruppert* emerged from the pack in about 67°36' S, 120°34' W and began the westward cruise toward the Bay of Whales. Snow squalls and intermittent fog continued to retard the vessel's progress. By January 10, the ship had sailed beyond the 150th meridian, west, and Byrd had the course changed to south to seek a possible shortcut through the belt of pack ice which usually blocks all but the western side of the Ross Sea. By 7:30 p. m. the ship had reached the edge of the pack ice at 69°02′ S, 152°21′ W, and the Admiral decided to attempt a flight from here straight south to the coast and then west to the Bay of Whales. Lincoln Ellsworth's Expedition on the *Wyatt Earp* was there at that time, and agreed to radio weather reports to Byrd. Byrd and the plane crew took off at 3:30 a. m., January 11. The sky gradually becoming overcast, they turned around at 5:35 a. m., in about 71°45′ S, 152° W. At 6:55 a. m. they were back over the ship.

The ship continued to grope along the edge of the pack ice in fog, snow, and haze, seeking a lead of open water to the south. They found one on January 14, in about 169° W, that led to open water all the way to the Bay of Whales. Passage southward was slowed by overcast weather and numerous snow squalls, but at 6:15 a. m., January 17, the Ross Ice Shelf was sighted. By 11:30 p. m., the *Ruppert* was moored in the Bay of Whales.

The *Bear of Oakland* had sailed from Newport News on November 1, 1933, had passed through the Panama Canal, and entered the Pacific Ocean on November 17. A course was set for New Zealand via Tahiti, where the *Bear* took on coal on December 12. The *Bear* was equipped with a sonic sounding device by which oceanographer S. Edward Roos made a continuous bathymetric profile across the Pacific. She docked at Wellington on January 6 and took on coal, lumber, and other stores for the expedition before departing on January 11. Two days later she reached Dunedin, where additional supplies were taken on board, and on January 19 the *Bear* sailed for Antarctica. The Antarctic Circle was crossed at about 177°42′ E on the afternoon of January 27. Setting a course south at about 178°45′ E, Lieutenant English saw few bergs, and surprisingly finding no pack ice, he was able to make a very fast passage of 12 days from New Zealand to the Bay of Whales, where the *Bear* was moored at 10:30 p. m., January 30.

ESTABLISHMENT OF THE BASE

On the afternoon of January 17 Admiral Byrd led a landing party to inspect Little America I. They found the old camp intact but buried by three to six feet of snow with only the ventilators, stovepipes, anemometer pole, and radio towers showing. The walls and ceilings of the buildings were covered with ice; the roof of the administration building had sagged, but there was no irreparable damage. The communication and lighting systems were in working order, and the stores of food were in good condition. Dr. Poulter was placed in charge of reestablishing the camp.

Reestablishment of the old base camp and the creation of Little America II was made extremely difficult by the tortuous trail through the pressure ice in the southern part of the Bay of Whales over which supplies had to be hauled from the ships to the camp site. In the 1930s the Bay of Whales was a long, narrow inlet in the seaward face of the Ross Ice Shelf, whose ice-cliff walls towered approximately 100 feet above the sea ice in the bay. Extending as tributaries both to the east and to the west, sometimes in opposing pairs, were small inlets roughly at right angles to the major axis of the Bay of Whales. Little America was located on one of these inlets, called Ver-Sur-Mer Inlet, on the east side of the bay about nine miles south of the Ross Sea in 1934. Differential movement of the parts of the ice shelf bordering the two sides of the Bay of Whales caused old bay ice, in the southern part of the bay that did not go out every year, to be crumpled into a series of pressure ridges.

By January 17, so much bay ice had gone out that it was possible to moor the *Ruppert* only 3 miles on an air line from the base camp, but by the only practical route, winding through and around the pressure ridges, the distance was 7.2 miles. Two crevasses exposing sea water, one 35 feet across, had to be bridged with telephone poles and hatch covers. Over this tortuous trail the tractors, towing loaded sledges, lurched and slid as they crawled over and around chaotically tilted slabs of ice. Even the dog drivers had difficulty guiding their teams over the trail, and in spite of strenuous efforts to prevent it, loaded sledges were frequently overturned. Alternatives to using this route were rejected as being even more costly in time and energy or too hazardous.

Stores and equipment were relayed inland and away from the outer edge of the bay ice, where they would be lost if a piece of ice should go out to sea. They were moved the first 100 yards inland by dog sledges and then transferred to tractor-drawn sledges and hauled to a temporary cache called Pressure Camp at the edge of the pressure ridges. By midnight, January 18, unloading was in full swing. One Citroën tractor was disabled by fire shortly after being landed, and the two snowmobiles stripped their gears. Without the mechanical aid of the other Citroën and the Cletrac, the 16 teams of 9 dogs each would not have succeeded in the tremendous task of moving several hundred tons of supplies and equipment over the difficult trail from the ships to Little America II. The Pilgrim monoplane also ferried 24 tons of stores between the ship and the base camp, but was grounded when the landing gear began to show the strain. With each storm more bay ice went out to sea. To avoid losing supplies, two additional caches were made on the ice shelf itself, one on each side of the Bay of Whales.

On January 30, when the *Ruppert* was almost unloaded, the *Bear* arrived. A third Citroën was now available for movement of supplies from the three major caches to Little America II, which was begun as soon as the bridge across the big crevasse was finished on February 1. By February 4 both ships had been unloaded, and the next day all of the stores at Pressure Camp had been moved off the bay ice, although 80 percent of the material still had to be moved to Little America II. Once the bridge was installed, however, the tractors kept the supplies moving up steadily, the Cletrac pulling loads of from three to five tons. At 10:10 p. m., February 5, the *Ruppert* sailed for New Zealand.

During the unloading, Dr. Poulter's crew renovated the old buildings, excavated the old caches of supplies and stored them along with new supplies coming up from the Bay of Whales. The first tractor to reach Little America II hauled a Kohler generating plant to supply the power for radio voice-test broadcasts to New York and Buenos Aires on February 1. The first regular broadcast to be used on a radio program in the United States was sent on February 3.

Eight new buildings were erected at Little America II while supplies were being hauled up from the caches, and two more buildings were put up later. The new structures were arranged in two parallel rows running roughly east and west. Most of them were specially designed, prefabricated structures with flat roofs, but some were improvised at Little America. They were all connected by a network of tunnels made by lining the walls with boxes of stores covered with chicken wire and canvas. In a short time snow had drifted over the buildings and supply dumps until the whole area was covered by a great mound of snow which was about a foot or two deep over the tallest buildings. Through this cover protruded the ventilators and chimneys. Towering above the camp was a steel tower supporting a wind-driven generator and a set of 45-foot telephone poles, upon which directional radio antennae were strung. The tunnel system of the new buildings was connected with that of the old, 20 feet lower, by a ramp, thus making it unnecessary to go out-of-doors to go from one part of the camp to another.

EXPLORATORY CRUISE OF THE *BEAR* BEYOND CAPE COLBECK

A major objective of the expedition was the delineation of the coast of Marie Byrd Land. By means of his three flights from the *Ruppert* earlier in the season Byrd had pushed back the area of the unknown, but the fact that he had not seen the coast made him eager to take the *Bear* on a cruise to the northeast, beyond Cape Colbeck, to investigate the possible existence of an archipelago where all ships had previously been stopped by heavy pack ice. Up to that time only two ships had been able to penetrate beyond Cape Colbeck, which had been discovered by Captain Robert F. Scott in 1902. Scott's *Discovery* had worked into a cul-de-sac east of 151° W, and Lieutenant Choku Shirase of Japan had sailed the *Kainan Maru* to 76°07′ S, 151°20′ W in 1912. Byrd himself was among those who had failed when, in 1929, he had been unsuccessful in trying to force the *City of New York* through the pack ice in that direction. Byrd was now starting later in the season than either Scott or Shirase, and he felt encouraged by the fact that he had seen no pressure ridges in the pack on his flight of January 11. Even if he failed to surpass his predecessors, Byrd felt that the line of sonic soundings which S. Edward Roos was prepared to make would be sufficiently valuable to justify the effort. Except for an occasional sounding with a line by earlier explorers, no bathymetric data were available in 1934 for this part of the Ross Sea.

On the evening of February 6 the *Bear* sailed out of the Bay of Whales, and Lieutenant English set a course for Cape Colbeck. By noon the next day the *Bear* was about 14 nautical miles northwest of the cape, skirting an extensive and unbroken field of pack ice fringing the Edward VII Peninsula. East of Cape Colbeck the water began to shoal noticeably until a minimum depth of 89 meters was recorded on the fathometer at about 76°51′ S, 157°15′ W.[5] A great number of stranded icebergs indicated that the area of shallow water was essentially linear, with a northwesterly trend, more or less as a submarine continuation of the Alexandra Mountains. Consolidated pack ice and shelf ice prevented the *Bear* from pushing south into Sulzberger Bay. The course was, therefore, continued northeastward along the edge of the pack ice. At noon, February 8, the position of the *Bear* was 75°43′ S, 151°00′ W. She had then surpassed the easting of both the *Discovery* and the *Kainan Maru*. Numerous tabular icebergs could be seen scattered throughout the pack.

The *Bear* spent most of the next 24 hours probing the edges of a great cul-de-sac in the icefield east of the 150th meridian and south of the 75th parallel. At 1:30 a. m., February 9, she made her farthest easting in about 75°06′ S, 148°08′ W, from where the northwesternmost peaks of the Ford Ranges were dimly visible to the southeast, about 75 nautical miles distant. The sonic sounding device was revealing depths of over 2000 fathoms, an indication of a very narrow continental shelf in this vicinity. From this point the *Bear* beat a short retreat to the southwest.

Shortly after noon on February 9 it was possible to work northward again, although for several hours the course was mostly west-northwest. Throughout most of this day the *Bear* moved through leads in very heavy pack ice, with great tabular icebergs on all sides. For another day and a half the vessel worked northward through the pack ice looking for an opening to the east, but between 74° S and 75° S heavy ice forced her westward to the 155th meridian west before she could push northeastward again. At 7:20 a. m., February 11, at 73°22′ S, 149°34′ W, heavy, unbroken pack ice again stopped further progress to the east. After withdrawing, the *Bear* was forced into another lead a little farther north with even less success. At this point Admiral Byrd decided to return to the Bay of Whales. A westerly course was set passing between 73°10′ S and 73°15′ S. At this latitude visibility from the crow's nest of the *Bear* almost extended to the limit of vision from the turning point of the flight of January 11 along the 152nd meridian. Byrd, therefore, felt that for all practical purposes a "corridor of exploration" had been driven along the 152nd meridian from 64°40′ S, Cook's record southing of 1773, to the Antarctic Continent.[6]

After working westward to a noon position of 73°35′ S, 157°30′ W, February 12, the *Bear* was headed southward toward Little America II. From 5:30 p. m., February 12, until the ship gained open water at 1:30 a. m., February 14, in about 75°50′ S she was constantly being maneuvered through narrow leads or forcing an opening through what appeared to be weak spots in an otherwise solid and hummocky pack. North of the 75th parallel most of the sonic soundings revealed depths of more than 2000 fathoms. South of that parallel, however, the bottom began to rise gradually, and, as Cape Colbeck was approached, again the water began to shoal to 200 fathoms, further evidence of the existence of a submarine ridge extending northwestward from Edward VII Peninsula. At 6 a. m., February 15, the *Bear* entered the Bay of Whales.

During the exploratory cruise of the *Bear*, the *Ruppert* was en route from the Bay of Whales to New Zealand, arriving at Port Chalmers on February 18, after sustaining minor damage in a severe southwesterly gale on February 11.

REMAINING VOYAGES OF THE *BEAR* DURING 1934

When Dr. G. O. Shirey, for reasons of health, decided to return to New Zealand on the *Ruppert*, the expedition was left without a physician, but a serious situation was avoided through radio communication with the outside world. Fortunately the British ship R.R.S. *Discovery II* was then at Auckland preparing for another cruise of oceanographic investigation in Antarctic waters. At Admiral Byrd's request, official permission was granted for the *Discovery II* to transport from Dunedin to a rendezvous with the *Bear* in the Ross Sea 21 tons of supplies and Dr. Louis H. Potaka, a New Zealand physician who had agreed to join the expedition.

Late February 18 the *Bear* steamed out of the Bay of Whales to keep the rendezvous. En route, between the 164th and 172nd meridians, another line of sonic soundings was taken. Depths of 225 fathoms, or less, at about 76° 30′ S indicated again the presence of the submarine ridge extending from Edward VII Peninsula to Pennell Bank which lies in about 74° S, 179° E. After maneuvering for 24 hours through the band of pack ice that stretches across the Ross Sea, the meeting with the *Discovery II* was effected in a snowstorm on February 21 with the assistance of radio communication and a radio direction finder. Six tons of supplies and 3000 gallons of gasoline were transferred in 16 hours, a difficult operation in the open sea, testifying to the seamanship of the two skippers, Lieutenants A. L. Nelson and R. A. J. English.

On the return voyage the *Bear* experienced little difficulty until she approached the Bay of Whales. Progress was slowed at first by pancake ice and loose pack. Then about 20 miles northwest of the bay the ship was forced by heavy pack ice to heave to until conditions improved. Finally, after bucking her way through the ice, at times foot by foot, the *Bear* entered the Bay of Whales at 11:15 p. m., February 25.

When the *Bear* cast off at 8:35 a. m., February 26, 12 of the men who had been helping establish Little America II were aboard. The "Ice Party" thus consisted of 56 men, the largest wintering party in Antarctica up to that time. For nine hours the *Bear* bucked new ice before reaching open water. She had no difficulty getting through the belt of pack ice in the Ross Sea, but shortly after crossing the 70th parallel late on March 2 the first of a succession of severe gales struck the ship. She finally reached Dunedin on the afternoon of March 12, 1934, after an extremely stormy passage.

RETREAT CAMP AND AUTUMN DEPOT-LAYING

After Admiral Byrd returned from the exploratory voyage of the *Bear*, he became alarmed at the series of cracks in the ice in the vicinity of the base. Knowing that the ice on which Little America II was located was afloat, he assumed that the slight motion noticeable along the cracks was due to the ocean swell in the Ross Sea. So much ice had gone out of the Bay of Whales that open water was visible in Ver-Sur-Mer Inlet, just west of Little America II. If more bay ice should go out, Byrd feared the restraining force which the bay ice had been exerting would be lost and that large portions of the ice shelf, including that part on which Little America II was situated, were likely to break loose and float out to sea. To prepare for such a catastrophe an emergency cache of food, gasoline, tents, and supplies, called Retreat Camp, was established on a higher and more secure section of the ice shelf about a mile southeast of Little America II.

The pressure ice had so delayed unloading that it was late in the season before Little America II was sufficiently completed to permit some of the men to begin depot-laying in preparation for the field season the following spring. On March 1 a sledge party, led by Captain Alan Innes-Taylor, chief of trail operations, set out on a journey to the south of Little America II to mark a trail that would be safe for the tractors and to lay down depots every 25 geographical miles for a distance of 200 miles. The party consisted of Innes-Taylor, Richard B. Black, Stuart Paine, and Finn Ronne, with three dog teams. The sledge loads, averaging 950 pounds, included nine 30-day rations for the explorers which were to be depoted. Richard S. Russell, Jr. and E. L. Moody, with two teams, comprised a supporting party. Immediately south of Little America II the trail crossed Amundsen Arm over a route newly discovered to replace the route of 1929-30 (via Ver-Sur-Mer Inlet) now closed by pressure ridges.

On the evening of March 5 Admiral Byrd dispatched Harold I. June, Bernard W. Skinner, and Amory H. Waite, Jr., in one of the Citroëns to investigate why Innes-Taylor had failed to keep any of the radio schedules. They carried 14 30-day rations which were eventually cached at 100-mile depot. The next morning they found the sledging party in good condition at 50-mile depot, but its radio had to be repaired. Byrd radioed that, after a day's rest, the Citroën, instead of returning, should set out that evening to overtake the sledging party and assist it to the 100-mile depot. They caught the dog teams 16 miles south of 50-mile depot. No longer needed, the supporting party returned to Little America II. The season's first blizzard forced the combined party to remain in camp for two days. When they set out again on the morning of March 9, the faster-moving tractor forged ahead of the dog teams, reaching 100-mile depot that evening.

Establishing the depot, the tractor party headed back for Little America II, which they reached at noon on March 10. Making an easterly detour around the crevasses, they covered 123 statute miles in 16 hours with three stops. In spite of difficulty in crossing crevasses, over which the snow bridges often collapsed as the tractor passed, the Citroën had definitely proved the practicability of long-distance mechanical transport.

Meanwhile the dog teams, slowly struggling southward through deep snow left by the blizzard, did not reach 100-mile depot until late on March 10. The sledging party pushed on from the 100-mile depot for four more days. On March 12 they established 125-mile depot, and late on March 14 they reached 80°54' S, 161°58' W, where they made the 155-mile depot. Temperatures had been very cold following the big blizzard, only two readings from March 9 to March 16 being above zero.[7] After resting a day at 155-mile depot, the sledging party headed back for Little America II.

BOLLING ADVANCE BASE

One of the objectives of the expedition was the establishment of an advance weather base where three men would spend the Antarctic winter making regular meteorological observations. Difficulties with the pressure ice during unloading operations had consumed so much time that any hope of establishing the advance base on the Polar plateau, or even at the foot of the Queen Maud Mountains, had to be abandoned. Because of the limited time remaining before the onset of winter darkness, Admiral Byrd decided that the advance base would be established at the 100-mile depot on the southern trail. Although this revised plan was much less ambitious than the original, it was feasible, and since no other station in Antarctica had ever been established this far inland, even in summer, valuable meteorological data could be expected from continuous observation over a period of several months.

During the latter half of March a concerted effort was made to establish Bolling Advance Base. The tractors, the southern sledge party, and even aviation contributed. In two flights the Pilgrim monoplane ferried 1800 pounds of material to 50-mile depot and on a third flight reached 100-mile depot. Unfortunately, the Fokker *Blue Blade* crashed while taking off on a preliminary test flight, and the weather closed in before the *William Horlick* could be readied for flight.

March 16, the day that the sledging party had turned back from 155-mile depot, a nine-man tractor party left Little America II for 100-mile depot with the material for Bolling Advance Base, the Cletrac pulling four sledges and the three Citroëns pulling three sledges each. Each tractor carried emergency camping gear, a man-hauling sledge, and two 30-day rations per man. Harold I. June was leader; E. J. Demas, Frederick G. Dustin, Joe Hill, Jr., and Bernard W. Skinner were drivers. Carl O. Petersen and Amory H. Waite, Jr. served as radio operators. Paul A. Siple and Ivor Tinglof, the carpenter, went along to assemble the hut. On the evening that the tractors set out the temperature was $-15°$ F, the sky was overcast, and a light snow was falling. Late the next night, March 17, they reached 50-mile depot. That same evening the sledging party reached 125-mile depot on their return journey. During the night Innes-Taylor's minimum thermometer registered $-45°$ F; the previous night it had registered $-54°$ F.[8] This was a severe test of men, dogs, and machines.

Also on March 17, aviation was again called on for an assist. W. H. Bowlin, with Clay Bailey at the radio, flew seal meat for the dogs and new sleeping bags for the men of the sledging party to 100-mile depot. Bowlin was also asked to search for the best route for the tractors through the crevassed area south of 50-mile depot. Shortly after circling the tractor party to drop a message on the return from 100-mile depot, a dense fog which had developed after he left Little America II forced Bowlin to land the Pilgrim monoplane in the field. Relief operations were not possible until the morning of March 19 when McCormick and Byrd in the autogyro soon spotted it south of Amundsen Arm. Fifty gallons of gasoline were hauled out by dog team, and when the autogyro developed mechanical difficulty during the operation, a mechanic with spare parts came to its rescue, also by dog team.

South of 50-mile depot the tractor party ran into a series of difficulties. First, on March 18, the Citroën driven by June and Skinner lodged in a crevasse about 18 miles southeast of 50-mile depot, while they were pioneering a trail through the pressure ridges. June and Skinner managed to get the Citroën out of the

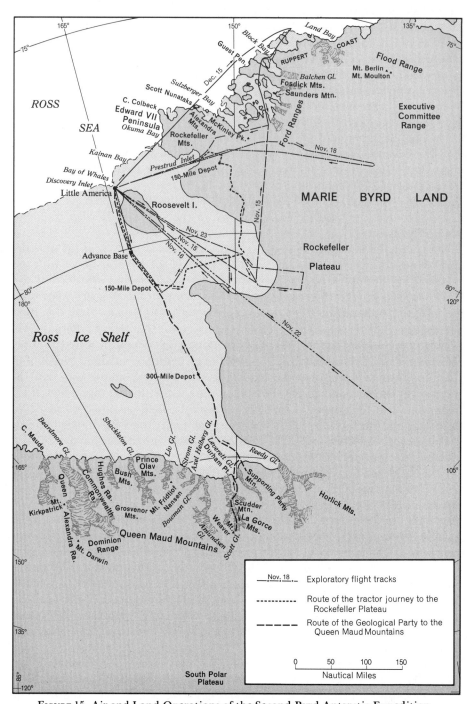

FIGURE 15. Air and Land Operations of the Second Byrd Antarctic Expedition.

crevasse by the time the remainder of the party arrived just before midnight on March 19. After breaking camp the next morning the Cletrac stalled and, because a pin had been sheared off the crank, could not be started. The expedient of towing the Cletrac, which had started the engine at 50-mile depot, this time was unsuccessful, and the Cletrac had to be left at this point. Setting a course to the southwest, the three Citroëns picked up the southern trail which had been marked by the sledging party, and on the evening of March 21 they reached 100-mile depot. A short time later Innes-Taylor's party arrived from the south.

It had taken the dog teams four days to travel from 125-mile depot to 100-mile depot, but on two of these days they had been held in camp by heavy snowstorms. They had only a day's rations of dog pemican on the sledges when they reached 100-mile depot.

The next morning, March 22, the two parties began the construction of Advance Base 100 yards to the east of the beacon marking 100-mile depot. At 11:55, a. m., Admiral Byrd landed at Advance Base, having been flown in by Bowlin and Bailey in the Pilgrim. Temperatures were bitterly cold for working on the base. The first night, the minimum thermometer recorded −52° F. During the day on March 22 the temperature remained in the minus 40s. That night, with the men working until 1:00 a. m., the temperature dropped to −60° F.[9]

The tractor party, in this same bitter cold, had gone back after the Cletrac's load and on the morning of March 23 arrived at Advance Base with the remainder of the supplies. Throughout the trip to Advance Base from Little America II the tractor party had been plagued by water condensing and freezing in the fuel lines, causing the engines to stall. Frequent stops were required to disconnect the gas lines and blow the ice out, a task that was extremely painful to the fingers and hands in such bitter cold.

The dog teams left Advance Base for Little America II on March 25, and on March 28 the tractors departed, leaving Admiral Byrd alone to man the meteorological station for the long winter months. The specially designed, prefabricated hut had a floor area of 9 feet by 13 feet, and was 8 feet high. Built in a pit, the hut was completely buried by snow which had drifted over its flat roof before the tractor party left. Only the 12-foot bamboo poles supporting the radio antennae, the 12-foot anemometer pole, and the instrument shelter projected above the snow. A trap door served as an entrance. Two tunnels extending out into the snow provided storage space for food and fuel and housed the generator for the radio. Located at 80°08′ S, 163°57′ W, Advance Base was actually 123 statute miles from Little America II due to the fact that the trail did not follow a meridian but had to detour around crevasses. The meridianal distance was 100 nautical miles (Fig. 15).

At 1:30 p. m. on March 29 the tractor party arrived at Little America II, a little more than 25 hours after leaving Advance Base. At 8:00 p. m. on March 31 Innes-Taylor's party arrived. Their last day's run had covered 34 miles. Cold and heavy drifts had kept them in camp on March 26 and 30. The teams suffered a great deal on account of extremely low temperatures, and three dogs were lost due to exhaustion on the return from 100-mile depot.

WINTER ACTIVITIES

During the depot-laying and the establishment of Advance Base, activities in preparation for the winter night had continued at Little America II, but much still remained to be done after the parties returned. Seal carcasses, cached at various points on the bay ice, had to be hauled in. The Bay of Whales having frozen over, the danger of a large piece of ice shelf going out to sea was greatly lessened. Many of the supplies at Retreat Camp now had to be hauled back to the main base. The tunnels and the directional antennae of the radio at the base camp had to be completed, and the planes and tractors had to be dug in for the winter. By the end of May all these tasks were completed, but the sun had already set for the last time on April 19. Consequently, the last phases of the work were done in darkness, and the temperatures were bitterly cold, causing the men frequent cases of frostbite.

Once the expedition had been made secure for winter, Little America II settled into a routine program. The mechanics worked on the tractors. Those destined to make overland journeys the following spring and summer devoted much time to planning and preparation of supplies and equipment. In addition, five programs of scientific observation were carried on through the winter.

1. Meteorology had a major place in the scientific program of the expedition, and it was essential to the success of the aerial exploration. Observations of temperature, pressure, wind, clouds, snow, and drift were made three times daily, at 8:00 a. m., 2:00 p. m., and 8:00 p. m. at Little America II from February 9, 1934, to February 3, 1935. Continuously recording thermographs and barographs were also used, as were maximum and minimum thermometers and a hygrometer. In order that the observations of the first and second expeditions might be comparable, the instruments of the second expedition were placed in the same position as those of the first.[10] The first pilot balloon observation was made on March 30, 1934, and thereafter two or more observations were made daily when the drift was not too thick nor the clouds too low to obscure the balloon from the view of the observer. The last pilot balloon ascent was made on February 2, 1935, making a total of 569 ascents for the second expedition.

Meteorological observations also included temperature soundings by aircraft. The use of kites during the first expedition had not been entirely successful, and an autogyro was included on the second for this purpose. The first temperature sounding with the autogyro was made on September 1, but after 10 flights had been made the operation was temporarily halted on September 25 by a crash of the machine, injuring pilot William S. McCormick. Observations were later resumed, however, by using one of the conventional aircraft. In all a total of 26 temperature soundings were made from September 1, 1934, to January 6, 1935.

2. Under Dr. Poulter's direction a program of meteor observations was carried

out at Little America II during the four months of winter darkness. This was a cooperative effort in which some 70 stations throughout the world agreed to participate in a system of synchronous and continuous observations. Observations began at Little America II on April 22 and were continued into August. Due to interference of bad weather, sunlight, moonlight, and auroral light, the actual time of meteor observations during the four-month period was limited to a total of a little less than seven days.[11] Observations were made on about 7000 meteors in this time.

Although several methods were used and some observing was done out of doors, most meteor observation was done by one of two methods from a shack with a specially designed plastic dome fitted with an eyepiece facing each of the cardinal directions. By one method each of four observers, working simultaneously, scanned his quadrant through a 50° reticle mounted outside the dome, reporting to a recorder the coordinates of each meteor's track, its color, magnitude, and duration of the train, if any. When it was discovered that, in spite of its limited field, a much greater number of meteors could be seen through a binocular than by the unaided eye, a 7 x 50 binocular was mounted in a zenithal position in place of the fifth reticle.

On July 11 and 12 favorable conditions revealed a great number of meteors flashing across the sky. A maximum of 300 an hour per observer were noted with the unaided eye looking through a reticle, but on the latter day in an observation period of 1 hour and 4 minutes over a 2-hour period, 1137 meteors were recorded as seen through binoculars.[12] In August a series of observations were made simultaneously at Little America II and at Advance Base on several hundred meteors, in an effort to determine real heights.

It had been estimated previously that from 10 to 20 million meteors enter the earth's atmosphere daily. Dr. Poulter's observations showed the number must be more than 1 billion. From meteor trains he was also able to calculate that at an altitude of approximately 100 miles the wind is blowing from west to east at about 150 miles per hour.[13]

3. Although the cosmic ray observations were not confined to the winter season only, it was one of the routine activities that occupied the attention of some of the men at Little America during the winter darkness. In cooperation with Dr. A. H. Compton's worldwide survey of the geographical distribution of cosmic rays, Dr. E. H. Bramhall and his assistant, Arthur A. Zuhn, began their observation of the intensity of cosmic rays while on board the *Jacob Ruppert* crossing the Pacific. The observations at Little America II were begun in April and continued at two-week intervals until February 1935. These observations were considered important in the worldwide study because of the nearness to the magnetic pole and because the continuous darkness of winter was an aid in determining a possible diurnal variation in intensity. Visual observations were carried out over a total of 800 hours.

4. The magnetic observatory consisted of two shacks of nonmagnetic material set up 100 yards apart in a north-south tunnel an eighth of a mile long. The southernmost shack housed the instruments to observe and continuously record

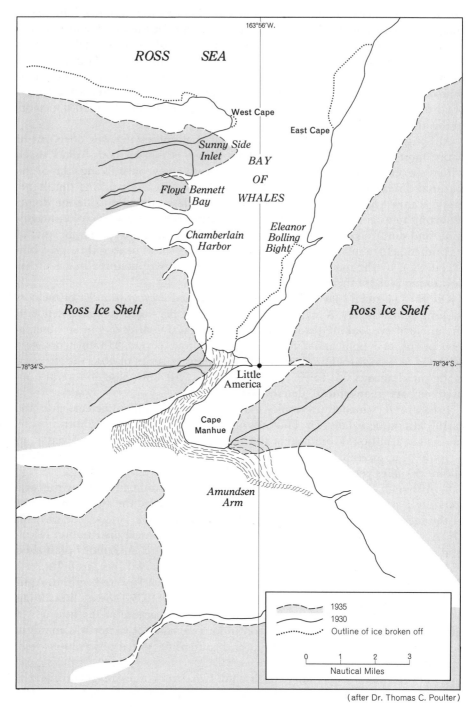

(after Dr. Thomas C. Poulter)

FIGURE 16. Ice Movement in the Vicinity of the Bay of Whales.

on sensitized paper variations in both direction and intensity of the earth's magnetic field. The other shack housed the magnetometer by which absolute values of the magnetic elements were periodically determined. To ascertain the magnetic declination, a mark light was set up on a timber in a tunnel 300 feet away from the "absolute" building. The bearing of the line running through the lamp and the center of the magnetometer pier was determined astronomically, as was the precise location of the pier. Records of the observations, sponsored by the Department of Terrestrial Magnetism of the Carnegie Institution of Washington, indicate at that time a mean value of inclination of about 82°. The horizontal intensity of the earth's field was approximately 0.09 c.g.s. units, and the magnetic declination was about 107.5° east of north. All values revealed regular fluctuations of various periodicities as well as the influence of transient disturbances.[14] In addition to the stationary observatory at Little America II, portable instruments were used in the field to record absolute and relative magnetic values.

5. The biologists, Dr. E. B. Perkins, Paul A. Siple, Alton A. Lindsey, and J. M. Sterrett, continued through the winter at Little America three investigations which were begun earlier in 1934 and which were carried into the following summer. These involved a study of plankton in the Bay of Whales, the examination of bacteria found in snow samples, and an investigation of the Weddell seals in the Bay of Whales (Fig. 16).

At the edge of the pressure ice in the Bay of Whales a hole was cut in the ice through which the plankton net could be lowered. As the winter set in, the ice became increasingly thick, but Dr. Perkins succeeded in getting samples of sea water and making hauls with the plankton net at about two-week intervals until the end of June. The plankton samples were placed in a thermos jug to be carried to the base, where they could be microphotographed. At the end of June it took four days of chopping to reach water, and then the mass of ice crystals under the ice would not admit the net, causing the suspension of the project until the following spring.

On June 26, Paul Siple, F. Alton Wade, Stevenson Corey, and Olin D. Stancliff set out on a journey down onto the Bay of Whales. The weather being too cold for dogs, the men hauled their own sledges. The trip had several purposes: to test equipment, to investigate the cause of the heavy sea smoke near the mouth of the bay, to search for evidence of Weddell seals remaining in the bay throughout the winter, to take snow samples for bacteria, and to observe glaciological conditions.[15] A current meter was also taken for tidal observations. On the night of June 27 they reached the Ross Sea at West Cape but were unable to approach close enough to use the current meter. No seals were observed. Heading back from the edge of the Ross Sea in the face of a stiff wind with temperatures in the minus thirties, Wade's face and hands were severely frozen. He and Stancliff remained in camp on June 28 while Siple and Corey went up Chamberlain Harbor onto the Ross Ice Shelf. At two places on the outward journey Siple opened sterile petri dishes which he collected on the return. Six random samples of snow were collected in sterile jars, and a precipitation meter for measuring snow accumulation was placed on top of a flat dome that rose above any surrounding elevation. Because of Wade's condition, the entire party then returned to Little America II on June 29. Snow samples were also taken at various times from positions in the vicinity of Little America for the purpose of investigating bacteria that might be present.

Alton A. Lindsey continued the study of seals begun by Siple during the First Byrd Antarctic Expedition. The most significant phase of this investigation dealt with Weddell seals, which remain in the Bay of Whales all year. Crab-eater seals spend the winter on the edge of the pack ice and in summer some of them frequent the Bay of Whales. Between February 9 and March 14, 1934, 61 crab-eater seals were taken and measured at the Bay of Whales.[16]

The study of the Weddell seals during the Second Byrd Antarctic Expedition began soon after the expedition arrived, and a supply of dog food had to be acquired by hunting seals. From February 9 to March 17, 1934, 233 Weddell seal carcasses were measured. Skulls from 73 seals of various ages were studied, and 43 specimens were collected for museums. Since the Weddell seals spend the winter under the ice beside "blow holes" in the Bay of Whales, they could be studied during the various stages of the life cycle. Their rookeries tend to be inland, away from the edge of the bay ice. The northernmost was eight miles from open water and two miles from Little America. There were 50 pairs of mother and young here, and two more rookeries farther south contained 24 and 80 pairs of seals. In all, 243 seals were branded. Forty-four births of known date were recorded from October 5 to November 10, 1934. With the help of Robert Young, Lindsey weighed 18 of these pups as often as every third day until they could no longer be lifted. Careful records were kept on the branded pups regarding aspects of growth, time of weaning, period of moulting, dentition, separation from mothers, learning to swim, and mortality. Of the 83 pairs of mother and young that were branded, Lindsey was able to keep records on 54 mothers and 48 pups.[17]

Those who were not engaged in scientific observations were preparing for the spring campaign in the field. Such preparations included making, weighing, and packing trail rations, repairing dog harnesses, making windproof clothing, modifying sledges, and testing equipment. Six tons of dog pemican were made from seal blubber and frozen into bricks for the trail. In the cramped quarters of the cold and drafty tractor garage, with its packing-crate walls and tarpaulin roof, each of the Citroëns was in turn remodeled so as to be more adaptable for trail work. To obviate the necessity for making camp, quarters for two men were built into an enlarged enclosure back of the driver's cab. A 145-gallon fuel tank was added, and petcocks were placed in the gas lines to facilitate blowing out the ice that condensed there. Other adaptations were added to conserve engine heat and to improve lubrication in the intense cold.

WINTER AT BOLLING ADVANCE BASE

When circumstances had prevented enough supplies being transported to Advance Base to support three men for the long winter, Admiral Byrd had decided that he would occupy the base alone. In addition to the routine of living, which in Antarctica is considerable, his duties consisted of making meteorological observations twice daily and maintaining a radio schedule with Little America II three times a week. The continuously recording instruments also had to be serviced regularly, and, due to frost formation, frequently. Once the sun set for the last time in April, Byrd also maintained a schedule of auroral observations which, like the meteorological observations, were synchronized with those at Little America II.

As it turned out, however, the mere business of staying alive proved to be much the greater problem. Although Byrd was aware of water vapor condensing and freezing in the ventilator pipe, the stovepipe, and the exhaust pipe of the engine which drove the radio generator, his improvisations failed to maintain proper ventilation, and he gradually became ill from carbon monoxide poisoning. He finally collapsed during the radio schedule on May 31, and remained critically ill for more than a month. His recovery was retarded by his inability to properly care for himself and to the fact that he was cold most of the time, since he dared have a fire only a few hours each day. In spite of his desperately weakened condition, Byrd succeeded in maintaining a continuous meteorological record for Advance Base. Although on the occasion of his first collapse and on subsequent relapses there was a total of nine times that he was unable to get to the surface for the scheduled observations at the instrument shelter, the continuity of the record was maintained by the continuously recording instruments which he managed to keep going.

TABLE OF MEAN AND ABSOLUTE TEMPERATURES AT BOLLING ADVANCE BASE*
FOR THE WINTER OF 1934

	April	May	June	July	August	September
Mean Temperature, °F	−31.9	−30.4	−25.0	−51.7	−46.8	−44.8
Absolute Maximum, °F	21	18	19	0	4	0
Mean Maximum, °F	−21.7	−20.4	−13.1	−42.7	−35.5	−32.2
Absolute Minimum, °F	−62	−72.5	−59	−78	−77	−72.5
Mean Minimum, °F	−42.0	−41.2	−35.0	−59.4	−57.8	−53.0

* George Grimminger, "Meteorological Results of the Byrd Antarctic Expeditions, 1928-30, 1933-35: Summaries of Data," *Monthly Weather Review*, supp. No. 42, pp. 68, 72.

The men at Little America II had become suspicious regarding Byrd's condition, although the Admiral was desperately trying to conceal it during scheduled radio contacts for fear his companions might take what he considered undue risks in a desperate rescue mission. Dr. Poulter had been contemplating a tractor trip to Advance Base for the purpose of meteor observation which would give him a base line of 100 miles for measuring the heights of meteor tracks. Such a trip was now considered doubly important — as a scientific operation and as a precautionary relief mission. Admiral Byrd gave his consent to the trip for the purpose of meteor observation, providing certain precautions were taken.

The tractor journey was scheduled to start during the full moon from July 18 to 23. Two false starts were made, however. The first attempt, begun on July 20,

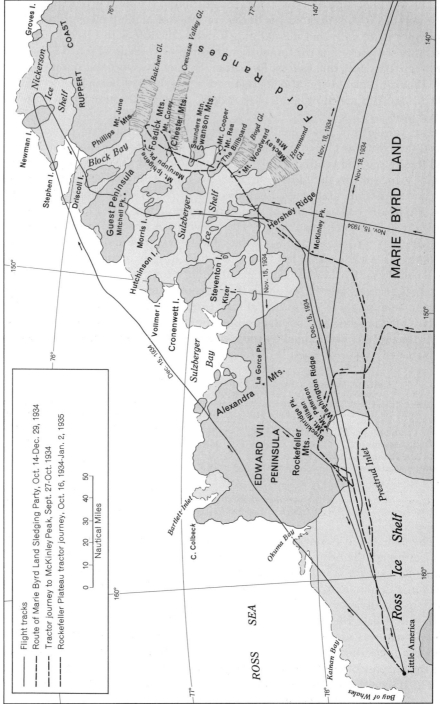

FIGURE 17. Detailed Map of Operations of the Second Byrd Antarctic Expedition in Northwestern Marie Byrd Land, 1934-35.

had to be abandoned south of 50-mile depot when the trail was lost due to darkness and drifting snow. The second, on August 4, was halted by mechanical difficulties just south of Amundsen Arm. Finally, Dr. Poulter, E. J. Demas, and Amory Waite set out in tractor No. 3 on August 8. Camping 30 miles out the first night, they covered the remaining distance in a continuous run, reaching Advance Base just before midnight on August 10. Here Byrd had been sending up flares to guide them to his shack.

Because of the weakened condition of Admiral Byrd, the tractor crew remained until he was strong enough to travel. Dr. Poulter immediately set up a reticle for the observation of meteors which he and Demas carried on as long as darkness lasted. Advance Base was closed on October 12 when Bowlin took advantage of good weather to fly the Pilgrim from Little America II. Byrd and Poulter returned in the plane; Schlossbach, who had flown out with Bowlin, returned with Waite and Demas in the tractor.

SPRING TRACTOR JOURNEY TO MCKINLEY PEAK

In support of and preceding a proposed trek by dog team for geological and biological investigations in the Ford Ranges, a remarkable tractor journey was made from Little America II to McKinley Peak, the southwesternmost peak in those mountains. In addition to marking the trail and laying food depots for the dog teams, the tractor party was instructed to select a landing field near McKinley Peak for refueling aircraft, whose range would thereby be extended. This was the first time that exploration had ever been carried on in Antarctica by means of mechanized land transport. Although the area over which the tractor was to travel had been seen from the air, no one had ever set foot east of the Rockefeller Mountains (see Fig. 17).

Late on September 27, Harold June, Ken Rawson, J. H. Von der Wall, and Carl Petersen set out in tractor No. 1, pulling two sledges with a total load of 7600 pounds.[18] The cargo consisted of 3600 pounds of food, supplies, and gasoline. Such a supply operation by dogs would have been impossible, especially with temperatures below −30° F. Because of the magnetic attraction of the radio equipment and of the steel in the tractor it was necessary to carry the compass on the rear sledge, which had been constructed so as to be nonmagnetic. From here Rawson, the navigator, by means of wires he had rigged to a set of signal lights on the dashboard of the tractor, was able to keep the driver on a true course. As they set out from Little America II, crunching through a heavy crust of snow which caused them to run in second gear a great part of the time, Petersen planted a trail-marking flag at regular intervals. Every 30 nautical miles they cached drums of gasoline for the return trip. At 60-mile depot they put down supplies for the dog teams that were to follow.

Having pulled abreast of the Rockefeller Mountains on the afternoon of September 30, the party camped that evening at the edge of ice ridges 120 miles (138 statute miles) east of Little America II. The next day, instead of breaking camp, they reconnoitered on skis, seeking a safe route through the pressure ridges. Clear weather that night permitted celestial observations, and a good geographical fix was obtained. The next day, by a short detour to the south, they managed to get through the pressure ridges. As they moved eastward the terrain rose gently and then more steeply. As they approached the 150-mile depot on the afternoon of October 3 a broken oil line stopped them temporarily. From the aneroid barometer they calculated that they had risen from 433 feet on the ice shelf west of the pressure ridges to 2339 feet at 150-mile depot.[19] As it later developed, they were ascending the western front of the Rockefeller Plateau, a feature whose existence was hitherto unknown. The oil line being repaired, they cached supplies at 150-mile depot and continued eastward with one sled. Bumping over hard sastrugi, the tractor gradually climbed another 1000 feet to the summit level of the Rockefeller Plateau. Wind and drift increased markedly as they laid 180-mile depot (207 statute miles). A blizzard of extreme violence struck from the northeast and held them in camp for six days. After spending most of October 10 digging out of the drift, they made only nine miles before being stopped by mechanical trouble. The next morning they were underway, traversing the rolling surface of the plateau, here about 3500 feet above sea level.

About 11 a. m. they sighted McKinley Peak and the Haines Mountains to the north. They altered course for the Peak and noted that the elevation dropped in a series of terrace-like slopes toward the base of the mountain. Reaching its base, they ascended part way up the gradual southern slope of the mountain where they made camp that night at about 2500 feet. The next day the men reconnoitered the slopes and climbed to the summit of McKinley Peak, finding on the north a sheer rock face 1200 feet high. From observations of both the sun and stars as well as a time signal on radio, Rawson found the mountain to be approximately 37 miles west of its previously estimated position.

On October 13 the party marked out an emergency landing field south of McKinley Peak and put down a depot for Siple's party. The high elevation of the field, however, made it unsuitable for refueling planes.

On the return to Little America II poor visibility and drift made it difficult to follow the trail, which had been partly obliterated across the Rockefeller Plateau. Hard sastrugi made the ride extremely rough. Once off the plateau, however, progress was more rapid, and at 2:13 p. m. on October 18 the tractor party arrived at Little America II, completing a round trip of 525 statute miles.

THE MARIE BYRD LAND SLEDGING PARTY

On October 14 the Marie Byrd Land party — consisting of Paul A. Siple, biologist and leader; F. Alton Wade, geologist; Stevenson Corey and Olin D. Stancliff, drivers — set out from Little America II over the eastern trail marked by the preceding tractor party. The first part of the journey was extremely difficult due to deep, soft snow which so taxed the dogs that, although they had traveled only 30 miles in the first four days, the fifth day had to be spent in camp to rest them. Finally a blizzard with temperatures between —25° F and —40° F, which forced the party to remain in camp on October 20, hardened the surface and daily progress improved accordingly. On October 23 the party sighted the Rockefeller Mountains on the north, and on the afternoon of October 30 they reached 150-mile depot on the western slope of the Rockefeller Plateau. By November 2 they had crossed the Rockefeller Plateau and were descending the terrace-like slopes toward the base of McKinley Peak. The next day they reached the cache laid by the tractor party at the foot of the mountain. The sledge meter recorded 216.9 miles since leaving Little America II.[20]

Six days were spent on McKinley Peak, during which time visibility was so poor that a solar observation could not be obtained nor could satisfactory bearings to other peaks be taken. One day was spent in making a magnetic observation. Wade examined the geology of the mountain, which is composed mostly of pink granite intruded by numerous dikes. Siple found several species of lichens growing in rock crevices. After being forced to remain in camp on November 8, the party departed the next day for the Haines Mountains to the northeast. They now had to break their own trail, and deep snow tired the dogs quickly. The descent of the steep slopes from McKinley Peak also gave trouble. On the way to Haines Mountains, which they reached late on November 13, the party crossed several low rock ridges, almost buried by snow and ice. Largest of these is Hershey Ridge. These ridges and the Haines Mountains were found to be composed of slates and schists, the first evidence of the origin of the Ford Ranges. A roaring blizzard on the night of November 10 had improved the surfaces for travel but had so deeply buried the camp that no progress was made on November 11. While Wade and Siple explored the Haines Mountains, Corey and Stancliff returned to McKinley Peak for food which they had been forced to abandon on November 9.

On the morning of November 19 the entire party broke camp and headed northeastward on a journey that would take them across or around the western ends of the westward projecting mountain ridges of the Ford Ranges and the great outlet glaciers which separated them. To the east lay a maze of hundreds of mountain peaks; to the west was the ice shelf in Sulzberger Bay. In a run of 18 hours the party crossed the heavily crevassed Hammond Glacier and camped at the base of Mount Woodward. This, like the Haines Mountains, is composed of black slates and schists, cut by igneous intrusions. November 20 was spent investigating Mount Woodward, the southernmost in the Ford Ranges. Here Siple found mosses. On November 21 the party crossed the much-disturbed ice of Boyd Glacier, then called Ames Glacier, and camped at the foot of Mount Rea. This and adjacent mountains are composed of red granite and possess remarkably steep slopes. One peak with an almost vertical face was called The Billboard. November 22 was spent mapping and investigating geological and biological conditions in the vicinity of Mount Rea and Mount Cooper.

The supply of dog food was running short, and to cover as much ground as possible in the time available, it was decided that the party should be split up. The three teams had already been reorganized into two to free Wade for geological work. On November 23 Siple and Corey, taking one team, left Mount Cooper, rounded Mount Rea, and headed north to the east of Saunders Mountain. By the close of November 24 they were at Mount Stancliff, overlooking Crevasse Valley Glacier, one of the great outlet glaciers. Snow and wind prevented them from crossing the treacherous surface of the glacier on November 25. The next day, in spite of poor visibility, they started across, but after having a narrow escape from plunging into a yawning crevasse, they camped on the ice until conditions improved. On November 27 they succeeded in crossing the glacier and camped beside the Chester Mountains. From the heights of the Chester Mountains, composed of gray granodiorite, many of the surrounding mountains were charted. From here they headed northeast for an imposing black peak which rose from the side of the higher Fosdick Mountains, a range of gray granite. When they reached the peak on November 28 they discovered it to be an extinct volcano. Ice which filled small depressions contained algae. That night a blizzard bore down from the north and kept them confined to camp until December 1.

This was the outward limit of the journey, and on December 2 they headed directly south, passed Mount Corey, toward Crevasse Valley Glacier. Finding this route impassable, they detoured westward to their northward crossing. On December 3, while making the second attempt to cross Crevasse Valley Glacier, both sledges fell into a crevasse. Fortunately the men were able to retrieve everything but some food and a set of dishes which fell beyond the reach of Corey, who was lowered into the crevasse at the end of a rope held by Siple. That night they camped beside a low peak supporting a surprising amount of vegetation, apparently due to the presence of a skua gull retreat beside a melt-water lake. Two days remained to keep the rendezvous with Wade and Stancliff at the Haines Mountains, but in spite of a great deal of fog, they covered first 20 and then 30 miles a day to reach the Haines Mountains on December 5. Wade and Stancliff were already there.

After Siple and Corey had departed from Mount Rea, Wade and Stancliff spent the remainder of the day, November 23, examining the contacts between the metamorphosed sedimentaries and the granite intrusions. The next day they headed for the west side of Saunders Mountain. They made a couple of stops to examine the granites and leave their trailer sledge before starting north toward Balchen Glacier. As they crossed Crevasse Valley Glacier in poor visibility, the sledge broke through the snow bridge of a huge crevasse. To recover the sledge it was necessary for Stancliff to descend into the crevasse on the end of a line held by Wade. Most of the gear and food were saved, but much of the dog pemican was lost. This necessitated an immediate retreat to the rendezvous at the Haines Mountains, and even then it was necessary to put the dogs on half rations. While waiting for Siple and Corey, Wade carried on investigations in the Haines Mountains. On December 7 the reunited party reached McKinley Peak, where they had clear weather to make the postponed solar observations and establish fixes.

As a result of their exploration, the Marie Byrd Land sledging party found that the more southerly mountains in the Ford Ranges serve as dams to the northwesterly flow of glacial ice, which rises in a gentle slope up to the very crest of the mountains on the south while the northerly face of the mountain, often a sheer rock wall, is free of ice. On the other hand, the upper parts of the more northerly mountains were found to be free of ice on all sides. Evidence of more extensive glaciation in the past was found in polished rock surfaces bearing striae, grooves, and chatter marks.[21] The Ford Ranges consist of highly folded and metamorphosed slates and schists into which granite and granodiorites have been intruded. Axes of the folds are not parallel, but diverging westward. Steep slopes, sometimes almost vertical walls, result from glacial plucking and frost action on rocks in which the major joint planes are almost vertical.[22] Structurally, the Ford Ranges appear to be related to the mountains of the Antarctic Peninsula. Petrographic relationships, however, are not so clear cut, for chemically the rocks bear a greater resemblance to those of the Queen Maud Mountains.[23]

As Siple and Corey traveled north across the Ford Ranges they found the temperatures less severe and the vegetation less sparse. In general, vegetation is to be found where rock outcrops, intercepting the sun's rays, raise the temperature sufficiently to induce melting. This results in small melt-water ponds, or more often, patches of blue ice.[24] Spots protected from the wind are more favorable to vegetation than unprotected places, and the presence of bird droppings also encourages plant growth. A total of 89 species of lichens and five species of mosses were collected from 215 locations on 12 different mountains.[25]

The necessity for standing by at 150-mile depot for the plateau tractor party had prevented the Marie Byrd Land sledging party from skirting the southern shore of Sulzberger Bay on their return to Little America II. After the rendezvous with the tractor party on December 16, the Marie Byrd Land party made a detour to visit the Rockefeller Mountains. On December 18 they reached Washington Ridge, where they met F. S. Dane, E. L. Moody, and Paul Swan who had come out with a dog sledge to salvage the engine of the Fokker plane wrecked there in 1929. Lichens were found in abundance on the pink granite outcrops of Washington Ridge, and algae, teeming with microscopic life, were present in the melt-water ponds on the mountain slopes. On the peak of the mountain, more than 50 miles from the nearest water, the party found a rookery of snowy petrels, and Siple suspected from the number of Antarctic petrels flying about that a rookery of these birds must have been present on an adjacent peak.[26] From the Rockefeller Mountains the Marie Byrd Land sledging party headed for Little America II. On Christmas day they met Ronne and Black taking spare parts to the plateau tractor party. At 3 p. m., December 29, they arrived at Little America II, after covering 862 miles, exclusive of side trips, in 77 days.

THE SOUTHERN JOURNEYS

The scientific program called for two overland journeys to the south. A geological party of three men with two dog teams was to explore the Queen Maud Mountains to the east of the Supporting Party Mountain, 85°27′ S, 147°33′ W, the easternmost point reached by the geological party of the First Byrd Expedition. A geophysical party of four men with four dog teams, after reaching the base of the Queen Maud Mountains, expected to ascend Scott Glacier and determine the thickness of the Polar plateau icecap. This posed a logistic problem. In addition to supplies depoted along the trail for 150 miles south of Little

America II in March 1934 and the supplies that the parties themselves could carry, it would be necessary to deliver 3000 pounds of supplies to the foot of Scott Glacier. The equipment for geophysical exploration alone weighed 850 pounds.[27]

This called for tractors, one to lay depots as far as the 300-mile mark and a second to haul supplies all the way to Scott Glacier. The success of the geophysical party depended on the ability of the tractors to cross the east-west belt of crevasses just south of the 81st parallel. It was planned that the dog teams should rendezvous with the tractors just north of the crevassed area, to assist them in finding a safe path through this treacherous belt. Because of the different speeds, the two groups would otherwise travel separately along the same trail to the south. The tractors, starting with loads of 8000 pounds each, would haul the bulk of the supplies for the depots.

As an alternative plan, it was proposed, as the party was ready to depart, that if the tractors could not get through the crevassed area, they should turn to the east and head for the Rockefeller Plateau which the eastern tractor party had just discovered, where geophysical and magnetic work would be of value. The geological party, with the support of the dog teams of the geophysical party, would continue on its original mission.

The combined parties left Little America at 11:15 a. m., October 16. The geological party consisted of Quin Blackburn, geologist and leader, Stuart D. L. Paine, radio operator and navigator, and Richard S. Russell, Jr. Their transport consisted of two teams of nine dogs each. The geophysical party consisted of Charles Gill Morgan, geologist, Dr. Ervin H. Bramhall, physicist, Finn Ronne, and Albert Eilefsen. Morgan and Bramhall were the coleaders. The party had four dog teams. The geophysical party reached Advance Base on October 22, the geological party 1½ days later. Up to this point the sledges had been only lightly loaded. Nevertheless, the soft surfaces and drifting snow had been hard on the dogs. Now full loads were taken on. By October 31 both parties were at the edge of the belt of crevasses at 81°10′ S, 161°05′ W, 192 miles south of Little America II.

While the dog teams were traveling toward Advance Base, Citroëns No. 2 and No. 3 had been completely overhauled. On October 25 the tractors, each pulling 8000-pound loads, headed over the southern trail. E. J. Demas was driving No. 3 and Joe Hill, Jr., accompanied by Amory H. Waite, Jr., radio operator, was driving No. 2. On October 28 the tractors reached Advance Base where two days were spent working on the machines before again heading south. On November 1 Paine radioed that the combined parties were camped at 81°22′ S, 161°24′ W, 209 miles south of Little America II, where they awaited the tractors. They had crossed a belt of crevasses, some of which were 30 feet across, but they felt the tractors could get through. When the machines did not appear that noon, the geological party retraced its route to the 193-mile point where they found the tractors, No. 3 being precariously wedged down in a crevasse. They finally recovered the tractor but there was no hope of the tractors proceeding any farther south at this point. It was also clear that the dog teams were useless in breaking

PLATE VII-A. Aircraft and tractors of the Second Byrd Antarctic Expedition. From the left, the autogyro, the Pilgrim, Condor, and TWA Fokker. Two converted Citroëns are at the bottom of the picture. U. S. Information Agency Photo No. 306-NT-548-16 in the National Archives.

PLATE VII-B. Digging the Condor out from its winter hangar. Some of the snow-block walls are still visible. U. S. Information Agency Photo No. 306-NT-548B-9 in the National Archives.

PLATE VIII-A. The foredeck of the *Wyatt Earp*. The ship is moored at the edge of the land ice at Snow Hill Island, February 28, 1935. U. S. Information Agency Photo No. 306-NT-557E-1Y in the National Archives.

PLATE VIII-B. Lincoln Ellsworth and Herbert Hollick-Kenyon. Ellsworth (r.) and his pilot are standing beside their tent with the *Polar Star* in the background at Dundee Island in November 1935. U. S. Information Agency Photo No. 306-NT-108.163 in the National Archives.

a trail, for snow bridges that permitted dogs and sledges to cross would not support the tractors. Many of these crevasses were so completely camouflaged that they were not apparent until the tractors broke through them.

After radio consultation with Admiral Byrd, the geophysical party was recalled from the 209-mile camp where it had been waiting, and the entire group retreated to 159-mile depot. From this point they headed eastward on November 3 in hopes that a safe route to the south would be found about 10 miles to the east. This attempt, however, proved no more successful than the first.

Admiral Byrd was again consulted, and since time was becoming critically short, it was decided to put the alternate plan in operation. Ronne and Eilefsen were detached from the geophysical party to constitute a supporting party for the geological party, to lay down depots at 173, 204, 250, and 300-mile points, and then return to Little America II. The dog teams were regrouped into five teams and each given a load of 1000 pounds. The geophysical apparatus was taken over by the tractors, and Morgan and Bramhall joined the tractor party to form a self-supporting group on a journey eastward up onto the newly discovered Rockefeller Plateau for the purpose of making magnetic observations and determining by seismic methods the thickness of the icecap. On November 6, from 81°09′ S, 161°07′ W, the reorganized parties set out on their missions.

The geological party crossed the crevassed belt and headed southeastward. Travel was at first difficult due to heavy loads and the fact that the sledges continued to break through a hard crust of snow on the surface. Winds were mostly in a southerly quarter. Blizzards on November 8 and 13 made travel extremely difficult and on the latter day the party was forced to remain in camp at 83°02′ S, 157°15′ W. Sandwiched in between was a cold spell with temperatures dropping below −30° F.[28] Leaving camp on the morning of November 14 they soon reached 300-mile depot at 83°09′ S, 157°06′ W. Here Ronne and Eilefsen turned over the remainder of their loads and Eilefsen's dog team and at 9 a. m. they started for Little America II with Ronne's team. Making a remarkably fast run, they reached Little America II nine days later, about midnight on November 22. On November 19, their best day, they had covered 47 miles (from 150-mile depot to Advance Base) in 13 hours.

From the 300-mile depot the geological party had three dog teams with 1440 pounds of dog food and 450 pounds of food for the explorers. About 3 p. m., November 15 they sighted the Queen Maud Mountains. A blizzard with southeast winds up to 50 miles an hour kept the party in camp on November 17. At 4 p. m. the next day they reached the site for 350-mile depot at 83°56′ S, 153°40′ W, and erected a beacon. At this point high land appeared to the east, a fact which seemed to disprove the existence of a strait between the Ross and Weddell Seas in this latitude. A half mile south of the beacon there began a nine-mile wide belt of crevasses, hummocks, and monoclinal pressure ridges with a northwest-southeast orientation.[29] The insubstantial bridging of the crevasses led Blackburn to conclude that the pressure causing the ice disturbance was active, perhaps related to the highlands to the east.[30] The party traveled tied together with alpine rope, and several times dogs or sledges crashed through a snow bridge into a crevasse from which they could be rescued only by one of the men descending into the chasm on the end of a line. On November 20, south of 84° 14' S, 152° 40' W, the geological party encountered a series of great east-west rolls in the surface of the ice shelf. The crests were from two to six miles apart and from 100 to 200 feet above the trough.[31] Huge bridged crevasses with north-south axes were found 13 miles beyond the 375-mile depot. At 10:30 a. m., November 23, the geological party reached the foot of the Queen Maud Mountains. From the 350-mile depot they had traveled through and over disturbed ice surfaces — great east-west swells and several belts of crevasses. Almost steady south-east winds, stinging the face and eyes with drift, made the task of crossing this treacherous belt extremely difficult.

At this first camp at the base of the Queen Maud Mountains, 85° 16' S, 148° 46' W, they marked out a smooth area, one mile square, as an emergency landing field and depoted supplies for the return trip. A blizzard with easterly winds up to 50 miles per hour struck on November 23, holding them in camp until November 26. On this day they made Supporting Party Mountain, 12 miles to the southeast, where they found the cairn that Gould's party had erected in 1929.

From the summit of Supporting Party Mountain, 85° 27' S, 147° 33' W, Blackburn scanned the mountain front, which he was to explore to the east, and Leverett Glacier, which he hoped would provide a route for him. He noted that Supporting Party Mountain was the westernmost of a line of low mountains which formed the northern boundary of Leverett Glacier. The glacier is not one of the great outlet glaciers from the Polar plateau but is fed from ice flowing off the Rockefeller Plateau to the east of the Ross Ice Shelf. The south wall of Leverett Glacier, 30 miles away, is formed by the Watson Escarpment, which here marks the fault-line scarp of the Queen Maud horst. Blackburn could find no way of ascending the escarpment to the south. He was disappointed to note that, to the east, the Queen Maud Mountains, except for the highest peaks, were practically ice-drowned and offered little opportunity for geological investigation. After discussing the matter, the party decided to retreat westward to the foot of Scott Glacier, then called Thorne Glacier, and ascend it to the Polar plateau.[32]

On November 28, they left Supporting Party Mountain and the next day began the ascent of Scott Glacier. The peaks bordering the lower part of Scott Glacier were found to be mostly gray, gray-brown, or reddish-brown granitic rocks. At two different locations among these granite peaks bordering the foot of the glacier — Durham Point, approximately 85° 32' S, 151° 12' W, at an elevation of 1200 feet, and Scudder Mountain, at about 86° 07' S, 149° 36' W — the party discovered a total of eight different species of lichens, the southernmost known examples of plant life.[33] What appeared to be diabase dikes cut the northernmost rock exposures, but farther up the glacier the dikes were found to be pegmatite. Where the tributary glaciers join the main glacier, the party had to skirt areas of greatly disturbed ice. Mountains bordering the upper part of Scott Glacier, like those farther west, were found to be capped by a great thickness of horizontal beds of sedimentary rocks. In other respects, too, the geological sequence is similar to the mountains farther west. The major difference is that the basement complex, consisting of highly folded and faulted gneisses and schists apparently of Precambrian age, is in the Scott Glacier area represented only in the lowest and northernmost peaks at the edge of the Ross Ice Shelf. The great bulk of the peaks which border Scott Glacier are made of granitic rocks which rest on the older basement complex. Above these rise the great tabular peaks with the sedimentary caps.[34]

On December 7 the geological party reached the foot of Mount Weaver at the head of Scott Glacier and on the brink of the Polar plateau, 212 miles from the South Pole. In 10 days they had traveled 120 miles, while climbing approximately 6000 feet in the face of biting winds which cascaded down off the Polar plateau, sometimes at velocities as high as 50 miles per hour. Surfaces varied from glare ice to hard packed snow.

Mount Weaver was climbed on December 11 and a note recording the fact was placed in a tin can in a cairn at the summit. The temperature there was −13° F. The elevation of the peak, which is located approximately 86°58′ S, 153°50′ W, was barometrically determined to be 8411 feet above sea level.[35] A recent survey showed the elevation to be 9780 feet, 3010 meters. This is 1500 to 3000 feet lower than comparable peaks, such as Mount Fridtjof Nansen, which border Axel Heiberg Glacier and Liv Glacier, and is indicative of the decreasing elevation of the Queen Maud Mountains to the east. The ascent of Mount Weaver revealed an interesting meteorological phenomenon, the shallow nature of the cold air mass on the Polar plateau which funnels down through the passes between the highest peaks. On the glacial surface the men had been plagued by the bitterly cold wind sweeping down from the plateau, but some distance up Mount Weaver they found the air comparatively calm, although the swirling drift below indicated that the wind was still raging there.[36]

The 2000 feet of sediments that form the upper part of Mount Weaver are sandstones and shales lying on a basal conglomerate. Beds of coal, ranging from lignite to bituminous and varying from a few inches to 10 feet thick, are interbedded with the sandstones and shales. The topmost bed contains many fossil stems and leaves of plants, while fossil tree sections as much as 18 inches in diameter were found in the moraines at the foot of the mountain. Dikes and sills of a fine-grained, greenish, igneous rock cut through the sediments and form the uppermost 170 feet of the mountain.[37]

From the summit of Mount Weaver the relationships between the various geographic features stood out more clearly. The fault-line scarp marking the southern margin of the Queen Maud Mountains horst, represented by the southern flanks of the great tabular mountains, extends eastward from Scott Glacier and may even have a northeasterly trend. It does not trend southeastward, as suggested by Amundsen.[38] The Queen Maud Mountains act as a dam for the out-flowing glacial ice of the Polar plateau. The ice covers the southern flanks of these mountains almost to the summits, while the northern slopes are ice-free rock walls.

At 9:30 a. m., November 12, the geological party broke camp and began the descent of Scott Glacier. Stopping for as much as a day to triangulate the various mountain peaks, the party reached the foot of the glacier on the night of December 22. Two days earlier the men were surprised to see four skua gulls fly over their camp. On December 23 they started the long trek across the Ross Ice Shelf toward Little America II. Southeast winds, reaching a velocity of 30 miles per hour for hours at a time, created a great deal of drifting from December 24-29. Fortunately the wind was at their backs, but even so the men were confined to camp the greater part of December 26 and 28. Beginning December 26, they started traveling each day at about 4 p. m. so as to have the sun on their backs, thus cutting down the glare. On the morning of December 30 they camped at 300-mile depot. By the morning of January 4 they were through the great crevassed area south of 81° S, and at 7:05 on the morning of January 11 they arrived at Little America II, having traveled 527 miles across the Ross Ice Shelf in 16 sledging days.[39]

When the geological party and the geophysical party separated on November 6 in the belt of crevasses in about 81°09' S, 161°07' W, the geophysical party, now the plateau party, retreated with the tractors to 159-mile depot on the southern trail. Here all the depoted gasoline was loaded on the sledges, and the tractors set out eastward in hope of making a third and successful attempt to cross the crevassed belt. Fog set in, however, and they were forced to stop about 2 a. m. on November 7. When the fog finally lifted on November 10 the party got under way again, headed in an east-southeast direction so as to cross the crevasses at right angles to their major axes. In the first hour of November 11 tractor No. 3, with Demas at the controls, crashed through a crevasse into what looked like a hopeless situation. The machine was wedged down at a precarious angle in the crevasse. After four hours of struggle the machine was brought out with the aid of the other tractor. The party camped at this point, 81°06' S, 157°28' W, until November 16. Bramhall set up his apparatus for magnetic observations, and Morgan, assisted by Waite, made several seismic soundings while Demas and Hill made necessary repairs on the machines.

This procedure was the usual pattern of events on the entire journey of the plateau party. It was so difficult to start the cold engines, a process requiring several hours of heating with blow torches, that the men were inclined to keep moving as long as possible when the tractors were performing properly. Four things were a cause to halt, at which time they would go into camp for a day or more. These were scientific observations, mechanical breakdown, bad weather, and crashing into a crevasse. Scientific observations were made every 25 to 50 miles. Since there was flexibility in the location of the observation points, scientific work was often done when the crew was stopped for other reasons, and mechanical breakdowns were often anticipated and prevented by making adjustments while the crew was stopped for scientific observations.

The scientific observations and getting an accurate geographic fix generally consumed a day. Consequently, this work was done while the party was in camp. Bramhall, with Waite's help, required about four hours to occupy a magnetic station, and Morgan took from 8 to 15 hours for each set of seismic soundings. All hands assisted in this rather complicated process. Morgan usually developed the records on the spot, using the cook tent for a photographic laboratory. The difficulties involved in doing the precise kind of instrumental work that Bramhall and Morgan accomplished can be appreciated when it is noted that at no time in the entire meteorological log of the journey was a temperature above freezing recorded. Over half of the recorded temperatures were below zero.[40] During the journey 19 magnetic stations were occupied and seismic soundings were made at 80 points.

Pulling heavy loads, traveling almost constantly in low gear, slamming over rough sastrugi or crunching through a four-inch crust of snow, it is not surprising that the tractors broke down frequently. Eight times during the journey the engine pans had to be dropped to take up bearings or to make other repairs, often in temperatures well below zero, with only a blowtorch to keep the men warm.[41]

On November 14 the repairs and scientific work having been completed, the plateau party left the tractors at the camp beside the crevasse into which No. 3 had plunged and reconnoitered ahead on skis, looking in vain for a safe passage. On November 16 the tractors were started and a retreat northward was begun. They were soon halted, however, by a radio message from Little America II informing the party that a plane was flying out to aid them in finding a safe route. At 9:55 p. m., June, Bowlin, Rawson, Bailey, and Pelter flew over in the *William Horlick*. The perilous situation of the tractors and the impossibility of their getting across the crevassed belt was readily apparent to the plane crew. First they sought a line of retreat for the tractors, which surprisingly had penetrated six miles into the crevassed belt. Then a practical route to the Rockefeller Plateau was explored and the information radioed to Little America II and to Waite, who was also tuned in.

After sitting through a day-long blizzard, the plateau party finally got the tractors under way on the evening of November 17. They retraced their tracks northwestward for 28.7 miles to a beacon they had built at 81°01′ S, 159°45′ W. Reaching the beacon shortly after midnight, they headed the tractors northeastward. After 40 miles on this course, a burned out bearing in tractor No. 2 forced a halt at about 80°37′ S, 157°11′ W. Early on November 21 the tractors were under way again, continuing northeasterly for another 16 miles before heading straight east toward the Rockefeller Plateau, 100 miles distant. On November 23 they camped at about 80°27′ S, 149°04′ W, about 20 miles from the edge of the plateau. This was the day on which the fifth major exploratory flight was being made. On the way out a pair of connecting rods were parachuted to the plateau party. That evening, on their return flight, Admiral Byrd and the flight party landed beside the tractors. Morgan, Bramhall, and Hill were taken aloft in search of a safe route for the tractors up onto the Rockefeller Plateau. Although crevasses marked the lower slopes along the margin of the plateau, what appeared to be a satisfactory place for an ascent was found some miles to the north. The party was camped at a point where the margin of the plateau forms a broad embayment so that north of the camp the border of the plateau has a northwest-southeast trend. A northward course would therefore bring the tractors up onto the plateau on the north side of the embayment.

After bad weather forced the party to remain in camp for three more days, they set out northwestward and then northward toward the proposed route onto the plateau. After 40 miles on this northward course they found themselves in a crevassed belt at the foot of the plateau border. Here on November 28, fog and mists forced them to camp, for they dared not venture blindly through such terrain. A reconnaissance on skis showed an easterly course to be impossible, but a continued northerly direction seemed feasible. On December 1 they threaded their way northward through the crevasses, and crawling over a series of rolling terraces and hills they climbed more than 1600 feet in 11 miles. After a run of 28 miles, the aneroid barometer began to show a declining elevation, and they camped in about 79° 17′ S, 149° 00′ W. For the next several days, often with bad visibility, the party probed its way northward through badly crevassed areas. Late on December 11, at about 79° 00′ S, 150° 24′ W, tractor No. 2 had to be abandoned when it rammed a connecting rod through the crankcase as it was being run at full speed across the thin snow bridge of a treacherous crevasse. All its useable parts were salvaged and piled on the sledges of tractor No. 3.

From this point conditions improved, and by December 14 the party, now traveling with one tractor, reached elevations of over 2700 feet above sea level where they camped at 78° 33′ S, 150° 29′ W. They were now certainly on top of the Rockefeller Plateau. Morgan calculated from results of his geophysical work here and at other places on the plateau that the glacial ice was from 1000 to 2000 feet thick. Where the surface elevations vary from 2000 to 3000 feet above sea level it is obvious that the greater part of the height of the plateau, at least in this sector, is due to ice.[42]

On December 16 the plateau party reached 150-mile depot on the eastern trail, where they met Siple's party. After completing magnetic and seismic investigations, they left the next day for Little America II, but about 15 miles west of 150-mile depot their tractor broke down. In response to a radio message asking for spare parts, Ronne and Black, when flying weather failed to materialize, were dispatched with a dog team on December 20. Ten days later they reached the stalled tractor. On December 31 the tractor was running again, and at 4:30 a. m., January 2, 1935, it arrived at Little America II in wretched mechanical condition after a grueling 815-mile journey. Meanwhile Morgan, with Black and Ronne, had left the tractor party for a side trip to the Rockefeller Mountains. Here, on top of Mount Nilsen, Morgan found mica schist, indicating that the granite which makes up most of the mountains of this group was actually intruded into previously existing metamorphics.[43] On January 6 Morgan, Ronne, and Black arrived at Little America II.

EXPLORATORY FLIGHTS

While the several parties were on long journeys afield, Admiral Byrd and the aviation group were carrying out the program of aerial exploration. The quickening tempo of affairs at Little America II toward the end of August included getting the aircraft ready for the flying season, beginning about November 1. The autogyro was dug out first, on August 29, for the meteorologists' atmospheric sounding flights. The Pilgrim was brought out next, on September 12. The task of shoveling out the planes was made more difficult by the continuing low temperatures, mostly below $-30°$ F, and sometimes dipping below $-50°$ F and $-60°$ F. A blizzard interrupted the job of digging out the big Condor, but it was finally dragged to the surface on September 22. Some time later the Fairchild, buried since 1930, was dug out. The autogyro went into service on September 1, but several weeks were required to overhaul the engines and recondition the other planes, especially the *William Horlick,* which had suffered damage to its fabric. A test flight was made on the big plane on October 26.

With everything in readiness at the beginning of November, the flying crew became impatient for good weather, so as to begin the flying program. On November 2 a short photographic flight was made over Little America, but it was not until November 15 that the meteorologists were satisfied with the weather. At 5:49 that morning Smith and Zuhn took off in the Pilgrim which had been specially prepared for a flight for 3 hours at an altitude of 12,000 feet, where the intensity of cosmic rays was 15 times greater than at the surface at Little America II. Smith landed the plane at 10:01 a. m.

Meanwhile emergency gear and rations were being loaded into the big Condor, *William Horlick,* for an exploratory flight. The crew consisted of June (chief pilot), Bowlin (copilot), Bailey (radio operator), Rawson (navigator), Pelter (aerial cameraman), and Admiral Byrd. The plane took off at 10:58 a. m., and three minutes later squared away on a course to the southeast to close the gap of unexplored land between Supporting Party Mountain, at the base of the Queen Maud Mountains, and the eastern trail between Little America II and the Ford Ranges. Three belts of crevasses were crossed, the first two trending at right angles to the flight track. The third belt formed a great horseshoe curve with west and northwest limbs. Over each belt the plane flew low, the altimeter indicating an elevation of 400 feet each time. The ice surface was 100 feet lower.[44] In all directions the snow-covered surface of the Ross Ice Shelf seemed to have comparable elevation.

A short distance beyond the horseshoe-shaped belt of crevasses, at about 81° 05' S, 146°30' W, and 275 miles from Little America, the plane was turned toward McKinley Peak to begin the second leg of a great triangular flight. As the flight continued northward the surface seemed to rise as the plane flew over the border of the Rockefeller Plateau which here has a northwest-southeast trend. Dropping low over the surface and using the altimeter as a sounding device, between 78° and 79° S, they determined the elevation of the snow surface to be 1975 feet. Farther north the process was repeated. This time the surface elevation was estimated to be 3200 feet. As McKinley Peak and the Ford Ranges came into view Bowlin climbed to 10,000 feet. Now it was apparent to Admiral Byrd that the Ford Ranges really were a series of east-west ranges and not, as he had thought in 1929 when he flew over Sulzberger Bay, a north-south range.[45] South of the range, the Rockefeller Plateau extended beyond the horizon to the east and south. They passed McKinley Peak on the east, and at 4:30 p. m., at about 77°30' S, 146°30' W, close by the Haines Mountains, the plane was headed westsouthwest for Little America II. This was over familiar territory. A jog to the south placed them over the Rockefeller Mountains, where they discovered the wreck of the Fokker plane, abandoned there in 1929. At 5:50 p. m. the plane landed at Little America II after a flight of 6 hours and 43 minutes for a distance of 777 miles.

The weather continued good, and the *William Horlick* took off again at 7:30 p. m., November 16. The crew remained the same, except that Admiral Byrd did not go on this flight. A major objective was to assist the plateau party to find a safe route up onto the Rockefeller Plateau. The plane first was flown south along the 164th meridian to 159-mile beacon and then along the southern trail to beyond the crevassed belt. Then, as described earlier, the plane crew explored for a practical route for the tractors of the plateau party. When this had been accomplished the plane was headed south along the 151st meridian. By midnight they reached 81°20′ S, 151° W. Clouds forming to the south and a rising gale forced them to turn the plane at this point and head for Little America II, where a landing was made shortly after 2 a. m., November 17. As a result of this flight it was now possible to plot on the map a belt of crevasses stretching across the Ross Ice Shelf south of the 81st parallel from 140° E to 175° E.[46]

November 18 at Little America proved to be another fine day for flying and reports from all the field parties were also favorable. A checkup on the engines of the *William Horlick* had been started the previous day. This was now rushed to completion and the plane was made ready for a flight to the east over the Ford Ranges. At 2:37 p. m. she took off with June at the controls, accompanied by Bowlin, Rawson, Pelter, and Petersen, who replaced Bailey as radio operator. Admiral Byrd remained at Little America II where he followed the progress of the flight on radio, the plane being in continuous contact with the base. Over the Rockefeller Mountains at 10,000 feet, June flew a circular course to permit Pelter to photograph the entire 360° of the horizon. At 4:56 p. m. the plane was flying over McKinley Peak at 10,000 feet. Here another photographic circle was completed, and the plane headed eastward over unexplored territory. Again the east-west trend of the Ford Ranges was apparent. At 6:40 the plane was abeam of MacKay Mountains, a massif in the Ford Ranges which Admiral Byrd had seen with the aid of binoculars on the flight of November 15. Here a third photographic circle was flown. Far to the north the plane crew detected the appearance of water sky but did not see the coast. Then jogging southward, the flight was continued on an easterly course along the 78th parallel. As the flight continued, two prominent mountain peaks stood out, one on the distant northern horizon and the other straight ahead. The distant peak was later identified as the main peak of the Flood Range by the U. S. Antarctic Service Expedition; the latter was named Mount Sidley. About 69 miles from Mount Sidley, on a course that would have brought the plane close by the mountain, threatening weather at 7 p. m. caused June to turn around at an estimated position of 78°00′ S, 135° W and head for Little America II. After making the turn they dropped down to skim the plateau-like surface which seemed an endless expanse of level to rolling snow. The corrected altimeter reading gave an elevation of 4486 feet.[47] Racing the approaching cloud banks, the plane landed at Little America at 10:32 p. m., after a flight of 7 hours and 36 minutes.

After hearing from the geological party on November 19 and 21 of the highland which they had sighted to the east of 350-mile depot and of the crevasses between it and the 375-mile depot, Admiral Byrd became eager to make a flight to the southeast to investigate this area, which had a direct bearing on the presence or absence of a possible strait between the Weddell and Ross Seas. Favorable weather, however, was not forthcoming until the night of November 21, and even then Haines was afraid it would not last long.

June, Smith, Bailey, Pelter, and Rawson took off in the *William Horlick* at 12:10 a. m., November 22. At Little America II Dyer kept almost continuous radio contact with the plane as it flew out over the Ross Ice Shelf on a southeasterly course between the flight tracks of November 15 and 16. At 1 p. m. the plane was 56 miles southeast of Little America on a course 141° true. This was changed to 126° at 2:55 when the plane was 267 miles from Little America II at 81°10′ S, 152°30′ W. Using the altimeter as a sounding device, June skimmed the surface to determine the elevation in this vicinity, which was later calculated to be 1370 feet. At 3:40 the plane was at 81°42′ S, 146°15′ W and the surface, which was steadily rising, was found to be 1840 feet above sea level. From the plane the crew looked out over a great white expanse unmarked by a topographic feature anywhere on the horizon. The altitude varied somewhat, for at 4:35 a. m., shortly before the plane reached 82°19′ S, 138°20′ W, the level of the surface declined to 1760 feet above sea level. At 5:30 the course was changed to 104° true. Ten minutes later, again skimming the surface, the elevation was found to be 2480 feet. At 5:45 the plane's position was 82°52′ S, 125°15′ W.[48]

Just as the plane reached the limit of the outward flight, which was determined by the amount of gasoline remaining in the tanks, Smith, now at the controls, noted on the distant horizon a group of snow-covered mountains — too distant to be photographed. Holding the plane on course long enough to confirm with binoculars the reality of the distant mountains, the plane was wheeled about at 6:05 a. m., in about 83°05′ S, 119° W. At this point, 552 miles from Little America, calculations based on an altimeter sounding showed the elevation of the surface to be 2810 feet. The distant mountains were estimated to be in the vicinity of 85°30′ S, between 110° and 115° W.[49]

As the plane was returning to Little America II, low clouds and ground fog obscured the surface and hid the tractors of the plateau party. The plane reached Little America II and landed at 11:09 a. m., a half hour before the weather closed in.

As a result of this flight, the existence of a strait between the Ross and Weddell Seas now seemed doubtful, insofar as surface expression was concerned. Moreover, the eastern boundary of the Ross Ice Shelf was determined at still another point. The distant mountains that the flight crew had seen at the turning point of the flight, probably an eastern continuation of the Queen Maud Mountains, Admiral Byrd named the Horlick Mountains.

The overcast weather soon changed for the better and the next day, November 23, the meteorologists again gave approval for a flight. The plane, with June, Bowlin, Rawson, Petersen, and Admiral Byrd aboard, took off at 5:16 p. m., again toward the southeast, dropping low over Roosevelt Island for altimeter soundings of 1070 feet and 1237 feet, respectively. A third sounding on the shelf ice farther south gave an elevation of only 275 feet. Altering course, they headed for the plateau party now moving eastward toward the Rockefeller Plateau and dropped a pair of connecting rods to them. They then flew south southeast toward the great horseshoe-shaped belt of crevasses, seen on November 15, to determine the extent of the large reentrant in the Rockefeller Plateau at this point. Over the crevassed belt the elevation was determined to be 771 feet. Heading eastward at latitude 81°10′ S for 60 miles, the crew sounded with the altimeter three times, getting elevations of 1105, 1204 and 1338 feet.[50] Then, with land rising to the eastward, the plane was headed north for 16 miles. At that point the surface elevation was 1591 feet. Turning westward, three more soundings of 1138, 1085, and 669 feet, in that order, seemed to eliminate the possibility of a strait at this position and further delineated the eastern margin of the Ross Ice Shelf.[51] At 9:55 the plane landed and took Bramhall, Morgan, and Hill aloft in search of a tractor route up onto the Rockefeller Plateau. At 10:49 the plane crew took off for Little America II, where they landed 2 hours later.

Wind, fog, snow, and overcast weather associated with the warmer temperatures of approaching summer prevented any long-distance flying for several weeks. During this time the *William Horlick* was given a complete overhaul in preparation for the last long flight, a penetration along the coast of Marie Byrd Land to the northeast. The first break came late on December 7, and the plane crew took off from Little America at 2:37 a. m., December 8. Fifteen minutes later, however, the weather closed in, and Haines radioed that they should return. That afternoon the weather cleared enough to permit June to fly 150 gallons of tractor gasoline to 120-mile depot on the eastern trail.

On December 15 weather conditions improved and the situation looked promising to the meteorologists. Consequently a flight was scheduled and at 7:27 p. m. June, Bowlin, Rawson, Petersen, and Pelter took off in the *William Horlick*. Flying just south of the seaward edge of the Ross Ice Shelf, Rawson set a course across Edward VII Peninsula, passing over Scott Nunataks at 9:15 at an elevation of 6000 feet. Here June flew a photographic circle, and then set the course at 52° true, to bring them about 30 miles north of Balchen Glacier. The northern margin of the bay ice in Sulzberger Bay had begun to break up, but most of the bay was still frozen over. The ice shelf in the upper part of the bay was much disturbed by pressure. At 10:40 p. m. the plane was at 76°08′ S, 148°45′ W, flying at 14,500 feet. They were above the clouds which extended everywhere to the eastward and southward. The surface of the earth was visible only occasionally through breaks in the cloud bank, but the clouds hung too low over the land to permit the plane to fly beneath them. At 11:35 the position of the plane was 75°22′ S, 144°30′ W. Here heavy clouds ahead forced June to turn and head back on a course of 222°.[52] At this point they were 360 miles northeast of Little America II, about 45 miles beyond the point reached by Admiral Byrd, June, Parker, and McKinley in a flight on December 5, 1929. The course was soon altered so as to fly south along the western ends of the Ford Ranges. Flying over the eastern part of Sulzberger Bay, they were able to get down under the clouds which hung over the peaks. From this level Pelter was able to photograph the mountains. The plane rose up over the Haines Mountains, and over McKinley Peak a photographic circle was flown. The crew then headed the plane for Little America, where they landed at 3:21 a. m., December 16.

The flight of December 15 ended the long-range aerial exploration. Although the aviation group stood by for another attempt, the weather was never satisfactory for a long flight except on December 31, and on that date the plane was turned back by a wall of clouds before it reached the Ford Ranges. Meanwhile, the planes made short photographic flights, mostly in the vicinity of the Bay of Whales, and flew Dr. Poulter's party and equipment to the more distant seismic stations on the Ross Ice Shelf. The Fairchild of the First Byrd Expedition having been reconditioned, Schlossbach test flew it on December 12, and on January 1, 1935, Smith flew it on a successful photographic mission over the Rockefeller Mountains.

GEOPHYSICAL STUDIES OF THE ROSS ICE SHELF

While the far-ranging flights were pushing back the margin of the unknown and while the trail parties were filling in details, a less spectacular but equally important activity was going on in the vicinity of the Bay of Whales. Here Dr. Thomas C. Poulter was carrying out his geophysical investigation of the Ross Ice Shelf, a project which proved to be one of the major accomplishments of the Second Byrd Antarctic Expedition.[53]

Up to 1934 any theories or conclusions relating to the nature of the Ross Ice Shelf were based on direct surface observation and estimates deduced therefrom. Dr. Reginald A. Daly and the Harvard Committee on Geophysical Research suggested that quantitative data on the thickness of the ice shelf, the extent to which it is aground, and the depth of the water beneath that part which is afloat could be obtained by the application of methods used in geophysical exploration for petroleum. For this purpose seismograph equipment was designed light enough and compact enough to be transported by dog sledge and sensitive enough to obtain good reflections from relatively small charges of TNT or Trojan powder.[54]

Dr. Poulter and his assistant, Richard B. Black, worked out an efficient method of field operations using two dog sledges in tandem. The first carried explosives, navigational instruments, radio, and camping equipment. On the rear of the second sledge was attached the seismograph instrument with four geophones and a reel carrying five cables. The augers for drilling the holes for the explosives could be fastened together to serve as a skeleton framework to which runners were fixed to form additional sleds. With explosives and caps for several stations and a shooting battery fastened to these auger-sleds, they were trailed behind the instrument sledge. The total weight of the outfit, including the instruments, explosives for 25 stations, food for men and dogs, camping equipment, and two sledges totaled 950 pounds.[55]

The excellence of the design of the field rig and the efficiency of the method of operation can be judged by the fact that the normal crew of four men could occupy a station, make four shots, and be ready to move in as little as 15 minutes. Rarely did the operations take more than 30 minutes. From 10 to 30 nautical miles were covered in a day, and as many as 12 stations would be occupied.[56] In addition to Dr. Poulter and Black, the seismograph crew was variously made up of Finn Ronne, Bernard Fleming, Albert Eilefsen, and E. L. Moody.

Beginning in mid-October 1934, after the various field parties had left Little America II, about six weeks were spent in experimenting with the seismographic equipment in the vicinity of the base camp. By November 27 Dr. Poulter and his assistants had made 78 test shots and were ready for more distant journeys. Preliminary tests showed that it was not necessary to develop the photographic records of the seismograph at each station, and that satisfactory results could be obtained by carrying the film in a magazine to be developed after returning to camp. This saved a great deal of time on the trail and it afforded better working conditions. As often as possible the crew returned at the end of each day to Little America II, but distance and bad weather sometimes prevented this convenience. The first line of stations was run on November 29, and the work continued daily until January 18 except when bad weather held the crew in camp. Exclusive of preliminary testing, 73 stations were occupied in the vicinity of the Bay of Whales and south beyond Amundsen Arm. A line of eight stations was run southeast from Amundsen Arm to the northwestern edge of Roosevelt Island at an elevation of 710 feet. Six more stations were placed east of Amundsen Arm within the heavily crevassed area.[57]

At the close of the season for aerial exploration, the *William Horlick* flew the seismographic crew and equipment to a series of seven stations forming an arc around the Bay of Whales on a radius of approximately 30 miles (35 statute miles) from Little America II. The first was on the west side of Kainan Bay. Two stations were occupied southeast of Little America on the northwestern corner of the large dome in the surface of the ice shelf, which was subsequently found to be ice-drowned Roosevelt Island. The surface elevation at one of the stations was 1400 feet. Another station was located on the trail to the south near the 25-mile depot, and the arc was completed southeast of the head of Lindbergh Inlet. On one flight a station was occupied at Bolling Advance Base and a landing was made to locate a station about 75 miles south of Little America. On another flight a station was occupied just south of Discovery Inlet. While the use of the plane did not permit as close a network of stations as was possible by dog team, the much greater range that was possible in a shorter time was a compensation.

The geophysical work was completed in January when a line of stations was occupied by dog team from the mouth of the Bay of Whales westward to Discovery Inlet. Here on January 18, the *Bear of Oakland,* by prearrangement, called on its return from New Zealand to pick up the geophysical crew and take the men back to the Bay of Whales. During the survey the crew had traveled a distance of 2000 miles, half of it on skis with dog teams. Good records were obtained for over 95 percent of the 122 stations occupied. For plotting the stations a detailed map was constructed from aerial photographs controlled by a triangulation of all existing markers from the survey made by the First Byrd Expedition.[58] As a result, quantitative data were available for about 5000 square miles of the Ross Ice Shelf.

Only the more significant facts revealed by the geophysical exploration and the conclusions based thereon can be summarized here. One of the most important discoveries, geographically speaking, was the existence of an ice-drowned island, subsequently named Roosevelt Island, underlying the high snow area southeast of the Bay of Whales where surface elevations of 1400 feet were recorded. This island, which rises to an elevation of 850 feet above sea level, is approximately 90 miles long and 40 miles wide, and is covered by over 500 feet of ice. The greater part of the ice shelf east of 164° W, from 10 miles north of Roosevelt Island to 80° S (the southern limit of the area of geophysical investigation), is grounded below sea level all the way to the Rockefeller Plateau. It is also grounded below sea level south of Discovery Inlet, probably over a considerable area. From Kainan Bay to Discovery Inlet the ice shelf is floating for a distance of at least 10 miles to the south.[59]

A current up to one knot moving across the Ross Sea from east to west passes under the floating margin of the Ross Ice Shelf, entering at Kainan Bay and emerging at Discovery Inlet. At the Bay of Whales this current follows a trough over 2000 feet deep. This current, Dr. Poulter believed, melts the denser, drift-bearing, glacial ice at the bottom of the ice shelf, accounting for the fact that glacial drift was not seen at any point along the front of the ice shelf nor embedded in the bottom ice of overturned bergs. The drift thus freed by melting accumulates as morainic material on the seaward slope immediately north of the edge of the grounded ice shelf. As this moraine accumulates, it is prevented by overriding ice from rising above the common level at which the ice is grounded — here about 500 feet below sea level. At the same time, this process slowly extends the area of grounded ice northward. The presence of the moraine prevents action of the sea from breaking up the ice shelf beyond it to the south.

Although exact measurement of snow accumulation for limited periods is made almost impossible by the great amount of drifting on the surface of the ice shelf, evidence indicates that the greatest amount of accumulation takes place a short distance inland from the edge of the ice. The average thickness of the ice at the floating edge of the ice shelf east of Discovery Inlet is 525 feet, while at a point from one to three miles south of the edge it averaged 755 feet. For another 10 miles south the ice gradually thins to less than 500 feet in some places, but south of this zone it again increases in thickness to about 700 feet.

Aerial photographs revealed a series of tidal cracks parallel to the ice front between the Bay of Whales and Discovery Inlet. Each of the lateral inlets bordering the Bay of Whales was found to correspond with the position of one of these tidal cracks. Motion along the cracks near the Bay of Whales was noticeable, and it apparently continues as long as part of the ice is aground at either end. Once adjoining segments are free floating, freezing of the water in the crack at sea level prevents movement, and drifting snow bridges the crack at the surface. The crack remains as a zone of weakness, however, and as the ice moves forward segments of the floating shelf break off along these lines to form the great flat-topped icebergs, tens of miles in length.

A resurvey in 1934 of the 1929 triangulation carried out in the vicinity of the Bay of Whales showed that the portion of the ice shelf east of the bay was moving westward while that west of the bay was moving northward, the latter at a rate of 6.6 feet per day.[60] Consequently the bay was, in the 1930s, becoming narrower and the bay ice being folded into pressure ridges. In recent years the bay has been obliterated, and a large bite in the ice shelf has replaced it. Dr. Poulter estimated that the ice shelf between the Bay of Whales and Discovery Inlet was moving northward at the remarkable rate of more than 12 feet a day.

CLOSING THE EXPEDITION

As the year 1935 dawned at Little America II, the program of the Second Byrd Antarctic Expedition was rapidly drawing to a close. The last major exploratory flight had been completed on December 15. An attempt at a second flight over the coast of Marie Byrd Land on December 31 had been turned back by heavy clouds. Siple's Marie Byrd Land party had returned on December 29 and the other field parties were approaching Little America II. When the geological party arrived on January 11, only Dr. Poulter's crew remained in the field, and they continued to work until picked up by the *Bear* at Discovery Inlet. The meteorological and magnetic observations were continued to the very last, but the biologists, while squeezing in every opportunity for additional work, were beginning to pack their specimens and notes.

All supplies, equipment, and stores that could be salvaged were sorted and packed for return to the United States. Citroën No. 1 had been overhauled after its return from the winter journey to Advance Base, and on January 5 Demas, Boyd, Skinner, Tinglof, and Wade set off with the tractor to salvage the shack at Advance Base and to bring back the Cletrac for use in embarkation. Ten days later the quintet was back at Little America II, having accomplished their mission, and, for good measure, they brought back the snowmobile that had been abandoned in 1929.

During their winter sojourn in New Zealand both the *Bear of Oakland* and the *Jacob Ruppert* had been reconditioned. Heavily loaded with coal, the *Bear* put out from Dunedin on the afternoon of January 2. Aboard were Charles F. Anderson, U. S. Postal Inspector, to handle the cancellation of mail at Little America, and Glenn H. Bryan of the Seismograph Service Corporation who was coming out to check on the seismic sounding methods employed by Dr. Poulter and Morgan. During the first part of the voyage the *Bear* was buffeted by heavy squalls with rainy overcast weather. On January 9 the ship was hove to in a very strong gale south of 61°30′ S. On January 12 Scott Island was sighted.

As the *Bear* moved south along the 180th meridian and then to the west toward Ross Island, very little ice was encountered. The sea was surprisingly open. Late on January 17 the *Bear* was cruising along the north shore of Ross Island. From Cape Crozier to the Bay of Whales, Lieutenant English sailed close to the edge of the Ross Ice Shelf, which he carefully surveyed. The survey showed that a general advance of about 12 miles had been made since Pennell had made a similar survey in the *Terra Nova* in 1911. The contour of the ice cliffs, their height, and irregularities in the front of the ice shelf were not materially changed.[61] During the cruise southward through the Ross Sea and then eastward along the edge of the ice shelf, Roos ran a line of sonic soundings to obtain a submarine profile, and 12 hydrographic stations were occupied en route. On the afternoon of January 18, the *Bear* entered Discovery Inlet, where the seismograph crew came aboard. The next morning, shortly after 10 o'clock, she hove to in the Bay of Whales.

The *Ruppert* sailed from Port Chalmers late on January 16 and, except for some fog and drizzle, had a favorable passage to the Ross Sea. Here Commodore Gjertsen set a course down the 177th meridian, but on January 22 the belt of pack ice forced a westerly detour, after which he was untroubled by ice although some patches of pack ice and numerous bergs were seen. On January 25 and 26 an easterly gale brought snow and high seas. On the morning of January 27, with the seas still rough, the *Ruppert* slid into the Bay of Whales.

Loading operations began soon after the arrival of the *Bear*. The pressure ice in the Bay of Whales was as bad as it had been a year earlier. It was decided, therefore, that the tractors would haul the material to be put on board as far as the head of Eleanor Bolling Bight, north of Little America on the east side of the Bay of Whales. From here the dog teams would ferry the material down onto the bay ice beside the ship. Finally the bay ice broke out beyond Eleanor Bolling Bight, and it was necessary to work the *Bear* up against the edge of the ice shelf in the bight. Such a position was too dangerous for the thin plates of the *Ruppert*. Therefore, with decks piled high, the *Bear* ferried the cargo out to the *Ruppert,* hove to in the Bay of Whales. This process continued until only the heavy tractors and the aircraft remained on the ice. Since these were too heavy for the tackle of the *Bear,* it was necessary to move the *Ruppert* into the bight long enough to take on these items. Shortly before midnight February 3, the *Ruppert* moved into the bight. The sea was calm, but pack ice moving up the bay across the mouth of the bight threatened to trap the vessel. Consequently, before the tractors could be taken aboard, she was forced to cast off and move out into the bay about 6 p. m., February 4. The *Bear* moved in to clean up the job, but the Cletrac, Citroën No. 2, two snowmobiles, and a small amount of miscellaneous material had to be left behind as the two vessels steamed out of the Bay of Whales on the afternoon of February 5, 1935. On board, en route to the Ford Museum in Dearborn, was the plane in which Byrd had flown to the Pole in 1929.

Both ships hove to at Discovery Inlet to pick up additional penguins destined for American zoos. On February 7 the two vessels put out in company for Dunedin but the slower *Bear*, whose progress was retarded by the oceanographic investigations, soon fell astern the flagship. Finally, on the morning of February 20, the *Bear* docked at Dunedin. On May 10, 1935, she arrived at Washington, followed by the *Bear,* for an official welcome. Five days later the *Ruppert* docked at Boston.

NOTES

1. Richard E. Byrd, *Discovery* (New York, 1935), p. 16.

2. E. J. Demas, "Tractor Operations on the Second Byrd Antarctic Expedition," *Polar Record*, vol. 2, No. 12 (July, 1936), pp. 175-184.

3. Byrd, *op. cit.*, p. 18.

4. *Ibid*, p. 21.

5. S. Edward Roos, "The Submarine Topography of the Ross Sea and Adjacent Waters," *Geographical Review*, vol. 27, No. 4, October, 1937, p. 580.

6. Byrd, *op. cit.*, p. 110.

7. George Grimminger and William C. Haines, "Meteorological Results of the Byrd Antarctic Expeditions, 1928-30, 1933-35: Tables," *Monthly Weather Review*, supp. No. 41, 1939, p. 45.

8. *Ibid.*, p. 46.

9. *Ibid.* The position of Advance Base, 80°07'30" S, 163°55' W, as given on p. 7, differs from that reported by Byrd, *op. cit*, p. 167 (80°08' S, 163°57' W).

10. *Ibid.*, p. 5.

11. Thomas C. Poulter, "The Scientific Work of the Second Byrd Antarctic Expedition," *Scientific Monthly*, vol. 49, 1939, p. 17; and *Meteor Observations in the Antarctic, Byrd Antarctic Expedition II, 1933-1935*, Part I, Stanford Research Institute, Stanford, Calif., July 26, 1955, pp. 8-9.

12. Poulter, *Meteor Observations . . ., op. cit.*, pp. 17-19.

13. *Ibid.*, p. 16.

14. Byrd, *op. cit.*, p. 222n.

15. Paul A. Siple, *Scout to Explorer* (New York, 1936), p. 113.

16. Alton A. Lindsey, "Notes on the Crab-eater Seal," *Journal of Mammalogy*, vol. 19, 1938, p. 456.

17. Alton A. Lindsey, "The Weddell Seal in the Bay of Whales, Antarctica," *Journal of Mammalogy*, vol. 18, 1937, pp. 127-144.

18. Byrd, *op. cit.*, pp. 244-245, 260.

19. Grimminger and Haines, *op. cit.*, p. 47. The meteorological record kept on each field journey, including notes of the observer, serves as a valuable abstract log.

20. Siple, *op. cit.*, p. 161. Discovered by the First Byrd Antarctic Expedition on the flight of December 5, 1929, this mountain was then called Mount Grace McKinley.

21. F. Alton Wade, "Northeastern Borderlands of the Ross Sea: Glaciological Studies in King Edward VII Land and Northwestern Marie Byrd Land," *Geographical Review*, vol. 27, 1937, p. 597.

22. F. Alton Wade, "Petrologic and Structural Relations of the Edsel Ford Ranges, Marie Byrd Land, to other Antarctic Mountains," *Bulletin, Geological Society of America*, vol. 48, 1937, p. 1388.

23. *Ibid.*, pp. 1394-1395.

24. Paul A. Siple, "The Second Byrd Antarctic Expedition — Botany, I. Ecology and Geographical Distribution," *Annals of the Missouri Botanical Garden*, vol. 25, 1938, pp. 480-481.

25. *Ibid.*, p. 500.

26. Siple, *Scout to Explorer, op. cit.*, p. 193.

27. Byrd, *op. cit.*, p. 259.

28. Grimminger and Haines, *op. cit.*, Table 20, p. 51.

29. Quin A. Blackburn, "The Thorne Glacier Section of the Queen Maud Mountains," *Geographical Review*, vol. 27, 1937, p. 598.

30. Byrd, *op. cit.*, p. 308.

31. Blackburn, *op. cit.*, p. 600.

32. *Ibid.*, p. 601.

33. Siple, "The Second Byrd Antarctic Expedition . . .," *op. cit.*, p. 496.

34. Blackburn, *op. cit.*, pp. 611-612.

35. Grimminger and Haines, *op. cit.*, p. 53.

36. Byrd, *op. cit.*, p. 368.

37. Blackburn, *op. cit.*, pp. 609-610.

38. *Ibid.*, p. 613.

39. Byrd, *op. cit.*, p. 370.

40. Grimminger and Haines, *op. cit.*, Table 20, pp. 55-57. Temperatures were recorded 127 times, although not on every day of the journey. Of the recorded temperatures, 70 were below zero.

41. Byrd, *op. cit.*, p. 353.

42. C. G. Morgan, "The Geology of the South Polar Region," *Tulsa Geological Society Digest*, 1935, p. 60. Although over-snow traverses in the 1960s have not covered the same area, modern investigations support Morgan's conclusions. See C. R. Bentley and others, "Physical Characteristics of the Antarctic Ice Sheet," *Antarctic Map Folio Series*, American Geographical Society, Folio 2, 1964, plates 1, 2, and 3.

43. Byrd, *op. cit.*, p. 357; also C. G. Morgan, "Geology of the South Polar Region," *Tulsa Geological Society Digest*, 1935, p. 54.

44. Data regarding the exploratory flights are mainly from Byrd, *op. cit.* (pp. 281-334), or from Grimminger and Haines, *op cit.* The latter contains a meteorological log for each flight with times based on the 180° meridian (pp. 126-134). Except for the flight of November 15, the two sources agree, or the difference is only a matter of a few minutes, which could be due to interpretation of exactly when the flight began and ended, e. g., touchdown or end of taxi. On November 15, Grimminger and Haines report 180th meridian time, but Byrd gives times that are unaccountably 36 to 55 minutes faster. The *New York Times* account (November 18, 1934, p. 1), does not agree with either. Local sun time at Little America was 64 minutes faster than 180th meridian time. The *Times* account gives takeoff at 12:12 p. m. and landing at 7:12, reportedly for local sun time which it stated is one hour and 19 minutes faster than 180th meridian time. In this chapter, times reported by Grimminger and Haines are used for the flight of November 15; times reported by Byrd are used for all other flights.

45. *Ibid.*, p. 293.

46. *Ibid.*, p. 301.

47. *Ibid.*, p. 306. This and other elevations are corrected after correlation with barometric pressures at Little America II, but it should be remembered that elevations so obtained, even when corrections are made to take into account several variables, are only approximate. See Grimminger and Haines, *op cit.*, p. 127. They give a corrected elevation of 1345 meters which approximates elevations obtained in over-snow traverses in the region since 1956.

48. *Ibid.*, pp. 309-314. Grimminger and Haines, *op. cit.*, p. 128, give other figures for other positions.

49. *Ibid.*, p. 314.

50. *Ibid.*, p. 316.

51. *Ibid.*, p. 317.

52. *Ibid.*, p. 333. Grimminger and Haines, *op. cit.*, p. 131, give the A turning point as 75°43' S, 145°14' W.

53. Thomas C. Poulter, "Seismic Measurements on the Ross Shelf Ice," *Transactions of the American Geophysical Union*, vol. 28, No. 2, pp. 162-170, No. 3, pp. 367-384, 1947, and *Geophysical Studies in the Antarctic,* Stanford Research Institute (Stanford, Calif., 1950).

54. Poulter, "Seismic Measurements . . .," *op. cit.*, p. 162.

55. Poulter, *Geophysical Studies . . ., op. cit.*, pp. 8, 11.

56. *Ibid.*, p. 12.

57. Poulter, "Seismic Measurements . . .," *op. cit.*, Fig. 3, pp. 164-165, Fig. 5, pp. 370-371.

58. *Ibid.*, p. 168.

59. Poulter, *Geophysical Studies . . ., op. cit.*, pp. 104-105. All of the summary statement is based on Poulter. Investigations by A. P. Crary and others since 1957 show that most of the Ross Ice Shelf and other ice shelves in Antarctica are afloat. See Charles Swithinbank, and James H. Zumberge, "The Ice Shelves," *Antarctica* (Trevor Hatherton, ed.) (London, Methuen, 1965), pp. 199-217.

60. Poulter, "Seismic Measurements . . .," *op. cit.*, p. 374.

61. Comdr. Robert A. J. English, *Sailing Directions for Antarctica*, No. 138, U. S. Navy Hydrographic Office (Washington, 1943), p. 211.

BIBLIOGRAPHY

Published Material

Bartram, Edwin B., "The Second Byrd Antarctic Expedition — Botany, III. Mosses." *Annals of the Missouri Botanical Garden*, vol. 25, No. 2, April, 1938, pp. 719-724.

Blackburn, Quin A., "Some Geographical Results of the Second Byrd Antarctic Expedition, 1933-35, III. The Thorne Glacier Section of the Queen Maud Mountains," *Geographical Review*, vol. 27, No. 4, October, 1937, pp. 598-614.

Byrd, Richard E., *Alone* (New York, Putnams, 1938) xii, 296 pp.

——, *Discovery* (New York, Putnams, 1935) xiv, 405 pp., 2 maps. This is the official narrative of the expedition.

——, "Exploring the Ice Age in Antarctica," *National Geographic Magazine*, vol. 68, No. 4, October, 1935, pp. 399-474. This is a preliminary narrative of the expedition.

Compton, Arthur H., "Studies of Cosmic Rays," *Carnegie Institution Yearbook*, No. 32, 1933, p. 334; No. 33, 1934, p. 316.

Darling, Chester A., and Paul A. Siple, "Bacteria of Antarctica," *Journal of Bacteriology*, vol. 42, No. 1, July, 1941, pp. 83-98.

Demas, E. J., "Tractor Operations on the Second Byrd Antarctic Expedition," *Polar Record*, vol. 2, No. 12, July, 1936, pp. 175-184.

Dodge, Carroll W., and Gladys E. Baker, "The Second Byrd Antarctic Expedition, Botany II. Lichens and Lichen Parasites," *Annals of the Missouri Botanical Garden*, vol. 25, No. 2, April, 1938, pp. 515-718.

Fenner, Clarence N., "Olivine Fourchites from Raymond Fosdick Mountains, Antarctica," *Bulletin, Geological Society of America*, vol. 49, 1938, pp. 368-400.

Fleming, John A., "Antarctica and the Pacific, Annual Report of the Director of Terrestrial Magnetism," *Carnegie Institution Yearbook*, No. 34, 1935, pp. 248-249, 257.

Grimminger, George, "Preliminary Results of Pilot-balloon Ascents at Little America," *Monthly Weather Review*, vol. 67, No. 6, June, 1939, pp. 172-175.

——, "Meteorological Results of the Byrd Antarctic Expeditions, 1928-1930, 1933-35: Summaries of Data," *Monthly Weather Review*, supp. 42, February, 1941, vii, 106 pp.

——, and William C. Haines, "Meteorological Results of the Byrd Antarctic Expeditions, 1928-1930, 1933-35: Tables," *Monthly Weather Review*, supp. 41, October, 1939, iv, 377 pp.

Haines, William C., "Meteorological Observations in the Antarctic," *Bulletin, American Meteorological Society*, vol. 12, 1939, pp. 169-172.

Hill, Joe, Jr., and Ola Davis Hill, *In Little America with Byrd* (Boston, Ginn, 1937), 264 pp.

Lindsey, Alton A., "Biology and Biogeography of the Antarctic and Sub-Antarctic Pacific," *Quarterly Review of Biology* vol. 15, No. 4, December, 1940, pp. 456-465. Also published in *Proceedings of the Sixth Pacific Science Congress*, vol. 2, 1940, pp. 715-720.

——, "Notes on the Crab-eater Seal," *Journal of Mammalogy*, vol. 19, No. 4, November, 1938, pp. 456-461.

——, "The Weddell Seal in the Bay of Whales, Antarctica," *Journal of Mammalogy*, vol. 18, 1937, pp. 127-144.

Morgan, C. G., "The Geology of the South Polar Region," *Tulsa Geological Society Digest*, 1935, pp. 50-61.

Nichols, J. T., and F. R. La Monte, "Pagothenia, a New Antarctic Fish," *American Museum Novitates*, No. 839, April 10, 1936, 4 pp.

Perkins, Earle B., "Animal Life in the Antarctic," *Proceedings of the American Philosophical Society*, vol. 82, No. 5, June, 1940, pp. 833-834 (Abstract).

——, Biological Photography in Antarctica," *Journal of Biological Photographic Association*, vol. 7, 1938, pp. 49-53.

——, "Plankton and Invertebrates of the Antarctic," *Scientific Monthly*, vol. 43, 1936, pp. 568-574.

——, "Pond Life in the Antarctic," *Educational Focus*, June, 1936, pp. 6-9, 18-19.

Poulter, Thomas C., "Application of Seismic Methods in Discovery of New Lands in the Antarctic," *Armour Engineer and Alumnus*, March, 1937, reprinted in *Polar Times*, vol. 1, No. 7, October, 1938, pp. 6-7.

——, *Geophysical Studies in the Antarctic*, Report for U. S. Office of Naval Research, Contract No. N8-onr-526, Project No. NR-081-020, Stanford Research Institute (Stanford, Calif.), n.d. [1950], vii, 109 pp., plus separately paged and unpaged appendixes, illus., maps, tables, and diagrams.

——, "The Scientific Work of the Second Byrd Antarctic Expedition," *Scientific Monthly*, vol. 49, No. 1, July, 1939, pp. 5-20. Reproduced as a facsimile in his Report in *Geophysical Studies*, above.

——, "Seismic Measurements on the Ross Ice Shelf," *Transactions, American Geophysical Union*, vol. 28, No. 2, April, 1947, pp. 162-170; No. 3, June, 1947, pp. 367-384. Reproduced almost verbatim in his Report in *Geophysical Studies*, above.

——, *Meteor Observations in the Antarctic, Byrd Antarctic Expedition II, 1933-1935*, Part 1, Stanford Research Institute (Stanford, Calif.), 1955, 49 pp.

Roos, S. Edward, "Some Geographical Results of the Second Byrd Antarctic Expedition, 1933-1935, I. The Submarine Topography of the Ross Sea and Adjacent Waters," *Geographical Review*, vol. 27. No. 4, October, 1937, pp. 574-583.

Siple, Paul A., *Scout to Explorer* (New York, Putnams, 1936), xiv, 239 pp., map. General narrative with emphasis on the author's personal experiences.

——, "The Second Byrd Antarctic Expedition — Botany I. Ecology and Geographical Distribution," *Annals of the Missouri Botanical Garden,* vol. 25, No. 2, April, 1938, pp. 467-514.

——, and Alton A. Lindsey, "Ornithology of the Second Byrd Antarctic Expedition," *Auk,* vol. 54, No. 2, 1937, pp. 147-159. Also reprinted in the *Polar Times,* vol. 1, No. 6, March, 1938, pp. 1-5.

Stetson, H. C., and J. E. Upson, "Bottom Deposits of the Ross Sea," *Journal of Sedimentary Petrology,* vol. 7, No. 1, 1937, pp. 55-66.

Stewart, Duncan, Jr., "Notes on Some Marie Byrd Land Rocks," *American Mineralogist,* vol. 26, 1941, pp. 42-49.

——, "The Petrography of Some Instrusive Rocks From King Edward VII and Marie Byrd Lands," *Proceedings of American Philosophical Society,* vol. 89, No. 1, April, 1945, pp. 148-151.

Wade, F. Alton, "Some Geographical Results of the Second Byrd Antarctic Expedition, 1933-1935, II. Northeastern Borderlands of the Ross Sea: Glaciological Studies in King Edward VII Land and Northwestern Marie Byrd Land," *Geographical Review,* vol. 27, No. 4, October, 1937, pp. 584-597.

——, "Petrologic and Structural Relations of the Edsel Ford Ranges, Marie Byrd Land, to other Antarctic Mountains," *Bulletin, Geological Society of America,* vol. 48, No. 10, October, 1937, pp. 1387-1396.

MANUSCRIPT MATERIAL

Siple, Paul A., "Adaptation of the Explorer to the Climate of Antarctica," parts I-III of Ph. D. dissertation, Clark University Library, Worcester, Mass., 1939.

Wade, F. Alton, "Some Contributions to the Geography, Geology and Glaciology of Antarctica," Ph. D. dissertation, Johns Hopkins University, Baltimore, Md., not dated.

19

ELLSWORTH'S TRANSANTARCTIC FLIGHT, 1935

ORGANIZATION AND ACCOMPLISHMENTS

SIGNIFICANCE OF THE FLIGHT

On three successive years Lincoln Ellsworth organized and led expeditions to Antarctica with the intention of making an airplane flight across the continent. Thwarted by damage to his plane on the first expedition, and prevented by bad weather from making his flight on the second, he accomplished his objective on the third. With Herbert Hollick-Kenyon as pilot, he took off from Dundee Island at the tip of the Antarctic Peninsula on November 23, 1935. On December 5 they landed, their gasoline supply exhausted, on the Ross Ice Shelf approximately 16 miles from Little America. With four stops en route, they had completed the first transantarctic flight in history. Covering 2200 miles in approximately 20 hours, this was the longest flight and the only transcontinental flight in Antarctic history until January 1956.[1]

This was an extremely daring undertaking because there was no intention of returning to the point of departure. No other plane was available for a quick rescue in the event of a forced landing, and no dog teams or tractors were available for an overland rescue mission. If the men survived a crash landing, there was no alternative to an overland march of up to 1000 miles, dragging camping equipment on a man-hauling sledge. On such an inland trek they could not depend on penguins or seals for food to supplement their emergency rations. That the flight was successful was the result of a combination of a good plane, an excellent pilot, excellent navigation, exceptional courage, and a great deal of good fortune.

ESTABLISHMENT OF THE PROJECT

Lincoln Ellsworth began serious consideration of an Antarctic expedition in 1930. He had gained fame from his Arctic flights with Roald Amundsen. In 1925 the two had been forced down short of the North Pole on a projected flight across the pole from Kings Bay, Svalbard, to Alaska in two Dornier-Wal flying boats. In June of the following year they made the flight successfully in the dirigible *Norge*. In June 1930 Ellsworth met Sir Hubert Wilkins, just returned from his second Wilkins-Hearst Expedition. Byrd had just concluded his first Antarctic Expedition, and Riiser-Larsen, who had accompanied Ellsworth and Amundsen on the two Arctic flights, had also completed a successful campaign of aerial exploration in the Antarctic that spring. In July 1930, Ellsworth's intention of leading an expedition to the Antarctic was further motivated by his acceptance of an invitation to serve as navigation expert on the *Graf Zeppelin* in a flight over the Siberian Arctic.[2]

Later in 1930 Ellsworth and Wilkins met in New York and discussed plans for an Antarctic expedition. Ellsworth was interested in penetrating into the interior of the continent between the Weddell and the Ross Seas, particularly to determine whether or not there was any connection between the mountains of the Antarctic Peninsula and the Queen Maud Mountains. He first considered the use of a base ship with a catapult mechanism for launching seaplanes. A number of flights could then be made into the interior from the ship, which would cruise along the coast. Wilkins was to assume responsibility for the ship and any base that might be used. Bernt Balchen was approached by Ellsworth and agreed to be chief pilot. However, he counseled against the use of a catapult ship as being too risky, but agreed to an alternative plan of a nonstop flight from Byrd's old base at Little America to the head of Weddell Sea and return. This was later changed to a plan whereby the plane would land at intervals to wait out bad weather and to determine geographical fixes by celestial observation. Wilkins was made technical adviser and manager. The entire expedition was financed by Ellsworth. He signed a contract for newspaper rights with the *New York Times* and the North American Newspaper Alliance, and received a grant-in-aid from the National Geographic Society. In the summer of 1933 the expedition was ready to depart for the Antarctic.

COMPOSITION OF THE EXPEDITION

Ellsworth had suggested that Wilkins go to Norway to purchase one of their stout wooden fishing vessels to be used as an expedition ship. Wilkins agreed with the suggestion and subsequently purchased the *Fanefjord,* a herring vessel of 400 tons with a 15-foot draft. The 135-foot craft was built in 1919, at Molde, of Norwegian pine and oak. She had a single deck and was powered by a semi-diesel engine capable of driving the ship at a speed of seven to eight knots. Later fitted with auxiliary sails, the vessel was capable of nine knots under a favoring wind. Wilkins supervised the refitting of the ship, which included sheathing the hull from bow to midships with oak planking and armor plate to strengthen her for work in the pack ice. She was given a fore and aft rig of Marconi-type sails — long, peaked, triangular sheets. Extra fuel and water tanks were installed, giving her a cruising range of 11,000 miles. The inside of the hull was remodeled to provide living quarters for 14 men, and an electric lighting system was installed. Ellsworth rechristened the remodeled vessel the *Wyatt Earp* after a famous frontier marshal of the old west whom he much admired.

Ellsworth's plane, the *Polar Star,* was built by the Northrop Corporation of Inglewood, Calif. It was an all-metal, cantilever, low-wing monoplane powered by a Wasp 600-horsepower engine, giving a top speed of 230 miles per hour. The plane could accommodate two passengers and was well suited for polar work. Equipped with wing flaps which reduced landing speed, it could land at 42 miles per hour. The low wing was advantageous for landing in the field, for two men could quickly scoop out trenches in the snow into which the skis would fit, bringing the wing to rest on the surface of the snow. In this position, wind could not get under the plane which could be secured easily against a blizzard. With a full load of gasoline the *Polar Star* had a cruising range of 7000 miles.

Including Ellsworth, the leader, and Sir Hubert Wilkins, technical adviser and manager, the expedition personnel numbered 17 men. Originally Bernt Balchen was airplane pilot and Chris Braathen served as mechanic. Dr. Jorgen Holmboe was meteorologist, Walter J. Lanz of Brooklyn was radio operator, and Dr. Reals Berg of Oslo served as medical officer. Captain Baard Holth and eight officers and crewmen of the *Wyatt Earp* were Antarctic veterans of the Norwegian whaling fleet.

On the second attempt at a transantarctic flight in 1934-35, Dr. Francis Dana Coman of The Johns Hopkins University, medical officer on the First Byrd Antarctic Expedition, replaced Dr. Berg, and Alistair Duthie of Dunedin replaced one of the Norwegian crewmen who had returned to Europe.

Further changes in personnel were made by the time the *Wyatt Earp* left Montevideo in October 1935 for Ellsworth's third trip to the Antarctic. Balchen had resigned and was replaced by Herbert Hollick-Kenyon, British-born Canadian from British Columbia. Hollick-Kenyon's background was similar to that of almost all of the early pilots in Antarctica. He had been a pilot in World War I, serving with the Royal Air Force, and as a transport pilot for Canadian Airways he had had considerable experience in the Arctic flying planes equipped with skis. J. H. Lymburner, also a Canadian Airways pilot flying out of Montreal and who had flown with skis and floats in the Hudson Bay country, was signed as reserve pilot. Braathen was replaced by Patrick Howard as engine mechanic. Dr. Theodore Schlossbach succeeded Dr. Dana Coman as physician. Captain Holth had resigned as master of the *Wyatt Earp,* and first mate Hartveg Olsen was promoted to captain. Liavaag was advanced to first mate, and Olsen's younger brother, Magnus, became second mate. This time no meteorologist was included. As on the first two expeditions, the party consisted of 17 men in October 1935. William J. Klenke, Jr., airplane mechanic, joined the expedition in December 1935.

OBJECTIVES AND ACCOMPLISHMENTS

Ellsworth's intention in 1933 was to make a transantarctic flight from the Bay of Whales to the Weddell Sea and return, the round trip covering approximately 2500 nautical miles (2000 statute miles). By this flight across the interior he hoped to determine whether these two great seas were connected by a strait which would thus divide the continent into two parts. An equally important objective was to learn the disposition of the mountains of the Antarctic Archipelago[3] as they extend into the continent. Did this axial range, generally considered a structural continuation of the Andes of South America, diverge like the frayed ends of a rope into a number of ranges, as predicted by the Swiss geologist Staub[4] or did it continue across Antarctica as a single range to join the Queen Maud Mountains at the head of the Ross Sea?

When the transantarctic flight had to be postponed because of damage to the plane in January 1934, the original plan was discarded, and a new one was proposed for a second attempt in 1934-35. The best season for flying in Antarctica is November and December, but the Ross Sea is generally blocked by pack ice until January. Consequently, it was decided that the takeoff should be made from some place in the Antarctic Peninsula area, probably Deception Island with which Wilkins was familiar and which would be accessible in November. The experience of previous expeditions in the Weddell Sea did not afford any hope for making a start from there. Instead of a round trip, a one-way flight was proposed. Ellsworth and his pilot would fly south from Deception Island to the head of the Weddell Sea and then westward to the Bay of Whales, where they would wait to be picked up by the *Wyatt Earp* sometime in January. The newly proposed flight would be shorter by from one hundred to several hundred miles, depending on how far south the plane flew before heading westward, but several hundred miles of additional unexplored territory would be flown over in this shorter distance because the duplication of a return trip would be eliminated. Moreover, the new plan afforded an equal opportunity for finding the answer to the two major geographical problems which Ellsworth hoped to solve.

When a broken connecting rod and continued bad weather delayed the flight beyond any hope of success during the summer of 1934-35, Ellsworth proposed to try again the following season. His plan of operation remained unchanged except that after further study he was more convinced than ever that he could land en route to wait out bad weather or to obtain geographical fixes.

The geographical discoveries and other accomplishments of the three expeditions relating to Lincoln Ellsworth's transantarctic flight are here briefly enumerated.

(1) The transantarctic flight, starting at Dundee Island on November 23, 1935, and ending about 16 miles from Little America on December 5, covered a distance of 2200 miles. Of this distance 1200 miles was over unexplored territory.[5]

(2) The transantarctic flight penetrated farther into the interior than any other exploring mission with the exception of the overland treks of Amundsen and Scott to the South Pole and the polar flight of Byrd.

(3) Although the total operations of larger expeditions may have exceeded it, no other single exploratory mission until the flights of the U. S. Navy Task Force 43 in January 1956 revealed as much of the interior as did Ellsworth's transantarctic flight.

(4) Four landings were made in the field while en route. At each, sun sights were made which fixed the position of the flight and served as a basis for the subsequent map by Joerg and his associates at the American Geographical Society.[6]

(5) The ice-covered upland which Ellsworth discovered between 80° and 120° East Longitude he claimed for the United States and named it James W. Ellsworth Land.[7]

(6) The several mountains which surmount the Antarctic Peninsula south of the great transverse valley occupied by Fleming and Bingham Glaciers Ellsworth named the Eternity Range. Three prominent peaks whose identity cannot be determined with certainty he named Mounts Faith, Hope, and Charity.

(7) Ellsworth observed and photographed the major fault depression which Rymill's British Graham Land Expedition later surveyed from the surface and named King George VI Sound.

(8) Individual features which Ellsworth discovered and named also include the Hollick-Kenyon Plateau, the Sentinel Range, and Mount Ulmer.

(9) From photographs of salient topographic features seen on the short flight of November 21 and on the transantarctic flight two days later it was subsequently possible to construct a topographic map[8] of portions of the east coast of the Antarctic Peninsula in the vicinity of Cape Keeler, the middle portion of George VI Sound, and the Sentinel Range. More recent ground surveys have shown the delineation of the first two areas to be accurate.

(10) While waiting in vain for suitable weather for the transantarctic flight during the 1934-35 season, Ellsworth collected 150 specimens of 28 species of fossils on Snow Hill Island. Three of the species had never before been found in the Antarctic. These were all turned over to the American Museum of Natural History along with souvenirs collected at Nordenskjöld's old hut on Snow Hill Island.

(11) During the 1934-35 season two short flights were made from Snow Hill Island southward along the Nordenskjöld Coast, and features which were not indicated or not correctly located on the latest charts were noted.

DETAILED RECORD OF OPERATIONS

THE FIRST ATTEMPT, 1933-1934

Under the command of Captain Baard Holth, the *Wyatt Earp* sailed from Bergen, Norway, July 29, 1933, and proceeded — via Cape Town, the Indian Ocean, and Melbourne — to Dunedin, New Zealand. All members of the expedition were aboard except Ellsworth, who joined the ship upon its arrival at Dunedin on November 9. After refueling and taking on provisions for two years, the expedition sailed from Dunedin on December 10, 1933. A week later they entered the pack ice of the Ross Sea. It took 22 days for the *Wyatt Earp* to work its way through the pack ice, and the gears of the ship were seriously worn by the constant backing and bucking forward against the pack. On January 9, 1934, the *Wyatt Earp* reached the Bay of Whales and was moored to the edge of the bay ice.

The *Polar Star,* which had been assembled ready for flight in Dunedin, was hoisted onto the bay ice on January 9. Three days later Balchen and Ellsworth flew south over the Ross Ice Shelf on a 30-minute test flight and pronounced the plane ready for the transantarctic flight. That evening, when the edge of the bay ice began breaking off under the pounding of a heavy sea, Balchen and some of the men moved the plane about a mile back from the outer edge of the bay ice as a precautionary measure.

Shortly after 4 a. m., January 13, a cry of alarm rang through the ship. Heavy swells moving beneath the great Ross Ice Shelf had begun to break up the apparently rigid bay ice. Within 15 minutes the Bay of Whales for five miles south had become a grinding mass of ice floes, heaving with the swell.[9] The *Polar Star* was rocking precariously on one of these heaving floes which was not much larger than the plane itself. Soon this floe split in two, and the skis and hull of the plane dropped down into the newly opened crack. Only the wings which were resting on the two halves of the floe kept the plane from sinking into the bay.

For six hours the men worked urgently with boats and lines to save the plane. First they succeeded in getting it up onto safer ice, and from there it was hoisted aboard the *Wyatt Earp*. The damage was such that only a factory could make repairs. The skis were broken and one wing was bent. The flight had to be abandoned for that year.

As soon as the *Polar Star* was secured on board, the *Wyatt Earp* was headed into the Ross Sea and a course was set for New Zealand. Because of the wear on its gears while bucking through the pack ice on the way into the Ross Sea, the ship was unable to travel at half speed. As a result, when coming into Dunedin against the tide on January 28, 1934, she smashed her bow against the dock. The *Wyatt Earp* remained in Dunedin to undergo repairs in preparation for another Antarctic voyage the following year. With Balchen in charge, the *Polar Star* was shipped to the United States aboard an oil tanker, and Ellsworth took passage for San Francisco aboard the Matson liner *Mariposa* at Auckland.

THE SECOND ATTEMPT, 1934-1935

As has been pointed out above, the plan of operation had been greatly changed for the second attempt at a transantarctic flight. It was now proposed to use Deception Island as a starting point and fly to the Bay of Whales. The *Polar Star* had been reconditioned at the Northrop factory and was shipped back to Dunedin where the *Wyatt Earp* had been undergoing repairs to her bow and driving mechanism. Here the members of the expedition who had returned to the United States reassembled.

The plane was stowed in the hold of the *Wyatt Earp*, and supplies for 20 men for two years were taken aboard along with gasoline and oil, spare parts, and quantities of assorted gear. The ship sailed from Dunedin on the morning of September 19, 1934. For 26 days under almost constantly leaden skies the *Wyatt Earp* rolled and wallowed through 4000 miles of storm-lashed seas. A succession of gales and blizzards buffeted the ship. A lookout was kept in vain for the elusive Dougherty Island, reported by whalers in approximately 59° 20′ S, 120° W, but never sighted by expedition ships which sought it.[10] A form looming up through the thick, snowy weather in the reported vicinity of the island turned out to be an iceberg.

The most violent storm of the entire passage struck the ship as it approached Deception Island. The weather was so thick that Smith Island was passed without being seen. Fortunately, the ship's officers were well acquainted with these waters. Early on the morning of October 14 they spotted, through the whirling snow, the jagged outline of Castle Rock from which they set a course for Deception Island. Sail Rock was next sighted and at 2 p. m. the tall cliffs guarding the entrance to Deception Island's Whalers Bay could be dimly seen through the murk. The *Wyatt Earp* squeezed past an iceberg which partially blocked the entrance into the protection of the bay.[11] Later the wind shifted from the northeast to the south. The weather gradually cleared and the temperature dropped, but floe ice was now blown in from the sea. Soon the *Wyatt Earp,* at anchor off the whaling factory, was surrounded by ice (Figs. 3 and 19).

It was a distinct disappointment to find Port Foster, the body of water inside Deception Island, free of ice because Ellsworth had hoped to take off from its frozen surface. For that reason the expedition had sailed early. Balchen took advantage of the clearing weather on October 15 to prospect for an alternative landing field. He concluded that the deep snow left by the blizzard of the previous day on the lower slopes near the whaling factory would serve for a takeoff. Since the snow fields apparently would last for a month, they decided to unload, but because of ensuing bad weather it was five days before the *Polar Star* could be taken off the ship. The plane was assembled in one of the whaling company sheds. On the evening of October 29 it was decided to start the engine, but after the propeller had made a half turn a connecting rod broke. After a fruitless search among the spare parts it was necessary to radio Pan American Grace Airways to make a new connecting rod available at Magallanes, Chile.

With Wilkins aboard, the *Wyatt Earp* set out for Magallanes while Ellsworth, Balchen, Braathen, Dr. Holmboe, and Dr. Coman took over one of the whaling company cottages. During the following days there was a great deal of fog and rain, interspersed with an occasional snow storm and blizzard. Thawing predominated, and gradually the snow fields from which they hoped to take off thinned. By the time the *Wyatt Earp* returned on November 16 patches of black volcanic ash showed through the snow. Fog and mild temperatures continued and ten days later, when the engine was repaired, most of the snow had disappeared. On November 27, with all hope of flying with skis from Deception Island gone for that season, they restowed the ship and hoisted the plane aboard. Shortly after noon they headed south in search of a new base.[12]

That evening they approached Trinity Island, which was almost blotted from view by a thick snowstorm. During the night they cautiously entered Gerlache Strait, and as they sailed south through the strait they encountered little ice until they approached Bismarck Strait by which they hoped to exit. Unfortunately, this strait was blocked by ice. Forced to retreat, they decided to give up the idea of trying to reach Adelaide Island and to seek instead a base on the Weddell Sea side of the Antarctic Peninsula. On November 29 the *Wyatt Earp* was moving northeastward through Bransfield Strait in heavy weather. About midnight the ship entered Antarctic Sound at the tip of the Antarctic Peninsula. The wind had risen to a full gale, driving sleet and fog from the southwest. High seas in the sound forced them to run into Hope Bay to ride out the storm.

At noon, November 30, they headed south from Hope Bay and slowly worked through Antarctic Sound into Erebus and Terror Gulf, where the next morning they found only a few bergs and no pack ice. A course was set to pass Seymour Island and Snow Hill Island, intending to come up against the Larsen Ice Shelf where they hoped to find a field suitable for a takeoff. Fog settled down as the ship entered the loose outer fringe of the pack ice within sight of Seymour Island, and they passed Snow Hill Island without seeing it. Pushing through the pack, they were soon halted by a solid sheet of ice, but its pitted surface made it unsuitable as a field from which to take off.

Thwarted again in his search for a suitable surface from which the plane might take off, Ellsworth now had the *Wyatt Earp* return northward, forcing its way through the pack to Snow Hill Island. It was now December 2, and the first half of the flying season was about over. Ellsworth would have liked to anchor near Nordenskjöld's old hut facing Admiralty Sound on the northwest side of the island, but when the strait between Snow Hill Island and Seymour Island proved too shallow to permit the ship to enter Admiralty Sound from that quarter, the *Wyatt Earp* came to anchor off the southeast side of the island.

When the fog cleared they could see that the low northern part of Snow Hill Island was bare of snow but the southern part, which rose to an elevation of 900 feet, was covered by a thin, uncrevassed glacier cap. Gentle slopes extended from the shore to the icecap. Here a satisfactory flying field could be established. The *Polar Star* was unloaded at a point where the glacier came down to the water's edge, and the plane taxied up the glacier on its own power. The men hauled the gasoline and oil up on sledges. Ellsworth crossed the island to visit Nordenskjöld's old hut, where he collected numerous souvenirs which were later presented to the American Museum of Natural History.

On Deception Island radio contact had been made twice daily with Admiral Byrd's base at Little America for the exchange of weather information. On December 2, 1934, this contact was reestablished from Snow Hill Island and continued until January 11.[13] Thus, before he took off on a transantarctic flight, Ellsworth would have the benefit of knowing what kind of weather he might expect on the other end. Unfortunately, day after day brought snow, fog, gales, and blizzards. Rarely did the sun shine.

Ellsworth took advantage of this poor flying weather to hunt for fossils on the snow-free northern end of Snow Hill Island made muddy by melting snows. In addition to fossils of invertebrate marine life, he collected samples of tree sections and imprints of leaves of Mesozoic trees related to present-day trees in South America. During several trips he collected a total of 150 specimens of 28 species, three of which were previously unknown from the Antarctic. These, plus those which he found at Nordenskjöld's hut, Ellsworth later gave to the American Museum of Natural History.[14]

December 18 was the first clear day that the expedition experienced since it landed on Deception Island two months earlier. The day was spent digging the plane out of the snow and getting it ready for flight. At about 9:30 a. m. Balchen and Braathen took off on a test flight to the southern end of the Nordenskjöld Coast.[15] At midnight they were back at Snow Hill Island, and conditions appeared so favorable that Ellsworth was certain he and Balchen would take off on the transantarctic flight in the morning. December 19, however, brought a falling barometer, an overcast sky, and snow squalls. An overcast sky with intermittent snowfall and long periods of fog continued until the end of the month.

The second break in the weather occurred on December 30. The sky was clear and there was only a slight wind from the southwest. A sounding balloon with a radio broadcasting device was sent aloft. Light airs prevailed as high as 50,000 feet.[16] Weather reports from Little America were also favorable. The *Polar Star* was dug out and that evening was ready for flight. Takeoff, however, was delayed until 4 a. m., December 31, the most advantageous hour from the standpoint of navigation. The next morning the fog had closed in again.[17]

The season for flying was now about closed. Although there were only two days in December when flying had been possible at Snow Hill Island, there was an even smaller chance of getting a good day in January. Because of large pieces of ice calving from the glacier it had been necessary to move the *Wyatt Earp* from its mooring and anchor it offshore, but otherwise they had experienced no great difficulty up to now. Winds, mostly from the south, southwest, or west, had kept the pack ice away from the ship. Now, however, north or northeast winds, which would soon drive the pack ice against the islands and the Larsen Ice Shelf, were becoming more frequent. If the wind held in this direction for long, the ship would be trapped, perhaps crushed. Caution dictated an early departure. Consequently the crew began moving gasoline and oil drums down from the flying field on January 3. That afternoon as the plane was being dug out preparatory to putting it aboard ship, the weather, which had been showing signs of improvement, became clear. The radio report from Little America was favorable.

At Ellsworth's suggestion, Balchen agreed to make a try at the transantarctic flight. The plane was made ready, and after a hot meal the two men climbed aboard. Even though calculations had not been made in advance, and navigation would be more difficult than if departure had been delayed until 4 a. m. the next morning, Ellsworth was desirous of taking off immediately. The wind was blowing down the glacier, and patches of sastrugi on the ice made it impossible to get sufficient speed for a takeoff going up the slope. After almost an hour's bumpy but ineffectual taxiing, Balchen, by a bold maneuver, finally got the plane in the air on a side wind. It was then about 6 p. m.

Ellsworth was soon to find that Antarctic weather would once again prevent him from achieving his goal. The following excerpts from his radio dispatch to the *New York Times* tell the story.

> . . . we found after flying southward for about 160 miles that snow squalls on a wide front, extending northwest and southeast, barred our way.
> Near Robertson Island, the clouds closed in above us. In a few minutes we could see heavy snow squalls descending and we had to turn southwestward. The air conditions were extremely bumpy and visibility was reduced at times to two miles. By turning due west we came to clear weather.[18]

At this point Ellsworth and Balchen were several hundred miles north of the point at which they had planned to turn westward. Consequently, with such ominous looking weather to the south, there was no alternative to returning to Snow Hill Island. The return flight was made in a generally northeastward direction along the eastern side of the Antarctic Peninsula to beyond James Ross Island and then southward across the island to their base, where they landed 2 hours and 28 minutes after takeoff.

Since James Ross Island and the adjacent part of the Antarctic Peninsula had not previously been seen from the air, it is not surprising that Ellsworth found inaccuracies in the maps which had been made from ground surveys or from shipboard, often at a distance. He was especially impressed by the discrepancy between the maps and reality in the vicinity of Cape Sobral.

One big feature discovered yesterday is a fjord directly behind what is marked on the charts as Cape Sobral, and which we found was in fact an island off North Graham Land. The fjord, walled with glaciers and floored with gaping crevasses, runs for about thirty miles northwest.

Following a precedent established by other explorers, I have named it James W. Ellsworth Fjord, after my father, a pioneer himself in the field of industry and through whose generosity I have made this and other flights in the interest of Geography.[19]

Ellsworth described the return flight to Snow Hill Island and the features he observed as follows:

We reached the high coastal area a few miles south of Evans Inlet, then turning north came to Hektoria Fjords. Here we turned easterly and saw a long fjord ending in two steep glaciers extending for about fifteen miles to the north.

Following closely along the coast, we observed behind Sobral, marked as a cape but really Sobral Island, the deep, wide fjord, the most conspicuous feature of our discoveries, which I have already mentioned. Ten miles to the northeast of this another deep uncharted fjord was seen. Several mountain peaks reached up to near our altitude, which was then 5500 feet. One uncharted island was remarkable for its sharp-topped peak and three other islands of considerable size, also uncharted, were observed in Prince Gustav Channel. The northwestern coast of Ross Island is much indented with bays and fjords, and lying between Ross and Vega Islands is another one, conspicuous but hitherto uncharted.[20]

On January 6 Ellsworth radioed a dispatch to the *Times* containing the following:

The results of our flight last Tuesday [an error; the flight was made on Thursday] have now been accurately checked and the discoveries considerably alter the contour of Nordenskjöld Coast as marked on the latest charts.

Running from Cape Ruth is a fjord, its southern side forming an almost exact right angle with Hektoria Fjords, which was indicated on the chart but the depth of which was unknown until we observed it to be nineteen miles deep and eight miles across at its widest part.

Two huge glaciers tumble into this fjord at its easterly and westerly extremities. Directly behind Sobral Island, which was previously marked as a cape, there is a long, wavy coastline fjord twenty-five miles deep, averaging about seven miles wide and ending in a much crevassed glacier six miles wide. This fjord I have named after my father, James W. Ellsworth.

Ten miles northeastward along the coast is the southern side of another fjord that extends for twenty-three miles inland from the bottom of Larsen Bay. This I have named after my wife, Mary Louise Fjord.

Numerous other details will be included on the maps to be published upon our return.[21]

The maps which Ellsworth promised were never published, and the foregoing excerpts from his dispatches have been included here because they constitute the most complete report ever published of his observations on the flight of January 3, 1935. Because Ellsworth neglected to publish maps which incorporated the observations which he made on this flight, maps of the area subsequently published by others do not reflect his findings. The descriptions of this area contained in the *Sailing Directions for Antarctica* do, however, include Ellsworth's observations.[22] Large-scale topographic maps compiled by the Falkland Islands Dependencies Survey from ground surveys carried out between 1945 and 1948 from the base at Hope Bay generally confirmed Ellsworth's findings.[23] Because Ellsworth's descriptions are not always precise, however, the correct identity of the feature to which he refers is in some cases impossible to determine.

Cape Sobral is the seaward end of a north-south ridge which may well be an island, for it is separated from the main body of the Antarctic Peninsula by Muskeg Gap whose floor is close to sea level and almost two miles wide. It is impossible to tell which feature on the coast Ellsworth named James W. Ellsworth Fjord. To the east of the feature which Nordenskjöld named Cape Sobral he also mapped a broad indentation which he named Larsen Bay.[24] This is now known to be an inlet over 6 miles long with a glacier entering its upper end. This feature, now called Larsen Inlet, is possibly the same that Ellsworth named Mary Louise Fjord, but the correlation is uncertain. The conspicuous but uncharted fjord which Ellsworth mentioned between James Ross Island and Vega Island is undoubtedly Croft Bay, which Nordenskjöld did not show as a sufficiently deep indentation. The existence of Wilkins' Hektoria Fjords is questioned, as is Nordenskjöld's Drygalski Bay. Both are perhaps represented by the very broad glacier shown by the Falkland Islands Dependencies Survey in this vicinity and named Drygalski Glacier.

In *Beyond Horizons* Ellsworth describes a low pass cutting across the northern end of the Antarctic Peninsula, through which he could see the peaks of the South Shetland Islands 100 miles away.[25] He must have been referring to Russell East Glacier and Russell West Glacier, which on the latest maps occupy a great transverse valley. Heading on a low divide, the two glaciers flow in opposite directions.

After the flight of January 3 was cut short there was little hope that another flight could be made that season. The pack ice was beginning to close in. A succession of gales and blizzards prevented the *Polar Star* from being put aboard the *Wyatt Earp* until January 9. The next afternoon the ship started north. A snowstorm accompanied by a northeast gale held them in the shelter of Seymour Island for the night. Then for three days they bucked pack ice trying to cross Erebus and Terror Gulf. When they found Antarctic Sound blocked with ice on the night of January 12, they retreated again to the shelter of Snow Hill Island to wait for a northerly wind to clear the passage. For five days the *Wyatt Earp* remained in Admiralty Sound.

When the pack loosened, the *Wyatt Earp* again ventured out toward Antarctic Sound. On the night of January 17 she sought shelter during the short period of darkness behind Cape Gordon on the east end of Vega Island. During the night a wind shift brought the pack down on the ship, threatening to crush her against the red rock cliffs. Fortunately, on January 18 the *Wyatt Earp* was able to work her way into Antarctic Sound and open water through an opening in Fridtjof Sound less than three miles wide. After a stop at Hope Bay in a fruitless search for the fossils supposedly left there in 1903 by Dr. Andersson and Lieutenant Duse of Nordenskjöld's expedition, the *Wyatt Earp* sailed for Deception Island.

Arriving at Deception Island on January 20, the *Polar Star* was dismantled and stowed in the ship's hold. At 3 p. m., January 21 the party sailed for Montevideo where they arrived February 2, 1935. Some of the members remained here with the ship until the following October; others, including Ellsworth, returned to the United States.

THE THIRD ATTEMPT, 1935-1936

Soon after Ellsworth returned to the United States in February 1935, he definitely decided to set out on a third expedition to the Antarctic to try once more to complete a transcontinental flight. Plans for the expedition were essentially the same as those for 1934-35. Herbert Hollick-Kenyon replaced Balchen as pilot, and Dr. Theodore Schlossbach replaced Dr. Coman as medical officer. With Hollick-Kenyon's consent, Ellsworth did not include a meteorologist on this expedition. In Dr. Holmboe's place he took J. H. Lymburner as a reserve pilot. When preparations were completed, the members of the expedition assembled at Montevideo.

On October 18, 1935, the *Wyatt Earp* sailed from Montevideo under command of Captain Hartveg Olsen. The ship called at Magallanes, Chile, where her fuel tanks were filled, additional supplies were put on board, and the last mail was picked up. On October 28 she sailed for Deception Island which five days later was found to be surrounded by pack ice. Captain Olsen waited a few days for the wind to disperse the pack, and on the morning of November 4, forced an entry through the ice into the harbor at Whalers Bay.[26] Here the *Polar Star* was taken from the hold, assembled, and lashed on deck. On November 11 the expedition sailed for Dundee Island where, from observations made the previous season, Ellsworth hoped to be able to find a flying field.

At 3 a. m., Tuesday, November 12, the *Wyatt Earp* entered Antarctic Sound through a maze of icebergs. Moving over toward Dundee Island, Captain Olsen entered the mouth of Active Sound. Here Ellsworth and his men found the northwest corner of Dundee Island bordered by a rim of relatively smooth, snow-covered sea ice about a half mile wide. Investigation showed it to be fast to the shore. Back from the shore they found a gently sloping, snow-covered area more or less triangular in shape which offered a runway 1200 feet long in each of three directions.[27] Here was what they had been hoping for. On the night of November 12 the *Polar Star* was let down onto the sea ice and dragged the half mile to the shore of Dundee Island.

In contrast to the previous year, the weather now, a month earlier in the season, was mostly favorable. Storms were few and there was little fog. The temperature usually rose to slightly above freezing during midday, making the snow surface soft and sticky. This meant that the takeoff could best be made in the morning while the surface was still frozen. From the standpoint of navigation, the most favorable time for takeoff was also in the morning, at 4 a. m. With good weather prevailing, takeoff on the big flight was imminent.

To simplify the problem of navigation while in flight, Ellsworth computed in advance and plotted as curves on cross-section paper the altitude and azimuths of the sun for the estimated hourly positions of the plane. Since these would be different for each day, Ellsworth spent several hours each evening on these calculations in anticipation of a takeoff the following morning. It was planned to fly at a constant ground speed of 150 miles per hour (130 knots). A nonstop flight to Little America, where local time was 7 hours earlier than at Dundee Island, was calculated to take 14 hours. By starting from Dundee Island at 4 a. m. the plane, if on schedule, should reach the continental interior at the time when the sun would be at meridian, or due north, and easily sighted from the right-hand window.[28] Because of the rapid change in local time when traveling either east or west in high latitudes, Ellsworth decided to use Greenwich civil time (G.C.T.) as his standard while on the flight. This was 3 hours and 44 minutes later than local time at Dundee Island.

In addition to working out the flight plan, Ellsworth also prepared a detailed statement of his intentions in the event that he lost radio contact with the *Wyatt Earp* after a forced landing from which it would be impossible to get the plane into the air. As a guide to Wilkins he outlined the route which he and Hollick-Kenyon would travel from each of several positions to reach a likely rendezvous with members of the expedition trying to effect their rescue.[29]

Tuesday, November 19, the *Polar Star* was ready for the big flight. It had been given a short test flight by each of the pilots, and all day November 18 the men worked sledging gasoline, oil, food, emergency camping equipment, a light sledge, and a field radio from the ship up to the plane. At midnight it was loaded and ready for takeoff which was first attempted in midmorning on November 19. The snow had thawed just enough, however, to make a sticky surface from which the heavily laden plane was unable to lift.

The favorable weather continued, and at 4 a. m. (7:44 G.C.T.) on November 20, after the mechanics had helped loosen the skis which had frozen to the snow during the night, Hollick-Kenyon and Ellsworth had no difficulty in taking off with a run of less than a half mile.[30] They climbed to 2400 feet and headed south, rising later to 4500 feet. As far as they could see to the southeast the Weddell Sea was open. Just beyond Robertson Island, 1 hour and 45 minutes after takeoff, a fuel-flow gauge on which the glass had been broken by a bump during the takeoff began to leak badly. In a few moments it threatened to burst completely, and Hollick-Kenyon radioed the ship that they were returning. They landed on Dundee Island at 7:11 a. m., 3 hours and 11 minutes after taking off.

After the plane had been repaired and when the weather continued fair, preparations were made for a flight the next day, November 21. That morning the temperature was 32° F and the air was clear and motionless. Ellsworth and Hollick-Kenyon took off at 4:19 a. m. (8:03 a. m. G.C.T.) A half hour later they were flying over James Ross Island at an elevation of 5500 feet. South of Robertson

Island Ellsworth noted that they were still flying over open water, but off toward the southeast an ever-increasing amount of pack ice could be seen in the Weddell Sea. A thin haze spread from the south to the southwest. At 10:20 G.C.T. the Weddell Sea to the south and east of them was filled with pack. The weather was thickening over the land, and in a few minutes ground fog began to obscure some of the features. They were now approaching the area first seen by Wilkins and Eielson on their pioneer exploratory flight of December 20, 1928 (Fig. 12).

That Ellsworth and Hollick-Kenyon had difficulty in identifying features shown on the map they were using is understandable.[31] Instead of an archipelago formed by three great transverse straits, as reported by Wilkins, they found a highland dissected by four broad, steep-walled valleys, each occupied by a low-gradient glacier. Rising above the snow-covered uplands between the glacial valleys they found an unsystematic array of mountain peaks. Although the valleys were broad, they were much narrower than the straits they expected to find.[32] Moreover, it was difficult at ground speeds of 80 to 130 miles an hour to gain a clear or lasting impression of features close aboard, and many of the more distant landmarks were partially obscured by fog or low hanging clouds. Stefansson Strait, which Wilkins thought to be a broad strait separating the supposed Antarctic Archipelago from Hearst Land on the continent, was sought as the feature by which others might be identified. Although they thought that four different glaciers might be the elusive Stefansson Strait, unfortunately they did not succeed in making a positive identification.

Three attempts at reconstructing the flight track of November 21, 1935, have been published. The first attempt by Joerg in 1936 was a preliminary effort.[33] Later, in addition to analyzing Ellsworth's journal, Hollick-Kenyon's flight log, and the record of radio messages received by the *Wyatt Earp* from the *Polar Star* during the flight, Joerg and his associates at the American Geographical Society succeeded in identifying features which Ellsworth had photographed on November 21 and November 23, 1935, in the pictures taken by Wilkins in 1928. As a result they were able to construct from what were very meager data a remarkably accurate map which was published in 1937.[34] Although Joerg was unable to assign definite positions in terms of latitude and longitude to individual features, he estimated that the northern and southern limits of map A, plate III, were 68°10′ S, and 69°35′ S, respectively.[35] Subsequent ground surveys and aerial photography of the U. S. Antarctic Service show that the boundaries are approximately 68° S and 69°31′ S and that the relative position of features with respect to one another is accurately portrayed on Joerg's map. Working from the Ellsworth and the Wilkins photographs, Joerg was able to reconstruct the flight track of the plane, eliminating a long southwesterly loop, into what Ellsworth identified as Stefansson Strait, which he had shown on his first map in 1936 (Fig. 18).

The third attempt, by Stephenson and Hinks, to reconstruct the flight track of November 21 was published in 1940.[36] From material supplied by the American Geographical Society they were able to identify features appearing in Ellsworth's photographs A.5, A.10, and A.11 with Rymill's R.40, and Ellsworth's

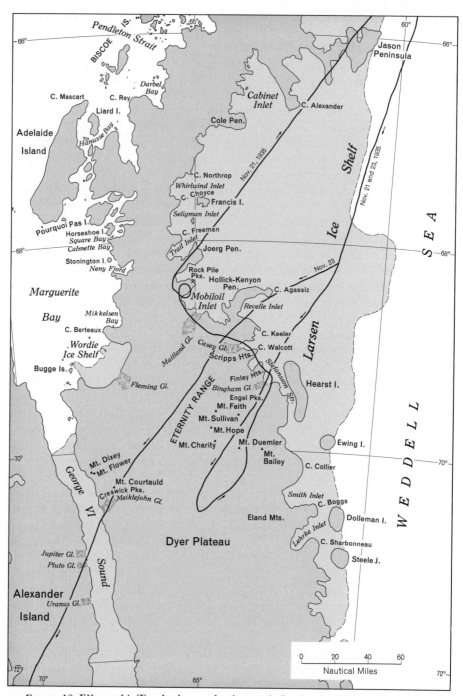

FIGURE 18. Ellsworth's Tracks Across the Antarctic Peninsula in November 1935.

photograph A.9 could be matched with Rymill's RD.85.[37] Stephenson and Hinks were able to show that Joerg's map A, plate III of 1937 belongs north of the traverse of Rymill and Bingham, that the great transverse glacier, now known as Bingham Glacier, which lay immediately north of their traverse was shown on the southern part of Joerg's map. By being able to identify Rymill's photograph RD.85 with Ellsworth's A.9, Stephenson and Hinks were able to pin down further the southerly loop of the November 21 flight for which Joerg had no confirming data beyond Finley Peninsula, which he identified as Wilkins' Finley Islands, and which is now known as Finley Heights.

Because Hollick-Kenyon and Ellsworth neglected to log the speed and compass course of the plane after 13:50 G.C.T. on the return to Dundee Island on November 21, some uncertainty exists regarding the track of the flight across Mobiloil Inlet. Stephenson and Hinks suggest (p. 180) that an unlogged loop westward up Casey Glacier is necessary to reconcile Ellsworth's notation pertaining to his photographs A.18 (taken to port, 14:30) and A.19 (taken to starboard, 14:42), since they were both taken from a point north of Casey Glacier, looking south across the glacier toward Scripps Heights. They point out that, insofar as this loop is concerned, Joerg's 1936 interpretation of the flight track may be more accurate than his more simplified version on the 1937 map. Such a loop may well have been made, but in solving one difficulty it only adds another, for Ellsworth reports in his journal that both photographs A.19 and A.20 were taken at 14:52. The latter, however, is a view of Rock Pile Peaks taken from the south near the foot of Maitland Glacier, 40 miles northwest of Scripps Heights. Obviously, there is an error someplace, but, while it leaves the flight track somewhat uncertain at this point, it has not affected the accuracy of Joerg's map.

As a result of Joerg's interpretation, amplified by Hinks and Stephenson and the work of subsequent expeditions, the flight track of the *Polar Star* can be determined with a fair degree of accuracy. The following account of the flight of November 21 is based on an analysis of these published materials, the data used by Joerg and made available to the writer through the generosity of the American Geographical Society, copies of aerial photographs taken by the U. S. Antarctic Service, and copies of aerial photographs taken by the Ronne Antarctic Research Expedition.

The *Polar Star*, flying on a compass course of 185° on November 21, was edging in toward the land from the Weddell Sea when, at 11:26 G.C.T., Hollick-Kenyon called Ellsworth's attention to what he thought must be Stefansson Strait ahead and Scripps Island to the right. Four minutes later Ellsworth noted in his journal, "Stefansson Strait dead ahead. High peaks away to left front." At the same time Hollick-Kenyon radioed the *Wyatt Earp*, "Can see about 30 miles along Stefansson Strait now." At 11:37 G.C.T. he radioed, "Just coming up Scripps now — think there must be strong wind off the land. Ring of peaks to left ahead. Not very high I think now." From the position they then must have been in, north of Hearst Island, they were probably looking up either Casey or Lurabee Glacier because they saw peaks to the left.

We now know Stefansson Strait to be the north-south strait, filled with shelf ice, 40 miles long and over 3 miles wide which separates Hearst Island from the mainland.[38] From the elevation of the plane at 11:37, approximately 6000 feet, Ellsworth and Hollick-Kenyon could have seen Stefansson Strait if they had known what to look for but it is probable that the gentle snow-covered slopes of the low dome that is Hearst Island were not obvious from their height. Certainly Hearst Island would present no peaks on their left.

At 11:50 G.C.T. the *Polar Star* was over the northern end of Stefansson Strait when Ellsworth took four pictures in rapid succession with his 35 mm Leica camera. In his journal he recorded, "11.50, Stefansson Strait (over) pictures 1, 2, 3, 4 from starboard side to 20° astern." A. 1, A. 2, and A.3 show Lurabee Glacier and Scripps Heights, which form its north wall. Photograph A. 4 may well be looking straight up Bingham Glacier, but clouds prevent a positive identification. Five minutes later, when the plane was just south of the foot of Bingham Glacier, Ellsworth took a picture which obviously shows Mount Sullivan and wrote in his journal, "Entered Hearst Land, picture 5 from starboard side at right angles." According to the then-accepted concepts he would have entered Hearst Land as soon as he crossed Stefansson Strait. He must now have been thinking of Bingham Glacier, which he had just passed, as Stefansson Strait. The greater breadth and lower gradient of Bingham Glacier, which heads opposite Fleming Glacier at the very divide of the peninsula, better fit the concept of a strait cutting clear through to Marguerite Bay than Lurabee Glacier. The glacier which he considered to be Stefansson Strait he described as follows:

. . . [If Stefansson Strait is a fjord], it is an immense one, for we could see its walls back for thirty miles, where they lost themselves in cloud and fog. I observed that it was much narrower than Wilkins had suspected — not over a mile or two wide in places. Also the Finley Islands [now called Finley Heights] were much closer together than the chart showed.[39]

From the foot of Bingham Glacier the *Polar Star* flew on a compass course of 190°, passing just west of Engel Peaks (4800 ft.) and some distance to the east of Mount Sullivan (6800 ft.) as shown by photograph A. 5, as it climbed toward Dyer Plateau. With the plane pitching and swaying on the bumpy air, Hollick-Kenyon put it into a steady climb, aiming for what appeared to be a pass between peaks whose bases were shrouded in fog. Ragged, low-hanging clouds revealed patches of blue sky ahead. At 12:16 he radioed the *Wyatt Earp*, "Lots of mountains here left and right at 8000 and still going up. Peaks on both sides are higher, perhaps 2000'. Strongish wind about SSW." Four minutes later he added, "Lots of good places to land tho. Cannot see to SSE low clouds looks like mountains run that way."

Fortunately at this time Ellsworth was using his Leica again. Between 12:19 and 12:22 G.C.T., while the plane was climbing from 8000 to 9000 feet, he took photographs A.6 to A.9 to the left, at right angles to the plane. Photograph A.9 has been correlated by Stephenson and Hinks with Rymill's photograph RD.85, which was taken from about 70°09'27" S, 63°58' W. This would place the *Polar Star* west of Mount Duemler (7300 ft.) at 70°01' S, 63°45' W at 12:19 G.C.T. when photograph A.6 was taken.[40] The picture must therefore show peaks between Mount Duemler and Rymill's position.[41]

As the plane continued to climb, air speed dropped to 80 miles per hour and the fog and clouds became more menacing. At 10,000 feet the surface was only 800 feet below the plane. At 12:36 G.C.T., Hollick-Kenyon radioed, "Compass course 190, Air speed down badly. Ground must be still going up, machine climbing slowly. Wind on ground S by W." Ellsworth recorded in his journal, "Can't see ground below, only mountain tops. (Sun on tail; no observation possible.)" At 12:45 G.C.T., he noted, "Heavy fog below. Alt. 10,300' High range of mountains parallel us to left." Hollick-Kenyon, in trying to explain the slow speed of the plane, suspected a downward air current. At 12:50 he radioed that if conditions did not improve he was going to turn back. At 13:00 G.C.T. Hollick-Kenyon decided conditions were too bad to continue. He radioed the *Wyatt Earp*, "Turning back, dense clouds at 12,000, Can not see any end of cloud. Bumps in distance look like mountains right on course." They were then flying at 11,500 feet.[42]

The turning point of the flight cannot be definitely determined. It was near the head of Clifford Glacier at approximately 70°35' S, 64°30' W. After a turn to the left the plane was put on a compass course of first 20° and then 10°, which placed the return flight between Mount Duemler and Mount Bailey (4700 ft.). With a stiff tailwind and decreasing elevation, the *Polar Star* was soon back at the Weddell Sea coast. At 13:41 G.C.T. Ellsworth took photograph A.10 to the left at right angles to the plane. The picture shows the Engel Peaks almost under the plane, with Mount Sullivan in the distance. Three minutes later the *Polar Star* was over the edge of Stefansson Strait at the foot of Bingham Glacier. If the times at which the photographs were taken are accurately recorded, it took 70 minutes to make the outward leg of the flight and 44 minutes to return to the foot of Bingham Glacier.

One important point pertaining to this part of the flight is still unsettled. Referring to the ascent toward Mount Duemler on the outward leg of the flight, Ellsworth has written as follows:

Uncertain as to what lay ahead, Hollick-Kenyon put the plane into a climb. Suddenly through a rift I saw a great mountain peak ahead and to the left, and therefore due south of us. Although we had reached an altitude of 7,000 feet, it loomed high above us. A minute later several other peaks had come into sight ahead, both to the left and right, and, as we climbed more appeared, jagged, rocky summits piercing the clouds to a height of ten and eleven thousand feet — until finally we confronted a great range crossing our track diagonally from north to southeast and extending off to the southeast at least seventy-five miles.
. . . At once the true name for these mountains came to me, and I wrote it down in my diary — the Eternity Range. Later, observing three central summits a little higher than the others, I gave them the names, in order from north to south, mounts Faith, Hope, and Charity.[43]

From his writings after the close of the expedition it is apparent that Ellsworth intended that all of the mountains of the Antarctic Peninsula south of Bingham Glacier be named Eternity Range. Which peaks he named Faith, Hope, and Charity cannot be identified with certainty, for in the transcript of his journal at the American Geographical Society there is no mention of these names in connection with the November 21 flight. The statements just quoted pertain to the part of the flight before the turn was made. Therefore, high peaks to the left or south of the plane could have been Mount Duemler, the unnamed peak south of it, peaks in the Eland Mountains, which exceed 8000 feet, about 30 nautical miles east of the turning point, or higher unnamed peaks farther south.

It is now thought that the trio of peaks on the peninsular divide immediately south of the heads of Fleming and Bingham Glaciers are Ellsworth's Mounts Faith, Hope, and Charity. The middle peak, named Mount Wakefield by Rymill, highest and most conspicuous peak in the vicinity, is 9400 feet high. Though it is a logical conclusion overall, specific proof for it is lacking from the November 21 flight. Perhaps, however, they are the three central peaks which, in the quotation just cited, Ellsworth says he observed a little later, for he does not say how much later nor from which side he viewed them. It is worthy of note that the northernmost of the three peaks appears in Ellsworth's photograph A.5 in the left center background behind Mount Sullivan.[44] The three peaks of Mount Wakefield must also have been seen by Hollick-Kenyon. In a radio message to the *Wyatt Earp*, dispatched at 13:15 G.C.T., when the *Polar Star* was about one-third of the way toward Bingham Glacier on the return leg of the flight, he indicated that two mountains seen to the north-northwest on the way up were now abreast.[45] If the message, whose reception was not entirely clear, has been correctly interpreted, it is logical to assume that Hollick-Kenyon was referring to Rymill's Mount Wakefield and one of its two neighbors.

From the foot of Bingham Glacier the plane was headed northwestward in a great arc, concave westward, across the foot of Lurabee Glacier, Cape Walcott, and diagonally across the lower part of Casey Glacier. Meanwhile, the altitude of the flight was decreasing from 9000 to 7500 feet. Ellsworth and Hollick-Kenyon were still having difficulty trying to identify Stefansson Strait. At 14 G.C.T. Ellsworth took photographs A.14 and A.15 which show Finley Heights. At the same time Hollick-Kenyon thought he might be over Cape Eielson but he soon changed his mind in favor of Cape Walcott. At 14:30 G.C.T., when the plane was crossing Casey Glacier and Ellsworth took photograph A.18 looking south across the glacier, Hollick-Kenyon recorded in his log that he was now over Stefansson Strait. This would, of course, be consistent with his interpretation of Cape Walcott as Cape Eielson. Ellsworth's journal shows that he dropped a flag here, but no purpose is indicated.

At this point the question of a westerly loop up Casey Glacier is raised. The flight log and Ellsworth's journal, however, give no clue to this except for the timing of the pictures to which Stephenson and Hinks called attention. It was here that Hollick-Kenyon recorded, "Clouds and snow right down to bottom." Since the pictures show the lower part of the glacier to be clear, he must have been referring to the upper part which he could have seen from the coast. It is not probable that he would have flown into such conditions. Joerg's map shows that they flew a northwesterly arc, concave eastward, across the head of Mobiloil Inlet. The flight log indicates that Hollick-Kenyon brought the plane down low to have a look up some of the glaciers. No doubt Maitland Glacier, indicated as a "major valley depression" on Joerg's map, was one reason for the closer investigation. At 14:55, when the plane was over the foot of Maitland Glacier, Ellsworth took photograph A.21, showing Rock Pile Peaks, and recorded in his journal, "Picture 21 to starboard side of plane at right angles — over Stefansson Strait."

Hollick-Kenyon now began flying a clockwise loop around Rock Pile Peaks, and then, deciding that there was little chance of completing the flight to the westward, he flew diagonally across the length of the Joerg Peninsula and headed for Dundee Island. At 15 G.C.T. he concluded a radio dispatch to the *Wyatt Earp* with, "Well, enuf, am turning back to Weddell Sea then north along coast." This was extremely disappointing to Ellsworth, at least for the time being, for he had hoped to land here and wait for better weather if they could not have crossed the mountain ranges and reached as far as 80° W.

At 18:30 G.C.T. (11:46 local time) the *Polar Star* landed at Dundee Island after a flight of 10 hours and 27 minutes. Although it was a temporary disappointment to Ellsworth, the flight eventually made an important contribution to the solution of the geographic problems pertaining to Stefansson Strait.

THE TRANSANTARCTIC FLIGHT

Most of November 22 was spent servicing the *Polar Star*. The weather was fitful and not too promising.[46] As November 23 dawned, however, the weather turned out to be excellent, and Ellsworth and Hollick-Kenyon were called at 1 a. m. Lymburner, Wilkins, and members of the crew had everything in readiness when Ellsworth and Hollick-Kenyon arrived at the plane. A gentle breeze was blowing from the southeast. At 8:04 a. m., G.C.T. (4:20 a. m., local time), the plane took off, heading southwestward over Prince Gustav Channel before straightening out on a compass course varying from 180° to 185°.

The first part of the flight was essentially over the course that had been flown on November 21. They passed five miles to the east of Robertson Island at 9:28 G.C.T. Across the Weddell Sea they maintained an altitude of approximately 7500 feet and an indicated air speed of 126 miles per hour. As they moved south, they found the pack ice increasingly heavy. Beyond Cape Framnes, which they passed 10 miles to the west, navigable leads were no longer apparent. Shortly after 11:00 they crossed over the seaward edge of the Larsen Ice Shelf. Hollick-Kenyon had now brought the plane up to 9000 feet and, thinking himself to be too far east, altered course to 190° at 11:13.

They were climbing steadily and soon, from an altitude of 11,000 feet, could see in the distance the maze of long, glacier-filled valleys in the vicinity of Stefansson Strait. At 11:28 G.C.T. Hollick-Kenyon further altered the course to 210° so as to bring them west of what he took to be Cape Eielson. As they drew closer, they found it as difficult as ever to reconcile the chart with the terrain. Hollick-Kenyon's radio dispatch to the *Wyatt Earp* at 11:45 contained the following: "Very confusing mass of islands in front. It's hard to say which is which." He had previously reported some low mist, and now he told of clouds over mountains to the left and ahead, which undoubtedly increased the difficulty of identification.

As they came in over the coast at an altitude of 13,000 feet, Ellsworth took 14 photographs between 12:20 and 12:59 G.C.T. Eight of these were from the right side of the plane and six from the left. They pretty well locate the flight track so that we know the plane passed almost over Cape Agassiz, crossed Revelle Inlet, and came in diagonally across the upper part of Casey Glacier. This placed them about 30 miles northwest of the northern end of what we now know is Stefansson Strait and the point where they reached the coast on November 21. As in the latter instance, they tried to orient themselves in terms of this strait as it was shown on their chart. As Joerg pointed out,[47] it appears from the notations in the flight log that they mistook Cape Keeler for Cape Eielson.

At 12:17 Hollick-Kenyon recorded in the flight log, "C. Eielson close left." Five minutes later Ellsworth took, from the left side of the plane, photograph 2 which shows the headland which we now know as Cape Keeler. Consistent with this identification, they also mistook Maitland Glacier, shown on Joerg's map of 1937 as a "major valley depression" at the head of what is now named Mobiloil Inlet, as Stefansson Strait.

Before recording the above entry in the flight log, Hollick-Kenyon had radioed a dispatch to the *Wyatt Earp* which was incompletely decoded as follows:

12:15 At cape in 3 min. . . . off now for 15 min. . . . Cape Eielson course is 138. To W 242. Both by compass. . . . Channel is one I was in last time and is Steff Str not Lurabee. Stef appears to be the coast. Hearst Land abeam poin . . . cloud over mts. . . . ahead to right 15 to 60° must be very high . . . chain . . . is in two parts now . . . is shorter than southern . . . about two fifty . . . must be 100 miles or so.

At 12:25 he made the following entry in the log:

Coast SE 138 c W 242 c Long Strait-channel is coast and is one I was in last time (Nov. 21) cc. 190.

Ellsworth's journal elaborates on this information in the following entry for 12:22:

Crossed Stefansson Strait. Confirmed Wilkins' discovery of a separation between Graham Land and the Continent of Antarctica, but observed Strait to be not more than one mile wide, which is much less than is shown on maps.

Compass bearing of coast S E 138° and W 242°. Low black conical peaks of Cape Eielson on our left. Climbed to elevation 13,400 feet, temp. minus 22° cent.

Heading for unknown. Bold and rugged mountain peaks across our route lay ahead, some of which seemed to rise almost sheer to 12,000 as far as the eye could see. I named this range "Eternity Range."

It is important to note that the compass bearing which Ellsworth gives for the coast of "Hearst Land" to the west, 242°, is the same as for the longitudinal axis of Maitland Glacier.

That Ellsworth and Hollick-Kenyon considered Maitland Glacier to be Stefansson Strait is further confirmed by the identification of photographs in Joerg's preliminary article of 1936.[48] Figure 2 (page 456) is denoted as "looking about northwest across the Stefansson Strait depression." This picture is Ellsworth's photograph 11, taken at 12:45, November 23, and shows the foot of Maitland Glacier, Mobiloil Inlet, and the Rock Pile Peaks.

Although Ellsworth took no photographs as they crossed the Antarctic Peninsula divide, the flight track can be fairly well determined from the landmarks which were photographed on the east and west side of the peninsula. Most of the time the plane was held on a compass course of 190°; at one point it was briefly changed to 210°. Flying at an altitude of 13,000 feet the *Polar Star* must have crossed the axial range just west of the opposing heads of Bingham and Fleming Glaciers. The head of the latter was crossed diagonally, placing the plane some distance north and west of the three prominent peaks of which Mount Hope (9400 ft.) is the middle and highest one. These three peaks comprise at least part of the high mountains mentioned in the entries just quoted. Unfortunately, the few entries which follow those are no more explicit regarding these mountains. Perhaps they were obscured by clouds which Hollick-Kenyon mentioned in a radio dispatch at 12:55.

From an examination of the evidence, one can be reasonably sure of Ellsworth's flight tracks on November 21 and 23. However, it is impossible to identify with certainty the peaks which he called Mounts Faith, Hope, and Charity. The three peaks which most nearly fit his conception of the Eternity Range are those on the crest of the Antarctic Peninsula immediately south of the opposing heads of Fleming and Bingham Glaciers. These three peaks were mapped in November and December 1936 by Rymill and Bingham of the British Graham Land Expedition while on a sledge journey across the peninsula. The middle and tallest peak was called Mount Wakefield, the other two peaks were unnamed, and the three have often been called informally the Wakefield group. It would seem quite certain that Ellsworth saw them on November 21, and it is possible that he saw them on November 23, 1935.

This interpretation of the evidence has been concurred in by a number of people for some time. It was expressed in 1956 in an alternate application of the name Eternity Mountains.[49] In 1962 the British Antarctic Names Committee and the U. S. Board on Geographic Names officially approved the name Eternity Range for these peaks, and the names Mount Faith, Mount Hope, and Mount Charity, respectively, were approved for the three high peaks from north to south. The name Wakefield was applied elsewhere, and the U. S. Board removed the name Eternity Mountains from the high mountains somewhat farther south.

Continuing southwestward on a compass course of 190°, the flight track approached a great structural trough, George VI Sound, one of the most interesting topographic features in Antarctica. The steep walls of this north-south trending fault depression are formed by mountains whose peaks range from less than 4000 feet to over 8000 feet high. The *Polar Star* passed very close to and southeast of Mount Courtauld (6900 ft.) and the Creswick Peaks as it flew the full length of Meiklejohn Glacier and out over George VI Sound to the foot of Pluto Glacier on the west side. From the notations in their respective logs it is apparent that both men were impressed by the magnitude of these mountains and the sheer slopes rising from the bottom of the sound.

At 14:25 G.C.T., as they were crossing the mountainous eastern wall of George

VI Sound, Ellsworth recorded in his journal, "Passed three prominent peaks of Eternity Range on our right. I named them Mt. Faith, Mt. Hope, and Mt. Charity. Saw no glaciers or crevassed surfaces." This would seem to eliminate the Mount Wakefield trio as the peaks Ellsworth intended for these names because they must have appeared on his left between 13:20 and 13:50. He could well have meant the three summits (3300, 4300, and 5100 feet, respectively) of the Creswick Peaks which he must have seen close aboard shortly before, and also he might well have included Mount Courtauld among the three. Farther north he must have seen Mount Dixey (4500 ft.) and Mount Flower (4400 ft.) for they were within range of his camera in photograph 19, taken at 14:13.[50] Whichever they were, they certainly were not the same peaks to which he had applied these names as of November 21.

Ellsworth took 13 photographs which show portions of George VI Sound. From these Joerg and his associates were able to make a reasonably good map of the sound.[51] Although somewhat out of position longitudinally, the relative position of the various topographic features with relation to one another has been confirmed by subsequent ground surveys.[52] In the interpretation of Ellsworth's photographs for the construction of map B, plate III, showing George VI Sound, Joerg was influenced by a preliminary report in the London *Times* regarding the independent rediscovery of this feature in 1936-37 by the British Graham Land Expedition which subsequently named it.[53] Yet, as Joerg pointed out, Ellsworth and Hollick-Kenyon were conscious of the corridor-like character of the sound at the time they discovered and photographed it for at 14:35, as the plane was flying across it, Hollick-Kenyon radioed the following dispatch to the *Wyatt Earp:*

> The big range to the right goes to the south for a long ways. To the left the country seems flat. On the east side of the range this wide, level-bottomed valley seems to run from the hinterland south right north towards the sea. The mountains here are sedimentary stratifications. Not very much folding.

This dispatch, although some of the words were missing due to faulty radio reception, was printed in the *New York Times* for November 24, 1935 (p. 36), along with other messages incorporated in a report radioed to the *Times* by Sir Hubert Wilkins.

The *Polar Star,* now at an altitude of 10,000 feet, flew on toward the southwest across the head of Uranus Glacier and across the southwestern part of Alexander Island. The western limb of George VI Sound was crossed in the vicinity of Eklund Islands, but neither Ellsworth nor Hollick-Kenyon made any note of it nor of the appearance of open water in the Ronne Entrance to the west.

Hollick-Kenyon held the plane on a southwesterly course (185° by compass) flying across the English Coast and over a vast, rolling, snow-covered surface above which rose an occasional nunatak. At 16:15 G.C.T., shortly after reaching the English Coast, the plane's radio failed to function due (as was later discovered) to a defective switch on the antenna lead. Prior to that, the *Polar Star* had been in continuous contact with the *Wyatt Earp* although the messages were not always completely clear to Walter J. Lanz, radio operator on the ship. The last message that was at all comprehensible, sent at 15:48 G.C.T., indicated that the plane was at 71° W and that everything was well. This was reassuring when, a short time later, all contact with the plane was ended. Lanz stayed at the radio for hours in an effort to regain contact with the plane and later, besides observing the prearranged schedule, sent a great many blind messages in the hope of making contact. Although Ellsworth knew the radio was not working, he decided not to land for repairs until they had at least crossed the 80th meridian.

At 17:09 G.C.T. Ellsworth estimated they had reached 80° W and he dropped an American flag as a sign of his having discovered this vast plain of glacial ice through which an occasional isolated range or nunatak protruded. Some of the latter were then visible to the right of the plane. He recorded in his journal his intention of naming this area James W. Ellsworth Land in honor of his father. At 17:18 Ellsworth photographed (Nos. 34 and 35) a small mountain range and some isolated nunataks to the right of the plane and shortly after photographed (No. 36), an isolated nunatak to the left. These were, of course, assumed to be west of 80° W as first reported by Joerg,[54] but when the navigation was later more thoroughly checked and corrected it was found that photograph 34 was taken from approximately 74½° S, 76° W. The flag was, therefore, also dropped east of the 80th meridian. Flags were dropped again, as shown by Hollick-Kenyon's flight log, at 17:45 when they estimated they had reached station nine (79°45′ S, 101°15′ W) on the precalculated navigation table. Corrections show, however, that this was still short of 80° W.

At 18 G.C.T., from an altitude of 10,000 feet, very distant peaks were visible on the port bow. An hour and a half later the nearest peaks were abeam and Ellsworth took the first of three photographs (No. 39) of the range which because of its solitary nature on the broad, featureless, snow-covered landscape he named the Sentinel Range. He estimated it was about 75 miles long. The highest peak, which he estimated to exceed 12,000 feet in elevation and which is located at 77°35′ S, 86°09′ W, he named Mount Mary Louise Ulmer[55] in honor of his wife. For a time another range, about 100 miles distant, was visible to the south. These were the last mountains they were to see. From now on it was just a broad expanse of white (Fig. 19).

Ellsworth and Hollick-Kenyon continued across the featureless upland of snow and ice for another two hours. From George VI Sound to a short distance east of the Sentinel Range the plane was flown at 10,000 feet on a course of 185°. At 18:45, 76½° S, 83½° W, the course was changed to 190° and this was held for two hours until the plane was west of the 95th meridian, when it was changed again to 186°. At 20:35 G.C.T., Hollick-Kenyon thought he saw water sky ahead and 10 minutes later he recorded the appearance of a heavy water sky to the north, in which quarter it was also hazy. Since they were then about 250 miles from the nearest water, Pine Island Bay, it is probable that the darkening of the sky to the northward was due to storm clouds. For the past 6 hours they had been flying at an altitude of 10,000 feet and at a speed of 120-125 miles per hour. They decided to drop down for a look at the surface and, finding the ground to be at an elevation of approximately 6000 feet, they leveled off at 6400 feet.

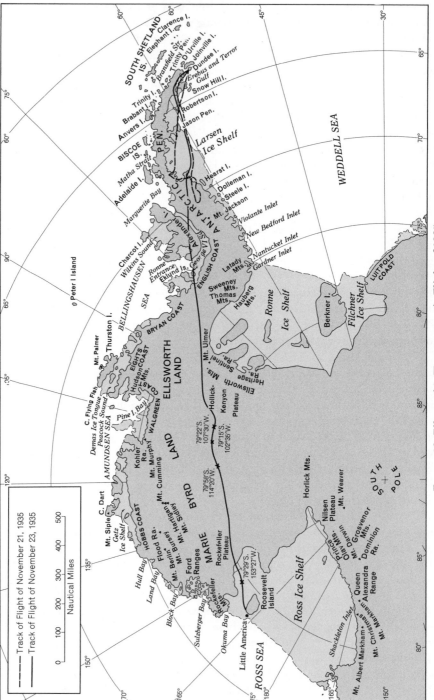

FIGURE 19. Ellsworth's Transantarctic Flight of 1935.

They had been in the air approximately 13 hours and, while they had followed the flight plan closely, they were not certain of their position. According to the plan, the elapsed flying time should have placed them near the 153rd meridian and not far from Little America but the position of the sun indicated otherwise. By 21:55 G.C.T. they decided to land to ascertain their position since visibility was getting poor. They had no trouble finding a smooth surface free of sastrugi but the plane landed hard on the granular snow covering the ice cap. The plane's skis hardly made an impression in the hard-packed surface. The altimeter showed the undulating plateau surface to be approximately 6400 feet above sea level. Over-snow traverses in the general area since 1957-58 indicate that this figure is about 1000 feet too high.

The location of this first landing was eventually determined to be 79°15′ S, 102°35′ W. They secured the plane and set up camp here, where they remained for 19 hours. Ellsworth raised the American flag and claimed the area between 80° W and 120° W for the United States. As he had done five hours earlier when he dropped the flag, he named this area in honor of his father. That part above 6000 feet he named the Hollick-Kenyon Plateau.

During the stay at camp I, Ellsworth and Hollick-Kenyon took sextant observations every three hours, but because the index error-adjustment screw had worked loose without their knowledge, they were unable to obtain satisfactory results. To save gasoline they set up the trail radio set rather than use the plane radio and the portable generator. They were unable, however, to contact the ship. On November 24, at 17:03 G.C.T. (shortly before noon, local time), they took off again for Little America.

The flight of November 24 was extremely short. After an easy takeoff from the hard surface with the now lightly loaded plane, the two men landed again in 30 minutes in the face of rapidly thickening weather. Here they remained for three days of unsettled weather during which time they took 30 careful sights of the sun's altitude. Since the sextant was still out of adjustment, the results were inconclusive. The large number of readings did prove advantageous, however, when the error was eventually discovered, for camp II finally became the point to which Joerg and his associates were able to fix the western end of the flight of November 23 in the construction of the maps from Ellsworth's photographs.[56] As finally determined, the position of camp II was 79°22′ S, 107°30′ W.

Late in the afternoon (23:35 G.C.T.), November 27, Ellsworth and Hollick-Kenyon took off again but the weather soon deteriorated. In 50 minutes they were forced to land for the third time. They scarcely had the plane secured and the tent pitched when a blizzard struck. The storm alternately raged and subsided, but for three days they were confined to their tent. During this time they discovered what was wrong with the sextant — that a loose set screw on the bubble had permitted the index scale to slip out of adjustment to the extent of 82 minutes of arc.

On December 1 the storm subsided and the lulls became longer. The occasional intervals of bright sunshine were used to take observations with the sextant. Putting the bubble on the snow horizon, Hollick-Kenyon set the index at zero and locked it there. This gave a reasonably accurate reading, and since the deviations in the readings taken at the other camps had been consistent, it was now possible to correct them. They now determined the location of camp III to be 79°58' S, 114°15' W, still more than 500 miles from their goal.

After he returned to the United States Ellsworth asked Lieutenant Commander P. V. H. Weems (USN, retired), an expert on aerial navigation, to make a postcalculation of his navigation. As a result, the 30 sights at camp II turned out to be the basis for correcting all others. The latitude originally determined for camp III was considered correct, but the longitude was changed to 114°20' W. So slight a modification was an indication of how successful the adjustment of the sextant on December 1 had been.

They also took advantage of the lulls in the bad weather at camp III to repair the plane's radio and to set up the portable generator, but at the first attempt to contact the ship on the prearranged schedule the magneto burned out. With the plane's radio dead they had to fall back on the trail set with the hand-cranked generator with which they had been trying three times daily to contact the *Wyatt Earp*. Although they failed to reach the ship, they succeeded on November 30 in getting three time signals from the Buenos Aires radio station which gave Ellsworth a check on his chronometer.

The three-day blizzard had practically buried the plane, and a great part of December 1 was spent shoveling out the plane and scooping out the snow which had sifted into the cockpit and tail section of the *Polar Star*. The next day they were prevented from taking off by snow which had drifted in and around the plane during the night and by continued unsettled weather. After more shoveling they started the engine and shortly after noon on December 3 they got the empty plane out of the drift that buried it. Before the plane was completely loaded, however, a storm broke from the southeast with thick snow and high winds.

Fortunately, this snowstorm did not last long and on the morning of December 4, although the weather looked ominous, the two men began once more to get the plane ready for flight. At 11:38 a. m. (19:15 G.C.T.) the *Polar Star* took off from camp III. An hour later the thick weather cleared and soon the sun shone brightly as they flew on toward the Bay of Whales. The undulating surface of the land was steadily dropping in elevation, and extensive areas of crevasses were seen.

At 23:10 G.C.T. they decided to land a fourth time to ascertain their position and to check their fuel supply. Although they erred slightly in their position, which was ultimately determined to be 79°29' S, 153°27' W, they knew they were now at an elevation of less than 1000 feet and near the edge of the Ross Ice Shelf, about 150 miles from the Bay of Whales. After spending the night here they took off again the next morning, December 5, at 8:58 local time.

During the next hour of flight a dark water sky was visible to the north and then at last the Ross Sea was visible. In a few minutes the engine began to sputter — the gas tanks were empty. The plane glided to a landing at 10:03 a. m. local time. The rest of the day was spent in securing the plane, making camp, and preparing to search for Little America, which dead reckoning told them was close at hand. They were, however, uncertain of the direction in which they should set out to find Byrd's camp, which they expected would be almost completely buried by snow with only ventilators and radio towers visible on the surface.

Although, as was later determined, they were only about 16 miles from Little America, they did not reach this haven until December 15, almost 11 days after landing. They were soon to find out how deceptive distances appear in the Antarctic. December 6 was spent in trying to reach a black object which they thought might be a stovepipe or ventilator at Little America but which turned out to be an empty gasoline can used by Byrd's expedition. Returning to the plane, they set out again the next day toward what looked like the ice-covered towers and roofs of Little America. Deceived by the apparent nearness of these objects they set out on what they thought would be a short hike, but later were forced to return for the sledge and food supplies stowed in the plane. By December 9 they discovered that the apparently ice-covered buildings and towers were in reality blocks of ice pushed up in pressure ridges.

Finally, on December 10, they were at last under way with the supplies and equipment necessary for a prolonged and serious search. Using a pocket compass for direction and traveling on a schedule of 15 minutes pulling in the harness and resting for 5, they sledged for 10 hours each day. Besides camping equipment the sledge carried a 10-day supply of food. The wet, heavy snow made pulling hard. Often they were plagued by fog and Ellsworth's foot was causing him trouble. It had been frostbitten, perhaps due to impaired circulation caused by the shrinking of a moccasin which had become wet at camp II on the transantarctic flight. They began to fear they would not find Little America, when on December 13 they came to the edge of the Ross Ice Shelf overlooking the Ross Sea. They then sledged westward where, as they had hoped, they came upon the Bay of Whales. Then trudging south they spotted two tractors half buried in the snow at Ver-Sur-Mer Inlet on December 15. Some time later they reached Little America where they entered the radio shack through a skylight.

On December 16 Ellsworth and Hollick-Kenyon busied themselves with making life comfortable at Little America until the *Wyatt Earp* should arrive in about a month. They found a small amount of coal, gasoline for the primus stove, and an assortment of food with which they could manage to get along until they were relieved by the ship. Later, at Ver-Sur-Mer Inlet, they erected the tent marked with two orange streamers as a signal to the *Wyatt Earp* when it arrived. A message was placed in the tent. As time dragged on, Ellsworth's foot became infected.

When radio contact with the *Polar Star* was broken off, a considerable popular alarm was felt for the safety of the two flyers. As a result, two different plans for relief of the men were put into effect.

1. On the initiative of Joseph A. Lyons, Prime Minister of Australia, the Commonwealth Government, along with that of New Zealand and the United Kingdom acting through the Discovery Committee of the Colonial Office, organized a joint relief effort. As a consequence the R. R. S. *Discovery II,* which was then

carrying out whaling and oceanographic investigations off the Queen Mary Coast, was ordered on December 3 to proceed to Melbourne. Here two airplanes, aviation personnel, sledging equipment, emergency supplies, and additional fuel oil were taken aboard. The *Discovery II* sailed for Dunedin, New Zealand, on December 23. Here additional fuel oil was taken on. Before the ship left Dunedin on January 2, 1936, a message was received from Sir Hubert Wilkins stating his confidence that Ellsworth had reached his objective, that he had sufficient food, and that he expected the *Wyatt Earp* to be at 70° S, 170° W by January 19.

The *Discovery II* reached the belt of pack ice in the Ross Sea on January 7, and spent a week in penetrating it to open water to the south. On two occasions a plane was sent aloft to reconnoiter a suitable passage to the south. On January 15 the edge of the Ross Ice Shelf was sighted and at 7:30 that evening the *Discovery II* entered the Bay of Whales, where Ellsworth's tent was soon sighted. When the ship's signals were not answered, a plane was sent aloft to circle the tent and to fly over Little America. While the plane was circling the latter, the noise of the motor attracted Hollick-Kenyon who ran out to signal the pilot. A message attached to an emergency food parcel was dropped by parachute.

In response to the message from Lieutenant Leonard C. Hill, Captain of the *Discovery II,* Hollick-Kenyon hurried down to Ver-Sur-Mer Inlet. Ellsworth's foot caused him to remain in camp. A party arrived from the ship on January 16, and that night Ellsworth returned with them to the *Discovery II,* where his foot was given medical attention. A radio message was sent to Melbourne announcing to the world that Ellsworth and his pilot were safe. The *Discovery II* had been in radio communication with the *Wyatt Earp* since leaving New Zealand and now, while awaiting the arrival of the latter, the *Discovery II* personnel engaged in scientific investigations in the Ross Sea in the vicinity of the Bay of Whales.

2. Finally, on November 26, after Lanz had been unsuccessful in his prolonged efforts to reestablish radio contact with the *Polar Star,* Sir Hubert Wilkins ordered the *Wyatt Earp* to sail for Deception Island. Drums of gasoline and a message placed in a cairn were left at Dundee Island. Arriving at Deception Island the next day, the *Wyatt Earp* was in a safer and much better position to carry out emergency relief action. Meanwhile Mrs. Ellsworth and friends, in regular contact with Sir Hubert, were organizing additional relief. A plane was chartered by them to fly to Magallanes, Chile, where it would be met by the *Wyatt Earp*. When this crashed at Atlanta, Georgia, on the way south, another Northrop "Gamma" monoplane, offered by the Texaco Company, was chartered and flown south by Dick Merrell, pilot, and William J. Klenke, Jr., mechanic. This plane was taken on board the *Wyatt Earp* at Magallanes on December 22, and the ship sailed the same evening for Charcot Island.

When the *Wyatt Earp* arrived off Charcot Island on December 28, a belt of dense impenetrable pack ice, 60 miles wide, lay between open water and the island. High wind, occasional snow squalls, and fog prevented the plane from taking off on a reconnaissance search to the south where a cache was scheduled to be laid according to the prearranged plan. On December 31 Sir Hubert decided it was futile to wait any longer, for he was confident that the *Polar Star* had reached her objective. If she had been forced down, he felt it was more likely to have been nearer the Bay of Whales than Charcot Island. Consequently, he proceeded directly for the Bay of Whales. The *Wyatt Earp* was sighted by the *Discovery II* at 6 p. m. on January 19, 1936, and the next day both ships were at the Bay of Whales.

It was now decided that Ellsworth should return to Australia on the *Discovery II* and that Hollick-Kenyon should join the *Wyatt Earp* to assist in the salvage of the *Polar Star,* which in the meantime had been spotted from the air by one of the pilots from the *Discovery II*. The *Discovery II* left the Bay of Whales at 12:40 a. m., January 22, sailing westward toward Cape Crozier, where a landing was made, and then north to Franklin Island — routine scientific investigation being conducted en route. The Balleny Islands also were visited and a running survey made. The ship arrived at Melbourne on February 16.

Meanwhile, Ellsworth's men had succeeded in getting one of Byrd's abandoned tractors started. With this they set out with a load of gasoline for the *Polar Star*. After crashing through a crevasse from which they rescued the tractor with much difficulty, they arrived at the plane, which was then flown to the Bay of Whales where it was placed on board the ship. A week after her arrival the *Wyatt Earp* sailed from the Bay of Whales, and by February 7 had cleared the pack ice of the Ross Sea. After a call at Valparaiso she passed through the Panama Canal and arrived at New York April 19, 1936. Ellsworth, having sailed from Australia on board the *Mariposa,* was there to greet his men.

NOTES

1. Between January 3 and 14, 1956, four planes attached to U. S. Navy Task Force 43 made nine long-distance, photographic flights from McMurdo Sound as part of the preliminaries to United States participation in the International Geophysical Year, 1957-58. Of these the following are especially noteworthy: On January 6 a 2PV Neptune Patrol Bomber, commanded by Lt. Comdr. John H. Torbert flew from McMurdo Sound to Vincennes Bay and then 120 miles farther west along the coast. The round trip, covering 2900 miles took 14½ hours. On January 13 a four-engine Skymaster transport (R-5D4), commanded by Lt. Col. H. R. Kolp (USMC), flew from McMurdo Sound to 82° S, 20° E, from there to the South Pole, and then back to the base, a distance of 2700 miles in less than 15 hours. A 2PV Neptune, commanded by Comdr. William Hawkes, took off from McMurdo Sound on January 13 and flew, via the South Pole, to the head of the Weddell Sea. The nonstop round trip, completed on January 14, covered 3450 miles in 19 hours. Although these three flights exceeded Ellsworth's one-way flight for distance, none of them exceeded his 1200 miles over unexplored territory.

2. Lincoln Ellsworth, *Beyond Horizons* (New York, 1937), p. 250.

3. In 1933, as a result of Wilkins' interpretation, based on his flight of November 26, 1928, the Antarctic Peninsula was considered to be a mountainous archipelago, and it was generally referred to as the Antarctic Archipelago.

4. Rudolf Staub, *Der Bewegungsmechanismus der Erde* (Berlin, 1928), pp. 117-118, map.

5. W. L. G. Joerg, "The Topographical Results of Ellsworth's Trans-Antarctic Flight of 1935," *Geographical Review,* vol. 26, No. 3, July, 1936, p. 461.

6. W. L. G. Joerg, "The Cartographical Results of Ellsworth's Trans-Antarctic Flight of 1935," *Geographical Review,* vol. 27, No. 3, July, 1937, pp. 430-444, Plate III.

7. The name first officially approved for this area by the U. S. Board on Geographic Names was Ellsworth Highland. As a result of five long-distance traverses over the surface of this area by U. S. parties between 1957 and 1962, it was found that a part of the area flown over by Ellsworth, north of the Filchner Ice Shelf from the base of the ·Antarctic Peninsula west to

about 100° W, was sufficiently distinctive to be called a land. In 1962 the name Ellsworth Land was officially approved for this area.

8. W. L. G. Joerg, "The Cartographical Results . . .," *op. cit.*, plates III-A, III-B, and III-C.

9. Ellsworth, *op. cit.*, p. 266.

10. *Ibid.*, p. 273.

11. *Ibid.*, p. 275.

12. *Ibid.*, p. 278.

13. *Ibid.*, p. 287, and George Grimminger and William C. Haines, "Meteorological Results of the Byrd Antarctic Expeditions, 1928-30, 1933-35: tables," *Monthly Weather Review,* supp. No. 41, October, 1939, pp. 58-59.

14. Ellsworth, *op. cit.*, pp. 289-290, and *New York Times,* March 6, 1935, p. 21.

15. *New York Times,* December 20, 1934, p. 21.

16. Ellsworth, *op. cit.*, p. 291.

17. *Ibid.*

18. *New York Times,* January 5, 1935, p. 15. Robertson Island is about 70 nautical or 80 statute miles from the point of takeoff on Snow Hill Island.

19. *Ibid.*

20. *Ibid.*

21. *Ibid.*, January 7, 1935, p. 14.

22. Comdr. Robert A. J. English, *Sailing Directions for Antarctica,* H. O. 138, U. S. Navy Hydrographic Office, Washington, 1943, pp. 267-268.

23. Falkland Islands Dependencies Survey, *South Shetlands and Graham Land,* 1:500,000, sheet B (1948); 1:200,000, sheets (65-60 (1955); 64-60 (1953); 64-58 (1955); 63-56 (1953). *Graham Land,* 1:100,000, sheets 64-56 NW. (1955); 63-58 SE. (1955); 63-56 SW. (1955). The Survey sheets, under the new scale of 1:200,000 were revised in 1964.

24. N. Otto G. Nordenskjöld and J. Gunnar Andersson, *Antarctica* (London, 1905), map, p. 316.

25. Ellsworth, *op. cit.*, p. 294.

26. *New York Times,* November 5, 1935, p. 32.

27. *Ibid.*, November 14, 1935, p. 14.

28. Ellsworth, *op. cit.*, pp. 304-305, 384-389.

29. *Ibid.*, pp. 308-310.

30. *New York Times,* November 21, 1935, pp. 1, 3.

31. *Map of the Antarctic,* 1:4,000,000, American Geographical Society (New York, 1929), American Quadrant. Also *Map of Antarctic Archipelago,* 1:2,500,000, insert on map of *Wilkins-Hearst Antarctic Expedition, 1928-1929,* 1:12,500,000, American Geographical Society (New York, 1929).

32. Ellsworth, *op. cit.*, p. 312. As features photographed and named by Wilkins have been identified as a result of work by later expeditions the generic portion of many of the names has been changed to conform to the latest concept regarding the nature of the feature. To assist readers who may wish to refer to the old maps, the following is a table of names of features named by Wilkins that are referred to in Chapter 19. Except for Scripps Island, on page 377, the latest accepted form of the name is used unless otherwise stated in the text. Name changes have been initiated by either the U. S. Board of Geographic Names or by the British Permanent Committee on Geographic Names, and approved by both.

Named By Wilkins	As Identified By Joerg, 1937	Special Publ. 86 U.S.B.G.N., 1947	Gazetteer 14-5 U.S.B.G.N., 1969
Casey Channel	Casey Glacier	Casey Glacier	Casey Glacier
Cape Eielson	——		——
Finley Islands	Finley Peninsula	Finley Ridge	Finley Heights
Hearst Land	——	Hearst Island	Hearst Island
Hektoria Fjords	——	——	Hektoria Glacier
Cape Keeler	Cape Keeler	Cape Keeler	Cape Keeler
Lurabee Channel	Lurabee Glacier	Lurabee Glacier	Lurabee Glacier
Cape Mayo	Cape Mayo	Cape Mayo	Cape Mayo
Mobiloil Bay	——	Mobiloil Bay	Mobiloil Inlet
Scripps Island	Scripps Peninsula	Scripps Ridge	Scripps Heights

33. Joerg, "The Topographical Results . . .," *op. cit.*, fig. 1, p. 455.

34. Joerg, "The Cartographical Results . . .," *op. cit.*, Plate III-A, opposite p. 444.

35. *Ibid.*, p. 430.

36. Alfred Stephenson and Arthur R. Hinks, "Diagram Relating the Discoveries of Wilkins and Ellsworth to those of the British Graham Land Expedition," *Geographical Journal*, vol. 96. No. 3, September, 1940, pp. 177-180, map opposite p. 234.

37. The Rymill photographs were actually made by Bingham on a sledging journey made by Rymill and Bingham from Marguerite Bay between October 26, 1936, and January 5, 1937. See John Rymill, *Southern Lights* (London, 1938), pp. 213-242, and John Rymill, "British Graham Land Expedition, 1934-37," *Geographical Journal*, vol. 91, No. 5, May, 1938, pp. 429-431.

38. K. J. Bertrand, W. L. G. Joerg, and H. E. Saunders, "The True Location of Stefansson Strait and Hearst Land, Antarctica," *Geographical Review*, vol. 38, No. 3, July, 1948, pp. 475-486.

39. Ellsworth, *op. cit.*, p. 312.

40. Stephenson and Hinks, "Diagram Relating the Discoveries . . .," *op. cit.*, opposite p. 234.

41. A careful examination of photographs 120 to 144 (right obliques) from flight M-6, December 22, 1947, of the Ronne Antarctic Research Expedition, fails to reveal features that resembled those shown in Ellsworth's A.6 and A.8. Correlation is especially difficult because the Ronne pictures were taken at right angles to the Ellsworth pictures.

42. It is quite probable that the altimeter of the *Polar Star* was recording inaccurately, for elevations of the peaks they had passed are lower than Ellsworth and Hollick-Kenyon estimated.

43. Ellsworth, *op. cit.*, p. 313.

44. *Geographical Journal*, vol. 96, No. 3, September, 1940, fig. EA, 5, p. 180.

45. "Back of coast range again, must be a howling gale here, haven't made much mileage. Two mountains passed on right NNW. . . . up are about abreast." [All messages between plane and ship were in Morse code.]

46. *New York Times*, November 23, 1935, p. 1.

47. Joerg, "The Cartographical Results . . .," *op. cit.*, p. 434.

48. Joerg, "The Topographical Results . . .," *op. cit.*

49. *Geographic Names of Antarctica*, Gazetteer No. 14, U. S. Board on Geographic Names, Washington, 1956, p. 122.

50. Joerg, "The Cartographical Results . . .," *op. cit.*, Plate III-B. On this plate Joerg has adjusted the time to show photograph 19 at 14:21. In this account the original time notation has been retained so as to correlate with the comment at 14:25.

51. *Ibid.*

52. Alfred Stephenson and Rev. W. L. S. Fleming, "King George the Sixth Sound," *Geographical Journal*, vol. 96, No. 3, September, 1940, pp. 153-166, map opposite p. 232. Also composite map on reverse side, opposite p. 233. *South Shetlands and Graham Land*, Falkland Islands Dependencies Survey, sheet G., 1:500,000, 1950.

53. Joerg, "The Cartographical Results . . .," *op. cit.*, pp. 440-442.

54. Joerg, "The Topographical Results . . .," *op. cit.*, figs. 15 and 16, p. 459.

55. The name officially approved by the U. S. Board on Geographic Names is Mount Ulmer. Its height was subsequently determined to be 8430 ft.

56. Joerg, "The Cartographical Results . . .," *op. cit.*, p. 433.

BIBLIOGRAPHY

PUBLISHED MATERIAL

Douglas, Vice Adm. Sir Percy, "Mr. Ellsworth and the *Discovery II*," *Polar Record*, vol. 2, No. 12, July, 1936, pp. 166-172.

———, "Mr. Ellsworth's Trans-Antarctic Flight," *Geographical Journal*, vol. 87, No. 5, April, 1936, pp. 351-358, map. An account of the voyage of the *Discovery II* to the Bay of Whales to rescue Ellsworth and Hollick-Kenyon.

Ellsworth, Lincoln, "To Antarctica Again," *Natural History*, vol. 34, No. 4, July-August, 1934, pp. 332-338.

———, *Beyond Horizons* (New York, Doubleday, Doran & Co., 1938), xii, 403 pp., illus., map. An autobiographical account, including both Arctic and Antarctic exploration.

———, "The First Crossing of Antarctica," *Geographical Journal*, vol. 89, No. 3, March, 1937, pp. 193-213, map. Reprinted in *Annual Report of the Board of Regents of the Smithsonian Institute for 1937* (Washington, 1938), pp. 307-321, plates 1-9. Also reprinted as Appendixes I, II, and III in Ellsworth's *Beyond Horizons*.

——, "My Flight Across Antarctica," *National Geographic Magazine*, vol. 70, No. 1, July, 1936, pp. 1-35, map. A preliminary narrative of the transantarctic flight. Some paragraphs repeated verbatim in Ellsworth's *Beyond Horizons*.

——, "Fortune and Misfortune in Antarctica, Adventures and Discoveries of the 1934-1935 Ellsworth Expedition to Graham Land," *Natural History*, vol. 35, No. 5, May, 1935, pp. 379-404. An account of Ellsworth's second attempt to make a transantarctic flight.

Grimminger, George, and William C. Haines, "Meteorological Results of the Byrd Antarctic Expeditions, 1928-30, 1933-35: Tables," *Monthly Weather Review*, supp. No. 41, October, 1939, Table 22, pp. 58-59. (Meteorological observations received by radio at Little America from the Ellsworth Expedition: October 22, 1934-November 26, 1934, from Deception Island; December 2, 1934-January 11, 1935, from Snow Hill Island.)

Joerg, W. L. G., "The Cartographical Results of Ellsworth's Trans-Antarctic Flight of 1935," *Geographical Review*, vol. 27, No. 3, July, 1937, pp. 430-444, maps. This article and the accompanying maps represent the principal geographical and scientific results of the Ellsworth transantarctic flight.

——, "Demonstration of the Peninsularity of Palmer Land, Antarctica, Through Ellsworth's Flight of 1935," *Proceedings of the American Philosophical Society*, vol. 82, No. 5, June 29, 1940, pp. 821-832.

——, "The Topographical Results of Ellsworth's Trans-Antarctic Flight of 1935," *Geographical Review*, vol. 26, No. 3, July, 1936, pp. 454-462.

The *New York Times* and North American Newspaper Alliance: Articles of Apr. 5, 1933, p. 21; July 30, 1933, sec. II, p. 1; Aug. 2, 1933, p. 17; Nov. 28, 1933, p. 23; Jan. 30, 1934, p. 11; Sept. 15, 1934, p. 17; Sept. 19, 1934, p. 4; Dec. 3, 1934, p. 19; Dec. 20, 1934, p. 21; Jan. 4, 1935, p. 1; Jan. 5, 1935, p. 15; Jan. 7, 1935, p. 14; Jan. 12, 1935, p. 17; Jan. 14, 1935, p. 5; Jan. 18, 1935, p. 25; Jan. 19, 1935, p. 15; Jan. 22, 1935, p. 21; Feb. 2, 1935, p. 15; Feb. 18, 1935, p. 4; Mar. 6, 1935, p. 21; Oct. 25, 1935, p. 17; Oct. 31, 1935, p. 14; Nov. 4, 1935, p. 23; Nov. 5, 1935, p. 32; Nov. 12, 1935, p. 21; Nov. 14, 1935, p. 14; Nov. 19, 1935, p. 2; Nov. 20, 1935, p. 1; Nov. 22, 1935, p. 1; Nov. 23, 1935, p. 1; and Nov. 24, 1935, p. 1. Scattered articles through April 1936.

Stephenson, Alfred, and Arthur R. Hinks, "Diagram Relating the Discoveries of Wilkins and Ellsworth to those of the British Graham Land Expedition," *Geographical Journal*, vol. 96. No. 3, September, 1940, pp. 177-180, map opposite p. 234.

MANUSCRIPT MATERIAL

Files of the Department of State.

Manuscript material on the Ellsworth Expedition on file at the American Geographical Society of New York, including typescript copies of Ellsworth's Journal, Hollick-Kenyon's flight log, and messages received by the *Wyatt Earp* from the *Polar Star*.

20

THE ELLSWORTH ANTARCTIC
EXPEDITION, 1938-1939

ORGANIZATION AND ACCOMPLISHMENTS

SIGNIFICANCE OF THE EXPEDITION

Lincoln Ellsworth's Antarctic Expedition of 1938-39 marked a renewal of American interest in the Indian Ocean sector of Antarctica. The United States Exploring Expedition under Lieutenant Charles Wilkes in 1840 initiated American interest in this sector. Captain John J. Heard discovered Heard Island in 1853, and New London whalers and elephant sealers during the middle of the 19th century were active in the vicinity of Kerguelen Island for decades, occupying Heard Island continuously for more than 20 years. This activity, however, had been reduced to insignificance for almost 50 years when Ellsworth again brought the American flag into the Antarctic margin of the Indian Ocean.

His expedition of 1938-39 was also the last Antarctic expedition of any nation to be financed entirely by private funds. Considering the increasing complexity of modern exploring expeditions, it is doubtful that such privately financed undertakings will be organized in the future (Fig. 20).

ESTABLISHMENT AND COMPOSITION OF THE PROJECT

As in the case of Ellsworth's previous Antarctic expeditions, that of 1938-39 was organized and personally financed by him. He also had, as before, a contract with the *New York Times* and the North American Newspaper Alliance for supplying exclusive news reports. As technical adviser and manager, Sir Hubert Wilkins assisted Ellsworth in the organization of the expedition.

On this, his fourth Antarctic expedition, Ellsworth again used the *Wyatt Earp,* the ship he had purchased in 1933 and had used on his previous Antarctic expeditions. It has been described in Chapter 19. At the close of his Transantarctic Flight Expedition in 1936 the vessel had been berthed at Aalesund, Norway, where in the early summer of 1938 it was reconditioned for this expedition.

The expedition was equipped with two airplanes. The larger was an all-metal Northrop Delta monoplane with a 750-horsepower Wright cyclone engine. All but two seats were removed from the cabin to make room for additional gasoline tanks which extended the cruising range of the plane to 2000 miles. As an auxiliary plane for reconnaissance work, for use in case of emergency, and for communication between the ship and the flying field that they hoped to establish on the ice, Ellsworth obtained a small Aeronca two-seated scouting plane. To take advantage of any flying opportunity, both planes were equipped with wheels, pontoons, and skis. Both also had two-way radios.

The personnel of the expedition of 1938-39 included 19 men. As on his pre-

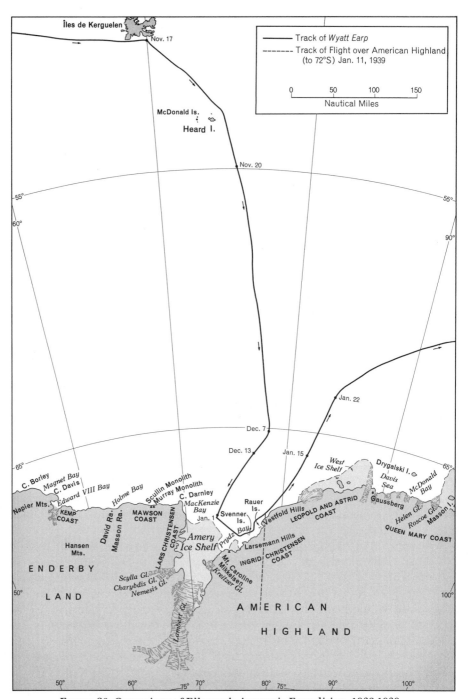

FIGURE 20. Operations of Ellsworth Antarctic Expedition, 1938-1939.

vious expeditions, Ellsworth was organizer, leader, and aerial navigator, and Wilkins was again technical adviser and manager. In the latter role Sir Hubert took an active part in the preparations and procurement for the expedition. J. H. Lymburner, who had served as reserve pilot on Ellsworth's 1935-36 Expedition, was appointed chief pilot. Burton J. Trerice of St. Johns, Quebec, and Amherst, Nova Scotia, was reserve pilot and flight engineer.[1] Trerice had been a transport pilot in northern Quebec. Dr. Harmon F. Rhoads, Jr., of Everett, Wash., was medical officer, and Frederick Seid of New York City was radio operator. All of the officers and crew of the *Wyatt Earp* were Norwegians. Captain Londer Johansen had been gunner and captain of a whale catcher in the Antarctic. First Mate Liavaag, Chief Steward Dahl, and Second Engineer Sperre were veterans of other Ellsworth expeditions.

OBJECTIVES AND ACCOMPLISHMENTS

The principal objective of the expedition was to launch a number of triangular flights into the Indian Ocean sector of Antarctica, an area of 750,000 square miles, the interior of which was then practically unknown. Of secondary importance, only because it was less certain of achievement, was Ellsworth's plan for a second transcontinental flight. If ice conditions allowed them an early start and if weather permitted, he hoped to fly from the Indian Ocean sector over the South Pole to the Bay of Whales, a distance of approximately 2000 miles. Here he and his pilot would wait until the *Wyatt Earp* picked them up later in the season. While this flight was something in the nature of the spectacular, it was not inconsistent with Ellsworth's purpose of discovering the character of the interior of the continent in this sector.

Ellsworth proposed to cruise along the edge of the pack ice until he was able to force his ship through the ice to the edge of the continent, where he hoped to find a surface suitable for taking off and landing the Northrop Delta monoplane. He hoped to be able to unload the plane directly on shelf ice, on solid bay ice, or on the sloping edge of the continental glacier from where it might be taxied or pulled to a suitable flying field. To facilitate flying operations a tent camp would be set up at such a point, but the *Wyatt Earp* would continue to be the headquarters of the expedition.

On the proposed triangular flights, covering a fan-shaped area, Ellsworth planned to photograph as much of the unknown interior as possible. He also hoped to be able to delineate the coastline more completely than it was then shown on the latest charts,[2] and also hoped to be able to locate a site for a possible future meteorological station.[3]

An extremely wide and difficult band of pack ice bordering the Indian Ocean sector in November and December 1938 prevented the *Wyatt Earp* from reaching the edge of the continent until the season of the best flying weather was over. This fact and the lack of a satisfactory surface for a takeoff with a full load of gasoline made a long flight impossible. The operations were further limited when a serious accident to First Mate Liavaag caused Ellsworth to order the ship northward on January 15. As a consequence the expedition fell considerably short of fulfilling its objectives. The accomplishments, briefly stated, are as follows:

(1) On January 11, 1939, a 3-hour flight was made inland from the coast along the 79th meridian for a distance of approximately 240 miles. This flight supplied the first knowledge of the interior in this part of Antarctica. The snow-covered surface, riffled by sastrugi but unbroken by terrain features, was found to rise steadily from the coast toward the interior.

(2) Three reconnaissance flights were made in the region of Prydz Bay. On January 1, 1939, a flight was made over the Amery Ice Shelf. Another was made along the Ingrid Christensen Coast on January 3, and a third was made along the same coast as far as the West Ice Shelf on January 10.

(3) Some of the Svenner Islands and some of the Rauer Islands were visited and geological specimens collected.

(4) As a result of the flight of January 11, Ellsworth claimed for the United States approximately 80,000 square miles of territory, which he named American Highland.

DETAILED RECORD OF OPERATIONS

DEPARTURE FOR ANTARCTICA

In May of 1938 Wilkins visited Aalesund, Norway, to arrange for the reconditioning of the *Wyatt Earp,* berthed there since 1936, and to hire a crew for the 1938-39 Expedition. On August 12, 1938, the *Wyatt Earp* arrived at the seaplane base of Floyd Bennett Field, New York, to take on board the two planes to be used by the expedition. The wings were removed from the larger plane, which was stowed in the hold, and the small Aeronca scouting plane was placed on deck. Meanwhile Ellsworth, with Mrs. Ellsworth, had sailed for Southampton on July 26. After a hunting trip in Africa he planned to join the expedition at Cape Town. Sir Hubert, after completing arrangements in this country, flew first to Australia and then to Cape Town to join the expedition.

At 12:30 p. m., August 16, 1938, the *Wyatt Earp* sailed for Antarctica. The ship put into port at Pernambuco, Brazil, on September 13, and after taking on supplies left the next day for Cape Town where she arrived on October 9.

THE OUTWARD VOYAGE

With the expedition fully assembled, the *Wyatt Earp* sailed from Cape Town at noon, October 29. After the usual rough passage through the "Roaring Forties" the expedition reached Kerguelen Island, November 14. Here the *Wyatt Earp* was moored for three days in Passe Royale (Royal Sound) while the engine was cleaned, the supply of fresh water replenished, and the deck cargo of fuel oil transferred to the bunkers to clear the deck for the heavy seas and storms anticipated in Antarctic waters. An abundance of rabbits and teal found on the nearby islands were killed to augment the supply of fresh meat, and a few Ross seals found on one of the beaches were also taken. They experienced the usual Kerguelen weather during the three days. Both anchors and three heavy mooring lines from both the bow and the stern were required to hold the ship as it was buffeted by a series of gales with snow and winds of more than 60 miles per hour.[4]

The *Wyatt Earp* cleared Passe Royale (Royal Sound) for Heard Island on November 17, but continued bad weather with snow, sleet, and very high seas prevented a landing there. In the vicinity of Heard Island the ship, sheathed in ice from sleet and frozen spray, wallowed through extremely rough seas whipped up by winds of more than 50 miles per hour. The storms subsided and the weather cleared on November 20. That night, at midnight, in about 55° S, 75° E, the *Wyatt Earp* encountered the outer edge of the pack ice. Visibility having been reduced to zero by a shower of ice crystals falling in the cold air, the presence of the pack was announced by the thumping of the floes against the hull as they rose on the swell.[5]

Experience of other expeditions and whalers who have cruised in the Indian Ocean bordering Antarctica reveals that ice conditions in this sector vary a great deal from year to year. Ellsworth was surprised to meet the pack this far north. It indicated that this was a year of exceptionally bad ice conditions. Forty-five days were spent working through this band of ice, approximately 800 miles wide.[6]

Fairly rapid progress was made the first seven days as the *Wyatt Earp* worked its way through 570 miles of generally heavy but scattered floes. As the vessel pushed southward the pack became tighter, and progress was slowed accordingly. Much of this heavy pack was two-year-old ice. On two occasions Lymburner took off in the small Aeronca plane from patches of open water to scout for promising leads through the pack. By December 7 the ship had reached 65° 09' S, 78°06' E, having made only about 70 miles in 10 days. During the last two of those days the propeller did not turn as the vessel drifted slowly with the pack.[7] With no room to maneuver between the tightly packed floes, the *Wyatt Earp* continued to drift with the pack until December 13. During that time the vessel was occasionally in danger of being carried by the drifting ice against icebergs which were scattered through the pack. Collisions were avoided in each case by squeezing to one side of the berg. This was accomplished by forcing the vessel at full speed through the brash ice that filled the spaces between the floes. On one of these occasions a hot spark from the engine exhaust was forced through the stack and ignited the fabric wing of the Aeronca plane. Fortunately, Lymburner, who was on deck at the time, extinguished the fire before irreparable damage was done.[8]

After seven days of imprisonment, the *Wyatt Earp* finally broke free of the tightly pressed pack at 1 a. m., December 13, but the freedom was short-lived. At 4 p. m. the same day, after having worked her way through loose pack for 70 miles, the vessel's position was approximately 66° S, 77° E, but to the south there were signs that the pack was closing up again.[9] Soon the ship met heavy, closely packed, impenetrable floes, and during the last 15 days of December she lay drifting with the pack. Although the pack drifted in several directions during this time, a southerly direction seemed to predominate.

During this period of idle drifting, waiting for the wind to shift and loosen the pack, it was discovered that two of the hardwood planks of the outer sheathing on the bow of the vessel had been ripped off by the ice. The main planking, too, bore a gouge an inch and a half deep and several feet long. This was a serious situation, but as Ellsworth related in a radio dispatch to the *New York Times*, the Norwegian crew took advantage of the ship's position to repair the damage at once:

> With a sling about a heavy mass of ice and a block and tackle to the mast head, the ship was careened, and by shifting oil and supplies from one side of the ship to the other we brought the damaged part above the water line and undertook repairs.
>
> Standing on a convenient ice floe the carpenter chiseled out the damaged parts and fitted in new planks and now the ship is as sound as she was when we entered the ice.[10]

Considering that the *Wyatt Earp* was a vessel of 400 tons and 135 feet long, this was no mean feat.

THE SEARCH FOR A FLYING FIELD

As the new year dawned the leads began to open and the *Wyatt Earp* began again to push southward. At 3 a. m., January 1, 1939, the icebound coast of Antarctica was seen. The ship was approaching the outer edge of the Amery Ice Shelf on the eastern side of Mackenzie Bay.[11] Shortly after sighting the continental ice, the southerly progress of the *Wyatt Earp* was halted by impenetrable pack ice. When a reconnaissance flight in the Aeronca showed the pack to be solidly pressed against the shelf ice, the ship was turned eastward, slowly pushing through heavy pack, brash, and slush in search of open leads across Prydz Bay toward Ingrid Christensen Coast.[12] At 11 a. m., January 2, they made the first attempt at getting up against the land, but were thwarted by a series of heavy snow squalls which blotted out all visibility. After cruising slowly in open water during the afternoon, they took advantage of a lull between squalls to try again at 7 p. m. This time a band of heavy pack ice fringing the shore prevented their landing.[13]

Early on January 3 the weather cleared sufficiently to permit the Aeronca, fitted with floats, to be taken aloft on a scouting flight along Ingrid Christensen Coast. In a short time a passage through the pack ice was discovered, enabling the *Wyatt Earp* to work free into a broad area of open water in Prydz Bay. The ship was thus able to sail within a short distance of the Svenner Islands which lie about 10 miles off the Ingrid Christensen Coast near the head of Prydz Bay.[14] The *Wyatt Earp* was moored at approximately 69° 10' S, 76° 30' E, against the edge of an expanse of level bay ice lying between the Svenner Islands and the mainland. This ice looked as though it would provide a satisfactory flying field, but it was only one year old and considerably honeycombed by melting. Consequently, Ellsworth feared that it would not safely hold the weight of the big Northrop Delta plane on takeoff.

While they were moored against the ice on January 3, Ellsworth landed on one of the Svenner Islands to collect geological specimens. He found the island to consist mainly of coarse-grained granite and gneiss, presumably of Precambrian age. One band of weathered rock contained many garnets.[15] Although the Svenner Islands had been discovered by Klarius Mikkelsen in February 1935, this was apparently the first landing that had been made there. Taking advantage of the mooring place, the Northrop plane was brought on deck for the first time, and the crew began to assemble it.

Since the area of bay ice adjacent to the Svenner Islands was not completely satisfactory as a flying field, Ellsworth decided to seek further. He saw that the continental ice also was unsatisfactory. The slope of the glacial ice down to the sea was much too steep and was also badly crevassed. Consequently, they decided to move over to the Rauer Islands which they could see over against the mainland about 20 miles to the northeast. Late on January 3 the *Wyatt Earp* got under way.

AT THE RAUER ISLANDS

On January 5, after having reconnoitered the Rauer Islands and the Ingrid Christensen Coast both to the north and the south, the *Wyatt Earp* was moored to a piece of level bay ice so located that adjacent members of the Rauer Islands formed a protected harbor for the ship. A huge serrated iceberg which had broken off a nearby glacier tongue lay grounded about two miles from shore and only 200 yards from the ship. Ellsworth thought that the iceberg was responsible for the bay ice having been held in place. This expanse of one-year-old ice was not entirely satisfactory, but Ellsworth called it "the only possible flying field in this vicinity."[16] It was thin, somewhat pitted by melting, and considered treacherous during the warmer part of the day.

Early on January 6 the big Northrop plane having been brought out of the hold on January 3 and now assembled on deck, was made ready for a flight. Before the plane could be put down on the ice, however, clouds began to roll in from the northeast. The weather continued to deteriorate until even the little Aeronca could not be taken aloft. Once the planes were secured, Ellsworth, in company with others of the expedition, landed on some of the Rauer Islands to gather geological specimens while waiting for the weather to improve.

Conditions were still unsatisfactory for flying on January 7. Early in the morning the men were alarmed when the big neighboring iceberg, which they had assumed to be grounded, began to move, threatening to crush the ship against the edge of the bay ice. The gasoline drums standing on the ice in preparation for loading the plane were hurriedly taken on board. Lines were cast off and the *Wyatt Earp*, with no room for maneuvering, moved astern quickly to a position farther out on the sheet of bay ice.[17]

After avoiding this disaster, another day of waiting for satisfactory flying conditions followed. Serious trouble occurred again on January 9. For a second time they were forced to move the *Wyatt Earp* away from the edge of the sheet of bay ice among the Rauer Islands, where it was moored. This time they were threatened by a large and heavy ice floe which was being forced down upon them by several icebergs. The *Wyatt Earp* was moved to the other side of the sheet of bay ice. Here, however, conditions were not suitable for flying, and it was just a matter of waiting for an opportunity for returning to the former mooring. In the meantime Ellsworth went ashore on the rocky strand of the continent which projects from under the wasting edge of the continental glacier.

On the evening of January 9, when the wind changed from west to east and began blowing offshore, Ellsworth decided to return to the old mooring to wait for satisfactory flying weather. They were surprised to find conditions completely changed when they arrived there. What had been fast ice had broken loose and had moved several miles north, blocking off the entrance to the island harbor. The bay ice from which they had hoped to take off had broken up, and part of it was drifting out to sea; that which remained was hopeless as a flying field.[18] If they were to take off from skis, there was no alternative to going in search of another suitable expanse of ice. Since the weather was showing signs of clearing, it was important to begin the search immediately.

The *Wyatt Earp* was now, on the evening of January 9, headed northeastward beyond the Rauer Islands and along the shore of the Vestfold Hills. Reaching the limit of their former reconnaissance of a week earlier, Lymburner took off from the water in the Aeronca plane to reconnoiter the coast and the ice conditions to the northeastward. Presumably going as far as the West Ice Shelf, he returned after a flight of 1 hour and 40 minutes to report "a possibility of finding room enough to take off in a small fjord, just where the end of the Great West Barrier meets the bare granite hill at Long. 79° E."[19] After Lymburner returned to the ship it took the *Wyatt Earp* five hours of tortuous maneuvering through fields of floating icebergs, dodging the capsizing sides of the bergs and the calving fronts of ice tongues, and avoiding submerged or partially submerged rocks to reach the site selected for the airfield. A small boat, powered by an outboard motor, was used to pilot the vessel through the most dangerous places.

During the night of January 10, after the *Wyatt Earp* had reached the new mooring place northeast of the Vestfold Hills, a strong easterly wind set in and heavy seas began pounding against the ice to which the ship was moored. The edges of the ice began to crumble, and the vessel was constantly being pounded against the ice. To risk running against a submerged rock, of which there were many in the area, seemed even more dangerous, so instead of moving away they held the *Wyatt Earp* against the ice until an iceberg began bearing down upon the ship. Then they slipped the moorings and moved cautiously into a little bight in the ice right next to its junction with the solid rock. Here they were afforded a small degree of shelter.

The January 11 Flight into the Interior

The area of level ice to which the *Wyatt Earp* was moored seemed to be the last hope for a takeoff with skis in this area, for in his reconnaissance flight Lymburner had found no other suitable site. While it was fairly smooth it was only large enough to permit a takeoff with a limited load of gasoline, so a flight of much more than three hours duration was out of the question. Even this seemed doubtful for, as the waves continued to pound the outer edges, more and more ice broke off and floated away. Fortunately the wind died down about noon on January 11 before all of the ice was broken up.

As the weather cleared, the Northrop plane was swung onto the ice and the smaller tanks filled with gasoline in preparation for a test flight because the plane had not been flown since it left New York. The test flight takeoff confirmed the poor condition of the ice for that purpose. By the time the plane returned from the test flight the sky had already begun to cloud up to the north, but since the weather appeared clear to the south Ellsworth and Lymburner decided to take a chance on a flight over the continent to the south. Enough gasoline for a little more than a three-hour flight was put in the tanks and provisions for two men for five weeks were put aboard.

Just after 6 p. m. local time (12:55 p. m. Greenwich mean time), Ellsworth and Lymburner took off and headed south along the 79th meridian. To the north, the sea was dotted with thousands of icebergs, and in the distance could be seen the band of pack ice. The Vestfold Hills, a peninsular and insular area of bare rock roughly 10 miles long and 15 miles wide, stood out darkly to the southeast in contrast to the white continental icecap which no longer covered them. To the south and to the east all was white. For the first 50 miles inland the continental glacier surface was greatly crevassed. Ellsworth noted that landing a plane would have been disastrous here and even foot travel would have been hazardous if not impossible over this steep continental slope.[20]

As they flew inland they climbed quickly to 7000 feet and then to 11,500 feet as the continental slope rose below them. Once in from the coast no rock features were visible, and beyond the 50-mile belt of crevassed ice the surface smoothed out to "a vast and apparently limitless expanse of ice and snow. . . . The horizon was, for 180 degrees and as far as we could see, straight edged and unmarked by color or contour. Visibility was perfect in all directions except north, where, behind us, the ominous storm clouds were thickening and banking higher."[21] The interior surface was marked by huge sastrugi running from east to west which gave the appearance "somewhat like a gigantic white plowed field."[22] There were, however, patches of smooth snow which Ellsworth estimated would permit a safe emergency landing.

When the gasoline supply had been about half consumed, Ellsworth estimated the plane's position at 72° S, 79° E, about 210 miles from the coast where they had taken off at 68°30' S. In the clear visibility then prevailing, Ellsworth estimated that they could see more than 110 miles farther over the snowy surface, which seemed to rise steadily toward the Polar plateau. It was now time to return to the ship, and, as a formal act of laying claim to the territory which he had just discovered, Ellsworth dropped a brass cylinder containing the following message:

To whom it may concern: Having flown on a direct course from latitude 68:30 south, longitude 79:00 east, to latitude 72 degrees south, longitude 79 east, I drop this record, together with the flag of the United States of America, and claim for my country, so far as this act allows, the area south of latitude 70 to a distance of 150 miles east and 150 miles west of my line of flight and to a distance of 150 miles south of latitude 72 south, longitude 79 east which I claim to have explored, dated Jan. 11, 1939. Lincoln Ellsworth.[23]

Lymburner then put the plane in a turn, and they flew back over their outward course into the clouded northern sky. They came out directly over the ship and, after circling a few times, landed.

High winds were pounding the *Wyatt Earp* against the ice, and huge pieces were breaking from the edge of the ice and floating out to sea. Since it was evident that the ice could not last long if this situation continued, little hope was held for its further use as a flying field. The big plane was hoisted aboard and the lines cast off.

As the *Wyatt Earp* moved slowly and cautiously along the coast seeking shelter from the strong east wind, Ellsworth sent a radio dispatch to the *New York Times* giving an account of the flight and of his formal act of claiming the territory for the United States. Thus the world was first informed of his discovery in the *New York Times* of January 12 and of his territorial claim (including a copy of the message contained in the cylinder dropped at the turning point in the flight) in the *New York Times* of January 13, 1939.

EXPLORATION TERMINATED BY AN ACCIDENT

The storm which drove the *Wyatt Earp* away from its moorings on the night of January 11 continued for two days. Then an accident occurred to First Mate Liavaag, which caused Ellsworth to give up any further work and return north. Three men were on a bergy bit, from which they were chipping pieces of ice to fill the fresh water tanks, when part of the block of ice broke off and threw the men into the water. Liavaag was caught between two pieces of ice, crushing his knee and breaking his kneecap. After the three were pulled from the icy water and examined by Dr. Rhoads it was apparent that Liavaag's injury required surgery which would be difficult to perform on board ship. At this point Ellsworth decided to give up further attempts at flying over the interior and return at once to the nearest port where hospital facilities were available.[24]

THE RETURN VOYAGE

The *Wyatt Earp* had clear running to the northeastward, roughly paralleling the margin of the West Ice Shelf, until the afternoon of January 15 when very heavy pack ice was encountered at about 66° S, 82° E. During the night of January 14, on its run to the northeast, the vessel was pounded by very heavy seas which stove in the bridge and carried away the heavy iron stanchions. It took five days of bucking through heavy pack in overcast weather with repeated snow squalls for the *Wyatt Earp* to break through into the open sea to the north. Part of the 150-mile struggle through the pack was negotiated almost a foot at a time by repeated ramming and slewing through the heavy floes.[25] On February 4, 1939, the *Wyatt Earp* arrived at Hobart, Tasmania.

POSTSCRIPT TO THE EXPEDITION

After Ellsworth arrived at Hobart he publicly reaffirmed his claim to the territory over which he had flown on January 11 and increased the area involved from the original estimate of 80,000 square miles to 430,000 square miles. His claim was immediately disputed by the Australian Government, and high officials began considering further Australian exploration in the Antarctic. As a result, at the recommendation of Sir Douglas Mawson, the Government purchased the *Wyatt Earp* from Ellsworth for £4400. On February 13, 1939, Prime Minister Joseph A. Lyons announced that the *Wyatt Earp* would be used by the Government for Antarctic exploration.[26]

After the sale of the *Wyatt Earp,* the Expedition was disbanded, with the various members returning to their homes by commercial carrier. Ellsworth announced on February 29 in Sydney that he intended to name the area of 80,000 square miles which he claimed as a result of discovery on his flight of January 11 "American Highland." He also announced plans for further explorations, but these eventually were canceled due to World War II.[27] On March 20, 1939, Lincoln Ellsworth arrived in Los Angeles. On April 18, 1939, he turned over to the Department of State, during a conference with Secretary of State Cordell Hull, a full report, dated April 17, 1939, of his four expeditions to the Antarctic. In this were accounts of his formal acts of making territorial claims in 1935 and 1939.[28]

NOTES

1. In his news dispatches Ellsworth listed the name as T. R. Trerice, but the *New York Times* article of Aug. 17, 1938, p. 3, describing the departure of the *Wyatt Earp* from New York, gave the full name as used above.

2. At the time he announced his plans in the *New York Times,* May 6, 1938, Ellsworth may not have known that practically the entire coast from Enderby Land to the West Ice Shelf, 15°30′ E to 81°20′ E had been photographed by Widerbøe and Romnaes of Lars Christensen's Expedition in 1937. A preliminary report (Lars Christensen, *My Last Expedition to Antarctica 1936-1937*) was published in Oslo in 1938. The charts resulting from this work were not published until 1946. See H. E. Hansen, *Atlas of Parts of the Antarctic Coastal Lands* (Oslo, 1946). By the time his expedition sailed, however, Ellsworth must have learned of the 1937 photography from his Norwegian crew. Certainly in his subsequent reconnaissance flights along the Ingrid Christensen Coast he made no efforts to photograph it. To be thus anticipated was not a serious setback for Ellsworth, for he was primarily interested in the interior. The proposed delineation of the coast would have been only incidental to the exploration of the interior.

3. Ellsworth's plans were outlined in three articles in the *New York Times,* May 6, 1938, p. 1; May 19, 1938, p. 7; and July 25, 1938, p. 4.

4. *New York Times,* November 19, 1938, p. 15.

5. *Ibid.,* November 22, 1938, p. 25.

6. Lincoln Ellsworth, "My Four Antarctic Expeditions," *National Geographic Magazine,* vol. 76, No. 1, July, 1939, p. 129.

7. *New York Times,* December 8, 1938, p. 20.

8. *Ibid.,* December 14, 1938, p. 27.

9. *Ibid.*

10. *Ibid.,* January 3, 1939, p. 5.

11. Discovered by Sir Douglas Mawson's B.A.N.Z. A.R.E. in February, 1931. See Sir Douglas Mawson, "B. A. N. Z. Antarctic Research Expedition, 1929-31," *Geographical Journal,* vol. 80, No. 2, August, 1932, p. 120.

12. *New York Times,* January 3, 1939, p. 5.

13. *Ibid.,* January 4, 1939, p. 23.

14. The Ingrid Christensen Coast was discovered by Capt. Klarius Mikkelsen of the Norwegian tanker *Thorshavn* on February 19, 1935. The next day he, his wife, and seven men landed at 68°39′ S, 78°36′ E. On February 21 he completed his exploration of Prydz Bay under ice conditions apparently much more favorable than those prevailing in 1938-39. See "Norwegian Discoveries in the Antarctic, 1935," *Polar Record,* vol. 2, No. 10, July, 1935, pp. 126-129. "Nytt Norsk Land I Antarktis, *Polar-Arboken"* (Oslo, Norsk Polarklubb, 1935), pp. 131-132.

15. *New York Times,* January 4, 1939, p. 23.

16. *Ibid.,* January 6, 1939, p. 23.

17. *Ibid.,* January 8, 1939, pp. 1-18.

18. *Ibid.*, January 12, 1939, pp. 1, 7.
19. *Ibid.* In view of the coastal representation shown on sheets 11 and 12 of H. E. Hansen's *Atlas of Parts of the Antarctic Coastal Lands, op. cit.*, based on aerial photographs taken by Widere and Romnaes in 1937, and also in consideration of aerial photography by U. S. Operation Highjump in 1947 and later Australian work, it would seem that Ellsworth was mistaken in his longitude. Terrain fitting his description was much more likely to have been found immediately northeast of the Vestfold Hills in the vicinity of 78°30′ E. Beyond the Vestfold Hills, which are free of ice, the continental ice sheet spills over the land directly into the sea.
20. *New York Times,* January 13, 1939, p. 21.
21. *Ibid.*
22. *Ibid.*
23. *Ibid.*
24. *Ibid.*, January 16, 1939, p. 17.
25. *Ibid.*, January 23, 1939, p. 15.
26. *Ibid.*, February 9, 1939, p. 5, 20, February 14, p. 20. The proposed expedition was postponed until after World War II.
27. *Ibid.*, March 1, 1939, p. 23.
28. State Department File 031.11, Ellsworth Antarctic Expedition/III.

BIBLIOGRAPHY

PUBLISHED MATERIAL

"The Course of Antarctic Exploration Between Longitudes 20° W and 110° E: Notes on a map compiled to accompany the paper by Mr. Lars Christensen," *Geographical Journal*, vol. 94, No. 3, September, 1939, pp. 204-208. (See p. 206.)
Ellsworth, Lincoln, "My Four Antarctic Explorations," *National Geographic Magazine*," vol. 76, No. 1, July, 1939, pp. 129-138, illus., map.
"Ellsworth Antarctic Expedition, 1938-39," *Polar Record*, vol. 3, No. 17, (Cambridge, Scott Polar Research Institute, January, 1939), pp. 76-77.
"Ellsworth Antarctic Expedition, 1938-39," *Polar Record*, vol. 3, No. 18, (Cambridge, Scott Polar Research Institute, July, 1939), pp. 174-175.
"Lincoln Ellsworth's Antarctic Expedition, 1938-39," *Polar Record*, vol. 4, No. 27, (Cambridge, Scott Polar Research Institute, January, 1944), p. 114.
The *New York Times* and North American Newspaper Alliance for the following dates: May 6, 1938, p. 1; May 19, p. 7; July 25, p. 4; July 27, p. 19; Aug. 11, p. 19; Aug. 13, p. 27; Aug. 14, p. 16; Aug. 15, p. 17; Aug. 16, p. 19; Aug. 17, p. 3; Sept. 7, p. 27; Sept. 14, p. 9; Oct. 10, p. 9; Oct. 30, p. 30; Nov. 2, p. 26; Nov. 14, p. 21; Nov. 19, p. 15; Nov. 22, p. 25; Dec. 8, p. 20; Dec. 14, p. 27; Jan. 3, 1939, p. 5; Jan. 4, p. 23; Jan. 6, p. 23; Jan. 8, p. I-18; Jan. 12, p. 1; Jan. 13, p. 21; Jan. 14, p. 19; Jan. 16, p. 17; Jan. 19, p. 3; Jan. 22, p. 29; Jan. 23, p. 15; Feb. 4, p. 17; Feb. 9, p. 5, 20; Feb. 14, p. 20; Feb. 17, p. 13; Mar. 1, p. 23. Most of these articles are based on radio dispatches from the *Wyatt Earp* and appear under Lincoln Ellsworth's "by-line." Some articles printed before the departure of the expedition are also under Ellsworth's authorship. Many of these articles have been reprinted in the *Polar Times*, Nos. 7 and 8, October, 1938 and March, 1939.
Rønneberg, Harald, Jr., "Med Ellsworth Til Sydpollandet," *Polar-Årboken* (Oslo, Norsk Polarklubb, 1939), pp. 84-91.

21

THE UNITED STATES
ANTARCTIC SERVICE EXPEDITION, 1939-1941

SIGNIFICANCE OF THE EXPEDITION

The United States Antarctic Service Expedition, 1939-41, was more than another post-World War I demonstration of continued American interest in the Antarctic. The widespread popular interest which had been developed by Byrd, Wilkins, and Ellsworth had been sufficiently vital to provide the principal financial support for the expeditions led by Wilkins and Byrd. This support, however, had all been from private or institutional sources. Medals had been granted Byrd and his men by an act of Congress, but nothing more tangible of an official nature was forthcoming.

In the late 1930s, however, government officials were becoming cognizant of the popular concern for the Antarctic that had been generated by the two expeditions of Rear Admiral Richard E. Byrd, and the importance of American interests there. Thus, 100 years after Lieutenant Charles Wilkes led the first United States Exploring Expedition to the Antarctic, the United States Antarctic Service was formed to carry out Antarctic exploration and establish bases there that would be more or less continuously occupied. Except for the cooperation of the learned societies in the formulation of a scientific program and the participation of civilian scientists, the United States Exploring Expedition was carried out by the Navy. By contrast, and reflecting the breadth of American official interest in 1939, the United States Antarctic Service was organized as a civilian service under the auspices of four cabinet agencies. Although the United States Antarctic Service was established to support one expedition, President Franklin D. Roosevelt apparently had the idea of making it an ongoing thing, with bases continually occupied by rotating personnel.

This broad base of support, in spite of the very short time allowed for organization and preparation, enabled the United States Antarctic Service Expedition to be the largest Antarctic expedition up to that time. Each of its three fields of operations was the equivalent of the entire program of many earlier expeditions.

ORGANIZATION AND ACCOMPLISHMENTS

ESTABLISHMENT OF THE PROJECT

The United States Antarctic Service was created by the Second Deficiency Appropriation Act, Fiscal Year 1939, approved May 2, 1939,[1] and by the Urgency Deficiency and Supplemental Appropriation Act, Fiscal Years 1939 and 1940, approved June 30, 1939,[2] both granting funds to the United States Department of the Interior for "Expenses, Division of Territories and Island Possessions." The first appropriated $10,000 for planning; the second provided $340,000 for expenses "in the investigation and survey of natural resources of the land and sea areas of the Antarctic regions."

From its inception, President Franklin D. Roosevelt took an active interest in the United States Antarctic Service. It was at his instigation that proposals for two separate Antarctic expeditions, one by Richard B. Black and Finn Ronne and another by Admiral Richard E. Byrd, were coordinated to form the U. S. Antarctic Service Expedition. Moreover, the records reveal that during the planning stages of the expedition Admiral Byrd was in frequent contact with the President.

In November 1937, Dr. Ernest Gruening, Director of the Division of Territories and Island Possessions of the Department of the Interior, being aware of certain somewhat vague requirements of the Government for an official American venture into the Antarctic regions, invited Black, then Field Representative of the Division, to prepare a memorandum on the subject. That memorandum, dated May 5, 1938, dealt with the Government's interest in the Antarctic and outlined a plan for a small Antarctic expedition jointly proposed by Black and Ronne, both veterans of the Second Byrd Antarctic Expedition, 1933-35. Gruening actively encouraged such an enterprise, with the result that the Department of State and the President subsequently were made aware of Black's memorandum. Moreover, as developments began to take shape, Black was summoned to Washington in February, 1939, to start active coordination of plans for a U. S. Government expedition.

Meanwhile, in Boston, Admiral Byrd and his associates had been planning his third Antarctic expedition which, like the first two, was to be privately financed. The Department of State also had been considering the subject, and a departmental representative had consulted with Byrd late in 1938. This was brought to the attention of President Roosevelt, for in a memorandum to the Acting Secretary of State, Sumner Welles, on January 7, 1939, the President approved the preliminary cooperative planning that had been done by the Departments of State, War, and Navy.[3] He suggested that the Department of Interior be included in such planning and that the group consider the feasibility of maintaining a party each summer season "at Little America and at the region South of the Cape of Good Hope" by way of annual colonization. He also recommended that Admiral Byrd and Lincoln Ellsworth be consulted concerning the estimated costs.

Two important developments resulted from the President's memorandum of January 7. After being consulted again by Department of State representatives as to estimated annual costs, and now cognizant of the President's latest views, Admiral Byrd decided to cancel plans for his private expedition and devote his energies and his extensive Antarctic experience to the furtherance of plans for an official Government undertaking.[4] From then on he was accepted as the leader of the proposed expedition and began to take an active part in planning and organization.

The second result of the President's memorandum of January 7 was the formation of an interdepartmental committee which eventually became the Execu-

tive Committee of the United States Antarctic Service. On January 13, as a result of the President's suggestion, the Secretary of State invited the Secretaries of
War, Navy, Treasury, and Interior to appoint representatives to serve on an Antarctic Committee. This committee began immediately an intensive program of
consultation and planning. On July 7, 1939, the President himself addressed letters to the Secretaries of State, Treasury, Navy, and Interior asking them to designate representatives to form a committee to organize, direct, and coordinate
the Antarctic investigations authorized by Congress in the act approved June
30. As a result, the original planning committee became what the President designated as the Executive Committee of the United States Antarctic Service. Representation of the four Departments continued throughout the life of the organization, although there were some personnel changes. Captain (later Rear Admiral) C. C. Hartigan and Mr. Hugh S. Cumming, Jr., represented the Navy
and State Departments, respectively, during the life of the Committee. Rear Admiral R. R. Waesche was later succeeded by Commander E. G. Rose as representative of the Coast Guard (Treasury). The Department of the Interior was
represented in turn by Ernest Gruening, Mrs. Ruth Hampton, R. A. Klein-
dienst, Paul W. Gordon, Rupert Emerson, and Guy J. Swope.[5] Lieutenant Commander (later Commander) Robert A. J. English, USN, commander of the *Bear
of Oakland* on the Second Byrd Antarctic Expedition, was appointed Executive
Secretary. In February 1942 he was succeeded by J. E. MacDonald, who had previously been administrative assistant to Admiral Byrd. As Commanding Officer
of the U. S. Antarctic Service Expedition, Admiral Byrd was an ex-officio member of the Committee, having received his formal appointment from President
Roosevelt on July 7.[6]

Although the expedition was organized and dispatched under the authority
of the United States Antarctic Service, it was also supported by donations and
gifts from private citizens, corporations, and institutions. The Department of
the Interior requested and was granted an appropriation which was inadequate
for a unilateral operation of the magnitude proposed, but the deficiency was
to be overcome by the cooperative efforts of the other departments concerned,
with exchange of funds for the equipment, services, and supplies provided by
these departments.[7] In addition, Admiral Byrd made available much equipment
and many supplies which had been assembled for his proposed private venture.
The largest item was the barkentine *Bear,* which was chartered by the Department of the Navy for one dollar a year. Further, by certain emergency acts of the
Executive Committee and the departments and bureaus of government concerned, procedures were established by which quantities of equipment, stores,
and even services could be accepted for nominal sums, somewhat in the pattern
of private expeditions. Some of the donors later felt that they had not been allowed to gain sufficient advertising advantage because of their donations. Apparently they had not understood completely the governmental nature of the
expedition. Well over 100 firms and individuals contributed money, supplies,
and equipment to the expedition, including tractors, food, clothing, instruments, tobacco, and books.[8] Charles R. Walgreen of Chicago and William Hor-

lick of Racine, Wisconsin, helped equip the barkentine *Bear,* and the Kohler family of Kohler, Wisconsin, and George F. Getz and Justin W. Dart of Chicago supplied the Barkley-Grow seaplane carried by the *Bear.*[9]

OBJECTIVES AND ACCOMPLISHMENTS

Objectives. The objectives of the United States Antarctic Service Expedition were outlined by President Roosevelt in an order dated November 25, 1939, and received by Admiral Byrd at Balboa, Canal Zone, as he boarded the *North Star* on November 30.[10] The President directed that two bases be established. One, to be designated East Base, was to be established in the vicinity of Charcot Island or Alexander I Land, or on Marguerite Bay if no accessible site could be found on either of the specified islands. The second base, designated West Base, was to be established in the vicinity of King Edward VII Land, but if this proved impossible, a site on the Bay of Whales at or near Little America was to be investigated.

The objectives, as specified by the President, were primarily concerned with geographical exploration.

(1) The principal objective was "the delineation of the continental coast line between the meridians 72 degrees W., and 148 degrees W., and the consolidation of the geographical features of Hearst Land, James W. Ellsworth Land, and Marie Byrd Land." Since the delineation of the coastline from approximately Alexander I Land to Sulzberger Bay was to be accomplished by long-range photographic flights whose limits were to be extended by supply caches, the significance of the proposed sites for the two bases is obvious. It was also suggested that flights be made from the *Bear,* if practicable, along the 75th, 101st, 116th, 134th, 150th, and 152nd meridians of west longitude.

(2) A secondary objective involved the delineation of the then-unknown west coast of the Weddell Sea between Cape Eielson and Luitpold Coast.[11]

(3) The eastern extremity of the Queen Maud Mountains and the Horlick Mountains and their relationship to the Sentinel Range, discovered by Ellsworth, were to be determined.

(4) The President also expressed a desire that an aerial investigation be made in the vicinity of the south magnetic pole and in the unexplored areas between the Weddell Sea and the South Pole, although it would seem that he considered these objectives secondary.

(5) The scientific program to be carried out at the two bases included observation of the aurora australis, cosmic rays, and meteors. It also included investigations in geology, glaciology, geophysics, terrestrial magnetism, botany, zoology, oceanography, and meteorology. The medical officers were to carry out physiological observations on the base personnel.[12]

(6) The President requested that the U. S. Antarctic Service cooperate with the Argentine meteorological station on Laurie Island in the South Orkneys and with the Chilean Meteorological Service in the exchange of data.

(7) One of the vessels was directed to determine the extent of Pactolus Bank. Although this submarine feature, located about 230 miles west of Cape Horn

(56°28′ S, 74°20′ W), is not in the Antarctic, it was near the track of the ships when en route to or from Valparaiso or Punta Arenas, Chile, and Marguerite Bay.

Accomplishments. As outlined by the President, the objectives of the expedition called for a broad scale of operations and were apparently predicated on the assumption that the work begun by the men in 1940-41 would be continued by others who would replace them at East and West Bases. In view of the broad scope of the objectives and the unpredictable but difficult circumstances that are bound to arise in Antarctica, it is remarkable that the members of the expedition were able to accomplish most of the objectives set for them. These included:

(1) The establishment and occupation for a year of two separate bases 1600 miles apart by air and 2200 miles by sea.

(2) As a result of flights by seaplane from the *Bear* and by landbased aircraft from Little America III, about 700 miles of coastline was added to the map of Antarctica. These discoveries included the Hobbs Coast, the Walgreen Coast, the Thurston Peninsula (found to be an island in 1960), and the Eights Coast.

(3) Aerial reconnaissance revealed for the first time all of the previously unknown parts of the Ross Ice Shelf and filled in the unexplored gap between Beardmore and Liv Glaciers in the Queen Maud Mountains.

(4) A sledge journey down the George VI Sound resulted in the discovery of its western outlet and demonstrated the insularity of Alexander Island. On this journey 12 control points for the aerial survey were determined by sun sights.

(5) Aerial reconnaissance from East Base extended the known coastline of Antarctica westward to about the 85th meridian, west, resulting in the discovery of the Bryan Coast and Carroll Inlet at its eastern border. By the same means the western coast of Alexander Island was roughly delineated.

(6) In flights from East Base the east coast of the Antarctic Peninsula was photographed from Trail Inlet and Three Slice Nunatak (approximately 68° S) to beyond Nantucket Inlet (74°35′ S). The last part was covered in a photographic circle made at the turning point of the flight at Wright Inlet (74° S). From this point the coast could be seen in the distance beyond Nantucket Inlet, trending gradually to the southwestward. The east coast of the Antarctic Peninsula from 70° S to 75° S and perhaps as far as to 76°30′ S was first seen by personnel from East Base.

(7) A route was discovered across the Antarctic Peninsula from Stonington Island to the head of Trail Inlet. This was used by a sledge party from East Base which completed a ground survey of the east coast of the Antarctic Peninsula from Trail Inlet south to Hilton Inlet (71°57′ S).

(8) A sledging party explored the Dyer Plateau, establishing 11 control points and triangulating the position of 58 mountains.

(9) A sledging journey was made from West Base northeastward along the east side of Sulzberger Bay to the Fosdick Mountains to study the biology of the region. A large quantity of biological and geological specimens and photographs were brought back.

(10) A geological survey party sledged from West Base to the Swanson Mountains, laying base lines and running intersections to 57 peaks, expanding the triangulation net laid by Siple in 1934 on the Second Byrd Antarctic Expedition. The groundwork was thus laid for a geological map, and a large quantity of geological and biological specimens was brought back.

(11) A 1200-mile round-trip sledge journey was made to the Flood Range for the purpose of determining ground control positions and making a survey en route. Official U. S. General Land Office brass monuments were set and claim sheets deposited at McKinley Peak and at Mount Berlin.

(12) A seismic station, established on the easterly slope of Mount Franklin in the Rockefeller Mountains, was operated for 41 days. A triangulation survey was made of the mountains, and the geological investigation begun in 1934 was extended.

(13) Detailed surveys were made at both East and West Base. The survey at West Base provided further data on the rate of movement of the different components of the Ross Ice Shelf.

(14) Meteorological observations, including upper air sounding, were carried on for a little more than a year at West Base and for a little less than a year at East Base.

(15) The first high-altitude meteorological station in Antarctica was operated during November and December, 1940, at 5370 feet, on the plateau-like summit of the Antarctic Peninsula east of Stonington Island.

(16) Cosmic ray observations were conducted on both voyages (1939-40 and 1940-41) of the *North Star* to and from Antarctica and during the occupation of West Base at Little America III.

(17) By means of two pits excavated in the ice shelf at West Base, the density, crystallization, compaction, banding, and temperature of the firn and underlying glacial ice were investigated.

(18) Auroral observations were carried out at West Base from April 1 to September 15, 1940.

(19) Biological studies on seals, birds, lichens, and mosses were made by members of both bases, and marine life studies were carried out on samples obtained through the ice at East Base.

(20) Tidal and magnetic measurements were made at East Base.

(21) Physiological studies were carried out at West Base to determine the effect of cold on the human body.

In those instances where Expedition personnel were unable to fulfill the objectives set for them, such as determining the relationship between the Sentinel Range and the Horlick Mountains, and the delineation of the coast of the Weddell Sea as far as the Luitpold Coast, the inability was due to the inadequate range of the aircraft. An insufficient number of tractors for surface transport and scientific equipment not properly adapted for Antarctic conditions also necessitated curtailment of scientific investigations that the men had hoped to accomplish. Fundamentally, this was due to the insufficient time in which the expedition was organized and the equipment assembled. In many cases the expedition had to make do with what was available in the way of equipment rather than obtain what was most desirable.

COMPOSITION OF THE EXPEDITION

Ships. Two ships were used by the expedition. Admiral Byrd's old ice ship, the *Bear of Oakland,* which had been used on the Second Byrd Antarctic Expedition, was chartered by the Navy for one dollar a year. The ship was reconditioned, including the installation of a diesel engine, by the Navy and commissioned the U.S.S. *Bear* before being assigned to the expedition. The *North Star,* a 1434-ton, wooden ice ship with diesel power, was built for the Bureau of Indian Affairs of the U. S. Department of the Interior in 1932. It was used each summer to transport supplies to Alaska. Because the two voyages to the Antarctic were made in the Alaskan winter season when the ship normally would be idle, it was possible for the Department of the Interior to lend the *North Star* to the Antarctic Service without interrupting the Alaskan service.

Aircraft. The expedition was supplied with four aircraft. A twin-motored Barkley-Grow seaplane was carried by the *Bear* on the 1939-40 cruise in the Antarctic. Both bases were supplied with twin-motored Curtiss-Wright Condor biplanes which had seen previous service for five years with the U. S. Marine Corps. These craft were the same as the *William Horlick,* the large plane used on long exploratory flights of the Second Byrd Antarctic Expedition. The fourth plane was a new, light, single-motored Beechcraft which was supposed to be used in connection with the Snow Cruiser.

The Snow Cruiser. The Second Byrd Antarctic Expedition, 1933-35, had proved the feasibility of long-distance, unsupported travel by motorized vehicles on the Antarctic continent. Experience in 1934, however, revealed the need for specially adapted vehicles which could operate under extremely low temperatures, have sufficient power and adequate traction to travel in deep, soft snow, cross at least small crevasses without bogging down, and provide living quarters for the crew. To meet these requirements, Dr. Thomas C. Poulter, who had led the mid-winter tractor journey to Bolling Advance Base in 1934, conceived the Snow Cruiser.

In 1939 Dr. Poulter was scientific director of the Research Foundation of the Armour Institute of Chicago, where the massive vehicle was designed. It was built at the Pullman Company shops at a cost of $150,000, which was defrayed by "Friends of the Research Foundation" and by 70 cooperating manufacturers.

The shell of this motorized giant was 55 feet long and 20 feet wide, with sled runners attached to its toboggan-like bottom. With the wheels down, it was 16 feet high. Inside the shell were sleeping quarters with four bunks, a scientific laboratory, a photographic laboratory, a radio room, a chart room, and a galley. Power was supplied by two 150-horsepower diesel engines connected to generators which provided current for the 75-horsepower electric motor which drove each wheel. The four rubber-tired wheels were 10 feet in diameter, and they could be retracted to permit the Snow Cruiser to toboggan downgrade. It was designed to cross crevasses up to 15 feet wide by retracting first the front wheels while the rear wheels powered the cruiser half way across, and then retracting the rear wheels while the front wheels provided traction to complete the crossing.

A single-motored, 5-passenger Beechcraft monoplane, mounted on skis, was meant to be carried on top of the Snow Cruiser for aerial reconnaissance and exploration within a radius of 300 miles. Enough food for a year could be stored in the cruiser, whose tanks carried 2500 gallons of diesel oil, enough for 5000 miles, and 1000 gallons of aviation gasoline. The Snow Cruiser had a maximum speed of 30 miles per hour on a hard surface, and could climb grades of 37 percent, turn in its own length, and move sideways at an angle of 25 degrees.

Other Transport Facilities. For the purpose of unloading ship, constructing the base camps, and laying gasoline caches and supply depots in the field, West Base was supplied with a T-20 International Harvester crawler-type tractor; East Base had an Army artillery tractor. Both bases were also provided with a light Army tank. For long-distance trail journeys, however, reliance was to be placed on the sled dogs. For this purpose 160 were taken to the Antarctic. Some of them were veterans of the Second Byrd Antarctic Expedition, seven having been born in Antarctica. West Base was given 70 dogs, and East Base the remainder.

Personnel. A total of 125 men departed from the United States in the two ships of the United States Antarctic Service Expedition, the third Antarctic and the first government expedition to be commanded by Admiral Byrd. The *North Star* was manned by its regular officers and crew, commanded by Captain Isak Lystad. The *Bear* was commanded by Lieutenant Commander Richard H. Cruzen, USN, and Bendik Johansen was ice pilot.

Most of the men on the expedition were selected from solicited lists of volunteers from all the military services and several civilian agencies of government, and from scientific institutions which work in close cooperation with the government. These received their regular salaries, paid by the cooperating agencies or institutions. A few volunteers were employed for the purpose by the Department of the Interior at $10 per month, food and clothing. Some of the men made the voyage for the purpose of setting up specialized equipment and instructing men in its operation. Eric T. Clarke of the Bartol Foundation, Swarthmore, Pennsylvania, set up the cosmic ray recording equipment at West Base and carried on observations aboard the *North Star* on the outbound and homeward voyage of 1939-40. On the 1940-41 voyage he was succeeded by Dana K. Bailey. Dr. Thomas C. Poulter also made the voyage to assist in unloading and making preparatory tests of the Snow Cruiser. Malcolm Davis, biologist, and Milton J. Lobell, icthyologist, were also aboard the *North Star* on the 1939-40 cruise.

The 59 men who wintered in Antarctica were initially divided into three groups. Dr. F. Alton Wade, geologist and Senior Scientist of the expedition, was in charge of the Snow Cruiser and the three other men assigned to it. When the Snow Cruiser failed to function as expected it was parked at West Base, and the four men joined the West Base party of 29 men under the leadership of Dr. Paul A. Siple. East Base was occupied by 26 men under the leadership of Richard B. Black.

The roster of the U. S. Antarctic Service Expedition shows how a body of experienced Antarctic personnel was being built up. Including Admiral Byrd, 13 of the men were veterans of previous expeditions. Bendik Johansen and Paul A. Siple were veterans of both the First and Second Byrd Antarctic Expeditions. Jack Bursey, dog driver, had been a member of the First Byrd Antarctic Expedition. Wade; Clay W. Bailey, chief radio operator; Vernon D. Boyd, master mechanic; Louis P. Colombo, assistant mechanic; and Lieutenant Commander Isaac Schlossbach, USN (retired), executive assistant, were veterans of the Second Byrd Antarctic Expedition who were stationed at West Base. Black, the leader; Joseph D. Healy, dog driver; and Finn Ronne, transportation engineer, at East Base were also veterans of the Second Byrd Expedition, as was Frederick G. Dustin, aide to Admiral Byrd aboard the *Bear*.

It is significant that many of the men who participated in the U. S. Antarctic Service Expedition also played important parts in subsequent Antarctic expeditions. Ronne led his own expedition in 1947-48, and Schlossbach was skipper of the Ronne expedition ship. Harry Darlington, III, of East Base and Sigmund Gutenko, cook at West Base, also were members of Ronne's expedition. In 1946-47 (then-Rear Admiral) Richard H. Cruzen was commanding officer of Task Force 68 of the U. S. Navy Antarctic Developments Project, commonly known as "Operation Highjump." Captain George J. Dufek, commander of the Eastern Task Group of "Operation Highjump," was, as Lieutenant Dufek, navigator on the *Bear* in 1939-40. From 1956-59, Admiral Dufek was commander of "Operation Deep Freeze," Task Force 43, U. S. Naval Support Force, Antarctica, supporting the United States participation in the International Geophysical Year. Siple, Ronne, and Carl Eklund, ornithologist at East Base, subsequently were leaders of U. S. bases during the first winter (1957) of the International Geophysical Year, Richard B. Black, Captain USNR, was called to active duty for "Operation Deep Freeze I," 1955-56. James C. McCoy, Charles C. Shirley, Vernon D. Boyd, Murray A. Wiener, Jack E. Perkins, and Paul A. Siple, all of West Base, and Frederick G. Dustin were active in "Operation Highjump."

DETAILED RECORD OF OPERATIONS

TRANSPORTING THE EXPEDITION TO ANTARCTICA

Early on November 15, 1939, the *North Star,* heavily laden with supplies and equipment and with the Snow Cruiser on deck, sailed from Boston en route to Philadelphia, where two airplanes and a supply of meteorological instruments were taken aboard. On November 21 she sailed down Delaware Bay en route to the Panama Canal. The *Bear* left Boston on November 22, calling at Norfolk on November 25 to take aboard one of the twin-motored airplanes of the expedition. On November 26 she cleared the Virginia Capes en route to the Panama Canal.

Admiral Byrd, who had stayed behind to clear up a host of last-minute administrative details, flew from Washington to the Canal Zone, where he boarded the *North Star* at Balboa on November 30. The *North Star* then cleared for New Zealand. En route, she called at Pitcairn Island, December 13 and 14, and at

Rapa (Easter) Island on December 17. She arrived at Wellington, New Zealand, on December 27 for a three-day stay before proceeding to Dunedin. On January 3 the *North Star* sailed from Dunedin for the Ross Sea, where only a narrow belt of loose pack ice was encountered. The Ross Ice Shelf was sighted on January 11. The ship stopped briefly at the Bay of Whales and proceeded eastward along the ice front. After investigating conditions at Kainan Bay and Okuma Bay, Admiral Byrd and Dr. Siple decided to establish the West Base at the Bay of Whales, which was re-entered on January 12, 1940. Meanwhile the *Bear,* after refueling at the Canal Zone, had sailed on December 6 for the Bay of Whales, which she entered on January 14, 1940.

Antarctic veterans found that the Bay of Whales had changed in shape and had become constricted in size since their departure in 1935. A strip of bay ice at the entrance to Eleanor Bolling Bight, however, provided space for unloading equipment and supplies. Drifted snow formed a ramp from the bay ice to the top of the ice shelf. Working in two 12-hour shifts, the men began immediately to discharge cargo. In less than a week after arrival, the smaller *Bear* was unloaded, and by January 24 the *North Star* was able to sail for Valparaiso, Chile.

At Valparaiso 600 tons of supplies, including a Navy twin-motored Curtiss-Wright Condor plane and prefabricated buildings, had been collected and stored in custody of Supply Officer Robert Palmer and Aviation Machinist's Mate William A. Pullen, USN. Here, too, waiting to join the *North Star* when she arrived on February 15, were Lieutenants 1st Class Ezequiel Rodriguez and Federico Bonert of the Chilean Navy and Lieutenant 1st Class Julio Poch and Lieutenant (jg) Emilio L. Diaz of the Argentine Navy, who at the invitation of the United States Government had been appointed to join the ship as observers on the voyage. On February 23, 1940, the *North Star* again sailed for Antarctica.

Meanwhile the *Bear,* with Admiral Byrd in command, was working eastward from the Ross Sea along the edge of the pack ice looking for opportunities for exploratory flights to the southward in the Barkley-Grow seaplane. Following the last of three such flights on February 24, 25, and 27, the *Bear* pushed eastward to a rendezvous with the *North Star* in Marguerite Bay. In the process Byrd attempted to approach Charcot Island to investigate the possibility of establishing a base there, but the pack ice held him off. For several days snow and fog prevented celestial observations for the determination of position. On the afternoon of March 2, as the *Bear* approached the northwestern tip of Alexander Island, six rocky, partly snow-covered islands, surrounded by pack ice, were discovered about 50 miles north northeast of Charcot Island.[13] Darkness, menacing pack ice, and shoaling water caused Lieutenant Commander Cruzen, master of the *Bear,* to heave to until the next morning.

At the same time, the *North Star* was approaching Charcot Island from due north, and on March 3 the island was sighted through haze and fog. Shunted to the east by the pack ice, observers on the *North Star* soon saw the high peaks of Alexander Island. More interesting, however, was a dark water sky over a lead to the south between Alexander Island and Charcot Island. Darkness and an intervening sea of pack ice caused Captain Lystad to heave to for the night, but

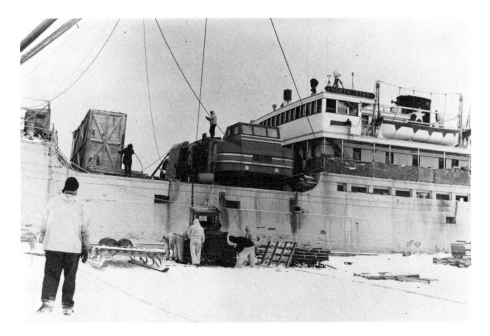

PLATE IX-A. Unloading the *North Star* at the Bay of Whales. The International Harvester tractor is being lowered to the bay ice. Note the snow cruiser on the deck of the ship. Photo No. 126-USAS-206 in the National Archives.

PLATE IX-B. Unloading the *North Star* at East Base. Stores are being transferred from the ship to Stonington Island on an improvised barge. Photo No. 26-USAS-1068 in the National Archives.

PLATE X-A. Admiral Byrd standing on the Barkley-Grow seaplane. He has just returned to the *Bear* from an exploratory flight, January 26, 1940. Photo No. 126-USAS-3033 in the National Archives.

PLATE X-B. Science building under construction at West Base in February 1940. Note double floor and panel construction. Main building in background. Photo No. 126-USAS-4426 in the National Archives.

prospects were no better on the morning of March 4. The two ships of the expedition had been in radio communication, and on the evening of March 4 the *Bear* reported that she had found a safe anchorage at Horseshoe Island. The *North Star,* meanwhile, was having difficulty identifying landmarks as she slowly felt her way across Marguerite Bay through fog and snow squalls. On March 5 the weather cleared sufficiently for better identification, and it was possible to make a reconnaissance flight of the bay in the Barkley-Grow seaplane. With improved visibility and an assist from the seaplane, the *North Star* was able to anchor beside the *Bear* that evening.

A suitable site for a base had not been discovered during a preliminary reconnaissance by the *Bear,* but pictures taken on the flight of March 5 provided clues for investigation by the two ships on March 6, the *Bear* examining Neny Fjord and the *North Star* going southward to the limit of open water, opposite Black Thumb. Ice floes and bad weather halted operations on the 7th and proved the unsuitability of two sites that had tentatively been chosen. Finally, a reconnaissance flight by Admiral Byrd, Richard B. Black, East Base leader, chief pilot Ashley C. Snow, and Earl B. Perce, co-pilot and radio man, on the afternoon of March 8, resulted in the discovery of two islands on the north side of Neny Bay which warranted investigation. A landing by boat on the more northerly one, subsequently named Stonington Island, confirmed its suitability as a base. A steeply inclined ramp of drifted snow connected the island to the foot of a mainland glacier and afforded an all-season passage to the interior. Deep water would permit the ships to moor a few hundred yards from a low ice foot attached to the shore, and to use boats and a scow, as lighters, to transfer cargo and the Condor biplane from ship to shore.

The start of unloading operations had to be postponed until March 11, and they were interrupted on several occasions because of strong easterly gales which swept down through the glacial valleys from the plateau-like summit of the Antarctic Peninsula. While such occasions afforded an opportunity for rest, they also caused great anxiety for the safety of the ships. During these gales it was necessary for the *Bear,* top-heavy with sails and rigging, to seek shelter at Horseshoe Island. While the *North Star* remained anchored off Stonington Island, there was always danger during the gales that she might drag her anchors or that a cable might part.

By all hands turning to from sunrise to sunset (a little more than 12 hours at this time of year), the ships were unloaded by the evening of March 20. The next morning the two ships sailed for the United States, Admiral Byrd remaining aboard the *Bear.* Both ships called at Punta Arenas, Chile. The *Bear* then sailed for Boston while the *North Star* headed for Seattle, from whence she was scheduled to make her regular summer cruise to Alaska for the Department of the Interior.

EXPLORATORY FLIGHTS FROM THE *BEAR*

The Ruppert and Hobbs Coasts. Even with advance caches of gasoline in the field, there had been doubt that the range of the twin-engined Curtiss-Wright

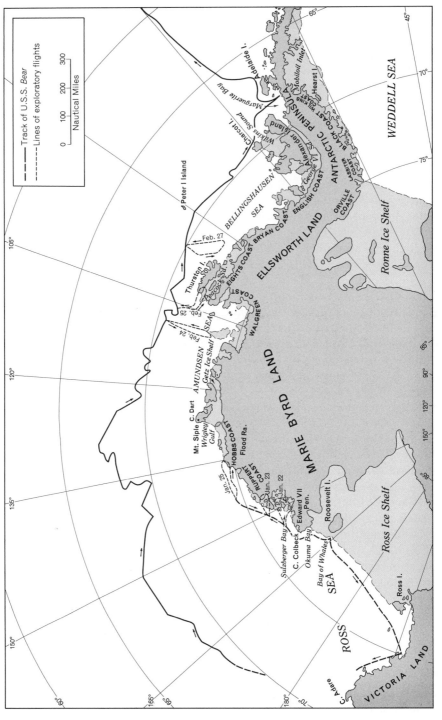

Figure 21. Track of the U.S.S. *Bear* on the Exploratory Cruises of 1940.

Condor biplanes would be sufficient to close the gap in the 1700-mile stretch of unexplored coast between the Ross Sea and Marguerite Bay. When conditions prevented the establishment of West Base other than at Little America, this doubt became a certainty and gave special significance to Admiral Byrd's plan to explore part of the coast by seaplane flights from the *Bear*. First, he planned to test once more his theory that in the latter half of the warm season offshore winds created a stretch of open water between the shoreline and the pack ice. If this were true, much of the coast could be explored by ship, provided it could reach the open water. Byrd had been unable to penetrate the pack in 1929 in the *City of New York*, but in February 1934 he had succeeded in getting to 75°06′ S, 148°08′ W in the more powerful *Bear of Oakland*. Now that old ship, as the U. S. S. *Bear*, had a diesel engine which increased its thrust, and when impenetrable pack was met, the Barkley-Grow seaplane could extend the field of exploration still further. Experience had shown in 1933-34 that the belt of pack ice in this longitude was too broad for a small seaplane to reach the coast from its northern edge. In 1940 Byrd hoped to reach the expected belt of open water by pushing through the pack while working the *Bear* eastward beyond Cape Colbeck.

On the 19th of January, five days after his arrival at the Bay of Whales, Lieutenant Commander Cruzen, with Byrd and 10 members of the East Base party aboard, headed the *Bear* toward Cape Colbeck, the northwestern extremity of Edward VII Peninsula. In 1940, ice conditions were favorable and the *Bear* had little difficulty in pushing eastward some distance beyond the cape. While near Cape Colbeck on January 21, a test flight was made in the Barkley-Grow seaplane for the purpose of calibrating the radio direction finder (Fig. 21).

On January 22 the first of four major flights during the cruise was made from the *Bear*, hove to in about 76°45′30″ S, 157°27′ W.[14] The three-hour flight by Admiral Byrd, with Ashley C. Snow and Earl B. Perce serving as pilot and co-pilot, respectively, circled the shores of Sulzberger Bay and up over the bordering peaks of Marie Byrd Land on the east. Cloud shadows and mirages hampered observations. To the north and east a large expanse of open water was sighted, and open leads through which the *Bear* might reach it were also observed.

Taking advantage of these leads, the *Bear* moved northeastward to about 76° 39′ S, 154° W on January 23, from where Byrd, Snow, and Perce took off again in the seaplane on a four-and-a-half hour flight over the Ruppert Coast and the more northwesterly mountains of the Ford Ranges. Clouds were encountered in the vicinity of the Chester Mountains. As the plane turned to the northward on a counterclockwise course, it emerged from a cloud bank just in time to avoid a mountain peak by going into a steep climb. Ice reconnaissance showed an open channel extending about 100 miles to the northeast, close to the coast.

Again the *Bear* moved northeastward along the open water revealed on the flight, but a gale prevented flying again until January 25. The ship was then moored against heavy old pack ice in 74°43′ S, 143°52′30″ W, the farthest east and south that any ship had reached in this area. Two flights were made from this point. The first, on January 25, was of little value because of poor visibility.

The second, on January 26, covered essentially the same track, 120 miles eastward to about 135°W and roughly parallel to what was subsequently named the Hobbs Coast. Broad glaciers, probably Land and Hull Glaciers, were seen flowing toward the coast between 4000-foot mountains. High mountains, probably Mount Berlin and Mount Moulton of the Flood Range, were seen 70 to 80 miles farther south. On the return flight, the plane passed over a snow-covered island whose northern shore rose 200 to 300 feet above the water. Hummocky old pack ice or shelf ice lay between it and the mainland. This newly discovered island (74°47′ S, 140°42′ W) was subsequently named Cruzen Island in honor of the captain of the *Bear*.

At this point Admiral Byrd decided to return to the Bay of Whales. Ice conditions were becoming unfavorable, and with East Base yet to be established he could not risk being beset. This proved to be a sensible decision, for the *Bear* met increasingly difficult ice conditions on the return leg of the cruise. Several times large floes menaced the ship, and often the *Bear* had to buck through the pack in passing from one lead to another. North of Edward VII Peninsula, two ice reconnaissance flights were necessary on January 28 to enable the *Bear* to work her way into the open water of the Ross Sea. On January 30 the *Bear* returned to the Bay of Whales, Admiral Byrd having added 300 miles of new coastline to the map of Antarctica.

Magnetic Investigations. Among the objectives of the expedition listed in the President's letter of November 25 was an investigation by air of the vicinity of the south magnetic pole. This, however, was only a secondary objective. The area of the south magnetic pole, being then approximately 70° S, 145° E, was considerably removed from the other areas of operations of the U. S. Antarctic Service Expedition. To achieve this objective would have required a special effort unless very favorable conditions permitted this flight to be made incidental to one of the other operations. Admiral Byrd hoped that the latter would be the case, but the favorable conditions did not materialize.

The *Bear* departed from the Bay of Whales on February 1, and it was Admiral Byrd's intention to spend about a week investigating the south magnetic pole while en route to Marguerite Bay. Since he felt that ice conditions in the Amundsen and Bellingshausen Seas would improve during the month of February, this plan would fit in well with other operations. Consequently, the *Bear* proceeded to the west side of the Ross Sea. The pontoons of the Barkley-Grow plane were replaced by skis to lighten the plane sufficiently to fly over the high plateau of Victoria Land. This meant that a satisfactory air strip had to be found along the coast. Ice conditions all along the coast of Victoria Land were unsatisfactory, and the only place the *Bear* could be moored suitably was alongside the Drygalski Ice Tongue. Its surface was covered with sastrugi, and strong variable winds were blowing. Attempts to smooth off an airstrip were abandoned when it became apparent that a takeoff would be extremely hazardous due to the changeable winds, including unpredictable crosswinds. Having cancelled the flight to the magnetic pole, Admiral Byrd attempted to gain relevant information by taking dip needle observations on the surface of the Drygalski Ice Tongue. From

this point, which he determined to be 75° 10′30″ S, 163°37′30″ E, the south magnetic pole bore 310° true, but the results were otherwise inconclusive.

Discovery of the Walgreen and Eights Coasts. The *Bear* left Victoria Land on
February 7, passing near Iselin Seamount on a northeasterly course and then
eastward north of the 70th parallel. In typical weather of the latitude, a succession of gales and snow squalls, the old polar ship began skirting the outer edge
of the pack ice. Following an essentially southeasterly course, she succeeded in
reaching the 70th parallel at about 137° W on February 15. Following a long
lead about 60 miles into the pack, she was forced to retreat by impenetrable ice
floes to the south and east. At about the 68th parallel she began working eastward again, and by February 16 had reached 67°04′ S, 129°38′ W; not, however,
before she had been buffeted by a 60-mile-an-hour gale which blew her 180° off
course. Gales and high seas continued for four days. On February 20 the weather improved sufficiently to permit Snow, Perce, and the navigator, Lieutenant
George Dufek, to make a one-hour reconnaissance flight in the Barkley-Grow
seaplane from approximately 70° S, 115° W. A 75-mile stretch of open water was
sighted to the southeast, and the ship began working in that direction. Continued bad weather and high seas, however, prevented further flying until February 24.

On that day, in about 70°44′ S, 108°26′ W, the third attempt to take off from
the lee of a tabular iceberg was successful, and Byrd, Snow, and Perce flew due
south 190 miles to discover the Walgreen Coast. After flying over 70 to 80 miles
of unbroken ice, land was sighted in the distance. Two mountain ranges, which
appeared to be about 7500 feet high and which paralleled the coast, extended
in an east-west direction for 100 miles. Behind these ranges appeared to be an
elevated, snow-covered plateau. Visibility was good, and during this flight, lasting three hours and 15 minutes, about 200 miles of coastline were photographed
and roughly sketched in on the map.[15] An ice-locked sea, 40 miles wide, was
sighted far to the west, and a snow-covered island, five or six miles long, was
sighted about 80 miles off the coast and 110 miles from the *Bear.*

After proceeding eastward during the night, the *Bear* was hove to, February
25, at about 70°57′ S, 105°47′ W. From here Snow, Perce, and Dufek took off,
and after flying south for about 50 miles, sighted land to the southeast. Changing course to the southeast, they were soon abreast of two parallel mountain
ranges, estimated at from 3500 to 4000 feet high.[16] These were apparently the
same ranges sighted on February 24. On the three-hour flight Dufek plotted
about 100 miles of coast to the east of that covered by Byrd the previous day.

Two days later, February 27, the *Bear* had reached 70°04′ S, 95°19′ W at the
edge of the pack ice. From this point Byrd, Snow, and Perce made another three-
hour flight over the coast which resulted in the discovery of Thurston Island,
then thought to be a peninsula. On February 25 Dufek, Snow, and Perce certainly must have seen the western tip of the island, later named Cape Flying
Fish, for Dufek reported parallel mountain ranges, 3500 to 4000 feet high, running in an east-west direction. Their flight track would also bear this out. However, it apparently was not until the flight of February 27 that enough of the

coast between 90° W and 100° W was seen to indicate any conception of its true nature.[17] Byrd estimated the peninsula to be 100 miles long, terminating in about 72°45′ S. The mountains which ran the length of the peninsula were estimated to be from 2000 to 3000 feet high. A mountain, about 4000 feet high, could be seen clearly to the southeast in what Byrd estimated to be the vicinity of the 96th meridian. These might well have been the Jones Mountains in about 73°35′ S, 94°15′ W, surveyed by a U. S. geophysical traverse party in 1962. The highest peak rises to 5980 feet. The two islands were reported on the east side of the peninsula, and the west side of the peninsula formed the irregular shore of a huge bay.

Byrd estimated that the three flights of February 24, 25, and 27 added 800 miles to the known coastline of Antarctica.[18] According to plan, the *Bear* proceeded eastward along the edge of the pack ice to establish East Base, but the weather failed to provide opportunities for additional flights until Marguerite Bay was reached.

OPERATIONS AT WEST BASE

Establishment of the Base. Admiral Byrd and Dr. Siple decided to establish West Base at the Bay of Whales after an inspection of Kainan Bay and Okuma Bay revealed a lack of suitable bay ice for unloading the Snow Cruiser. Once the *North Star* was moored to the strip of bay ice at the Bay of Whales, all hands cooperated in unloading operations. The two planes, minus the wing sections, were slung over the side very early and moved 500 yards from their precarious position on the bay ice up onto the Ross Ice Shelf, where an aviation cache was established about 200 yards from the edge. The Beechcraft was dragged up by dog teams and men, but a "flying fox" (an endless line running from the ship's winch through a block fastened to a "dead man" on the ice shelf), was used to drag the big Condor up the slope. Because they were needed for transport, the T-20 International tractor and the Army tank were also among the first things unloaded. Equipment and supplies, as they were unloaded, were placed in temporary caches on the bay ice. Due to the suddenness with which the bay ice can break up, often without warning, the contents of these temporary caches were transported as quickly as possible by dog sled and tractor-drawn "scoots" up onto the ice shelf to the site selected for the base camp. The "flying fox" rigged for the Condor was also used later for dragging supplies up the slope to the edge of the shelf from the bay ice.

The West Base camp was established a short distance south of Eleanor Bolling Bight, about two miles from the ship. Transport facilities were not adequate to move the supplies and equipment farther inland in the limited time available, and considerable difficulties would have been encountered in renovating the buildings used by the Second Byrd Antarctic Expedition in 1933-35 because the roofs of the larger ones had caved in badly. Little America I-II was six miles south of West Base, which was designated Little America III.

While West Base was under construction, the men were housed in a temporary camp of Army tents. The three main buildings were prefabricated structures. The largest one measured 60 feet long by 24 feet wide, while the dimensions of the other two were 30 by 24 feet. The wall panels were filled with 4-inch thick insulating material. A double floor, 16 inches above the main floor, permitted the heat from the galley to create circulation between them. This innovation, conceived by Siple, provided West and East Bases with buildings in which the floor was ice-free. Small buildings for special purposes were constructed on the spot. Supplies were stacked systematically in parallel rows which were roofed over to form a network of tunnels between the buildings. When the whole assemblage was covered with drift snow, it was possible to go from one building to another without going out-of-doors. Side tunnels, at right angles to the main tunnel, were used to house the dog teams during the winter, each team having its own tunnel. The main tunnel ran from the main building, containing the living quarters and galley, past the blubber house and chopping room to the magnetic hut. Airplane hangars were constructed of snow blocks roofed over with lumber and heavy canvas. By March 6, 1940, everything at West Base was under roof.

The Snow Cruiser. Great hopes were held for the Snow Cruiser, and in theory at least, its design seemed to justify them. Assumed to have a cruising range of 5000 miles and designed to cross crevasses up to 15 feet wide, its own potential was extended by the Beechcraft plane which it was to carry on its back. This plane would have been invaluable in reconnaissance flights to assist in finding a feasible route through crevassed areas or over rough terrain, to say nothing of its worth as an exploring instrument. If the Snow Cruiser had worked at all, it might have been possible for it to have reached the South Pole, especially if a route could have been found toward the southeast by which the Queen Maud Mountains might have been bypassed or surmounted. From the very beginning, however, the Snow Cruiser was plagued with misfortune. Several difficulties had arisen on its overland trip, via highway, from Chicago to Boston. Some of these could be explained by the fact that the trip was somewhat in the nature of a "shakedown cruise," the machine having had no previous testing. Other difficulties arose because the roads were inadequate for this giant vehicle. As the 30-ton Snow Cruiser was being disembarked at the Bay of Whales, a steel and timber unloading ramp partly collapsed under its weight, and Dr. Poulter, who was at the controls, averted disaster by instantly applying full power, causing the machine to make a crunching forward lunge onto the bay ice.

In spite of their great size, 10 feet in diameter, it was soon apparent that wheels did not provide adequate traction in the snow. The huge pneumatic tires kept 12 square feet of rubber on the surface at all times, but the machine's weight was too great. Investigation showed that the snow structure collapsed to a depth of three feet beneath the machine. Therefore, although the Cruiser sank only to a depth of six inches in the snow, its electric motors were not powerful enough to push it forward. If facilities to change the gear ratio had been available at West Base, the situation might have been remedied by reducing the speed and increasing the power. After a week's work the Snow Cruiser was only half way up the slope from the bay ice to the top of the ice shelf. Finally, after prolonged effort, the machine reached West Base, where it was enclosed in a shelter made of snow blocks roofed over with canvas. It was now clear that the Snow Cruiser could not be used as planned. Consequently, its Beechcraft plane and its crew, Dr. F. Alton Wade, Leader; Sgt. Felix L. Ferranto, USMC, Radio Operator; Clyde W. Griffith, Machinist's Mate, 2nd Cl., USN, Mechanic; and T. Sgt. Theodore A. Petras, USMC, Aircraft Pilot, joined forces with the West Base party under the leadership of Dr. Paul A. Siple.

Late Summer Flights, 1940. The twin-motored Curtiss-Wright Condor biplane and the smaller Beechcraft were readied for flight soon after they were unloaded to be ready to take off whenever the weather might prove satisfactory. The first flight by the Beechcraft was made on January 26 and by the Condor on January 31. Between January 26 and February 8 six short flights were made in the vicinity of the Bay of Whales. They were mostly test flights, but on February 3 Petras and Wade made a flight in the Beechcraft to observe cosmic rays. On February 8 and 9 they also flew the Beechcraft on a reconnaissance flight to the Rockefeller Mountains and back.

On February 9 the first major flight was made northeastward into Marie Byrd Land as far as Land Glacier. Flight personnel consisted of James C. McCoy, pilot; Walter R. Giles, radio operator and co-pilot; Charles C. Shirley, photographer; Dr. Paul A. Siple, mission leader, geographer, and navigator; and Lawrence A. Warner, geologist and observer. The purpose of the flight was to obtain aerial photographs for constructing a map to be used for planning and as a guide for sledging journeys into the area. The flight line crossed the Rockefeller Mountains and the head of Sulzberger Bay, which was mostly obscured by fog and low-lying clouds. To the east of Mount Woodward, bright sunshine made photography possible. The first of eight photographic circles was made over Arthur Glacier, immediately south of the Swanson Mountains. The course was set to the north-northeast and lines of photographs were taken on alternate sides. The second photographic circle was made over Crevasse Valley Glacier, from where the plane proceeded north to a third circle over the Phillips Mountains at the head of Balchen Glacier. The plane was then headed northeastward along the Hobbs Coast, newly discovered by Byrd in a flight from the *Bear.* After completing a photographic circle over Mount McCoy, a nunatak rising above Land Glacier, the plane was forced to begin its return flight by heavy clouds moving in from the north. A photographic strip was made to the northward on a course westward from Mount McCoy, passing along the south side of Balchen Glacier to Marujupu Peak, the center of the seventh photographic circle. During the winter darkness the photographs obtained on the flight were used by Siple, Leonard Berlin, and Raymond A. Butler to compile a four-sheet map on a scale of one mile to the inch for the use of field parties in the spring. Photographs were plotted by the Canadian grid method. The area covered (75° 57′ S to 77°03′ S and 143°30′ W to 146°30′ W), about 5000 square miles, is about the size of the state of Connecticut (Fig. 22).

As a result of British expeditions based on McMurdo Sound and Amundsen's and Byrd's expeditions based at the Bay of Whales, the western and eastern por-

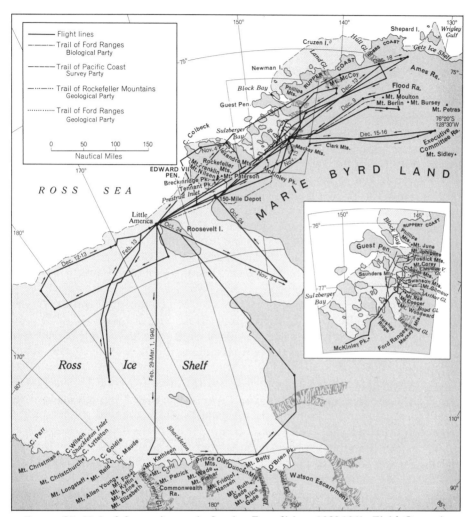

FIGURE 22. United States Antarctic Service Expedition, 1939-1941. Field Operations from West Base.

tions of the Ross Ice Shelf were fairly well known, but the vast expanse in the middle was unexplored. Siple hoped to investigate as much as possible of this unknown area, and although the Presidential orders indicated that operations should concentrate on the area to the east of Little America, he was given permission to fill in the unknown gaps as far west as the 180th meridian.[19] On three occasions when weather was unsuitable for flying to the east of the Bay of Whales, but satisfactory to the west, he sent flights over the Ross Ice Shelf. The first of these was made on February 12 and 13, 1940. Siple and Wade, with Petras as pilot, took off in the Beechcraft and headed westward along the seaward edge of the Ross Ice Shelf to Lindbergh Inlet, where they turned southwestward to avoid clouds. An area of crevasses, oriented northeast-southwest, was found to occupy a wide zone between 70°30′ S and 80° S and 175° W and 176° W. An even larger area of disturbed ice which appeared to be at a higher elevation than the first was discovered 100 miles to the southwest. At the turning point of the flight, at approximately 81°20′ S, 178° E, the high mountains of Victoria Land appeared in a semicircle to the south and west about 150 miles distant. The return flight was made roughly parallel, 10 miles to the northwest of the outward track. Near the 79th parallel and between 166° and 168° W, they noted an ice rise about as high but smaller than that associated with Roosevelt Island.

The next flight from West Base was also over the Ross Ice Shelf. On February 29, 1940, Siple and Wade took off in the Condor with McCoy as pilot, Giles as co-pilot, and Shirley as photographer. A great circle course was set across the Ross Ice Shelf toward the foot of Beardmore Glacier. Three areas of disturbed ice were observed. The first was the edge of the area near 80°45′ S and west of 170° W, seen by Byrd in 1929. To the east, along the 81st parallel, the crevasses which had been so troublesome to Amundsen (1911), Gould (1929), and Blackburn (1934) were plainly visible. Incipient crevasses seemed to indicate a connection between the two disturbed areas. The third belt of crevasses, with an east-west axis, was discovered in about 82°15′ S, 176° W. To the south of the crevasses the ice was thrown into a series of pressure rolls striking east-west.

At the foot of Beardmore Glacier the plane climbed to an altitude of 9500 feet and the course was changed to the southeast along the front of the Queen Maud Mountains, which were photographed from Beardmore Glacier to Amundsen Glacier, closing an unexplored gap between the areas traversed by Shackleton and Scott in the west and Amundsen and Byrd in the east. Although shadows reduced the quality of the pictures, the area was carefully observed with regard to its topographic and geomorphic relationships.[20] One of the major discoveries was a huge glacier, since named Shackleton Glacier, immediately east of the Dominion Range and similar to the other great glaciers, Beardmore, Amundsen, Liv, and Scott, descending from the Polar plateau to the Ross Ice Shelf. A towering landmark, Mount Wade, rising to 15,000 feet, forms its eastern portal. Photographic circles were completed at the foot of Beardmore, Shackleton, Liv, and Amundsen Glaciers.

Beyond Amundsen Glacier heavy clouds prevented an extension of the flight to the eastward. Therefore the plane was turned northeastward, and through breaks in the clouds the Watson Escarpment could be seen to extend farther north than had previously been thought to be the case. At the foot of the escarpment the broad westward-flowing ice stream, Leverett Glacier, was clearly seen. The gently rising ice slope of Marie Byrd Land to the north and the 2000-foot outcrops of the Watson Escarpment on the south seemed to preclude any possibility of a low-lying trough separating Marie Byrd Land from the Transantarctic Mountains, of which the Queen Maud Mountains are a part. Of course, they had no means of determining subglacial conditions.

South of the 83rd parallel the course was changed to the north-northwest. Near the 81st parallel the surface sloped down to the Ross Ice Shelf in a series of ice falls and crevasses. To the north of the parallel a bulge in the ice shelf seemed to indicate another ice-drowned island. The gasoline tanks were almost empty when the plane landed at West Base at the conclusion of more than 11 hours in the air, the longest flight from West Base during the U. S. Antarctic Service Expedition.

The last flights of the season, a series of local flights in the Beechcraft to obtain meteorological data, were made from West Base on April 3. In the interval between then and February 29, several local flights had been made. On March 9 Petras and Griffith, in the Beechcraft, ascended to over 21,000 feet over Little America for the observation of cosmic rays. The following day Petras, Butler, and Berlin used the Beechcraft to observe the pressure ice associated with Roosevelt Island. Also on the 10th, Siple, McCoy, Giles, Shirley, Warner, and Passel, in the Condor, made a complete photographic survey of the vicinity of the Bay of Whales.

Scientific Investigations. As winter darkness and decreasing temperatures enveloped West Base, preparations for trail journeys during the coming summer season and a variety of scientific investigations occupied the men. Many of the investigations, such as meteorological observations, were carried on throughout the year, but during the confinement of winter they were brought into sharper focus. Other investigations, such as those pertaining to the aurora, were limited to periods of darkness.

1. The program of meteorological investigation was formulated by the scientists of the U. S. Antarctic Service with the assistance of the U. S. Weather Bureau, which supplied most of the instruments and the observer, Arnold Court. Marine weather observations were begun as soon as the *North Star* left Boston, and were continued throughout the entire cruise as well as on the voyage to evacuate West Base in 1940-41. Eric T. Clarke, physicist from the Bartol Foundation in charge of the cosmic ray observations aboard the *North Star,* assumed responsibility for the marine meteorological observations after Court disembarked at the Bay of Whales.

The *North Star* was moored at the Bay of Whales on January 12, and on the next day a temporary weather station was established at the equipment and supply cache on the edge of the Ross Ice Shelf. Observations were commenced at Little America III, two miles farther south, on January 25, and the temporary station was discontinued on February 15. Until March 1, when a regular six-hour schedule of observations was established, Court tried to read the instruments at midnight, 6:00 a. m., noon, and 6:00 p. m., but since he was assisting in transporting supplies and constructing the camp, he could not always adhere strictly to that schedule. Greenwich meridian time was observed so as to coordinate with radio operations, and magnetic and cosmic ray observations, although local time at the camp (164° W) was more than 13 hours later. Temperature, pressure, wind direction and velocity were observed regularly. In addition to conventional mercury thermometers, barometers, and sling psychrometers, continuously recording thermographs, barographs, and hydrographs were employed. Minimum thermometers were of the alcohol variety, and special thallium-mercury alloy maximum thermometers were used instead of the usual mercury-type instrument for obtaining maximum readings when the temperature dropped below −38° F. No attempt was made to measure precipitation, but surface accretion was measured daily by Wade, who for this purpose erected a pair of calibrated sticks in each of four directions from the camp. It was calculated that annual accretion totaled almost 40 centimeters.

Pilot balloons and radiosondes were used for upper-air observation. The first pilot balloon ascent was made on January 28, 1940; others followed at irregular intervals. From February 12, 1940, until January 29, 1941, ascents were made daily unless drifting snow or low visibility interfered. A total of 219 successful ascensions were made. From April 26, 1940 until January 15, 1941, 188 successful radiosonde ascents were made at West Base. Of these 180 reached or exceeded six kilometers. From the extent of this program, unprecedented for the Antarctic, a remarkable discovery resulted. In the winter there is a continual decrease in temperature with altitude averaging from −04° F at the surface to −112° F at 12 kilometers, the recording limit of the equipment. Thus the tropopause must be higher than 12 kilometers or the stratosphere disappears altogether. In summer, on the other hand, the tropopause was reached at from seven to eight kilometers where the temperature reaches a minimum of about −58° F.[21] In these operations Court was regularly assisted by Harrison H. Richardson and Malcolm C. Douglass, and at one time or another more than half of the men at the base assisted in the pilot balloon or radiosonde ascents.

While the major portion of the meteorological program was successful, difficulties resulted from the fact that the program was too large for one meteorologist with volunteer assistants from other activities.[22] Lack of manpower, and instruments which were not properly adapted to Antarctic conditions, were mainly responsible for unsatisfactory results in three phases of the meteorological program. One of these concerned a study of vertical temperature gradients by placing telethermometers in a box on the anemometer pole, in the regular thermometer shelter, and in the snow. Results of the solar and sky radiation measuring program were also unsatisfactory. From October 6, when difficulties with the instruments were finally overcome, until January 16, a total of 28 determinations were made of the amount of radiation. The number of these readings, each of which took more than an hour, was hardly adequate, yet the number was of necessity limited by the fact that observations could be made only when the sky was either entirely clear or entirely overcast. A broken sky caused wide variation in radiation over short periods. Dr. Siple set up a project to measure the amount of cold air drainage in Eleanor Bolling Bight, for which 10 minimum thermometers were mounted on exposed boards. When blizzards did not prevent it, these were read daily during the months of winter darkness by Isaac Schlossbach and

Loran Wells, but re-calibration in Washington of the instruments used in the project revealed that they were accurate only to within one degree in such low temperatures.[23]

2. Three physiological investigations having to do with the effect of the rigors of Antarctic climate on the human body were carried out at West Base. During the Antarctic winter night Dr. Siple and Charles Passel, assisted by Malcolm Douglass, carried on experiments to determine the extent to which increased wind velocity increases human discomfort in a given degree of cold. During a series of 89 experiments under variable atmospheric conditions, Siple timed the freezing of 250 grams of water in a freely suspended cylinder of pyrolin, recording also the atmospheric temperature and wind velocity in each instance. As a result, he was able to determine the variation in atmospheric cooling due to variation in wind velocity. Expressing the heat loss in terms of kilogram calories per square meter per hour per degree centigrade, he devised a wind-chill index which he reduced to tabular form and which became an accepted standard wind-chill index.

Dr. Russell G. Frazier, medical officer at West Base, carried on a series of tests on expedition personnel designed to determine the degree of body acclimatization to cold. Blood counts were taken in Boston before sailing, when near the equator in December, and monthly from February to November, 1940. Frazier cooperated with Siple in the development of his wind-chill index by having subjects expose part of the body while facing into the wind. The elapsed time from the first exposure to the appearance of a white spot on the exposed flesh was carefully noted. It was found that some men, those who had developed a dehydrated condition of the skin through spending long hours out of doors, could be exposed for as much as ten minutes before the white spot appeared, while men who lived indoors would freeze in 20 to 90 seconds.[24] Over a period of six months Dr. Frazier made a series of 100 blood pressure readings on camp personnel. With the subject stripped to the waist, his blood pressure, pulse, and respiration rate were first recorded in the building, where the temperature was about 70° F. He then stepped out of the door into the tunnel, where the temperature was well below zero, and readings were made at 1-minute intervals for 8 to 10 minutes. The subject then returned to the building for a final series of readings until he returned to normal. The tests showed that both respiration and pulse were slowed between 20 and 50 percent after exposure in the tunnel, but soon returned to normal upon re-entering the warm building. The blood pressure, on the other hand, showed a sharp rise immediately upon exposure to the cold. Its return to normal after the subject re-entered the building was more gradual.

Using volunteers among camp personnel, Dr. Ernest E. Lockhart studied the problem of acclimatization through a series of physiological investigations. He was concerned with the slightly lowered basal metabolism, a 13 percent increase above normal blood sugar, and changes in respiration and body temperature. The basal metabolism studies included tests on field men before and after a three-month period on the trail, during which they lived on a controlled diet.

3. For a variety of reasons, mainly inadequate transport, an elaborate plan for

auroral observation had to be considerably curtailed. In addition to an observatory at Little America III, it was also hoped to establish, before winter set in, an outpost in the Rockefeller Mountains, about 100 miles east of Little America III. Here the seismograph and the magnetograph were to be installed and an auroral observer was to spend the winter. The outpost was established the following spring. In the meantime, however, winter observations of the aurora had to be carried on at West Base, and height determinations were accomplished by establishing a temporary field observatory 15 miles east of Little America III for a week in July and for a second week in August. The auroral observatory, also used by the meteorologists for balloon ascents, was located on the roof of the science building. Within this 6 foot by 6 foot enclosure, with a trap door in the roof, a transit was set up to measure the angles of altitude and azimuths of auroral displays. A camera fitted to the transit was used for photographing the displays. Regular observations were begun on April 1 and continued throughout the winter night until September 15, 1940. During the period of 24-hour darkness, Murray A. Wiener, the regular observer, was assisted by Roy G. Fitzsimmons, physicist, or by Dr. Wade, to provide continuous observation.

On July 10 a field party consisting of Wiener, observer and leader; Fitzsimmons, navigator; Ferranto, radio operator; Passel, driver; and Griffith, mechanic, set out with the International Harvester T-20 tractor, drawing two sleds and a caboose on a 15-mile trip directly east of Little America III. The objective of the party was to establish a sub-base to record simultaneous radio-controlled photographs of the auroral displays with observations taken at West Base by Wade and Warner. The trigonometric function of the two angles, the azimuth, and the known length of the baseline extended to the sub-base would then give the computed altitude of the aurora observed. The trip was undertaken in midwinter, and extremely low temperatures were experienced. A minimum of $-71.1°$ F was recorded. Twenty-five film exposures synchronized with West Base were made of auroral activity, but difficulties were experienced in operating the camera in such low temperatures. After the party returned to West Base on July 17, the film was developed, and not a single picture appeared. Apparently the camera mechanism had been stalled by the extreme cold. The length of the established baseline was later determined to be 84,802.5 feet, approximately 16 statute miles.

A second attempt to establish an auroral sub-base for height determination was made two weeks later. On July 30 Wiener, Ferranto, Adam Asman, driver, Griffith, and Passel, navigator, set out in a sled train pulled by the modified Army M2A2 tank. This time they obtained 16 pairs of synchronized photographs, the first in the history of Antarctic exploration. The party returned to West Base on August 9 without having suffered any serious mishap during their period in the field, despite the continued low temperatures. From April 1 to September 15, a total of 1553 individual aurora were observed and recorded.

4. The U. S. Antarctic Service Expedition program for observation of cosmic rays consisted of three parts: (a) observations and experiments aboard ship, (b) long-term observations with meters installed at West Base, and (c) incidental

observations, such as "bursts" noted in the long-term observations and observations of altitude variation during airplane flights. Eric T. Clarke of the Bartol Foundation conducted the observations aboard the *North Star* on the 1939-41 round-trip voyage to Antarctica. Two Millikan-Meher meters which Clarke brought to Antarctica were installed in the science building at Little America III. Recording began on both meters on April 27, 1940, and continued until mechanical difficulties forced the shutting down of Meter No. 1 on September 15 and Meter No. 2 on November 16. The records were subsequently correlated with meteorological data, including temperatures at various elevations obtained by radiosonde.[25] On the 1940-41 Antarctic voyage of the *North Star*, the cosmic ray observations were carried out by Dana K. Bailey, who also dismantled the meters at Little America and returned the films to the Bartol Foundation.

5. To insure conformity with recent investigations by leading glaciologists, Dr. Wade invited the Association for the Study of Snow and Ice (London) to propose a research program in glaciology for the U. S. Antarctic Service Expedition and make suggestions relating to methodology and equipment. The program presented by the Association was the basis for the work carried out by Wade and Lawrence A. Warner, geologist. Two ice stations were planned, one on the Ross Ice Shelf at Little America and another on the Polar plateau, but the failure of the Snow Cruiser caused the cancellation of the plateau station.

A pit 2 meters square (6½' x 6½') and 7 meters (23') deep was excavated in the ice shelf beneath the ice laboratory. Snow blocks were easily cut and removed at the upper levels, but at the bottom of the pit blasting was necessary. For the purpose of comparing the profiles of the upper 2 meters and the densities of upper layers of névé, an auxiliary pit, 2 meters deep, was dug 200 meters (656 feet) west of the ice laboratory. Three compression meters were installed on the north wall of the main pit to determine the amount and rate of settling of the firn.[26] Density was determined by weighing samples of snow, névé, and firn obtained from the walls of the pit. Samples of firn with a density of less than 0.5 were obtained with a sampler by which 500 cc of firn could be extracted and sealed. Firn of greater density was sampled by cutting out carefully measured blocks of 500 cc or 1000 cc by volume. Crystallization was studied by means of thin sections viewed under a petrographic microscope. The U. S. Bureau of Standards devised a method for determining subsurface temperatures. A resistance bulb thermohm was sealed in the bottom of each of 14 holes, varying in depth from 0.25 to 41 meters. An additional thermohm was set up 10 cm above the surface. The thermohms were connected by way of a multiple switch to a modified wheatstone bridge, calibrated to permit direct temperature readings. The measurement of surface accumulation of snow, previously referred to as part of the meteorological observations, was actually carried out as a part of the glaciological study.

Results of the investigation, as reported by Wade,[27] revealed a general but not regular increase in density with depth from an average of 0.3 (gm/cm^3) at the surface to an average of 0.5 at 6 meters. Thin layers or bands of ice in the firn had an average density of 0.903. The pit revealed a definite stratification with a tendency for increased grain size with depth, but there was no apparent orientation of crystal grains. Perhaps because the ice at Little America III is afloat, there was no differential horizontal movement indicated. The rate of settling decreases with depth and varies directly with temperature. Temperature decreases in depth to about 5 meters, below which it remains fairly constant and approximately the equivalent of the average annual atmospheric temperature. Seasonal temperature variation was reflected to a depth of 5 meters. A slight rise in temperature was noted below 15 meters, perhaps due to the influence of warmer water below. No melt water existed in the firn, and transformation from snow results from continued settling, first rapidly and then at a steadily decreasing rate with depth.

6. The more important contributions to botany and zoology by West Base personnel resulted from collections made on sledge journeys which will be reported below. Because of lack of time and personnel, biological work at Little America III was limited to recording observations and collecting specimens incidental to other activities such as procuring seal carcasses for dog food. Some museum specimens were also prepared. It is noteworthy that three specimens of the relatively rare Ross seal were collected at the Bay of Whales. This seal had not been seen there by members of either the First or Second Byrd Expeditions. Three adult Weddell seals, bearing brands made by Alton A. Lindsey, biologist on the Second Byrd Antarctic Expedition in 1934-35, were observed in 1940, indicating their non-migratory nature. Jack E. Perkins, biologist at West Base, also collected at the Bay of Whales and at Discovery Inlet four Emperor and several Adélie penguins, five crab-eater seals, and one Ross seal for the National Zoological Park in Washington, but of these only three Emperor penguins reached the United States alive.

Depot-Laying Preliminary to Sledge Journeys. During the winter night at West Base, those who were to make long sledge journeys during the coming spring and summer season were busy with preparations. Equipment had to be readied; man and dog pemican had to be weighed and packaged, and all details had to be carefully planned. The shortest journey would involve a round trip of over 200 miles, and the longest more than 1200. To reach distances of from 350 to 600 miles from West Base would require supply depots along the trail, which would insure a full sledge load at the beginning of each of the more extended thrusts into the unknown, and on which returning parties could depend for food and fuel. To extend the flight range of the big Curtiss-Wright Condor plane, it was also planned to cache aviation gasoline in the field.

As soon as there were a few hours of daylight, the sun having risen for the first time on August 22, preparations for the first depot-laying journey were begun, but a spell of extremely cold weather in September delayed departure. With time slipping by, the tractor party finally left on September 18 in spite of a $-63°$ F temperature. Warner served as leader and navigator, Passel was radio operator, and Vernon D. Boyd was at the controls of the International T-20 tractor pulling a train of sleds loaded with man and dog food and tractor fuel. Richard Moulton was responsible for laying and marking the trail as the tractor train slowly headed eastward from Little America III. Breaking a trail over a snow-covered waste in temperatures that sometimes dropped below −60° F, the party finally established a depot 10 miles south of Breckenridge Peak in the Rockefeller Mountains. This cache, which subsequently became known as "105-Mile Depot" because of its distance from West Base, was located at 78° 16′45″ S, 155°32′08″ W. Caches of dog food were also laid at intervals along the trail between West Base and 105-Mile Depot. At one point in the journey, Boyd performed major repairs to the tractor without benefit of shelter, despite temperatures below −40° F. On October 3 the tractor party returned to West Base, leaving a well-marked trail for the first 105 miles to the east.

The day before the First Eastern Tractor Party returned, the Second Eastern Tractor Party set out on the trail that the first had marked. The party was led by Adam Asman, who drove the light tank, drawing the caboose and a train of sleds loaded with eight tons of supplies and tractor fuel. He was accompanied by Clyde Griffith and Louis Colombo. For trail work, Asman and Griffith had cut most of the armor plate from the tank to lighten it. The party's objective was to augment 105-Mile Depot and to transport to the Rockefeller Mountains the equipment for a seismic station. Because of an intervening area of crevasses which the tank could not cross, they were halted 11 miles short of Mount Franklin, the proposed site of the seismic station. On October 9 the tractor party was back at West Base. At one point during the journey their tent had been blown to shreds by a gale; at another, they were forced to halt in subzero weather to repair a sled.

The First Stage of the Sledge Journeys. The big push eastward, eventually involving five separate sledging parties, began on October 15, 1940, which marked the departure of the Ford Ranges Biological Party. Led by Jack E. Perkins, biologist, the party then consisted of Dr. Ernest E. Lockhart, physiologist and radio operator, and Louis P. Colombo, dog driver, with two dog teams, each pulling two sleds in tandem. Harrison H. Richardson, meteorological observer, transferred from the Pacific Coast Survey Party to the Biological Party at 105-Mile Depot. Their objective was the western mountains of the Ford Ranges, where they were to gather biological information and obtain, wherever possible, data relating to geology and glaciation. They were also assigned a number of problems of triangulation pertaining to the location and elevation of certain mountain peaks. Roy G. Fitzsimmons, the physicist who was to man the seismic station, accompanied the Biological Party as far as 105-Mile Depot.

The following day, October 16, the Third Eastern Tractor Party set out on the (by then) well-marked trail to 105-Mile Depot. Approximately five tons of building materials, fuel, man food, and dog food were loaded on the sleds pulled by the light Army tank. Only Asman and Griffith were aboard.

On October 17 two more sledging parties, the Ford Ranges Geological Party and the Pacific Coast Survey Party, left West Base for field assignments in Marie Byrd Land to the northeast. The Geological Party consisted of four men: Dr. Lawrence A. Warner, geologist and leader; Charles F. Passel, geologist and radio operator; Loran Wells, photographer and meteorological observer; and Harold P. Gilmour, recorder. Their sledges were pulled by two teams of nine dogs each. Their objective was the central Ford Ranges, where they were to map the geological structures and formations of as large an area as possible in the limited time available.

The Pacific Coast Survey Party, led by Leonard M. Berlin, cadastral engineer, included Jack Bursey, radio operator and dog driver, and Richard S. Moulton, photographer and dog driver. Harrison H. Richardson, meteorological observer for the Biological Party, accompanied the Survey Party as far as 105-Mile Depot. Because the Survey Party was to penetrate far to the eastward to reach the Flood Range, its two dog teams were made up of the best dogs at West Base, and the party was in other ways also organized for speed. Although the Survey Party and the Geological Party set out together, the slower dogs of the latter were soon trailing behind. There were now three sledging parties and a tractor train en route from West Base to 105-Mile Depot on the eastern trail.

The next day, October 18, another tractor party, the Fourth Eastern Tractor Party, set out for 105-Mile Depot. The party consisted of Boyd and Ferranto, with the International T-20 tractor pulling the sleds loaded with 1000 pounds of man food, 2000 pounds of dog food, and 500 gallons of aviation gasoline.

The three sledging parties and the two tractor parties, according to plan, made a rendezvous at 105-Mile Depot. Here they cooperated in transporting the equipment for the seismic station to a site selected by Fitzsimmons on nearby Mount Franklin in the Rockefeller Mountains. Because of the intervening crevassed area, dog teams and man-hauling had to be relied on for the last part of the trip to Mount Franklin.

Having completed this assignment, the three sledging parties reorganized their sledge loads for the next leg of the journey into Marie Byrd Land. On the 130-mile journey from 105-Mile Depot to McKinley Peak, the three sledging parties were supported by the Fourth Eastern Tractor Party of Boyd and Ferranto with the tractor. Part of the man and dog food on the tractor-drawn sleds was cached at regular intervals along the trail for use of the sledge parties on their return trip. The dog teams, in turn, were invaluable in seeking a safe route for the tractor train through crevassed areas as the combined parties ascended the terrace-like rises to the summit of the Rockefeller Plateau en route to McKinley Peak.

By November 11 all four parties had reached the foot of McKinley Peak, where the tractor party cached the remainder of the man and dog food and the 500 gallons of aviation gasoline. On November 13 the four parties climbed to the highest point on the southernmost ridge of the mountain, where a 20' x 200' outcrop of granite and diabase porphyry is exposed. Here the United States flag was raised and the men witnessed a document, claiming the area for the United States. The document, drawn up by Berlin, was placed in a glass jar and deposited in a stone cairn built there by Siple and his party in 1934. At that time, Siple's party had flown the United States flag there. In the bedrock beneath the cairn, Berlin set an official U. S. General Land Office brass monument marked "Station 2 Antarctica 1940." Through triangulation and astronomical observation, the site of the cairn was determined to be 70°54'35.4" S, 148°20'20.0" W.

PLATE XI-A. The first depot-laying tractor train leaving West Base for the Rockefeller Mountains on September 18, 1940. The temperature was −65°F. The tractor is pulling two loaded sledges and a "caboose." Note the buildings in background and the degree to which they have been buried by drifting snow since photo on Plate X-B was taken. Photo No. 126-USAS-5202 in the National Archives.

PLATE XI-B. The U. S. A. S. West Base Biological Party at McKinley Peak. The Beech-craft has flown in from West Base to the cache at the foot of the mountain and is being refueled. Photo No. 126-USAS-5758 in the National Archives.

PLATE XII-A. Field parties at Saunders Mountain, December 15, 1940. The U. S. A. S. West Base Pacific Coast Survey Party is in the foreground. The Geological Party is in the background. (Photo by Charles C. Shirley.) Photo No. 126-USAS-5761.

PLATE XII-B. Flight planning at West Base, U. S. A. S., November 10, 1940. Standing, l. to r., Orville Gray, Charles C. Shirley, Walter R. Giles, and (seated) James C. McCoy, Paul A. Siple, F. Alton Wade, and Theodore A. Petras, planning southeastern flight D. Photo No. 126-USAS- 5603 in the National Archives.

From McKinley Peak the tractor party returned to Little America III, which they reached on November 24. Ferranto and Clyde Griffith set out again six days later with the tractor, drawing a second load of aviation gasoline for the depot at McKinley Peak, where they remained for several weeks as a meteorological outpost, sending back weather information in support of the aviation program.

Field Journey of the Ford Ranges Biological Party. Meanwhile the three sledging parties headed north-northeast, across Hershey Ridge toward the northwestern end of the Haines Mountains. Since the Biological Party hoped to reach the Fosdick Mountains to the north, it was to their advantage to stay as much as possible on the ice shelf bordering the eastern side of Sulzberger Bay, where they could travel more rapidly. Moreover, this coastal area, in contrast to the drier and colder interior, was expected to yield a greater harvest of biological specimens. Since the Geological and Survey parties were destined for more inland locations, the Biological Party set out on its own after crossing the shelf ice at the foot of Hammond Glacier. First they headed for the low hills to the west of Saunders Mountain. Then the party crossed the foot of Crevasse Valley Glacier, after which they examined the southwestern corner of Mount Iphigene and neighboring peaks.

On November 25, 1950, the party raised the United States flag and witnessed and deposited a claim sheet in a rock cairn on the talus slope at the southwest corner of peak No. 167, which is on the west side of Mount Iphigene. The site of the cairn is approximately 76° 31' S, 145° 45' W.

The Biological Party next visited Marujupu Peak, which proved to be the richest locality for biological specimens on the trip. By Antarctic standards, plant life was abundant, perhaps, according to Siple's observations, because of a nearby rookery of Snow petrels.[28] Adjacent peaks having similar environmental conditions, but lacking a rookery, are barren.

From Marujupu Peak the Biological Party sledged over the southwestern corner of the Fosdick Mountains and up onto the plateau-like crest of this mountain block. Along this commanding summit the party trekked eastward 15 miles, visiting an area greatly disrupted by volcanic activity. Siple and Corey had visited the southern edge of this volcanic area at the extremity of their sledge journey in 1934.[29] Approaching from the west, the Biological Party was able to examine this volcanic area much more extensively than had Siple and Corey, who had approached from the south. From this volcanic area in the center of the Fosdick Mountains, the Ford Ranges Biological Party began the return journey to Little America III. En route to McKinley Peak they again stayed on the coastal ice shelf for much of the way, this time passing between Saunders Mountain and the low hills to the west which apparently are on an island. They picked up the outward trail at the foot of Hammond Glacier and on Christmas Day reached Little America III, having covered 725 miles in 72 days. The sledges brought back a considerable quantity of biological and geological specimens. A daily meteorological record, a well-written journal, and numerous photographs were tangible products of the journey.

The Ford Ranges Geological Party. When the Geological Party and the Survey Party left McKinley Peak, their immediate destination was Mount Rea, where a cache of food and gasoline had been laid by Siple, McCoy, Giles, Shirley, and Frazier on November 13 while on a photographic flight from West Base. With its faster dogs, the Survey Party pushed on ahead, breaking a trail around the northwestern end of the Haines Mountains, descending out onto the ice shelf bordering the shore of Sulzberger Bay. Cutting northeastward around the foot of Hammond Glacier and keeping well to the west of Mount Woodward, the Survey Party stayed on the ice shelf until it reached the foot of Mount Rea, a day ahead of the Geological Party.

After supplying itself from its Mount Rea cache, the Geological Party set out northeastward toward the western end of the Swanson Mountains. Here on a ridge one-and-a-half miles southwest of the peak designated No. 24 on the base map,[30] the party raised the United States flag on November 24 and deposited a claim sheet in a rock cairn at about 76°59′ S, 145°15′ W. A baseline was laid out and intersections were shot to the major peaks of the Swanson Mountains to test the accuracy of the base map compiled by Siple, Berlin, and Butler during the winter from photographs obtained on the flight of February 9, 1940, on which Warner was an observer.

Having completed this task, the party continued northeastward, visiting Wells Ridge and then Mount Gilmour before passing northward over the east end of Mount Passel. Side journeys were made to Mount Gilmour and to Mount Passel, as well as to one other large peak to the southeast of Mount Gilmour. From Mount Passel the party sledged east northeast to peak #232, in about 76°49′ S, 144°26′ W, where on December 1 they split into two groups. Passel and Wells with one team set off southward to the peaks overlooking the north side of Arthur Glacier, while Warner and Gilmour continued westward among peaks bordering the south side of Crevasse Valley Glacier. After visiting Peak #310, about 76°52′ S, 143°36′ W, Warner and Gilmour headed southwestward to the prearranged rendezvous with Passel and Wells at peak #345. On December 6, 1940, en route to the rendezvous, Warner and Gilmour raised the United States flag and deposited a second claim sheet in a rock cairn on a ridge in the vicinity of peak #328 in about 76°56′ S, 143°40′ W.

From the rendezvous, at about 76°57′ S, 143°53′ W, the four men and two teams crossed the head of Arthur Glacier to Mount Warner in about 77°05′ S, 144°00′ W. The Party then moved south a short distance and westward among the peaks forming the divide between Arthur Glacier and Crevasse Valley Glacier. Moving along the northeastern flank of Mount Cooper, they reached the Mount Rea cache on December 14. They had visited 59 peaks in a little less than one month. Often the going had been difficult because, in areas adjacent to the rock outcrops, radiation caused thawing on warm days and melt water had refrozen to solid blue ice. The rock outcrops on mountain flanks were often difficult of access because of "wind moats," depressions partly due to excavation of the snow by swirling winds. Compaction due to radiation-induced melting, no doubt, contributes to their formation. The southeastern Ford Ranges were found to consist of dark-colored sandstone and shales compressed into broad folds whose axes trend northwest-southeast. These folded sedimentaries have

been slightly metamorphosed by extensive intrusions of red and brown granodiorite and associated igneous rocks whose emplacement has been influenced by
the folds.[31]

The Pacific Coast Survey Party. From Mount Rea the Pacific Coast Survey
Party sledged eastward along the northern side of Arthur Glacier and up its
northeastern branch, making brief surveys en route. On November 26 they sighted an 11,400-foot peak, subsequently named Mount Berlin, rising above the western part of the Flood Range. On December 1 they made their easternmost camp
at the western edge of the range and about 14 miles southwest of Mount Berlin.
They ran a 2400-foot baseline from which peaks of the western part of the range
were intersected. Mount Berlin, the highest and most easterly of those surveyed,
was found to be located at 76° 03' S, 135° 52' W. On December 5 the Survey Party
raised the United States flag and deposited a claim sheet in a rock cairn on the
southwestern slope of the westernmost peak of the range. The spot was marked
by a United States General Land Office brass marker set in rock. The marker,
"Antarctica No. 4," was set at a position determined to be 76° 03'59.4" S, 136° 08'
25.43" W. The survey of the Mount Berlin area was completed on December 6.
Rock specimens of the area, which show evidence of igneous origin, were collected by the party.

On December 15 the Pacific Coast Survey Party joined the Geological Party
at the Mount Rea cache. Together they made the return sledge journey to the
cache at McKinley Peak, where they joined the two-man tractor party which had
been serving as weather outpost, radio relay station, and emergency rescue crew.
Boyd and Ferranto had reached Little America on November 24 with the tractor train on the return from the first trip to McKinley Peak. On November 30
Ferranto and Griffith set out with the International T-20 tractor for the second
trip to the McKinley Peak cache. The sleds were loaded with trail rations, aviation gasoline, and emergency supplies. This time, living in the caboose, they remained at the cache to radio weather reports to Little America III in support of
the aviation program. They also served as emergency ground crew for the planes
as they refueled at the cache, and acted as a radio relay station for both sledge
parties and the flight crews.

The four dog teams of the combined parties again served as a convoy for the
tractor train across or around dangerous crevassed areas en route to 105-Mile
Depot. The long treks, heavy loads, and the inadequacies of the trail diet began
to tell on the dogs, some of which had to be shot when they could not keep up
with the group even though freed from their harness. At 105-Mile Depot the
combined parties were joined by the Rockefeller Mountains Geological Party,
and all cooperated in dismantling the seismic station on the flank of Mount
Franklin.

The Rockefeller Mountains Geological Party. The other field parties were
already investigating their assigned areas when the Rockefeller Mountains Geological Party left West Base on November 25, 1940. The party consisted of Dr.
Wade and Dr. Frazier, base medical officer, and one team of six dogs. Dr. Wade's
objective was to complete the geological investigation of the Rockefeller Moun-

tains which he had begun on the return from the longer sledge journey with Siple, Corey, and Stancliff to Marie Byrd Land in 1934-35. En route, Wade and Frazier measured a 14-mile baseline between West Base and the site of the auroral observations during the winter night. On December 10 they arrived at the first mountain, Tennant Peak. Thirteen peaks were surveyed and geologically investigated in the next 18 days, and Dr. Frazier collected biological specimens at the sites visited. Wade found that the Rockefeller Mountains are geologically similar to the Ford Ranges, most of the peaks being part of a pink granitic batholith intruded into previously folded and metamorphosed sedimentary rocks.[32] The geological and survey work in the Rockefeller Mountains was greatly facilitated by a triangulation network established by the Rockefeller Mountains Seismic Station Party. On December 30 Wade and Frazier joined the other field groups in the return to West Base from 105-Mile Depot.

The Rockefeller Mountains Seismic Station. The Rockefeller Mountains seismic station was in charge of Roy G. Fitzsimmons, physicist, who was assisted by Isaac Schlossbach and Raymond A. Butler. Fitzsimmons had sledged out to 105-Mile Depot with the Biological Party, and Schlossbach and Butler were flown out from the Base. The equipment for the station had been carried by the Second Eastern Tractor Party, which had left the Base on October 2. With the assistance of the other field parties and two tractor parties, the equipment for the station was hauled 11 miles from 105-Mile Depot to the slope of Mount Franklin, where the construction was begun on November 1. When Schlossbach and Butler were flown out in the Condor by McCoy and Giles on the night of October 31, 1000 pounds of additional supplies were aboard. These Schlossbach and Butler man-hauled from 105-Mile Depot to Mount Franklin.

On November 17 a seismograph was set up and operated continuously thereafter for 41 days.[33] Fitzsimmons made a collection of gulls, Snow petrels and Antarctic petrels during his stay. The party was without dogs, but Fitzsimmons and Butler, backpacking their equipment and supplies, ran a series of base lines and made a triangulation of every peak in the Rockefeller Mountains, with the exception of the northern group. The geographic position of the main base line was determined by taking several series of sights on the sun. Butler occupied ground camera stations at several points for further assistance in the construction of an accurate topographic map. On December 12, 1940, the party raised the United States flag and witnessed and deposited a claim sheet in a rock cairn built on the central peak of Washington Ridge, 78°06′ S, 154°48′ W. With the assistance of return trail parties, the seismic station was evacuated on December 27, and the Seismic Station Party joined the other groups at 105-Mile Depot.

Return of the Field Parties from 105-Mile Depot. By December 30 all of the field parties and the Tractor Party of Ferranto and Griffith were prepared for the last leg of the return journey to Little America III, and on that day they all set out on the trail for West Base. The dog teams were in poor condition as a result of their long, hard travels, so the sledges carried only enough man and dog food to make the last 105 miles. Rocks, biological specimens, notebooks, and survey charts were loaded on the sleds of the tractor. A fresh fall of snow covered the surface like a soft blanket, causing the tractor to bog down. The dogs were in no condition to take on any addition to their lightened loads. Ferranto and Griffith discovered that by driving the tractor in reverse it was possible to make some progress through the soft snow. By abandoning the caboose they were able to pull the rest of the load slowly.

On January 3, McCoy, Giles, and Siple took off in the Condor with a load of seal meat and 50 gallons of gasoline for the trail parties. The plane landed beside the struggling Tractor Party, delivered the gasoline, and took on board the load of specimens. Intending to land again to deliver the seal meat to the dog teams who were ahead on the trail, McCoy, Giles, and Siple took off, but in a few minutes were forced to glide to a landing when the starboard engine caught fire 82 miles from West Base. The fire burned out quickly, but a piston and cylinder were blown out. In response to a radio message, Petras and Gray flew out to the disabled Condor in the Beechcraft. Petras delivered the seal meat to the dog teams, now 10 miles farther west, and then he and Siple explored for a possible salvage route northward to the edge of the ice shelf. Giles was then returned to West Base, and the next day Petras returned to the Condor for Siple and McCoy. On January 10 Petras and Giles were able to make another flight to the disabled Condor to salvage instruments, equipment, specimens and field records.

Meanwhile, the Tractor Party reached Little America III on January 6. The tractor had traveled the last 92 miles in reverse. On January 7 the combined trail parties arrived at West Base. The Pacific Coast Survey Party had covered approximately 1200 miles, and the Geological Party 796 miles, in 83 days.

Exploratory Flights from Little America III, October-December, 1940. In the latter part of August, 1940, as the hours of daylight increased, preparations for the aviation program kept pace with the preparations for the departure of the sledge parties. When the mechanics had the planes ready, all hands who could be spared cooperated in digging the aircraft out of the winter hangars made of snow blocks roofed over with lumber and canvas. Exceptionally cold weather in the latter part of August and the first part of September made the work even more difficult than usual. From August 31 to September 6 the temperature never rose above −60° F, dropping to a record low of −76.2° F. In spite of these handicaps, the Beechcraft, which was dug out first, was test flown in the vicinity of the base on August 29. Two other test flights were made on succeeding days. The Condor was not ready for its test flight, however, until October 25. In the meantime, five flights were made with the Beechcraft. Three of them, on September 12, October 16, and October 23, were local flights, the last one being made to study conditions of the pressure ice in the Bay of Whales.

On October 23, following the flight over the Bay of Whales, Petras, Shirley, and Siple made a photographic flight along the edge of the ice shelf to Kainan Bay and then headed south to the northeastern corner of ice-drowned Roosevelt Island. Turning west, they photographed the pressure ice along the north side of the island and then returned to West Base.

For the next several weeks the aviation group was principally engaged in laying caches to assist the trail parties and in transporting gasoline to field depots which were designed to extend the flight range of the planes. Photographic reconnaissance was incidental to two of these flights. On October 24, Petras and Siple flew southeastward from West Base in the Beechcraft, searching for a place for a gasoline cache where the snow surface would permit landing and taking off in the Condor. Marking the spot with a sack of lampblack, they turned north-northwest to observe the indefinite eastern margin of the Ross Ice Shelf as they flew toward 105-Mile Depot. From here they followed the trail to the Base.

Two flights to the eastward were made on October 31, both planes returning on November 1. Petras and Wade made a reconnaissance flight in the Beechcraft over the Edward VII Peninsula, but only as they were heading back did the cloud cover retreat enough to reveal the Alexandra and Rockefeller Mountains. The Condor, which had been test flown on October 25, was used by McCoy, Giles, and Gray on October 31 to ferry Schlossbach and Butler to 105-Mile Depot with the last of the supplies for the seismic station. After returning from the Edward VII Peninsula, Petras and Shirley took the Beechcraft over the Bay of Whales to make another of a series of photographs of ice conditions there.

Two flights were also made on November 3-4. McCoy, Giles, Gray, and Siple took off in the Condor with a cargo of 225 gallons of gasoline. They landed about 200 miles southeast of West Base at the spot designated with the lampblack as suitable for a gasoline cache. Sun shots were taken, and the position of the cache was fixed at 80°45′ S, 147°00′ W. The outward flight track was followed on the return flight, the plane landing at West Base on November 4. Meanwhile, Petras and Shirley made a photographic flight in the Beechcraft, which encircled Edward VII Peninsula. The photography, which was intended to supplement that taken on Byrd Antarctic Expeditions I and II, was concentrated between Cape Colbeck and Washington Ridge. Five photographic circles were flown. After the Condor returned from the flight of November 3-4, it was discovered that overloading had overstrained the big plane, which was grounded for repairs until November 13.

On November 13 two flights were made to the area bordering the east shore of Sulzberger Bay. Petras and Wade flew a reconnaissance flight in the Beechcraft. They landed at McKinley Peak and then flew northeastward, over Mount Rea to Marujupu Peak. As the Beechcraft headed homeward from Marujupu, several hilly islands were discovered in Sulzberger Bay, and a circle was flown around La Gorce Peak in the Rockefeller Mountains. The plane's altimeter indicated elevations in general higher than had previously been supposed. While Petras and Wade were in flight, McCoy, Giles, Shirley, Frazier, and Siple took off in the Condor on a photographic flight. A strip of excellent photographs, looking northward into Sulzberger Bay, was obtained from the Rockefeller Mountains to the Haines Mountains. The plane landed beside Mount Rea, where a cache of aviation gasoline and food was laid. Having made photographic circles over Hershey Ridge and over the center of Hammond Glacier on the outward flight, McCoy and his colleagues took off from Mount Rea southeastward across Boyd Glacier, where a third photographic circle was made just to the east of Mount Woodward. The photography was continued across the center of Sulzberger Bay on the homeward flight.

The gasoline cache which had been laid on the Ross Ice Shelf on November 4, about 200 miles southeast of West Base, was in anticipation of a flight to the Horlick Mountains, which form a segment of the Transantarctic Mountains. On November 26 the weather appeared promising for such a flight, so Petras and Siple took off in the Beechcraft on a southeasterly course. Cloud banks across their proposed line of flight forced them to return when they reached the approximate position of the gasoline cache. On December 7 Petras and Siple made a second attempt at a southeastern flight, but this time they were forced back while over Roosevelt Island.

Since the weather on December 7 continued to be satisfactory at the Base, Petras, Siple, and Shirley took off again in the Beechcraft for a flight to make one more series of photographs of local ice conditions. They flew as far west as Lindbergh Inlet and then southward, Dr. Siple sighting what appeared to be two ice-drowned islands to the west of Roosevelt Island. Three other flights, one in the Beechcraft and two in the Condor, were made that day in the vicinity of West Base.

The next day, December 8, a third attempt at the southeasterly flight was made by Petras and Siple, but clouds again turned them back 150 miles from West Base. In an attempt to salvage something from the flight, the return leg was made via Kainan Bay to observe ice conditions there.

While foul weather apparently prevailed to the southeast, the sky over West Base remained clear, and on December 9 favorable conditions to the eastward were also reported. Consequently, the first of four extended photographic flights was made over Marie Byrd Land, beyond the Ford Ranges. Again it was Petras and Siple in the Beechcraft. They landed to top off their gasoline tanks at 105-Mile Depot and at the Mount Rea cache and then set a course for the Flood Range. Two hours and 15 minutes later they were abreast of and south of Mount Berlin, the westernmost of several high, massive peaks that surmount this range. After flying along the south side of the range for another 100 miles, Petras headed the plane northward through a gap at about 133°15′ W occupied by the head of a large north-flowing glacier between Mount Moulton and Mount Bursey.

Several large glaciers were found to descend the north flank of the Flood Range into a vast glacial basin which appeared to empty through a gap in the coast ranges to the north. This great glacial flow, observed again more closely on December 13 and 18, was subsequently named Cordell Hull Glacier and, more recently, Hull Glacier. Open water was visible to the north. Also, when over the Flood Range, Siple and Petras could see and photograph Mount Sidley to the southeast.

Petras then turned the plane westward along the north flank of the Flood Range. On the return flight the Range was observed to extend westward, although partially ice-drowned, to the Ruppert Coast north of Block Bay. After landing at McKinley Peak, the plane continued to West Base.

December 12 was the kind of day that Siple had been looking for to complete the aerial survey of the Ross Ice Shelf. Reports of unsatisfactory weather over Marie Byrd Land precluded a flight in that direction, but conditions were promising to the west of Little America III. Consequently, McCoy, Giles, Shirley, and Siple took off from West Base in the Condor and headed southward to photograph the west side of Roosevelt Island. About 50 miles south of Little America, clouds made a continuation of this course impractical, and the plane was headed westward, taking a strip of pictures toward the north, the only direction that remained clear. Various evidences of ice motion, pressure rolls, tension crevasses, shear zones, and hinge lines were observed west of 175° W.[34] At 178° E a photographic circle was flown and the plane's position determined astronomically before heading north toward the Ross Sea. The peaks of Mounts Erebus, Terror, and Discovery were visible as they protruded above the clouds almost 150 miles to the west. At the seaward edge of the ice shelf, another photographic circle was flown and the plane was then headed eastward to photograph the edge of the ice shelf as far as the Bay of Whales. Photographic circles were flown at the mouth of Discovery Inlet and at the base of the tongue of ice shelf which enclosed it. With the conclusion of the flight of December 12, the front of the Ross Ice Shelf had been photographed from Edward VII Peninsula to within sight of Ross Island.

On December 13 Petras and Siple used the Beechcraft to make the second of four major flights to the eastward during the 1940-41 season. Landings were made at McKinley Peak and at Mount Rea to top off the gasoline tanks. From Mount Rea the course was set northeastward to pass south of Mount McCoy and the head of Land Glacier. When the plane reached Hull Glacier, heavy clouds were observed to the east, seeming to lie over an embayment in the coast. Two photographic circles were flown over Hull Glacier as the plane was set on its return course. All of the field parties were spotted from the plane, and on the return flight landings were made at Mount Rea, the Haines Mountains, and McKinley Peak to make contact with some of them.

An easterly flight by Petras and Shirley on December 14 was interrupted when the tail skid of the Beechcraft was broken in a landing at Mount Rea. They returned to West Base, and after repairs had been made, Petras and Siple took off late on December 15 on a flight designed to tie together photographically the Flood Range and the area about Mount Sidley. After they had refueled at the Mount Rea cache, a course was set to the eastward along the 77th parallel to a point directly south of Mount Berlin. Mount Sidley now appeared on the horizon, and when Siple estimated the plane to be midway between Mount Sidley and Mount Berlin, the first of three photographic circles was flown. The plane was now heading east-northeast, and Mount Sidley was discovered to be the highest peak of what was subsequently named the Executive Committee Range. To the north, more peaks of the Flood Range came into view. A peak estimated to be 12,000 feet high and resembling the volcanic peaks of the Fosdick Mountains lay to the east of, but slightly separated from, the Flood Range. It was subsequently named Mount Petras. The third photographic circle was made at the turning point of the flight at about 76°20′ S, 128°30′ W. Although neither man had noticed it, the photographs revealed the towering summit of Mount Siple on the distant northeastern horizon. The snow-covered surface of the inland ice seemed to descend to the northeast and east of the turning point. A landing was made to refuel at McKinley Peak on the return from the longest penetration from West Base into the unknown.

December 18, 1940, was the last big day in the aviation program of West Base. Petras and Wiener made a 15,000-foot ascent in the Beechcraft to observe cosmic rays over Little America. The Condor was given a short test flight which included weather reconnaissance. Then McCoy, Giles, Shirley, and Siple took off on the last of the four long flights to the east. A course was set east-northeast along the front of the Ross Ice Shelf and across Edward VII Peninsula. A continuous strip of photographs, looking south into Sulzberger Bay, tied the Scott Nunataks to the Ruppert Coast. As the plane came onto the Ruppert Coast from Block Bay, the first photographic circle was flown, tying this area to the Ford Ranges to the south. Strips of photographs, both landward and seaward, were taken as the plane continued to follow the coastline to the northeast. A belt of open water was visible to the north. A second photographic circle was flown just beyond Land Glacier at about 75°15′ S, 139°30′ W. Low mountains, from 1000 to 2000 feet high, were found to border the coast between Land and Hull Glaciers to the northeast. Shelf ice or a complex of partially grounded glacial ice and sea ice bordered the shoreline. Cruzen Island lay at the outer edge of the ice mass, and what appeared to be a second island was sighted at its western margin, north of Block Bay. Cruzen Island had been first sighted by Admiral Byrd in his flights from the *Bear* in January. A third photographic circle was flown at about 74°50′ S, 136° W, just beyond Hull Glacier. About 30 miles northeast of the edge of the glacier the crew could view the broad embayment in the coast which had been seen only vaguely at the turning point of the flight of December 13. What was subsequently named Getz Ice Shelf occupies the embayment, and in 1940 part of its northern margin was marked by a sharp tongue which projected into the sea. Another photographic circle was flown on the coast at the 134th meridian. At least 150 miles away, on the other portal of the embayment, the conical form of Mount Siple could be seen, towering to an estimated height of 15,000 feet. The plane continued toward the mountain on a course east-northeast, but had barely begun to fly out over the Getz Ice Shelf when the fuel gauges dictated a return to West Base. On the return, a course was set for a direct flight to 105-Mile Depot for a refueling stop. En route, the gyroscopic drift sight was used in an interesting experiment as a means of measuring ground elevations along the coast.

The flight of December 18 concluded the aerial exploration from West Base. The disabling of the Condor on the flight of January 3 to assist the returning field parties, and the subsequent flights of the Beechcraft on the same mission, have already been noted. Between January 16 and February 1, Petras piloted the Beechcraft on a number of flights in the vicinity of West Base. Three were in connection with the study of cosmic rays, and two were photographic.

OPERATIONS AT EAST BASE

Establishment of the Base. The search for a satisfactory site for East Base, the selection of Stonington Island, and the problems of unloading the *Bear* and the *North Star* have already been described. When the two ships departed on March 21, the 26 men who remained to carry out the operations from East Base were housed in tents. By utilizing every hour of daylight for construction, they were able to move into the main building by March 27. The site of the permanent camp was near the north end of the island on a patch of bare rock about 400 yards from the ice foot at the southwest side of the island, where cargo was unloaded from the barge and boats which served as lighters between ship and shore. The island was dotted with orderly piles of supplies and equipment dragged out of reach of the icy spray as quickly as possible after landing. For this work the tractor was particularly useful.

Just to the north of the camp site, which was determined to be at 68°28'36" S, 67°17'36" W, the foot of a glacier which descended from the Antarctic Peninsula tied Stonington Island to the mainland.

The completed base camp consisted of five buildings. As in the case of West Base, the buildings were assembled from prefabricated sections designed by Major André Violante of the Corps of Engineers of the U.S. Army. The arrangement, however, was different, for the interchangeable, insulated panels permitted variation to suit the particular site. The main building, 60 feet long by 24 feet wide, had five curtained cubicles on each side of a center aisle with two bunks in each cubicle. The galley was at one end, and the sick bay and quarters for the base leader were at the other. The science building and the machine shop were 32 feet long and 24 feet wide, the latter being without the double floor that was built into the main building and the science building. Two diesel-driven electric generators were set up on a separate rock foundation in the machine shop, which also contained power tools and the sail loft where tents and other canvas articles were made and repaired on two electric sewing machines. The science building housed the radio equipment, a photographic dark room, the base commander's office and library, and a cubicle for each of the scientific departments. Finn Ronne, Arthur J. Carroll, and Lytton Musselman erected one of the two small buildings (12 feet by 12 feet) as living quarters for themselves, since there were not enough bunks for all in the main building. The fifth building, the biologists' taxidermy hut, was constructed from an aircraft wing crate. The base was completed before the end of April and everyone housed for the winter.

East Base was occupied by 26 men under the leadership of Richard B. Black. The staff consisted of seven members. Finn Ronne, who with Black had been a member of the Second Byrd Antarctic Expedition, was chief of staff. Ashley Snow, chief pilot, was in charge of aviation. J. Glenn Dyer, Cadastral Engineer of the General Land Office of the U. S. Department of the Interior, was the science staff member. Dr. Lewis S. Sims, Lieutenant (jg) USN, was medical and personnel officer. Herbert G. Dorsey, Jr. of the U. S. Weather Bureau was meteo-

PLATE XIII-A. Staff meeting at East Base, November 2, 1940. Clockwise, J. Glenn Dyer, Elmer L. Lamplugh, Finn Ronne, Lewis S. Sims, Richard B. Black, Joseph D. Healy, Lytton C. Musselman, and Ashley C. Snow. Photo No. 126-USAS-733 in the National Archives.

PLATE XIII-B. Condor secured at high field after its initial flight of May 10, 1940. The sloping surface of this glacier, which was used as the flying field for East Base, created problems in taking off and landing. Photo No. 126-AS-439 in the National Archives.

PLATE XIV-A. The Condor at Batterbee Cache, November 12, 1940. Richard B. Black is taking bearings from the cache in George VI Sound to bordering peaks. Photo No. 126-USAS-776 in the National Archives.

PLATE XIV-B. Finn Ronne and Carl R. Eklund. The two men have just returned from their 1264-mile sledge journey to the southwestern end of George VI Sound, proving the insularity of Alexander Island. Photograph by courtesy of Finn Ronne.

rologist. Joseph D. Healy, U. S. Department of the Interior, was responsible for sea operations, and Elmer L. Lamplugh, R. M. first class, USN, was in charge of communications.

With the base established, the men turned to the Curtiss-Wright Condor bi-plane. The plane was rigged and its motors checked. It was decided to establish a flight strip about 500 feet above and approximately a mile from camp on a low mound of smooth snow on the lower portion of the glacier that descends the western slope of the Antarctic Peninsula at this point. First a trail was pioneered up the drifted snow slope which connected the island with the glacier foot and then through and over the crevassed areas of the glacier itself. A cradle of long bamboo poles and heavy canvas was rigged to protect the tractor driver, should the machine fall into a crevasse beneath him. Fortunately, all breakthroughs were minor, thanks to care in selecting the trail. At this time a tent was set up at the flying strip, and during the winter a hut was constructed from a wing crate to house a weather station outpost, a repair shop, and the flight operation head-quarters.

After two unsuccessful attempts with the tractor and tank at towing the Con-dor up onto the glacier to the flight strip resulted in a broken fitting on a strut of the ski pedestal, it was decided to fly the plane up. This was accomplished, after repairs, on May 10 when the plane took off from a small remnant of old bay ice in the inlet between the island and the mainland. There were anxious moments as the plane was taking off because of the shortness of the runway and again as one of the motors momentarily sputtered as the plane was airborne.

Early Winter Reconnaissance Flights, 1940. The weather being clear on May 20, it was decided to make a reconnaissance flight in the vicinity of East Base. Preparations were begun early in the morning at the flight strip. After some dif-ficulty in breaking the skis loose, Ashley Snow took off at 11:32 with Earle Perce as co-pilot and radioman, and Arthur J. Carroll as photographer. Black, Ronne, and Dyer were also on board. An aerial reconnaissance was made in the vicinity of the Base, and the least difficult surface route up onto the mountainous up-land of the Antarctic Peninsula appeared to be the large glacier descending from the east and northeast north of East Base. Because of its position, this was subsequently named Northeast Glacier. By 12:50 the plane had been sufficiently flight tested in the vicinity of the Base, and a course was set southward for Cape Berteaux at an altitude of 7000 feet. At Cape Berteaux the course was set south-westward along the outer margin of the Wordie Ice Shelf for Cape Jeremy. New bay ice was observed. A photographic circle was flown at Cape Jeremy, and the plane was headed into George VI Sound for about 10 miles. At 2:30 a turn was made and a direct course was set for East Base. When the plane landed at the flight strip at 3:13 p. m., the sun had already set and a full moon was showing. Haze shrouding the plateau-like upland of the Antarctic Peninsula had pre-vented a return flight along its summit. The men now had a better idea how to prepare for the sledging trips planned for the coming field season (Fig. 23).

The next day, May 21, the weather was still good, and a second flight was made to lay a cache of food and supplies on or near the Wordie Ice Shelf where

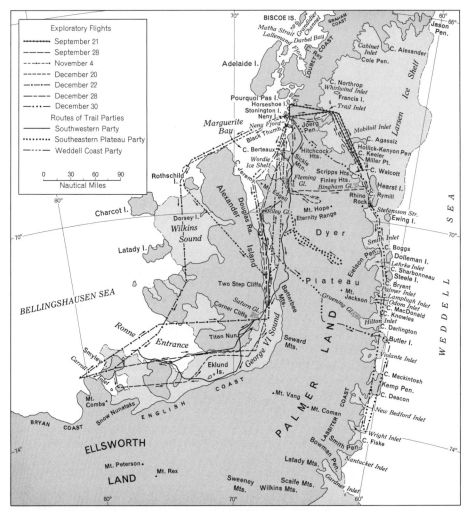

FIGURE 23. United States Antarctic Service Expedition, 1939-1941. Field Operations from East Base.

it would be accessible to trail parties returning from George VI Sound or from the Eternity Range, sighted by Ellsworth in 1935. As on the previous day, the crew consisted of Snow, Perce, and Carroll, and Black and Donald C. Hilton, surveyor, went along to determine the position of the cache. Takeoff was at 11:16 a. m. They flew toward Wordie Ice Shelf at an elevation of 4500 feet; hugging the coast so as to see possible landing sites. A landing was made on glacial ice at 12:48 p. m., and a cache was laid at a point later determined to be 69°50′ S, 67°30′ W.[35] The cache consisted of 296 pounds of man food, 180 pounds of dog food, and 321 pounds of equipment, including a complete trail radio with spare batteries. The cache was covered with a tarpaulin and surmounted by a United States claim sheet, dated May 21, 1940, and witnessed by all members of the party.[36] The elevation of the cache was subsequently determined barometrically to be 1625 feet. A round of angles was made to prominent peaks, but as the sun was setting, an astronomic fix was unreliable. Carroll took a round of still photographs.

After much difficulty in breaking the skis loose, the party took off at 2:06 and headed back over Cape Berteaux. At 2:55 the plane was headed up Neny Fjord. From the head of Neny Fjord a depression which might prove to be a possible sledging route was seen extending southeastward and southward. After flying eastward about 20 miles, they were over the rolling upland of the Antarctic Peninsula, and the party had its first view of the Weddell Sea. Two large peaks were also visible to the southeast. They returned to Stonington Island via Northeast Glacier. The plane landed safely at 3:29, but in the run-out passed over some hard sastrugi which broke the tail ski assembly, damaging the fuselage, stabilizer controls, and lower starboard langeron. To repair the damage it was necessary to make some of the parts; this misfortune, plus bad weather which kept the flying strip in poor condition, put an end to aerial reconnaissance until August.

Winter Activity at East Base. At Stonington Island the sun is below the sensible horizon from May 30 to July 12, but even on June 21, there is considerable twilight at midday. Consequently, outdoor work was possible throughout the winter, at least for a short period on every day that the weather was suitable. Moreover, the minimum temperatures normally fall to only about −40° F. These more favorable factors, compared to conditions at West Base, however, were counteracted by frequent high wind velocities and extended periods of foggy and overcast weather. Winds with gusts up to 85 miles per hour, sweeping down the glacial troughs and across Stonington Island, made it necessary to secure all the buildings with cables. After snow had drifted around the buildings, however, danger of wind damage was greatly reduced. Lights on the radio tower served to guide returning parties traveling about Stonington Island if they were overtaken by darkness while away from the Base during the short periods of winter twilight.

Winter preparations for the sledge journeys that were to be made the following spring and summer were handicapped by confusion concerning the geography of the area. Wilkins, following his pioneer Antarctic flight on December 20, 1928, had reported that the Antarctic Peninsula was in fact an archipelago segmented by ice-filled, sea-level straits. Ellsworth shed little light on the problem. Rymill, of the British Graham Land Expedition, 1934-37, showed that there was no such low-level strait north of 70° S. The damage to the plane at the end of the flight on May 21 had cut short reconnaissance flights which should have revealed possible routes across the peninsula. It was hoped to be able to fly men, dogs, sleds and supplies across the treacherous bay ice of Marguerite Bay to Alexander Land[37] for a journey along its west coast. It was proposed to extend the exploration of A. Stephenson of the British Graham Land Expedition beyond 69°30′ S in George VI Sound. This sea-level trough had been discovered by Lincoln Ellsworth in his transantarctic flight of 1935, and it had been explored by Stephenson on the ground and by other members of the British Graham Land Expedition from the air in 1936. It also was proposed to have a sledge party cross the Antarctic Peninsula and explore its Weddell Sea coast. Under the circumstances, winter planning for the spring journeys had to allow for a great deal of flexibility.

During the winter three short sledge journeys were made from East Base to select a suitable route to the crest of the Antarctic Peninsula for the spring sledging parties. The first of these began on July 21 when Black, Ronne, Healy, and Carroll set out on a scouting party up the lower slopes of Northeast Glacier, camping at the foot of the first steep icefall. At 10:00 a. m. the next morning it was light enough for Black and Ronne to proceed up the glacier to an elevation of 2184 feet, about 12 miles from East Base. A crevassed area of blue-green ice near the limit of their climb and a 1000-foot icefall on the southeast side of the glacier, from which small avalanches came crashing down every few minutes, made caution imperative, but the two men were convinced that by double teaming on the sledges, roping, and careful scouting this route could be used to reach the peninsular upland. They rejoined Healy and Carroll, and the party made a rapid descent to East Base.

On August 2 and 3 the same party, with one sledge and 15 dogs, made a second reconnaissance. This time it was to the southward, to investigate the possibilities of reaching the upland via one of the three glaciers that enter Neny Fjord. Ice cliffs prevented access to glaciers which had looked like possible routes on aerial photographs taken on the flight to Wordie Ice Shelf. On close examination in the field, steep slopes, crevasses, threatening rock falls, or incipient avalanches caused each site to be rejected. A successful route via Neny Fjord was used later during operations from East Base, but because of the short period of daylight, the party missed finding it on this trip. On August 3 it was concluded that Northeast Glacier offered the better route to the upland plateau.

The third winter sledge journey was an all-out effort to place a cache on the upland plateau of the Antarctic Peninsula. At 10:05 a. m., August 6, 1940, Black, Ronne, Healy, Dyer, and Paul H. Knowles, with a supporting party of Carl R. Eklund, Hilton, Carroll, Lytton C. Musselman, and Harry Darlington, III, set out with a total of 55 dogs in seven teams to ascend Northeast Glacier. At 3:30 p. m. they made camp after sledging 10½ miles and climbing about 2000 feet. From here on, however, the glacier was badly crevassed and the going was difficult. The next day they covered only 1¼ mile, climbing to an elevation of 3500 feet. A strong wind and drifting snow which cut down visibility kept them in camp on August 8. The going was extremely difficult on the 9th, but at about 1:30 the party reached the edge of the upland. Traveling over the rolling upland, they made camp at 3:00 p. m. at 68°08′ S, 66°32′ W at an elevation barometrically determined to be 5370 feet. From this point the supporting party was to return to East Base and the main party was to explore the upland for a suitable landing place for the aircraft which they hoped to use to lay a cache of sledging supplies on the upland. They were also planning to look for a route to descend to the Weddell coast and for a way into the Neny Glacier trough.

These plans had to be canceled, however, for a strong northeast wind increased to a gale. At 8:30 p. m. wind velocities ranged from 55 to 60 knots, and later rose to an estimated 100 knots or more. The drifting snow was scouring the surface and undercutting the tents, freeing the stakes and tangling the lines. The three-man tent was destroyed, and it was a continual struggle to keep the others from being blown away. The party could not break camp until August 12. By that time the men and dogs were wet and exhausted. There was no possibility of carrying out the original plan without great risk. A snow cairn was built to mark the cache of supplies, and the entire party started back to East Base.

The storm had scoured down the crevasse bridges on Northeast Glacier, making them especially hazardous. Skis could not be used on the bare ice surfaces, and several men broke through the snow bridges. Fortunately, the party was roped together with alpine lines. A sleepless night was spent in camp on a narrow, sloping ice block between two open crevasses. Throughout the night there were rumblings of "snow-quakes" beneath, and of many avalanches on nearby mountain slopes. When day broke they continued their descent, reaching East Base in mid-afternoon on August 13. On August 9 the plane crew had made a four-hour test flight to search for the sledging parties, with whom the base had lost radio contact. However, apparently due to drifting snow, the plane crew did not see the surface party nor they the plane. This was the last effort away from East Base until September, by which time the hours of daylight had become longer.

There was still much to be done at the Base. Sledges were rebuilt, dog harnesses were made or repaired and trail rations were packaged in quantities sufficient for one man for one month. Dog pemican also had to be prepared and packaged. At every opportunity, the dog drivers hauled gasoline up to the flying strip. This was a vitally necessary operation, and it helped to train and harden the dogs for the trail work ahead. In preparation for summer journeys, Dyer held classes in surveying and Lamplugh held classes in radio operation and repair for all field men.

Scientific Work at East Base. Although the major objective of East Base was geographical reconnaissance and discovery, considerable scientific work was carried on at the Base during the winter. Much of this work, especially in biology and meteorology, was also continued into the spring and summer. Scientific investigations were also carried on afield in the spring and summer on each of the long sledge journeys.

The biological work of East Base was under the direction of Herwil M. Bryant,[38] assisted by Carl R. Eklund, ornithologist.[39] Biological field kits were carried by each sledging party. Healy collected lichens in the mountains on the east side of the Dyer Plateau, Darlington made an extensive collection on the Weddell coast journey, and Eklund did the biological work on the southwestern journey. During the winter, in the process of preparing dog pemican, Bryant was able to prepare for exhibit skeletons, skulls, skins, and embryos of Weddell seals.

Bryant made eight trips to Red Rock Ridge rookery to study the habits and life history of the Adélie penguin and on one occasion spent a week there. Although Stonington Island was poor in plant life, collections were made in other places both far and near. Some of the neighboring areas were particularly rich, over 100 specimens of lichens and mosses being collected. The sea ice precluded dredging, but a snap bottom bucket sampler was used through holes chopped in the ice to collect marine life. A fish trap, a shrimp trap, and hook-and-line were also used.

Paul H. Knowles carried on extensive investigations in geology and also studied various forms of ice.[40] In addition to the longer trips as a member of a supporting party or as leader of the Weddell Coast party, Knowles made short trips in the vicinity of East Base to investigate the geology. One of these trips was made in company with Howard T. Odom and Harry Darlington up Northeast Glacier from August 19 to 22. A total of 125 rock samples were collected by Knowles or for him by other members of the expedition. Notations relating to its location accompanied each sample.

Magnetic observations were made at East Base and in the field by J. Glenn Dyer, and each field party made numerous determinations of magnetic declination at all places where astronomical fixes were taken.[41]

A daily schedule of meteorological observations was maintained at East Base for a little less than a year, under the direction of Herbert G. Dorsey, Jr. Observations were made four times daily: at 1:30, 7:30, 13:30, and 19:30. They included pressure, wind direction and velocity, temperature, humidity, precipitation, and a variety of visual observations of sky phenomena.[42] A total of 1200 synoptic observations was made and there were 370 pilot balloon runs at East Base. Data were transmitted daily to South American weather bureaus for use in their forecasts. Tides were observed, and there is a complete record of these observations for two months. Air samples and radiation readings were also taken at times throughout the year.

Plateau Weather Station. A unique feature of the science program of East Base was the establishment of a weather outpost at an elevation of 5500 feet on the pleateau-like upland of the Antarctic Peninsula. This station, which was maintained during November and December, was the first of its kind in Antarctica. Previous observations at high elevations were those made by trail parties on the move. While data from the journals of sledge parties are valuable, they are not suitable for direct comparison with data from sea-level stations.

Local meteorological conditions made the observatory at East Base not entirely reliable in forecasting weather for flight operations of the expedition. Surface conditions were affected by strong winds sweeping down off the glaciers and were not necessarily an indication of conditions aloft. Extended periods of cloudy weather due to orographic conditions in the vicinity of the Base limited the use of pilot balloons to obtain upper air data.

The weather outpost, called Mile-High Station, was located at 68°07′ S, 66°30′ W, about 12 miles east of the Base.[43] A specially reinforced tent of heavy canvas, an instrument shelter, and a 10-foot anemometer tower were among the things constructed at East Base for the weather outpost. Minimum weight, ease of assembly, and special durability to withstand high winds and abrasive snow drift were built-in qualities. Six men — Healy, Musselman, Darlington, Hilton, Lester Lehrke, and Robert Palmer — with four dog teams hauling 1300 pounds of equipment and supplies left East Base early on October 20 to set up Mile-High Station. They arrived at the site of the outpost at 10:00 a. m., October 25. It had taken three days to climb up Northeast Glacier, double teaming on the steepest grades. After the camp was established and radio contact made with East Base, the dog teams departed on the return trip.

Hampered by high winds and drifting snow, it took three days to set up the weather station. The first report was radioed to East Base on October 29, and from then until 1:45 a. m., January 1, 1941, four daily observations were reported twice daily by Lehrke and Palmer, who manned the outpost.[44] Observations were on the same schedule as those of East Base. During the period of major exploratory flights in December, the weather outpost was on almost continuous call for special weather reports. Observations from Mile-High Station, along with those from East Base, were reported to the South American weather bureaus.

The station included the customary weather instruments, mercurial barometer, thermometers, and automatic recording barograph, thermograph, and anemometer, as well as equipment for pilot balloon ascents. Of the latter, 25 were run. The barometer and the automatic recording instruments were placed in a snow cave to avoid condensation icing due to frequent temperature changes which occurred in the tent.

Lehrke and Palmer performed commendably under very trying conditions resulting mostly from high wind velocities over prolonged periods. The prevailing wind was from the northeast 33 per cent of the time. Wind velocities of gale force or greater were recorded at 46 per cent of the observations. A wall of snow blocks, which had to be repaired after particularly high-wind velocities, was built on three sides of the tent to prevent it from being buried by drifting snow. Even then, the men found it necessary to move the tent weekly because under continuous occupancy the floor melted away. The men also were plagued by rime forming on the walls of the tent.

Mile-High Station was closed on New Year's Day, and Lehrke and Palmer loaded 400 pounds of instrumental equipment and camping gear on a small toboggan which they hauled down Northeast Glacier. On the lower part of the glacier they were met by Musselman and Hendrik Dolleman with a dog team and were assisted on the remaining distance to East Base.

Exploratory Flights from East Base. A number of conditions made flight operations at East Base especially difficult. Under these circumstances, having only one plane made for a particularly precarious operation. East Base was plagued by frequent spells of overcast weather of many days duration. Strong winds often swept down the glaciers from the peninsular upland. As a result, good flying weather was infrequent and of short duration. Sites for taking off and landing a plane as large as the Condor were poor at best. The bay ice was unsafe or the surface was unsatisfactory for landing and taking off except in winter and early spring, which are periods of limited daylight. The high field, whose surface was crevassed, was not level and it was limited in size. Adjacent slopes left little room for maneuvering the plane while gaining altitude after takeoff. Consequently, the plane could not take off heavily loaded. This situation limited aerial reconnaissance and exploration, and adversely affected the sledging program. Considering the geography of the area and the state of development of the aircraft industry in 1940, however, it is difficult to imagine how the situation could have been different. Only an icebreaker could have possibly reached Charcot Island, and if (as was hoped) a base could have been established there, another set of difficult problems would have arisen.

Reconnaissance flights in the vicinity of Marguerite Bay and over the Antarctic Peninsula to the Weddell Sea coast were urgently needed in August and September to determine satisfactory routes for the sledge journeys planned for the coming field season. Until such routes had been definitely selected, preliminary depot laying, if carried on at all, would have had to allow for a great deal of flexibility. Otherwise there was a strong probability of much time being lost in backtracking. Consequently, anxiety increased at East Base as weeks passed without suitable flying weather. A number of times the plane was dug out of the snow, but the promising weather failed to materialize. Finally, September 14 was a good flying day, but the entire day was used up in digging out the plane and getting it ready for flight, and high winds prevented flying the next day.

Conditions were far from ideal on September 16, but Knowles, who was leading a sledge party which had left on September 10 with a load of supplies to be cached somewhere toward the Weddell Sea coast, had not made satisfactory radio contact with East Base. Consequently, in the hope of spotting Knowles' party from the air as well as scouting for possible sledging routes, Black, Snow, Perce, Carroll, Ronne, and Dyer took off at 5:04 p. m. The plane climbed to 9000 feet and was headed over the Peninsula in the direction of the cache that had been put down on August 9. The westerly wind unexpectedly strengthened, however, and drifting snow prevented the men in the plane from viewing the snow beacon that had been built at the cache. Under these conditions, Knowles' party would not be seen and it was decided to return to East Base. After turning, the plane was caught in a down draft and lost altitude so dangerously that it was enveloped in a cloud of drifting snow by the time it leveled off. All but the pilots were ordered as far aft as possible, and with full power on the engines, the plane gradually gained altitude as it moved slowly into the teeth of the westerly gale. Finally clearing the peninsular heights, the plane was landed safely at 6:42 p. m.

Flight of September 21. September 21 dawned clear and cold, and the forecast was promising. Heating the plane's engines and breaking the skis loose took longer than usual. At 12:48 p. m., Black, Snow, Perce, Carroll, Ronne, and Dyer took off on a photographic reconnaissance flight. Cruising in the area of Stonington Island for almost an hour, they climbed to 9000 feet and at 1:42 p. m. headed northeastward for the vicinity of Cape Northrop, discovered by Wilkins in 1928. The snow beacon at the upland cache of August 9 was sighted, as was the cache put down a few days earlier by Knowles' party. Ahead of the plane to the northeast the sky was hazy. At 2:11 p. m. the course was changed to 150° (true), and Carroll began a strip of oblique, overlapping photographs to starboard. At 2:30 p. m. the rounded, snow-covered Hollick-Kenyon Peninsula was crossed. Its tip, Cape Agassiz, was seen to port.[45] A photographic circle was started to the left at 2:46 p. m., but was broken off when a radio message was received from the Base that a balloon run showed a 50-knot wind from the southwest at 9000 feet. Immediately a course of 290° magnetic (310° true, or approximately northwest) was set, carrying the plane across Mobiloil Inlet and over the eastern slope of the Antarctic Peninsula. At 3:30 the Base reported 20-knot winds at 5000 feet with low clouds forming. The high clouds were also dropping. At about 3:40 the plane was up over the peninsular upland. The high peaks to the west were obscured by clouds at about 7000 feet. To get below these clouds the pilot dropped to 6000 feet, barely above the upland surface, where clouds also were beginning to form. It was clearer to the north, so the plane was headed in that direction and a narrow glacial valley with bare rock walls was followed in a descent which brought the plane out over Marguerite Bay near Horseshoe Island. From here the plane flew south at a low level and landed at the flying strip above East Base at 4:25 p. m.

The flight determined that it would be possible to descend to the Weddell Sea coast, and that travel southward on this coast would be possible along the ice shelf or piedmont ice. The surface of the upland also appeared suitable for sledging, but the experience of the members of East Base with the high winds at this level made extended sledging here seem ill-advised. On the flight Carroll had succeeded in photographing the Mobiloil Inlet area and some of the area to the south.

September 27 was another clear day. The towering mountains at the north end of Alexander Island, 90 miles away, could be seen clearly. It had been hoped to fly Ronne and Eklund, with sledges 15 dogs and supplies, to Charcot Island, from whence they would explore the area to the westward. Special crates in which to carry the dogs had been made during the winter. Exploring the coast between 72° W and 148° W had been given as a primary objective in President Roosevelt's instructions to Admiral Byrd. Since Charcot Island had proven to be inaccessible by sea, flying Ronne's party to the island from East Base seemed a possible alternative. As a start it was hoped to fly a cache of sledging supplies to the island, but this was not to be the day. The surface of the flying field had six to eight inches of new, light snow on it, and the plane could not take off with a heavy load from this kind of a surface. Since the plane had been readied for flight, it was decided to make two local flights, each 1½ hours in duration, to "joy-ride" as many of the base personnel as possible to familiarize them with the area. On the second flight Carroll photographed Northeast Glacier.

Flight of September 28. The next day, September 28, the weather was still excellent for flying, but the loose snow still made it impossible to take off with a heavy load. Consequently, it was decided to make a photographic flight over the Antarctic Peninsula. Much was still to be learned to reconcile the results of Wilkins' and Ellsworth's expeditions with Rymill's discoveries. Black, Snow, Perce, Carroll, and Ronne took off at 1:39 and in a few minutes set off on a course southward (186° true). At 2:18 the plane was over and east of Cape Berteaux. At 2:49 p. m., with the camera in the starboard sleeve, the plane began a left-hand circle over the Wordie Ice Shelf at an altitude of 7600 feet.

When the photographic circle was completed, a course was set eastward, at an elevation of 9000 feet, over the Antarctic Peninsula by way of Fleming Glacier. At 3:38 the prominent 9400-foot peak along the crest of the Antarctic Peninsula, which Rymill named Mount Wakefield, bore 210° true. This peak and the peaks on either side of it on the crest of the peninsula south of Fleming and Bingham Glaciers are probably the peaks which Ellsworth saw in 1935 and named Mounts Faith, Hope, and Charity. As the plane followed Bingham Glacier in its descent to the Weddell Sea, a prominent cape to the southward came into view at 3:50 on a bearing of 153° true. This was at first thought to be Wilkins' Cape Eielson. This, however, was later proven not to be the case,[46] and the cape was named Cape Boggs. Its position was later determined by Knowles and his sledging party to be 70°33′ S, 61°23′ W.

At 4:02 p. m. the plane was over the foot of Bingham Glacier. Looking south across the cape which Rymill had mapped as the easternmost projection of the coast of this area,[47] Black and the plane crew could see the high peaks that overlook that part of the Weddell Sea coast. To the east they discovered a low, snow-covered island separated from the coast by a strait five miles wide at its northern end. This island was first called Wilkins Island, but it was subsequently determined that the strait was actually what Wilkins had called Stefansson Strait. Therefore, the island was in truth what he had called Hearst Land, and it has been named Hearst Island. The eastern side of the island was not seen, but it was thought that icebergs could be seen about 15 to 20 miles to the east. The island was estimated to be about 40 miles long and 15 to 20 miles wide. A photographic circle was flown at this important juncture in the coast.

At 4:04 p. m. a course was laid northwestward (324° true), passing features which the men recognized as those discovered by Wilkins on his flight of December 20, 1928. At 4:22 the plane was over what the men at East Base identified as Wilkins' Cape Keeler. Continuing on the course, Three Slice Nunatak, a distinctive landmark, was discovered. Here a photographic circle was flown and then a course was set directly over the crest of the Antarctic Peninsula to East Base, where a landing was made at 5:54 p. m.

Traffic Circle Discovered. Following the flight of September 28, a month of bad weather grounded the men at East Base. On three different days during this period the weather improved, but attempts to take off in the plane failed because of the soft snow surface. The drag on the skis kept the speed below that necessary for the plane to take off. However, two short sledging journeys to investigate various approaches to Neny Glacier as possible sledge routes gave cause for optimism regarding surface operations.

On November 2 the weather was barely suitable, but crews were up early to make a flight to test take-off conditions. The plane was airborne with difficulty, and Snow radioed that he would not like to take off with an ounce more weight. Black, hoping to salvage something from the flight, instructed Snow to fly over Neny Fjord and scout the trough at its head, occupied by Neny Glacier. By now the men knew that from this ice-filled trough there was another glacial trough opening to the south, but the relationship was not entirely clear. Perce and Carroll, the photographer, were also aboard the plane, and Snow was instructed to make a photographic circle at the junction of the Neny trough with the trough that opened to the south.[48] When the plane returned to the base, the crew described a series of radiating glacier-filled troughs, the Neny Glacier trough to the northwest, Windy Valley to the west, and another broad glacier descending to the head of Mobiloil Inlet. It was ultimately found that five ice-filled troughs joined at this point on the peninsula upland between Mobiloil Inlet and Marguerite Bay. Because this pattern resembles traffic circles with radiating streets, this was called the Traffic Circle. In view of the fact that this route was used later by sledging parties from East Base and in 1947-48 by members of the Ronne Antarctic Research Expedition, the name is particularly appropriate. This discovery made this flight much more important than its two-hour duration would suggest. The return to East Base was made via Windy Valley and Marguerite Bay.

Flight of November 4. Shortly after midnight on November 4, the aviation crew began heating the motors preparatory to moving the plane to a new flight strip which had been prepared on the bay ice just west of Stonington Island. When bad weather threatened, the plane returned to the high field, but clearing weather enabled it to return to the bay ice in mid-afternoon.[49] Gasoline sufficient for an eight-hour flight was put in the tanks.

A fast but bumpy takeoff was made at 5:15 p. m. with Snow, Perce, Carroll, Black, and Ronne aboard. A course was laid across Marguerite Bay to the northern tip of Alexander Island. The ice over the bay looked suitable for sledging and even for a forced landing. At 6:10, Charcot's "Les Dents," four rocky spires at the north end of Alexander Island, were 45° off the port bow. Small rocky islets and signs of open water were viewed off the north end of Alexander Island. At 6:52 a view was had southeasterly into a channel between Rothschild Island and Alexander Island. Icebergs were frozen in the sea ice of the channel to the extent of visibility, and in the distant end of the channel a cape was seen jutting out from Alexander Island.

At 7:02, after passing Rothschild Island, the course was changed to due south. A fog, closing in from the sea to the northwest, prevented any view of Charcot Island. At 7:14 the course was changed to 140° true (southeasterly), and in 15 minutes new mountains began to appear in that direction. In a few minutes

Dorsey Island was discovered as the plane passed over the rocky crest, about 500 feet high. From this position, this time looking north through the channel seen at 6:52, it was again possible to confirm the insularity of Charcot's Rothschild Island.[50] As the plane continued on its course, it passed diagonally over the west coast of Alexander Island. At 8:00 p. m. a photographic circle was flown over the mountains on the west side of the island.

The course, 140° true, brought the plane out over George VI Sound, and at 8:26 mountains photographed by Ellsworth in 1935 were identified dead ahead of the plane.[51] A photographic circle was completed at 8:48, and the plane was headed north toward East Base. George VI Sound was filled with a low overcast which made a striking contrast with the bordering highlands. Thus, from the southernmost part of the photographic circle, the Sound could be seen far to the south, trending westward in a great arc as reported by Stephenson of the British Graham Land Expedition. As the plane headed on a northerly course to East Base along the high eastern border of George VI Sound, Mount Jackson was discovered at 9:07, bearing $112\frac{1}{2}°$ true. To the north of this towering landmark were high mountains which East Base men thought might have been the mountains which Ellsworth named Eternity Range. Because of growing darkness no pictures were taken on this leg of the flight. The plane landed on the bay ice at the edge of Stonington Island at 11:04 p. m. Red lanterns had been placed on several small bergs in the bay ice to guide the plane to the landing strip. When the pictures were developed, the huge peak which was named Mount Jackson and the mountains to the north of it showed clearly in the last photographic circle.

Supporting Flights of November 12 and 16. Good weather on November 12 was utilized to fly supplies into the field to be cached for use of trail parties. The flight around the north end of Alexander Island had come so late in the season that sledging plans had to be revised. Plans to fly the entire trail party with dog teams across Marguerite Bay to begin a southwesterly trek from the northern end of Alexander Island were abandoned because there was not enough time to fly the necessary caches. Instead, it was decided to make a combined assault southward, and the flights of November 12 and 16 were made in support of this new plan.

At 5:03 a. m., November 12, Black, Snow, Perce, and Carroll took off from the sea ice west of Neny Island with a 2340-pound load to be cached in George VI Sound. Supplies included 150 gallons of aviation gasoline, three man-month rations, 615 pounds of dog food, and 12 gallons of kerosene. Conditions of the ice at the northern end of George VI Sound were carefully observed. Photographs were taken of the west wall of the Sound on the southern leg of the flight. At 7:36 a. m., a landing was made on the floor of the Sound, abreast of Batterbee Mountains. A cache was laid at a position selected for the ease with which it could be located by means of bearings to surrounding landmarks. At 9:20 the plane took off into a 35-knot northerly wind. A course was set along the east wall of the Sound, allowing Carroll to photograph the areas missed because of darkness on November 4. The combined surface party was sighted at 11:33, toiling through an area of enormous crevasses. From the Wordie Ice Shelf,

the plane was flown over an inland course to check on the possibilities of an inland return route for the sledging parties, because by the time they would be
returning they probably would not be able to travel safely over the sea ice. A
landing was made at the high field at East Base at 12:42 p. m.

When the combined trail parties reached the Wordie Ice Shelf they reported
by radio that they could not find the Wordie cache, laid on the flight of May
21. A winter storm apparently had blown down the flagstaff, and the cache itself had been hidden by drifting snow. By mistake, the combined sledging party
had taken only one primus stove and one cooker, which made it necessary to
fly a new cache to Wordie Ice Shelf as soon as possible.

The first opportunity to establish a new Wordie cache occurred on November 16. At 1:06 a. m., Black, Snow, Perce, Sims, and Sharbonneau took off with
stoves, fuel, and food for a new Wordie cache. A landing was made beside the
trail parties at 2:09 a. m. at 69°33′ S, 66°55′ W. Dr. Sims checked each member
of the trail party. Ronne and Dyer were each given sets of photographs, taken
on November 12, which covered parts of the areas over which they were to travel,
and of the inland route north of the Wordie Ice Shelf. The plane landed at
East Base at 4:41 a. m.

On December 20, Black, Snow, Perce, and Carroll took off from the sea ice
northwest of Neny Island at 6:10 a. m. with the intention of making a long flight
south along the Weddell coast. They flew south to the Wordie Ice Shelf, which
they reached at 7:12, but in trying to cross over to the Weddell Sea coast they
found their route of September 28, the Fleming and Bingham Glaciers, obscured
by low clouds. Using Mount Hope (Rymill's Mt. Wakefield) as a landmark, they
tried to ascend south of their former track. The plane was heavily loaded, and
they had difficulty in gaining sufficient altitude. Twice Snow had to circle to
gain altitude as the surface rose too close beneath the plane for safety. Again, at
7:56, 20 miles west of Mount Hope at an altitude of 6600 feet, they turned westward to try for greater altitude. More and more high and low stratus clouds
were forming over the Weddell Sea, and haze hung over a ridge which they
would have to cross if they tried a course to the southeast. They finally decided
to return to East Base and landed at 9:35 a. m. Low fog over much of Marguerite
Bay blotted out Alexander Island and came in over the base at noon.

Flight of December 22. A long flight to the southwest had been planned for
some time. On the midnight schedule, early on December 22, Ronne reported
that he was, by dead reckoning, at 72°32′ S, 76°42′ W, ". . . camped on barrier
at edge of open sea . . ."[52] The weather was clear in the field and at the Base.
This was the time for the long flight to the southwest. For some days prior to
December 22, Black had been limping due to a hip injury received in a fall on
skis, making him a poor risk in a plane in case of a forced landing. To save his
weight and that of his emergency gear, Black remained at the Base, and in his
stead 80 extra gallons of gasoline were carried in tins in the cabin of the plane.
It was thus hoped to extend the range of the plane sufficiently to connect with
the discoveries made by Admiral Byrd, Snow, and Perce in flights from the *Bear*
in February 1940.

Snow, Perce, and Carroll took off at 4:50 a. m., on December 22. They set a course for the north end of Alexander Island which, since the receipt of Ronne's message, they now knew for certain to be an island. Halfway across Marguerite Bay they encountered a solid bank of overcast. Circling three times, they climbed above it and could see the peaks of Alexander Island protruding above the cloud blanket. Rounding the peaks of Rothschild Island, whose summits showed through the clouds, the plane was headed south. As the coast of Alexander Island was approached on the south side of Wilkins Sound, the overcast broke somewhat. The course was changed to the southwest following the northeast-southwest trending coast. At 9:00 a. m., just after sighting through broken overcast the low headlands of western Alexander Island, open water was sighted ahead on the starboard bow. Over the western portion of the island, the course was changed to west-southwest, crossing the open water of the western end of George VI Sound. The edge of the shelf ice in the Sound could be seen on the left. The southern shore was intersected at about 76° W. Here a turn was made, and the plane flew westerly along the coast for an hour and a half, crossing Carroll Inlet onto ice-bound Bryan Coast. At 10:30 a photographic circle was flown at about 72°55' S, 78°50' W. Westward from the turning point, the ice-covered land was seen to rise gradually southward from the low shoreline to heights surmounted by scattered mountains. Since the entrance to Carroll Inlet is at about 79° W, the turning point was west of the reported longitude.

As the plane flew eastward after the turn-around, overcast again obscured much of the land. The Batterbee cache was hidden in low overcast, and the plane landed in the Sound just south of Latitude 71°, where the gasoline was emptied from cans into the tanks. Taking off again, the plane landed at East Base shortly after 6:00 p. m.

Flight of December 28. In discussions with the staff and the aviation crew, Black decided that on the next period of good weather a flight would be made south into George VI Sound; there a decision would be made, based on the weather and on reports from the field, to continue southward, to turn southeastward, or to turn southwestward. An attempt was made to carry out this plan on December 27, but the surface of the bay ice had deteriorated, causing the skis to break through the snow crust to slush beneath. The load had to be lightened, and then the plane was flown up to the high field. Unfortunately, the plane could not take off with heavy loads from the high field, but with the bay ice surface deteriorating it looked as though the high field would have to be used exclusively for the rest of the season, in spite of this shortcoming.

On December 28 the weather continued good, and by 4:00 a. m. the plane had been serviced. At 6:11 a. m. Black, Snow, Perce, and Carroll took off from the high field, running upgrade into a 20-mile wind. With the head wind, the plane took off in 33 seconds; due to a heavy load, however, it had difficulty gaining sufficient altitude to rise above the higher part of the glacier. The plane staggered to hold the air as the pilot was forced to bank to the left over the crevassed area of the glacier. Fortunately, it continued a wavering climb to a higher altitude.

The north end of George VI Sound was entered at 7:18 a. m., and at 8:45 the

Batterbee cache was sighted. At Batterbee cache there was a great deal of haziness to the south and southeast. It was decided that the flight, if it was to continue, would have to be to the southwest. Consequently, the course was changed at 9:05 to 215° true, carrying the plane across the southeastern corner of Alexander Island. High mountains were sighted on the southern and south-southeastern horizons, but haze prevented good pictures from being taken. At 9:31 the course was changed again so that the plane flew along the high southern edge of Alexander Island, overlooking the western limb of George VI Sound. The largest of the Eklund Islands, the only one that was then ice-free, was sighted at 9:45 a. m. Fifteen minutes later the plane was over the outer, western edge of the shelf ice occupying the Sound. Like the northern edge opposite Cape Jeremy, the western edge was marked by great rifts. The flight continued across the open water of Ronne Entrance, first named Ronne Bay, and across the island which borders Carroll Inlet on the east. Beyond a line extending across Ronne Entrance straight north to the western capes of Alexander Island, the sea was entirely open to the horizon which, considering the elevation of the plane (5600 feet), was about 85 miles. In the distance the westward-trending mainland coast was marked by low, snow-covered capes. For some time, three peaks, subsequently named Snow Nunataks, were in sight on the port bow. Carroll Inlet and Sims Island, located in it, were in view at 10:54. At 10:55, over Smiley Island, the course was changed to the southward, after which a great mountain was viewed briefly to the southwestward at an estimated distance of 75 to 100 miles.

At 11:15 a. m. the course was changed again to the eastward, paralleling the outward flight but about 20 miles farther south. A short time later a photographic circle was completed. On the return flight most of the southern coast of Alexander Island was photographed. Two peaks were seen on the distant horizon: one at 11:45 a. m., to the southwest, the other at 12:02 p. m., to the southeast. Southeast of Two Step Cliffs, on the western side of George VI Sound, a photographic circle was flown, and half an hour later a landing was made at Batterbee cache. The spare man pemican was left and rock specimens left by Ronne and Eklund were picked up. At 3:10 p. m. the plane took off from the cache and landed safely at the high field at East Base at 5:32. The elapsed time of the flight was 11 hours and 21 minutes, 10 hours and 31 minutes in the air.

Flight of December 30. The last exploratory flight, to the Weddell Sea coast, was made on December 30 with Black, Snow, Perce, Carroll, and Dyer aboard. After an unsuccessful attempt at takeoff uphill into a 10-mile wind, an attempt was then made to takeoff downhill and downwind. The surface here was rough, and the takeoff was extremely bumpy. The plane took to the air only after it had reached the steepened slope at the edge of the field, with the engines at full throttle. By this time it was too late to cut the engines and try again, for the plane would have coasted down the ever-steepening slope and over a 60-foot cliff to the bay ice.

It was 5:50 a. m. and the plane was headed for George VI Sound, into which it was planned to fly until the plane had gained enough altitude to cross the

Antarctic Peninsula. By 7:30 the plane was well south of 70° S and at an altitude of 4750 feet. The course was changed to the southeastward (139° true)
through a pass in the east wall of George VI Sound. At 8:02 the peaks of the
high mountains north of Mount Jackson, discovered on November 4, were
coming into view over the port bow; at 8:13 they were in full view. The plane
was flying at about 6000 feet over a surface that was rising to the eastward. This
was the Dyer Plateau, over which a photographic circle was begun at 8:16.
Shortly after, Mount Jackson began to emerge from an envelope of clouds. The
course had to be changed to the southward to avoid overcast, and at 8:44 a
whole new range of mountains began to appear across the horizon ahead of the
plane.

At 9:00 a. m. a great eastward-trending, glacier-filled trough came into view
south of Mount Jackson. It appeared to offer a route through the range to the
Weddell coast, and a course was set to the east-southeast (112° true) to descend
to the coast. A photographic circle was made to tie in all the features before the
plane left the high plateau. The plane was flying down over the Gruening
Glacier to the Hilton Inlet, reaching the sea at about 72° S.

At 10:03 the course was changed to follow the coast to the south, a mountainous coast with great glaciers descending into broad inlets. The flight track
was over a narrow, snow-covered piedmont. Steep, rounded slopes, in some
places cliffs, descended to open water leads in the sea ice. Westward from the
piedmont, rocky escarpments rose to high mountains. Shortly after 11:15 a. m.,
a distinctive landmark was discovered at the head of a large inlet. Because the
arrangement of the rock walls suggested the appearance of a three-cornered hat,
the mountain was named Mount Tricorn by Black. The inlet was later named
Wright Inlet. Ahead, the mountains seemed to be getting lower and to be trending to the west of south. At 11:25 haze was beginning to form over the mountains to the south, and the gasoline supply had reached the point where safety
dictated a return to East Base. The plane was then over Wright Inlet, 73°57' S,
61°26' W. A photographic circle was flown at this point at an altitude of 8200
feet, and at 11:38 a. m. an official claim sheet was dropped in a metal cylinder,
wrapped in a United States flag, claiming this coast as far south as the men
could see.

On the flight north, Carroll tried to complete the photography of the coast
by using a Graflex camera from Hilton Inlet to Eielson Peninsula, the limit of
the flight of September 28. This expedient was made necessary when the aerial
camera ceased to function just as the photographic circle was completed over
Wright Inlet at the southern terminus of the flight. The return flight passed
Cape Keeler, crossed Mobiloil Inlet to Mercator Ice Piedmont, and ascended to
the Traffic Circle. Neny Glacier was followed to East Base, where a landing
was made at high field at 4:05 p. m., completing a flight of 10 hours and 15
minutes.

The exploratory flights were thus concluded. A local flight was made on January 15, and preparations were made for a flight to George VI Sound to aid
Ronne and Eklund, who, when last heard from, were resting their dogs at Bat-

terbee cache. In taxiing across the high field to prepare for a takeoff on this mission, the left ski dropped bodily into a crevasse, causing serious damage to the plane. Sufficient repairs were made to enable the plane to be used to evacuate East Base, but no further exploration was possible.

SLEDGE JOURNEYS FROM EAST BASE

Plans. In planning the program of geographic exploration from East Base, much reliance was placed in being able to support the sledge journeys by using the plane to place caches of food and supplies in the field. This might have worked very well if it had been possible to locate East Base other than in the vicinity of Marguerite Bay. The difficulties involved in flight operations based in the Antarctic Peninsula have already been discussed.

When bad weather delayed the flight program beyond any hope of flying caches to Alexander Island to support a sledging party which also would have been flown to the north tip of the island, it was necessary to revise the program. The plan to sledge over the crest of the Antarctic Peninsula and south along its Weddell Sea coast was retained. Instead of sledging westward from the north tip of Alexander Island, however, it was now proposed to sledge south into George VI Sound and explore a route westward from where the Sound seemed to be trending south-southwestward. All trail parties would move south in support of this effort. Knowles and his party would serve as a supporting party and then return to begin Knowles' own trek down the Weddell Sea coast. Somewhere in George VI Sound the main party would divide. Ronne and Eklund then would continue south in the Sound, looking for a route to the west, and Dyer would lead his party southeastward toward what was then thought to be the high mountains which Ellsworth called the Eternity Range.

Laying Caches. Before the long sledge journeys could begin, caches of food and supplies to support their return would be necessary. On May 21 a cache had been placed by air on the Wordie Ice Shelf, and attempts had been made to find a suitable route for sledging across the crest of the Antarctic Peninsula. In August a cache had been placed on the peninsula upland near the head of Northeast Glacier. These advance stores were insufficient, however, and a route for descending to the Weddell Sea coast had not been located.

On September 10 Paul H. Knowles, Donald C. Hilton, and Harry Darlington, III — the men who later were to sledge south along the Weddell Sea coast — left East Base to advance a 2300-pound cache of sledging rations and supplies across the peninsula upland and, if possible, down onto the Weddell Sea coast. They were supported by Joseph Healy and Lytton Musselman. Climbing up Northeast Glacier, they reached the upland, but bad weather prevented a descent to the Weddell Sea coast. It looked as though the glacier, which was later named Bills Gulch, would be suitable for this purpose under better weather conditions. Consequently, they cached the supplies at the head of this glacier and marked it with a beacon in which they placed an official claim sheet. The position was determined to be 68°05' S, 65°50' W. They returned to East Base late on September 20.

On September 27, Knowles, Hilton, Darlington, and Musselman left on a second, and this time successful, attempt to cross the Antarctic Peninsula. They visited but did not move the cache put down at the head of Bills Gulch. While descending Bills Gulch into Trail Inlet, Knowles broke through a snow bridge and fell into a crevasse. Fortunately he, Darlington, and Musselman were roped together, and his two companions were able to rescue him. They returned safely to East Base on October 15.

The last preliminary sledging trip before the long journeys began was made by Dyer, the leader, Knowles, and Eklund. They left East Base on October 26 with one dog team on a reconnaissance of Neny Fjord and the glaciers which enter the trough at its head. The reconnaissance of August 2 and 3 had been hampered by darkness, and a second investigation was deemed worthwhile. It was feared that the bay ice might not be safe to travel over on the return from the south in December. Consequently, finding an inland route for the returning parties was considered a safety measure. This October 26 trip into Neny Fjord also afforded Knowles an opportunity to extend his geological investigations, and the party was instructed to obtain preliminary ground control for the construction of a map from the aerial photography.

The party entered Neny Fjord by way of the low saddle east of Stonington Island overlooking the foot of Neny Glacier at the head of the fjord. Traversing the col, they traveled along the steep slope on the northeast side of the fjord until they were able to come down onto Neny Glacier. Little progress was made on October 27 because of a heavy snowfall. They moved forward during the middle of the day when visibility improved, but after five hours made camp again on Neny Glacier at an elevation of 1770 feet (by aneroid).[53] Continued snowfall on October 28 caused the party to leave the camp and advance the cache up the glacier. Because of the deep snow, a 7-percent grade and low visibility, they were not able to advance the cache as far above the camp as they had hoped. They left a cache of man and dog food and three gallons of kerosene well marked by flags at an elevation of 2680 feet, and then returned to their camp.

On October 29 visibility was still poor, but just as they were breaking camp the sun shone briefly, permitting the determination of position and a round of angles. On the return to base they succeeded in finding a snow ramp in a cleft of the glacier foot which permitted descent to the bay ice in the fjord. Thus, returning on the bay ice, they avoided traveling along the steep slope to the col over which they had come.

The big push south by the trail parties began on November 6. Ronne, Eklund, Dyer, Healy, and Musselman, with five teams totaling 55 dogs, set out over the bay ice with a combined load of 4850 pounds. This included clothing, instruments, equipment, 2618 pounds of dog food, 900 pounds of man food, and 290 pounds of kerosene. Knowles and Hilton accompanied them as a supporting party as far as the Wordie Ice Shelf. They traveled across the mouth of Neny Fjord to Red Rock Ridge and then over the sea ice to Cape Berteaux, crossing a number of open leads in front of Windy Valley. At the end of three days travel, the combined parties had reached the Wordie Ice Shelf and were camped south of Cape Berteaux.

The next four days they traveled slowly across the very heavily crevassed surface of the Wordie Ice Shelf. By November 12 the crevassed area had been crossed, and Knowles and Hilton started back to East Base, following the fresh tracks of the outward trek through the crevassed area. They arrived at East Base on November 15.

The combined party proceeded to the vicinity of the Wordie cache, 67°34.2′ S, 66°51.0′ W, but when they reached the locality there was no sign of the cache which had been deposited on a flight to this point on May 21. Apparently the bamboo flagstaff and the orange-colored canvas flag had been blown away and the cache drifted over. As we have learned, Ronne informed East Base by radio that the cache could not be located and that the combined party had only one cooker and one large primus stove. The entire group was ordered to remain until new supplies could be flown to them. In the meantime, they were to continue looking for the cache. Since each field party should have had one large cooker and one large and one medium primus stove with a kit of spare parts, it was imperative to fly out a new cache as soon as the weather would permit.

The evening of November 15 brought the first flying weather, and at 2:09 on the morning of November 16 the plane landed beside the combined sledging party with new supplies.[54] Ronne and Dyer were both given sets of aerial photographs, taken on the flight of November 12, of parts of the areas they were to travel over, including an inland route north of Wordie Ice Shelf. At 10:00 that morning the sleds were reloaded and a beacon, topped by a bamboo pole and flag, was erected to mark the position of the cache.

After leaving the Wordie cache, the two parties traveled southeastward up Fleming Glacier onto the plateau later named for Dyer. They traveled slowly through heavy snow, gradually climbing to a maximum elevation of about 7000 feet. Visibility was very poor, making it difficult to spot landmarks which Ronne had seen on the flight of November 4 and which were shown on the pictures taken on the flight of November 12. With clear weather on November 21, they were able to locate themselves with the aid of the aerial photographs. At this point it was decided that the parties would separate, with Ronne and Eklund continuing southward, looking for a route to the west, while Dyer, Healy, and Musselman would carry out a reconnaissance survey of the Dyer Plateau and the high mountains to the southeast, which the East Base personnel then considered to be Ellsworth's Eternity Range.

Ronne and Eklund continued southward with the intention of staying on the upland bordering George VI Sound on the east. They were traveling in what seemed like a broad valley extending southward behind the line of peaks which overlooked the Sound. They thought they might be able to continue thus to the vicinity of the Seward Mountains, which bordered the Sound at about 72°30′ S, before turning westward. However, they were ordered by radio from the base to descend into George VI Sound to locate the Batterbee cache and to make sure it was available in case of emergency. Accordingly, Ronne and Eklund descended slowly over the crevassed glaciers on the north side of Batterbee Mountains. On December 3 they reached the Batterbee cache on the ice of George VI Sound. Its position was fixed at 71°45′ S, 67°50′ W. They took bearings on prominent bordering peaks and tied the whole together with photographic circles.

From Batterbee cache, Ronne and Eklund sledged diagonally across to the west side of the Sound, passing Two Step Cliffs, the foot of Saturn Glacier, and Corner Cliffs. The two cliffs prominently display horizontal strata and make distinctive landmarks. Ronne and Eklund were surprised to encounter, about 19 miles south of Batterbee cache, a band of pressure ice extending southeasterly across the Sound. Salt water was found in openings in the pressure ice, suggesting that the ice was here afloat. They sledged diagonally over the southeastern corner of Alexander Island, passing along snow-covered and ice-filled valleys between the numerous flat-topped, rocky prominences and cliffs of horizontal strata that characterize this area. The maximum elevation of their route in this area was roughly 1600 feet. Fixes with bearings to prominent features and photographic circles were made whenever possible.

On December 7 Ronne and Eklund headed south, dropping down off Alexander Island to the ice of George VI Sound. Between the 69th and 70th meridians they crossed the Sound to the mainland coast, from where a huge peak was seen to the south, at least 50 miles distant. They followed the coast westward, noting that the ice-covered slopes dropping down to the Sound were heavily crevassed.

On December 13, near the western end of George VI Sound, they discovered a rocky mass protruding through the ice to a height of more than 1000 feet. The next day a stone cairn was built on top of the island, which Ronne named Eklund Island.[55] A snow cairn was built on the southwestern slope, and an official claim sheet was deposited therein.

On December 17 the surface of the ice was observed at a lower level. Salt water was sampled in open leads in which a 170-foot line failed to reach bottom. They saw some skuas and petrels, and there were tracks of seals and penguins. On December 21 ridges of pressure ice halted progress toward a small cape. Making a detour around the pressure ridges, they sledged up sloping land ice to about 1000 feet to reach the cape. Ahead of them was a vast expanse of sea, free of ice except for a few large icebergs. They now had proven definitely that what had been known as Alexander I Land was an island. They remained at this western terminus of their sledge journey for two days, surveying, determining positions, and delineating the coast to 72°23′ S, 78°00′ W. While at the cape, on December 21, they built a 10-foot snow beacon at 72°31′ S, 76°51′ W. Inside it they placed a metal container enclosing an official claim sheet and an account of their discoveries. It was during this time that Ronne and Eklund were at the western end of George VI Sound that the plane passed over the area on the flight of December 22, but neither of them heard or saw it, nor did the plane crew see them.

On the return journey Ronne and Eklund retraced their steps about 30 miles to approximately 72°46′ S, 75°43′ W and then took a more or less easterly course across the sea onto the shelf ice along the southern shore of Alexander Island. At about the 70th meridian they left the Sound and turned northeastward over the corner of Alexander Island. By now their dogs were in poor condition. Melting during the warmer part of the day made a slushy surface. If they traveled during the cooler hours, when the sun was low in the southern horizon, ice shards cut the dogs' feet. In four days, six dogs with cut and bleeding feet had to be shot. As they passed the stratified rock exposures in the vicinity of Titan Nunatak and Corner Cliffs, they collected rock samples, fossils, lichens, and petrel eggs. Changes in the pressure ice in the vicinity of Saturn Glacier since they had passed through on the outward journey made it necessary to find a new route for the return passage.

By the time Ronne and Eklund reached Batterbee cache only seven of their 15 dogs were left. They reported their position and the condition of the dogs to East Base. They remained at Batterbee cache for 10 days to allow the seven dogs to recuperate. Canvas boots were made to protect the dogs' feet. While at the cache their radio generator or transmitter failed, although their receiver continued to function. As a result, they were aware that the Base could not hear them and that there was much concern for their welfare, but they could do nothing about it.

On January 16 the two men with seven dogs set out from Batterbee cache with only essential supplies and equipment on the sledges. All sorts of surface conditions were encountered: melt water, slush, soft snow, and sharp ice crystals. They traveled north along George VI Sound to the foot of Riley Glacier on January 19. They ascended the glacier, which has a long, fairly gentle slope and few crevasses. This surface was much better for the dogs, and their feet improved rapidly. Riley Glacier proved to be a relatively easy route from the Sound over the divide to Fleming Glacier and the Wordie cache.

Once on the Wordie Ice Shelf the problem of traveling through the crevassed ice was met again. Melting had made conditions even worse than on the outward journey. They worked their way across the ice and headed for Sickle Mountain, guided by the aerial photographs that had been given them at the Wordie cache on the outward journey. They had no trouble selecting a suitable route, and they knew exactly where they were at all times. Anticipating that a party might be sent out to meet them and assist them back to East Base, they built snow cairns and enclosed messages at prominent landmarks along the route. This was a precaution against missing the other party. Passing Sickle Mountain, they crossed Clarke Glacier and ascended Meridian Glacier to the head of Windy Valley.[56] From this divide, where they camped on January 25, they could look out onto the Weddell Sea. They traveled eastward, down Lammers Glacier to the Hub Nunatak and the Traffic Circle.

From the Traffic Circle, Ronne and Eklund traveled northwestward in what they then called Neny Trough, for it led to the head of Neny Glacier. There is a divide in this trough at an elevation determined by Ronne to be 3180 feet above sea level. From this divide, Gibbs Glacier flows southeastward to the Traffic Circle and Neny Glacier flows northwestward into Neny Fjord. This divide is at approximately 68°22′ S, 66°16′ W. Near this divide, Ronne and Eklund met the party that had come out from East Base to meet them and assist them home. They had not been heard from on the radio schedule since January 7, and at last report their dogs were in poor condition. Consequently, it was assumed they might very well need assistance.

The party that had come out to meet Ronne and Eklund consisted of Black, Healy, Knowles, and Hilton. The latter two were a supporting party, for Black did not know how long the main group might have to be out. Supplies were organized to permit the main party to stay out 60 days if necessary — a bleak prospect, since the ships were expected in less than 60 days. The whole camp had assisted in the preparation after the plane had broken off a ski in a crevasse on the high field on January 19, and it was known that the plane could not be used to assist Ronne and Eklund. Various contingencies had to be allowed for in view of the fact that the party might miss Ronne and Eklund due to poor visibility or because they had taken different routes. Initial departure had been just before midnight on January 21, but due to a number of accidents and delays, the party had got no farther than the divide at the head of Neny Glacier where they met Ronne and Eklund on the afternoon of January 27, 1941.

After greetings, congratulations, and exchange of news, the supplies were cached and the entire group started down Neny Glacier toward East Base, where they arrived at 2:30 a. m. on January 28.

During the journey, 34 astronomical fixes had been made with 12 major control points. Photographic circles were made at each control point. By means of bearings from these control points and intersection stations, the positions of 320 major mountain peaks and nunataks had been determined.[57] Elevations were determined barometrically for each control point and intersection station. Alexander Land was proven to be an island, and 460 miles of new coastline were added to the map. A total of 1097 nautical miles (1264 statute miles) were sledged in 84 days, although the men did not travel every day. This was one of the longest sledge journeys in Antarctic history.

The Southeastern-Eternity Range Survey Party. This party, consisting of Dyer, as leader, Musselman, and Healy, left East Base on November 6 with Ronne and Eklund. They traveled together over the sea ice to the Wordie Ice Shelf and then by way of the lower part of Fleming Glacier onto the upland east of George VI Sound. According to the instructions given Ronne by Black, Dyer's party was under his command, to be retained or separated at his discretion according to conditions in the field. The division of the party, however, was recommended, and Dyer was to be the leader of the party if it were separated. The instructions directed,

> The detached party should operate . . . in a general southeasterly direction, aiming to clear the Eternity Range on the west. This will give better survey conditions for mapping the Range and entire area than would a direct course to the Range. This party should calculate its travel and supplies so that it will reach the Base, travelling over the outward course over the sea ice, not later than forty-eight days from today or the 24th of December.[58]

After several days of poor visibility, clear weather on November 21 permitted the party to identify landmarks on the aerial photographs with which they were supplied. At this point, 70°16′ S, 66°59′ W, Ronne decided to release Dyer's party, which was then called the Southeastern Survey Party. Dyer's group was supplied with dog food, kerosene, and man food to last 18 days. They had one 11-dog team.

Upon separating from Ronne and Eklund, the Dyer, Musselman, and Healy party started southeasterly. Moving around a high knoll, they reached a barometric elevation of 7150 feet from which they had a clear view for about 20 miles of their intended course. Clouds soon began forming, however, and by 2:30 visibility was down to zero. Dyer was concerned, however, by the fact that they were carrying supplies for a much shorter period of time than he had hoped for. Consequently, he felt compelled to travel in spite of the weather. They cached 44 cakes of dog food for the return journey, having made 17.8 miles before camping. The next day the weather remained the same, but since they were traveling over a gently rolling plateau surface with an average elevation of about 6700 feet, Dyer felt they should push on toward what they thought was Ellsworth's Eternity Range.

On November 23 they continued traveling in a southeasterly direction over the same gently rolling plateau surface. Both sledging surface and visibility were improving, but no topographical features were visible at any time.

Sunday, November 24, was their first good day. The weather cleared until there were very few clouds in the sky and visibility was excellent. Sun sights were taken at 10:00 a. m., and 11:30 the Eternity Range[59] was sighted. The following is an excerpt from Dyer's preliminary report.

November 24, 1940
> Sunday ... We stopped at 2:30 to have lunch and get a round of angles together with additional sun sights. Visibility had become almost 100% with very few clouds in the sky. Continued onward after taking a complete round of angles, with zenith distances to the principal peaks. Made 19 miles before establishing camp. Took additional sun sights and another round of angles from the camp site.[60]

The next day began with a continuation of conditions on November 24, but in the afternoon a northwest wind became a gale, forcing them to make camp in the lee of a small nunatak. Another 19 miles had been covered. They did not break camp on November 26 because of the drifting snow. The next day the wind had abated and shifted to the southwest. Although visibility was poor, they decided to travel in the hope of getting into position for more work when the weather improved.

They broke camp on November 28 and continued on course. They reached a small outlying peak at the north end of the "Eternity Range." Here they built a rock cairn, raised the United States flag and deposited a claim sheet in a metal tube fastened to a bamboo staff and placed in the cairn. The position of the cairn was determined as 70°53′ S, 63°38′ W. The wind was abating, but visibility was too poor to take bearings for surveying purposes. Man and dog food were dangerously low if some emergency or stormy weather should prevent travel for several days. Consequently, it was decided to return northwestward from the terminal cairn before camping for the night.

November 29 and 30 were excellent surveying days. Dyer's summary for the latter day is as follows:

November 30, 1940
>   This was another excellent surveying day. Stopped several times to get our sun sights and round of angles. On this part of the return route, we moved along a lower level closer to the Sound. Many clear and unobstructed views of the Eastern side of the Sound were to be had. It became cloudy in the P. M., and rapidly closed in after we had reached 150 mile cache.[61]

The weather deteriorated quickly and the party was kept in camp at the 150-mile cache all day on December 1. The tent had to be shifted to prevent its being torn up by the wind. Antarctic weather is changeable, and on December 2 the party was able to cover the 39 miles to the 111-mile cache in 15 hours. They used a different and better route than on the outward journey. The Wordie cache was reached at 7:00 p. m. on December 3, after another long run which included taking a great number of bearings to topographic features viewed en route. A snow storm kept them in camp at the Wordie cache for two days. The party then spent most of December 6 and 7 getting across the crevassed ice of the Wordie Ice Shelf. As they were emerging from the crevassed area and moving down the slope of a pressure ridge on the latter afternoon, Dyer's ski fitting failed, causing a bad fall in which he sustained a severely sprained ankle and torn ligaments of the left leg. This made it necessary for Dyer to ride the sledge for the remainder of the journey. Nevertheless a number of stops were made for surveying in the vicinity of Cape Berteaux. Once the party got down onto the sea ice north of the cape, low fog prevented further surveying and forced the party to use a compass to keep on course. Sticky new snow made for poor sledging. Under the circumstances, they kept pushing on toward East Base, arriving at 2:00 a. m. on December 11, having covered 38 miles on the last day.

The following is a summary of the surveying work done during the journey.

General Results:
>   During the period of our journey we established 23 astronomical fixes; 4 independent meridianal latitudes; 11 principal control stations and numerous resection stations. From these points the positions of 58 major mountain peaks and numerous nunataks were determined. Most of these features, also elevations determinants, based upon barometer elevation of observing station. This describes the amount of surveying accomplished on this journey. It will form the basic ground control for aerial mapping in this area.[62]

The Weddell Coast Sledging Party. Knowles and Hilton had served as a supporting party for the combined southern sledging party under Ronne. After assisting the party through the crevassed area of the Wordie Ice Shelf, they were released on November 12, returning to East Base on November 15. Preparations for the Weddell Coast journey began at once, but departure was delayed by bad weather until 9:00 a. m., November 19.

The party consisted of Knowles, geologist and leader, Hilton, surveyor and navigator, and Darlington, radioman. They had two teams of 11 dogs each and three sledges, one used as a trailer. Food for 70 days and equipment, including a spare tent, totaled 3200 pounds. The party reached the peninsular divide via Northeast Glacier. Bad weather and high winds, as usual, were experienced on the upland. They descended to the Weddell Sea coast by way of Bills Gulch; on this glacier they encountered many irregular and deep crevasses. By November 25 the party had reached the head of Trail Inlet.

Almost the entire extent of the east coast of the Antarctic Peninsula is bordered by Larsen Ice Shelf. The glaciers which descend the east side of the peninsula into the heads of the many fjord-like inlets which characterize this coast merge with the ice shelf in the inlets. In this respect Trail Inlet is typical. Knowles estimated the elevation of the shelf in Trail Inlet to be about 300 feet. Over the surface, "many narrow intersecting crevasses form a strained checkerboard pattern ... the margins ... are bounded by bold 2000′ cliffs...."[63] The party traveled northeastward through Trail Inlet toward Three Slice Nunatak, a distinctive landmark rising through the ice shelf at the end of the Joerg Peninsula. Three Slice was reached on November 27, and "The sledge course then turned southeasterly across a series of 'ice waves' which are about 800′ from crest to crest with a trough thirty feet in depth."[64] The party crossed the outer portion of Mobiloil Inlet, and the Hollick-Kenyon Peninsula was crossed on December 6. Samples were taken from the slate outcrop of Cape Keeler, and biological specimens were collected.

Traveling south from Cape Keeler, they were able to identify landmarks such as Cape Walcott and Miller Point, which were discovered, photographed, and named by Wilkins in his flight of December 20, 1928.[65] Great rifts in the ice shelf lay across their route, and the ice was stained with what appeared to be algae. Good sledging was found in Stefansson Strait. Although the nature of Stefansson Strait and the surrounding features were recognized, their true identity, with the exception of Cape Rymill, was not.[66] From the south end of Stefansson Strait to Cape Boggs, rifts even greater than those north of Stefansson Strait interrupted the surface of the ice shelf. There were leads of open sea water in the troughs, in one of which a Weddell seal was killed.

The party continued southward and reached what East Base personnel considered Cape Eielson at 12:30 a. m., December 16.[67] Its position was determined to be 70°33′ S, 61°23′ W, and a rock cairn was built adjacent to the rock outcrop of the cape. An official claim sheet, signed by Knowles and witnessed by Hilton and Darlington, was deposited in the cairn.

As the party continued southward past a series of rocky headlands and intervening ice-filled inlets, they discovered two ice-drowned islands similar to but smaller than Hearst Island. Dolleman Island was discovered just off Cape Boggs, and Steele Island, about 15 miles farther south, is bisected by the 71st parallel.

By December 18 the party was then in the vicinity of Steele Island, and the long journey had begun to show on the dogs. On December 22, at 3:30 a. m., they reached the opening of a broad inlet, subsequently named Hilton Inlet. On

December 23 they built a snow cairn in the vicinity at 71°57' S, 61°20' W and placed in it an official claim sheet. The geology of the locality was investigated and rock samples were taken from rock outcrops on the north side of the Inlet. Considering the date, the condition of the dogs, and the distances between caches, it was decided to return to East Base from this point. With an extra 12 hours of rest and an extra ration of food, the dogs' vigor was much restored, but one dog which had been carried on the sledge for two days had to be shot.

On the return journey, better visibility made it possible to take bearings on many additional features, especially those on the uplands farther west. The sledging surfaces were not as soft and were therefore easier on the dogs. On December 28 the party reached the 70th parallel, midway between Cape Boggs and Cape Rymill.

Several days were spent in the vicinity of Trail Inlet to gather scientific data, Knowles working on geology and Darlington on biology. Hilton did the surveying. On January 7 a three-foot rock cairn was built at an elevation of 1200 feet at Three Slice Nunatak. A claim sheet was deposited in the cairn, whose position was given as 68°00' S, 64°48' W.

A recent heavy snowfall hindered the party in crossing the Antarctic Peninsula. However, they stopped at the Mile-High Weather Outpost. The equipment which had been left there was loaded on the sledges and returned to East Base, which was reached on the morning of January 17, 1941. The party had covered 683.5 nautical miles (by sledge meter) during the 59 days in the field. On the sledges were 22 rock samples and many biological specimens. In addition to his survey data, accompanied by many pictures, Hilton had kept a weather record during the journey.

Local Journeys Near East Base. Three short journeys were undertaken. The first of these, planned as a long trek if necessary, was the journey already described in which Black led a party to meet Ronne and Eklund and assist them back to East Base. Herwil M. Bryant, biologist at East Base, and Heinrich Dolleman spent two weeks in the field in December 1940 and January 1941. One week was spent in biological study at the penguin rookery at Red Rock Ridge, south of East Base, and another week was spent making collections at Lagotellerie Island, north of East Base.

The last trail operation was a local one in which Healy and Dorsey left East Base on February 8, 1941, and traveled up Northeast Glacier and then along the upland to the north to survey and collect geological and biological specimens. On February 11, 1941, they set up a cache containing one week's rations for two men and seven dogs on a short ridge extending out from a nunatak at the head of McClary Glacier, and included in the cairn, located at 60°00' S, 66°48' W, an official claim sheet. They returned to base on February 11.

CLOSING THE EXPEDITION

Evacuation of West Base. The international situation had worsened since the U. S. Antarctic Service had been established, and it was considered advisable to evacuate the two bases rather than relieve the present personnel with new men who would continue to occupy the bases. To implement this decision, the *Bear* sailed from Philadelphia on October 13, 1940, and the *North Star* departed from Seattle on December 11. The *Bear* called at Dunedin and arrived at the Bay of Whales on January 11, 1941. The *North Star* arrived on January 24, encountering only a narrow belt of loose drift ice in the Ross Sea. Since it was hoped to some day reoccupy West Base, much equipment and supplies remained.[68] Instruments, records, and necessary materials were loaded, and the two ships sailed from West Base on February 1.

Evacuation of East Base. From the vicinity of Scott Island the two ships headed eastward toward Marguerite Bay. On February 24 both ships were off Adelaide Island, northwest of East Base, but dense pack ice prevented them from entering Marguerite Bay. To save fuel the ships returned north, where they anchored in Andersen Harbor, in the Melchior Islands, in the center of Dallmann Bay. While the ships remained here, the scientists from West Base occupied themselves with a variety of scientific investigations. From Andersen Harbor the *Bear* made a cruise in late February and again in mid-March to observe conditions at the northern edge of the pack ice, but each time she was unable to enter Marguerite Bay. The ice was rotten, but there were no easterly winds to blow it out; rather, north winds kept the ice in the bay. New falls of snow were occurring, and new ice was forming over pools in the bay.

The season being late, it was decided to evacuate East Base by air. Fortunately the Condor had been repaired and test-flown by the aviation unit after the accident on January 19 in which a ski had been cut off. The *North Star* was ordered on March 15 to proceed to Punta Arenas, Chile, where most of the West Base men would disembark and food and fuel for a second year would be put aboard for East Base in case the men could not be evacuated by air or in case the ships were beset. Meanwhile the *Bear* had been reconnoitering, and on March 16 a party was put ashore on Mikkelsen Island,[69] a low, snow-covered member of the Biscoe Islands, just north of the Antarctic Circle. The shore party laid out and marked a suitable landing strip, and arrangements were made by radio that evacuation by air would begin as soon as the weather was suitable.

The first flight took off from the high field at East Base at 5:30 a. m., March 22. In addition to Snow and Perce, there were 12 men aboard, along with records, specimens, and emergency gear. At 7:15 the plane had covered the 120 miles and made a safe landing. The West Base personnel and ship's men were ready to assist in the landing, unloading, and embarking the equipment and men. They had erected a series of lines down the face of the 400-foot cliff of rock and snow. Men and gear went down these lines to boats from the *Bear*. The plane returned to East Base, and a second takeoff was attempted at 11:30. The temperature had risen since the first takeoff, however, and the snow was too soft. Several hundred pounds of clothing, food, and emergency gear had to be unloaded to lighten the plane. A successful takeoff was made at 12:15 with the remaining 12 men. The plane was abandoned on Watson Island, and the *Bear* sailed immediately, reaching Punta Arenas on March 29. The *North Star* arrived in Boston on May 5 and the *Bear* on May 18.

APPENDIX

PRESIDENT ROOSEVELT'S ORDER OF NOVEMBER 25, 1939, TO ADMIRAL BYRD

November 25, 1939.

My dear Admiral Byrd:

1. By the Second Deficiency Appropriation act, Fiscal Year 1939, approved May 2, 1939, and the Urgent Deficiency and Supplemental Appropriation Act, Fiscal Years 1939 and 1940, approved June 30, 1939, the Congress has made available to the Department of the Interior, under heading "Expenses, Division of Territories and Island Possessions," a total of $350,000 for an "investigation and survey of natural resources of the land and sea areas of the Antarctic regions."

2. I have designated the organization of the Government activities in the Antarctic undertaken in pursuance of the foregoing Congressional authorization as The United States Antarctic Service.

3. By letters dated July 7, 1939, I requested the Secretaries of State, the Treasury, the Navy, and the Interior each to designate a representative to form a Committee for the purpose of organizing, directing, and coordinating the conduct of the investigation authorized by the Congress. This Committee is designated the Executive Committee of The United States Antarctic Service. It shall have authority to appoint an Executive Secretary, who shall perform such duties as may be assigned to him by the Committee.

4. Because of your experience and brilliant achievements in polar exploration and because of the confidence which the people of the United States have in you and in your qualities of leadership, I have designated you Commanding Officer of The United States Antarctic Service and an ex-officio member of the Executive Committee.

5. (a) I have directed all Departments and Agencies of the Government to cooperate with you as far as practicable in furthering the purposes of the investigation authorized by Congress. In pursuance of this request, the Secretary of the Interior has made available the U. S. M. S. *North Star.*

(b) Under the authority given him by the Third Deficiency Act, Fiscal Year 1939, approved August 9, 1939, the Secretary of the Navy has chartered and placed in commission the U. S. S. *Bear.*

(c) The Executive Committee has authorized, under certain conditions, the operation and control by the Service of a privately constructed snow cruiser.

(d) The foregoing vessels, and the snow cruiser, together with the personnel which has been made available by the several Government Departments and Agencies are hereby placed under your command as Commanding Officer of The United States Antarctic Service. The performance of your duties will involve flying.

6. When in all respects ready for sea, you will proceed to the Antarctic by routes chosen by you and there establish two continental bases, to be known as (a) East Base, and (b) West Base.

(a) It is desired that the East Base be established in the vicinity of Charcot Island or Alexander I Land; in the event that a suitable site in those areas cannot be reached by ship or by ship based parties, alternative sites on the shores of Marguerite Bay should be investigated.

(b) It is desired that the West Base be established on the East Shore of the Ross Sea in the vicinity of King Edward VII Land; in the event that this area cannot be reached by ship, or a base established without undue hazard, an alternative site in the Bay of Whales at or near Little America should be investigated.

(c) The principal objective in the field is the delineation of the continental coast line between the meridians 72° W, and 148° W, and the consolidation of the geographical features of Hearst Land, James W. Ellsworth Land, and Marie Byrd Land. It is desired that long range aerial flights equipped with mapping cameras, consolidate these areas; if practicable, supply caches to extend the cruising range of the planes should be established. Flights in this area should be made from the U. S. S. *Bear,* if practicable, and such flights so far as possible should be planned to supplement previous flights which have been made along the 75th, 101st, 116th, 134th, 150th, and 152nd meridians of West Longitude.

(d) Secondary geographical objectives are the delineation of the unknown west coast of the Weddell Sea between Cape Eielson and Luitpold Coast, and the determination of the eastern extremity of the Queen Maud Range and the William Horlick Mountains and their relationship to the Sentinel Range.

It is desired that you investigate by air the area in the vicinity of the South Magnetic Pole and the unknown areas between the Weddell Sea and the South Pole.

(e) The scientific program outlined by the National Research Council of the National Academy of Sciences shall form the basis for the scientific efforts at the bases. It is desired that the Antarctic Service cooperate fully with the Argentine Meteorological Station at Laurie Island and the Chilean Government Meteorological Service in the exchange of meteorological and similar data. It is desired that one of the vessels determine the extent of Pactolus Bank, located in Latitude 56°28′ S, Longitude 74°20′ W.

(f) The United States has never recognized any claims of sovereignty over territory in the Antarctic regions asserted by any foreign state. No member of the United States Antarctic Service shall take any action or make any statements tending to compromise this position.

Members of the Service may take any appropriate steps such as dropping written claims from airplanes, depositing such writing in cairns, et cetera, which might assist in supporting a sovereignty claim by the United States Government. Careful record shall be kept of the circumstances surrounding each such act. No public announcement of such act shall, however, be made without specific authority in each case from the Secretary of State.

(g) In the prosecution of the foregoing objective you will necessarily face situations which cannot be anticipated, and which may require independent action. In such emergencies your own judgment and discretion should be freely exercised to meet any situation so as to further the mission of the Antarctic Service.

(h) Upon the completion of your duties in the Antarctic during the spring of 1940 you will return to the United States, as your presence in this country at that time is essential for other duties in connection with the administration of The United States Antarctic Service.

7. The Commanding Officer shall be responsible for the correlation of the field operations and the performance of the Base Leaders. He shall require that the Executive Committee be kept informed of all field operations and the progress being made in accomplishing the objectives of the service. In this connection any plans for operations beyond the limits defined above, shall be referred to the Executive Committee for approval.

8. (a) The communication system of the Antarctic Service is an integral part of the Naval Communication System, as outlined in separate correspondence by the Chief of Naval Operations, and is governed by the U. S. Navy Communication Instructions. In this connection, those circuits authorized by the Interdepartment Radio Advisory Committee, the U. S. Army, and the Federal Communication Commission are restricted to the specific use intended and by their respective governing regulations.

(b) All official radio traffic to the United States will, therefore, be over Navy channels and shall be cleared through the Executive Committee. All releases, such as press, photographs, and motion pictures, shall be made through the Executive Committee, which shall also pass upon all radio broadcasting arrangements.

9. (a) You will direct Base Leaders and members of the Scientific Staff of the Service to maintain journals of the progress of the Service, and enter thereon events, observations, and remarks.

(b) You will prohibit all those under your command from furnishing any person not belonging to the Antarctic Service with copies of any journal, diary, chart, plan, memorandum, specimen, drawing, painting, photograph, film, plate, or information of any kind, which has reference to the object, progress, or proceedings of the Antarctic Service.

(c) As it is highly important that no journal or narrative of the enterprise, either partial or complete, should be published, without the authority and under the supervision of the Government of the United States, at whose expense this Service is undertaken, you will, before they reach the first port north of the Antarctic regions, require from every person under your command the surrender of all journals, diaries, memoranda, remarks, writings, charts, drawings, sketches, paintings, photographs, films, plates, as well as all specimens of every kind, collected or prepared during their absence from the United States.

(d) Such articles may be returned to the person concerned, or not, at the option of the Executive Committee; but such writer, in the published records, shall receive credit for such part or parts of his material as may be used in said records.

(e) After causing correct inventories of these to be made and signed by two responsible Service representatives and by the parties by whom they were collected or prepared, you will cause them to be carefully sealed by the said Service representatives and reserved for such disposition as the Executive Committee may direct.

(f) You will transmit your own journals and records, together with those enumerated above for such disposition as may be directed. The History of the Service will be prepared by yourself, from all journals and records of the Service, under the supervision of the Executive Committee. The records of the scientific results will be prepared, supervised, and edited under arrangements to be made by the Executive Committee with the National Academy of Sciences.

10. You will work out, with the Executive Committee, all necessary plans for the relief of the continental bases next season, or for the evacuation of those parties in the event that the Service is not a continuing project.

11. This undertaking is one which necessarily attracts the attention of the world, and I am sure that you leave the shores of the United States with the heartfelt wishes of our people for the success of the enterprise, and the safe return of yourself and your companions.

12. You will bring these instructions to the attention of every person under your command, but you will give them no other publicity until authorized to do so by the Executive Committee.

Very sincerely yours,

(Signed) FRANKLIN D. ROOSEVELT

Rear Admiral
    Richard E. Byrd, U. S. N.
        Commanding Officer
            The United States Antarctic Service

NOTES

1. 53 Stat. 627.

2. 53 Stat. 980.

3. Memorandum from President Roosevelt to Acting Secretary of State Sumner Welles, File No. 9-13-2, Administrative General, Records of the Division of Territories and Island Possessions, Record Group 126, U. S. National Archives.

4. See the "Statement of Rear Admiral Richard E. Byrd ..." in Hearings before the Subcommittee on Appropriations, House of Representatives, 76th Congress, 3rd Session, on the Secondary Appropriation Bill for 1940," pp. 227-235. Thus the government took advantage of the momentum developed by the two Byrd Antarctic expeditions, of Byrd's leadership, and of a body of experienced Antarctic personnel that had been built up. In addition to Black and

Ronne, Siple and Wade were called in. Siple was set up in the sail loft of the Boston Navy Yard as Technical Supervisor of Equipment. Wade worked on the science program and then was made Field Representative. By early summer, 1939, 100 people were at work.

5. All of the Division of Territories and Island Possessions. Mrs. Hampton was Assistant Director, and Emerson and Swope followed Gruening as Directors.

6. Letter from President Franklin D. Roosevelt to Rear Admiral Richard E. Byrd, July 7, 1939. Records of the U. S. Antarctic Service, General File I, Record Group 126, U. S. National Archives.

7. In addition to the $350,000 appropriated in the two bills in 1939, $171,000 was granted for continuing expenses in the bill enacted June 27, 1940 (54 Stat. 628). Other amounts were later granted for the preparation of reports.

8. Rear Adm. Richard E. Byrd, Commanding Officer, and J. E. MacDonald, United States Antarctic Service, Statement of, pertaining to "United States Antarctic Service," Interior Department Appropriation Bill for 1942. Hearings before the Subcommittee of the Committee on Appropriations, House of Representatives, 77th Congr., 1st Sess., Part I, pp. 1009-1026.

9. Richard E. Byrd, "Reports on Scientific Results of the United States Antarctic Service Expedition, 1939-1941," *Proceedings, American Philosophical Society*, vol. 89, No. 1, April, 1945, Preface, p. iv.

10. Orders from the President to the Commanding Officer, Records of the U. S. Antarctic Service, General File I, Record Group 126, U. S. National Archives. Reproduced as an Appendix to this chapter; also reproduced in "Records of the United States Antarctic Service," *Preliminary Inventories* No. 90, compiled by Charles E. Dewing and Laura E. Kelsay, The National Archives, Washington, 1955, pp. 15-18.

11. At the time these orders were written, the geography of much of the Antarctic Peninsula was still imperfectly known, and they reflect the mistaken conception that an archipelago instead of a peninsula extended north from Antarctica toward the southern tip of South America. Ellsworth's transantarctic flight of November, 1935 and the discoveries of the British Graham Land Expedition, 1934-37, proved there were no great, ice-filled, sea-level straits north of at least 72° S. However, the location of Stefansson Strait, Cape Eielson, and Hearst Land, discovered by Wilkins in 1928, was unknown, and there was some doubt of their very existence, at least as Wilkins depicted them.

For a discussion of these problems see Chapter 16, pp. 287-288; Chapter 19, p. 391, note 3, pp. 375-382; also see this chapter, p. 454. The insularity of Alexander I Land was proven by Ronne and Eklund on a sledge journey from East Base of the U. S. Antarctic Service Expedition. See p. 464. In some instances geographic nomenclature had not then been altered to fit then-known geographic conditions. Officially approved names today are Edward VII Peninsula, Alexander Island, Hearst Island, Ellsworth Land, and Eielson Peninsula. The last-named feature is not the same as the feature which Wilkins named Cape Eielson, for there is no such feature on Hearst Island near the north end of Stefansson Strait.

12. A lengthy prospectus for the scientific program was submitted by Dr. F. Alton Wade, Senior Scientist of the Expedition, to Mr. Paul Brockett, Executive Secretary of the National Academy of Sciences, on July 17, 1939. The Secretary of the Interior, Harold L. Ickes, requested that the National Research Council review the proposed scientific program and offer suggestions regarding it. With Dr. Isaiah Bowman as chairman, a meeting was held for this purpose July 28, 1939, to which 22 persons were invited. More than a score of representatives of government scientific agencies and private institutions attended. As a result of this meeting, an interim Advisory Committee to the U. S. Antarctic Service was appointed. It consisted of Dr. Bowman, President of Johns Hopkins University, chairman; Dr. Henry B. Bigelow, Director, Woods Hole Oceanographic Institution; Dr. John A. Fleming, Director, Department of Terrestrial Magnetism, Carnegie Institution of Washington; Dr. C. G. Rosby, Assistant Chief of the U. S. Weather Bureau; Dr. W. C. Mendenhall, Director, U. S. Geological Survey; and Dr. Robert Cushman Murphy, Curator of Oceanic Birds, American Museum of Natural History, New York. The correspondence of the committee, now in the central files of the National Academy of Sciences, however, shows that its advice was never requested by the U. S. Antarctic Service, much to the chagrin of the members.

13. These islands, centered in about 69°03' S, 72°52' W, have been named the Johansen Islands for the ice pilot on the *Bear*.

14. Data for this and other flights on the cruise are from the Log of the U.S.S. *Bear*. Records of the Bureau of Navigation, Record Group 24, U. S. National Archives.

15. Roger Hawthorne, "Exploratory Flights of Admiral Byrd (1940)," *Proceedings, American Philosophical Society*, vol. 89, No. 4, December, 1945, p. 398e.

16. *Ibid.*

17. The coastline as it was thought to be is illustrated on *Antarctica*, U. S. Hydrographic Office Chart 2562, 1943, and 2nd ed. 1947. Scale 1:11, 250,000. See also Lt. Comdr. R. A. J. English, "Preliminary Account of the United States Antarctic Expedition, 1939-1941," *Geographical Review*, vol. 31, No. 3, July, 1941, Fig. 1, p. 468. The map on page 418 of this chapter, indicating the track of the *Bear*, shows the coastline in much greater detail than was known in 1940. The greater detail is the result of the work of the Eastern Group of "Operation Highjump" in December and January 1946-1947. In February 1960 a U. S. Navy expedition, commanded by Capt. Edwin A. McDonald and consisting of the icebreakers *Glacier* and *Burton Island*, further explored this coast after a relatively easy passage through the pack ice. On February 15 a landing was made near Cape Flying Fish. The two ships sailed along the coast, and several helicopter flights were made. As a result it was found that the Thurston Peninsula was in fact a large island, and it has since been named Thurston Island.

18. Hawthorne, "Exploratory Flights . . .," *op. cit.*, p. 398e.

19. Paul A. Siple, "Geographical Exploration from Little America III, the West Base of the United States Antarctic Service Expedition, 1939-41," *Proceedings, American Philosophical Society*, vol. 89, No. 1, April, 1945, p. 46.

20. *Ibid.*, pp. 53-55; Paul A. Siple, and others, "A Summary of the Activities of the United States Antarctic Expedition, 1939-41," *Polar Record*, vol. 8, No. 22, July, 1941, pp. 437-438.

21. Arnold Court, "Tropopause Disappearance During the Antarctic Winter," *Bulletin, American Meteorological Society*, vol. 23, 1942, pp. 220-238. This somewhat anomalous phenomenon of a higher and sometimes disappearing tropopause in winter has been confirmed since the International Geophysical Year, 1957-58. See M. J. Rubin and W. S. Weyant, "Antarctic Meteorology," in *Antarctica*, edited by Trevor Hatherton (London, Methuen, 1965), p. 386.

22. During the IGY, 1957-58, such a program would have been handled by four men.

23. Arnold Court, "Weather Observations During 1940-1941 at Little America III, Antarctica," *Proceedings, American Philosophical Society*, vol. 89, No. 1, April, 1945, p. 342.

24. Russell G. Frazier, "Acclimatization and Effects of Cold on the Human Body as Observed at Little America III, on the United States Antarctic Service Expedition 1939-1941," *Proceedings, American Philosophical Society*, vol. 89, No. 1, April, 1945, p. 251. This was a preliminary contribution, but subsequent investigation added greatly to this phase of science.

25. S. A. Korff, D. K. Bailey, and E. T. Clarke, "Report on Cosmic-Ray Observations Made on the United States Antarctic Service Expedition, 1939-1941," *Proceedings, American Philosophical Society*, vol. 89, No. 1, April, 1945, p. 321.

26. In the process by which snow is transformed to glacial ice, two intermediate stages are recognized. Loose, granular snow on the surface of the glacier is called névé. Compacted granular snow and ice, intermediate between névé and glacial ice, is called firn. These two terms also have been used synonymously for all forms of granular snow.

27. F. Alton Wade, "The Physical Aspects of the Ross Shelf Ice," *Proceedings, American Philosophical Society*, vol. 89, No. 1, April, 1945, pp. 160-173. These findings are consistent with subsequent and more extensive investigation. Deformational recrystallization generally begins at 10 m.

28. Paul A. Siple, "The Second Byrd Antarctic Expedition — Botany," *Annals of the Missouri Botanical Garden*, vol. 25, No. 2, April, 1938, pp. 485-486; Jack E. Perkins, "Biology at Little America III, the West Base of the United States Antarctic Service Expedition 1939-1941," *Proceedings, American Philosophical Society*, vol. 89, No. 1, April, 1945, pp. 283-284.

29. Siple, "Geographical Exploration . . .," *op. cit.*, p. 27; Paul A. Siple, *Scout to Explorer* (New York, G. P. Putnam's Sons, 1936), pp. 181-182.

30. The original map, Map 27, is filed with the cartographic records of the United States Antarctic Service, U. S. National Archives. For a published photograph of this map, see Charles F. Passel, "Sedimentary Rocks of the Southern Edsel Ford Ranges, Marie Byrd Land, Antarctica," *Proceedings, American Philosophical Society*, vol. 89, No. 1, April, 1945, Map 1, p. 127.

31. Lawrence A. Warner, "Structure and Petrography of the Southern Edsel Ford Ranges, Antarctica," *Proceedings, American Philosophical Society*, vol. 89, No. 1, April, 1945, pp. 78-122.

32. F. Alton Wade, "The Geology of the Rockefeller Mountains, King Edward VII Land, Antarctica," *Proceedings, American Philosophical Society*, vol. 89, No. 1, April, 1945, pp. 73-74, 77.

33. The data, continuous recording and absolute measurements were deposited in the Department of Terrestrial Magnetism of the Carnegie Institution, Washington. Fitzsimmons was an early wartime casualty in an airplane accident in Cuba, and the results of his work were never written up.

34. Siple, "Geographical Exploration . . .," *op. cit.*, p. 51.

35. Richard B. Black, "Narrative of East Base U. S. Antarctic Expedition, 1939-1941," unpublished manuscript, pp. 41-43. This document, based on Admiral Black's Journal, is the source for many of the details relating to the activities of the men at East Base. It was lent to the author by Admiral Black. A copy is also on file in the National Archives, Scientific and Technical Reports, Logs and Related Material, Records of the U. S. Antarctic Service, Record Group 126.

36. A copy of the claim sheet is on file in the National Archives, Records of the Office of Territories, Record Group 126.

37. The insular nature of Alexander Island was unknown until Ronne and Eklund reached the west end of George VI Sound on December 21, 1940, and reported the fact by radio.

38. Herwil M. Bryant, "Biology at East Base, Palmer Peninsula, Antarctica," *Proceedings, American Philosophical Society*, vol. 89, No. 1, April, 1945, pp. 256-269.

39. Carl R. Eklund, "Condensed Ornithology Report, East Base, Palmer Land," *Proceedings, American Philosophical Society*, vol. 89, No. 1, April, 1945, pp. 299-304.

40. Paul H. Knowles, "Geology of Southern Palmer Peninsula, Antarctica," *Proceedings, American Philosophical Society*, vol. 89, No. 1, April, 1945, pp. 132-145; "Glaciology of Southern Palmer Peninsula, Antarctica," *Proceedings, American Philosophical Society*, vol. 89, No. 1, April, 1945, pp. 174-176.

41. J. Glenn Dyer, "Report of Magnetic Surveys and Studies," typescript, 2 pp., dated East Base, February 26, 1941. U. S. National Archives, Scientific and Technical Reports, Logs and Related Material, Records of the U. S. Antarctic Service, Record Group 126.

42. For a record of this material, see Herbert G. Dorsey, "Meteorology at East Base," typescript, 18 pp. U. S. National Archives, Scientific and Technical Reports, Logs and Related Material, Records of the U. S. Antarctic Service, Record Group 126.

43. Herbert G. Dorsey, Jr., "An Antarctic Mountain Weather Station," *Proceedings, American Philosophical Society*, vol. 89, No. 1, April, 1945, pp. 344-363. See p. 346.

44. Lester Lehrke, "Preliminary Report of Mile High Meteorological Outpost" [October 22, 1940-January 1, 1941], typescript, 2 pp., February 16, 1941. U. S. National Archives, Scientific and Technical Reports, Logs and Related Material, Records of the U. S. Antarctic Service, Record Group 126.

45. The entire peninsula was originally called Cape Joerg for W. L. G. Joerg, who was for many years a member of the U. S. Board on Geographic Names and of its Advisory Committee on Antarctic Names. At Mr. Joerg's request, the name was changed to Hollick-Kenyon Peninsula and Cape Agassiz.

46. K. J. Bertrand, W. L. G. Joerg, and H. E. Saunders, "The True Location of Stefansson Strait and Hearst Land, Antarctica," *Geographical Review*, vol. 38, 1948, pp. 475-486; also see Chap. 19, pp. 375-382 for a discussion of the problem of identifying features discovered by Wilkins and by Ellsworth.

47. J. R. Rymill, "British Graham Land Expedition, 1934-37," *Geographical Journal*, vol. 91, 1938, pp. 297-312, 424-434. See the map opposite p. 496. This map is also opposite p. 272 in Rymill's *Southern Lights*, London, 1938. A larger-scale map was published in September, 1940, but this was not available to the men at East Base until they returned home. See A. Stephenson, "Graham Land and the Problem of Stefansson Strait," *Geographical Journal*, vol. 96, 1940, pp. 167-180 and map opposite p. 232. The cape was named Cape Rymill by members of East Base and the name was officially approved by the U. S. Board on Geographic Names.

48. Black, *op. cit.*, p. 114.

49. The high field and the bay ice, after this date, were used interchangeably, depending on the condition of the respective runways, for take-offs and landings during November and December. Flight headquarters, however, remained at the high field, because facilities for servicing the plane and for tying it down during storms were lacking on the bay ice.

50. This island was discovered in January 1910 by Dr. Jean-B. Charcot of the Second French Antarctic Expedition, 1908-10. In a flight on August 15, 1936, Rymill thought the island to be connected to Alexander Land, although he saw it from a distance. See Rymill, *Southern Lights, op. cit.*, p. 165.

51. Black, "Narrative . . .," *op. cit.*, p. 119. The pictures were published in W. L. G. Joerg, "The Cartographical Results of Ellsworth's Trans-Antarctic Flight of 1935," *Geographical Review*, vol. 27, No. 3, July, 1937, Fig. 15, p. 440. These mountains were named Batterbee Mountains by the British Graham Land Expedition, 1934-37.

52. *Ibid.*, p. 134.

53. J. Glenn Dyer, "Report of Reconnaissance Sledging Trip into Neny Trough" [October 26-29, 1940], typescript, 2 pp., November 1, 1940. U. S. National Archives, Scientific and Technical Reports, Logs and Related Material, Records of the U. S. Antarctic Service, Record Group 126.

54. Ronne, in his account of the journey, "The Main Southern Sledge Journey from East Base, Palmer Land, Antarctica," *Proceedings of the American Philosophical Society*, vol. 89, No. 1, April, 1945, p. 15, gives the date as November 17. This is apparently an error, for his table of camps and their positions on p. 21 show they left the Wordie cache on the 16th, and this is consistent with all the other records of East Base which refer to this particular flight.

55. In 1949 V. E. Fuchs and R. J. Adie of the Falkland Islands Dependencies Survey discovered that the ice of George VI Sound had receded, revealing several smaller islands. The group is now called the Eklund Islands.

56. Windy Valley was named by Rymill in 1936 and Sickle Mountain by Black in 1940. The other features were unnamed at the time that Ronne and Eklund sledged through them, they being the first men to set foot in the vicinity of the Traffic Circle and the glacial troughs radiating from it.

57. Ronne, "The Main Southern Sledge Journey . . .," *op. cit.*, p. 20.

58. Richard B. Black, "Memorandum to Finn Ronne, East Base, November 6, 1940," paragraph 7, typescript, 5 pp. Appendix to Black's *Narrative, op. cit.*

59. At this time it was thought these high mountains in about 71° S were what Lincoln Ellsworth had seen in his flight in November 1935 and had called the Eternity Range. However, it is now generally agreed that his Mounts Faith, Hope and Charity are the three high peaks between 69°30′ and 70° S on the peninsular divide immediately south of the Fleming and the Bingham Glacier troughs. See Chap. 19, pp. 379-380; 383-384.

60. J. Glenn Dyer, "Report of Southeastern Survey to Eternity Range Area," typescript, 5 pp., U. S. National Archives, Scientific and Technical Reports, Logs and Related Material, Records of the U. S. Antarctic Service, Record Group 126.

61. *Ibid.*

62. *Ibid.*

63. Paul H. Knowles, "Weddell Coast Journey" [Nov. 19, 1940-Jan. 17, 1941], typescript, 7 pp., February 22, 1941. U. S. National Archives, Records of the U. S. Antarctic Service, Record Group 126.

64. *Ibid.*

65. Sir Hubert Wilkins, "The Wilkins-Hearst Antarctic Expedition, 1928-1929," *Geographical Review*, vol. 19, 1929, pp. 353-376.

66. Cape Rymill was seen from the 6000-foot uplands to the west on the south side of Bingham Glacier by Rymill and Bingham of the British Graham Land Expedition in December, 1936. See also notes 46 and 47, *supra*.

67. See note 46, *supra*. This feature cannot possibly be Wilkins' Cape Eielson, but it is practically impossible to identify what he did so name. Therefore, to commemorate Eielson's part in the pioneer flight of December 20, 1928, the peninsula on which this cape is located has been called Eielson Peninsula. This avoids the implication that this is truly the original Cape Eielson. The cape at the end of the peninsula is named Cape Boggs.

68. On February 24, 1963, in the vicinity of 77°32.5′ S, 174°22.5′ W, a lookout on the icebreaker U.S.S. *Edisto* spotted an iceberg which showed the buried remains of either Little America III or IV, probably III. See *Bulletin of the U. S. Antarctic Projects Officer*, vol. 4, No. 7, April, 1963, pp. 19-20.

69. The name has since been changed to Watson Island to avoid confusion with Mikkelsen Islets, off the southeast coast of Adelaide Island, and which had priority in the name.

BIBLIOGRAPHY

PUBLISHED MATERIAL

Bartsch, Paul, "Mollusks of the United States Antarctic Service Expedition, 1939-41," *Proceedings, American Philosophical Society*, vol. 89, No. 1, April, 1945, p. 294.

Berlin, Leonard M., "Ground Surveys Accomplished at West Base, Antarctica," *Proceedings, American Philosophical Society*, vol. 89, No. 1, April, 1945, p. 386.

Black, Richard B., "Geographical Operations from East Base, United States Antarctic Service Expedition, 1939-1941," *Proceedings, American Philosophical Society*, vol. 89, No. 1, April, 1945, pp. 4-12.

Boyd, Vernon D., "Motorized Surface Transportation in the Antarctic, U. S. Antarctic Service

Expedition, 1939-41," *Proceedings, American Philosophical Society,* vol. 89, No. 1, April, 1945, pp. 379-381.

Bryant, Herwil M., "Biology at East Base, Palmer Peninsula, Antarctica," *Proceedings, American Philosophical Society,* vol. 89, No. 1, April, 1945, pp. 256-269.

Bursey, Jack, *Antarctic Night* (New York, Longmans, Green, 1958), 256 pp.

Clark, Austin H., "Echinoderms of the United States Antarctic Service Expedition, 1939-41," *Proceedings, American Philosophical Society,* vol. 89, No. 1, April, 1945, p. 295.

Court, Arnold, and H. G. Dorsey Jr., "Antarctic Weather Observations," *Bulletin, American Meteorological Society,* vol. 21, September, 1940, pp. 386-387.

Court, Arnold, "Field Altitudes of West Base Parties, U. S. Antarctic Service Expedition, 1939-41," *Proceedings, American Philosophical Society,* vol. 89, No. 1, April, 1945, pp. 61-66.

——, "Insolation in the Polar Atmosphere," *Journal of the Franklin Institute,* Philadelphia, vol. 235, 1943, pp. 169-178.

——, "Meteorological Data for Little America III. Tabular and Graphical Results of Observations Made at the West Base of the United States Antarctic Service Expedition, 1939-41," *Monthly Weather Review,* Supp. No. 48, 1949, Washington, U. S. Govt. Printing Office, vi and 150 pp., illus.

——, "Temperature Measurements in Polar Ice," *Journal of Glaciology,* vol. 1, No. 5, March, 1949, pp. 227-230.

——, "Tropopause Disappearance During the Antarctic Winter," *Bulletin, American Meteorological Society,* vol. 23, 1942, pp. 220-238.

——, "Weather Observations During 1940-41 at Little America III, Antarctica," *Proceedings, American Philosophical Society,* vol. 89, No. 1, April, 1945, pp. 324-343.

Cushman, Joseph A., "Foraminifera of the United States Antarctic Service Expedition, 1939-41," *Proceedings, American Philosophical Society,* vol. 89, No. 1, April, 1945, pp. 285-288.

Deichmann, Elisabeth, "An Octocoral of the United States Antarctic Service Expedition 1939-41," *Proceedings, American Philosophical Society,* vol. 89, No. 1, April, 1945, p. 294.

Dorsey, H. G., Jr., "An Antarctic Mountain Weather Station," *Proceedings, American Philosophical Society,* vol. 89, No. 1, April, 1945, pp. 344-363.

——, "Meteorology at East Base of U. S. Antarctic Service Expedition 1939-41," *Bulletin, American Meteorological Society,* vol. 22, 1941, pp. 389-392.

Eklund, Carl R., "Condensed Ornithology Report, East Base, Palmer Land," *Proceedings, American Philosophical Society,* vol. 89, No. 1, April, 1945, pp. 299-304.

English, R. A. J., Preliminary Account of the United States Antarctic Service Expedition, 1939-41," *Geographical Review,* vol. 31, No. 3, July, 1941, pp. 466-478.

Ewing, H. E., "Mites of the United States Antarctic Service Expedition, 1939-41," *Proceedings, American Philosophical Society,* vol. 89, No. 1, April, 1945, p. 296.

Fleming, W. L. S., "Professor F. Alton Wade's Antarctic Glaciological Researches," *Journal of Glaciology,* vol. 1, No. 1, January, 1947, pp. 23-30. (Discussion, pp. 30-31.)

Frazier, Russell G., "Acclimatization and the Effects of Cold on the Human Body as Observed at Little America III, U. S. Antarctic Service Expedition, 1939-41," *Proceedings, American Philosophical Society,* vol. 89, No. 1, April, 1945, pp. 249-255.

Friedmann, Herbert, "Birds of the United States Antarctic Service Expedition, 1939-41," *Proceedings, American Philosophical Society,* vol. 89, No. 1, April, 1945, pp. 305-313.

Glance, Grace, "Collembola of the United States Antarctic Service Expedition, 1939-41," *Proceedings, American Philosophical Society,* vol. 89, No. 1, April, 1945, p. 295.

Hawthorne, Roger, "Exploratory Flights of Admiral Byrd (1940)," *Proceedings, American Philosophical Society,* vol. 89, No. 1, April, 1945, pp. 398a-398e.

Hoyt, Edwin P., *The Last Explorer, The Adventures of Admiral Byrd* (New York, John Day Co., 1968), 380 pp.

Knowles, Paul H., "Geology of Southern Palmer Peninsula, Antarctica," *Proceedings, American Philosophical Society,* vol. 89, No. 1, April, 1945, pp. 132-145.

——, "Glaciology of Southern Palmer Peninsula, Antarctica," *Proceedings, American Philosophical Society,* vol. 89, No. 1, April, 1945, pp. 174-176.

Korff, S. A., and Eric T. Clarke, "Report of Cosmic Ray Observations Made on the U. S. Antarctic Expedition in Cooperation With the Bartol Research Foundation," *Journal of the Franklin Institute,* vol. 230, 1940, pp. 567-581, 7 figures.

Korff, S. A., Dana K. Bailey, and Eric T. Clarke, "Report on Cosmic-ray Observations Made on the U. S. Antarctic Service Expedition, 1939-41," *Proceedings, American Philosophical Society,* vol. 89, No. 1, April, 1945, pp. 316-323.

Lockhart, Ernest E., "Antarctic Trail Diet," *Proceedings, American Philosophical Society,* vol. 89, No. 1, April, 1945, pp. 235-248.

Lockhart, Ernest E. and Arnold Court, "Oxygen Deficiency in Antarctic Air," *Monthly Weather Review,* vol. 70, 1942, pp. 93-96.

McCoy, James C., "Report on Aircraft Activities at West Base, Antarctica," *Proceedings, American Philosophical Society,* vol. 89, No. 1, April, 1945, pp. 387-398.

Passel, Charles F., "Sedimentary Rocks of the Southern Edsel Ford Ranges, Marie Byrd Land, Antarctica," *Proceedings, American Philosophical Society,* vol. 89, No. 1, April, 1945, pp. 123-131.

Perkins, Jack E., "Biology at Little America III, the West Base of the U. S. Antarctic Service Expedition, 1939-41," *Proceedings, American Philosophical Society,* vol. 89, No. 1, April, 1945, pp. 270-284.

Ronne, Finn, "The Main Southern Sledge Journey from East Base, Palmer Land, Antarctica," *Proceedings, American Philosophical Society,* vol. 89, No. 1, April, 1945, pp. 13-22.

Schmitt, Waldo, "Miscellaneous Zoological Material Collected by the United States Antarctic Service Expedition, 1939-1941," *Proceedings, United States Antarctic Service Expedition,* vol. 89, No. 1, April, 1945, p. 297.

Schultz, Leonard P., "Fishes of the United States Antarctic Expedition, 1939-1941," *Proceedings, American Philosophical Society,* vol. 89, No. 1, April, 1945, p. 298.

Shirley, Charles C., "Photographic Accomplishments and Photographic Technique at West Base, Antarctica," *Proceedings, American Philosophical Society,* vol. 89, No. 1, April, 1945, pp. 382-385.

Shoemaker, Clarence R., "Amphipoda of the United States Antarctic Service Expedition, 1939-1941," *Proceedings, American Philosophical Society,* vol. 89, No. 1, April, 1945, pp. 289-293.

Siple, Paul A., "General Principles Governing Selection of Clothing for Cold Climates," *Proceedings, American Philosophical Society,* vol. 89, No. 1, April, 1945, pp. 200-234.

——, "Geographical Exploration from Little America III, The West Base of the U. S. Antarctic Service Expedition, 1939-1941," *Proceedings, American Philosophical Society,* vol. 89, No. 1, April, 1945, pp. 23-60.

——, and Charles F. Passel, "Measurements of Dry Atmospheric Cooling in Subfreezing Temperatures," *Proceedings, American Philosophical Society,* vol. 89, No. 1, April, 1945, pp. 177-199.

Stewart, Duncan, Jr., "Preliminary Report on Some Intrusives of the Melchior Islands, Antarctica," *Proceedings, American Philosophical Society,* vol. 89, No. 1, April, 1945, pp. 146-147.

——, "Rocks of the Melchior Islands, Antarctica," *Proceedings, American Philosophical Society,* vol. 91, No. 3, 1947, pp. 229-233.

Sullivan, Walter, *Quest for a Continent* (New York, McGraw-Hill, 1957), xiv and 372 pp., endpapers, maps, illus. (See chaps. 12, 13, 14.)

T[anner], V[asco], M., "Antarctic Birds Contributed by Dr. Russell B. Frazier," *Great Basin Naturalist,* vol. 2, No. 3, 1941, pp. 122-124.

Wade, F. Alton, "The Geology of the Rockefeller Mountains, King Edward VII Land, Antarctica," *Proceedings, American Philosophical Society,* vol. 89, No. 1, April, 1945, pp. 67-77.

——, "An Introduction to the Symposium on Scientific Results of the United States Antarctic Service Expedition, 1939-1941," *Proceedings, American Philosophical Society,* vol. 89, No. 1, April, 1945, pp. 1-3.

——, "Oil in Antarctica," *The Oil Weekly,* vol. 121, No. 5, International Section, April 1, 1946, pp. 4-10, map.

——, "The Physical Aspects of the Ross Ice Shelf," *Proceedings, American Philosophical Society,* vol. 89, No. 1, April, 1945, pp. 160-173.

——, "Sub-Surface Temperature Measuring Equipment," *Journal of Glaciology,* vol. 1, No. 2, July, 1947, pp. 73-74.

Warner, Lawrence A., "Structure and Petrography of the Southern Edsel Ford Ranges, Antarctica," *Proceedings, American Philosophical Society,* vol. 89, No. 1, April, 1945, pp. 78-122.

Wiener, Murray A., "Results of Auroral Observations at West Base, Antarctica, April to September 1940," *Proceedings, American Philosophical Society,* vol. 89, No. 1, April, 1945, pp. 364-378.

MANUSCRIPT MATERIAL

I. Material in the National Archives

A great body of the records of the United States Antarctic Service is in the United States National Archives. These have been inventoried by Charles E. Dewing and Laura E. Kelsay,

"Records of the United States Antarctic Service," *Preliminary Inventories,* No. 90, The National Archives, National Archives and Records Service, General Services Administration, Washington, 1955. Those records used in this report are listed below under the various categories in which they are filed.

Record Group 126

Records of the Office of Territories, Records of the United States Antarctic Service

Scientific and Technical Reports, Logs, and Related Material

Berlin, Leonard M., "Preliminary Report of Ground Surveys Accomplished at West Base," typescript, 4 pp.

——, "Survey Notes," typescript, about 80 pp., Appendix VI (entry 9), item (11).

Black, Richard B., "Memorandum, dated November 6, 1940, to Finn Ronne, Chief of Staff, U.S.A.S., Leader of Combined Trail Parties; Subject: Operations by Sledging to South and Southeast," typescript, 5 pp.

Bryant, Herwil M., "Preliminary Report of the Scientific Work Accomplished at East Base, Biology," typescript, 5 pp.

——, "Summary Report, Biology Department [East Base]," February 16, 1941, typescript, 5 pp.

Bursey, Jack, "[Pacific Coast] Survey Party, Trail Log [West Base, October 17, 1940-January 7, 1941]," typewritten transcript of rough log in pencil, 25 pp.

Dorsey, Herbert G., "Meteorology at East Base," typescript, 18 pp.

Dyer, J. Glenn, "Report of Magnetic Surveys and Studies [East Base, February 26, 1947]," typescript, 2 pp.

——, "Report of Reconnaissance Sledging Trip into Neny Trough [October 26-29, 1940]," dated November 1, 1940, typescript, 2 pp.

——, "Report of Southeastern Survey to Eternity Range Area [November 20-December 10, 1940]," typescript, 5 pp.

Eklund, Carl R., "Ornithological Report, Biology Department [East Base, 1940-41]," typescript, 2 pp.

Gilmour, Harold P., and Lawrence A. Warner, "Geological Survey Party to Edsel Ford Mountains, October 17, 1940-January 7, 1941," typescript, 2 vols., 303 pp.

Healy, Joseph D., "Establishment of Meteorological Station on Central Plateau of Palmer Peninsula [October 23-26, 1940]," typescript, 1 p.

Knowles, Paul H., "Weddell Coast Journey, November 19, 1940-January 17, 1941," dated February 22, 1941, typescript, 7 pp.

——, "Ice Studies Summary, East Base [February 22, 1941]," typescript, 3 pp.

Lehrke, Lester, "Preliminary Report of Mile High Meteorological Outpost [October 22, 1940-January 1, 1947]," dated February 16, 1941, typescript, 2 pp.

Lockhart, Ernest E., "Journal of the Biological Party, West Base [October 15-December 25, 1940]," typewritten transcription, 63 pp., with incidental correspondence.

Snow, Ashley C., "Summary Report, Flight Operations [East Base, February 16, 1941]," typescript, 2 pp.

Warner, Lawrence A., "Survey Notes, Geological Party, Edsel Ford Ranges, Marie Byrd Land, Antarctica, November-December 1940," Pen-and-ink copy of original, 50 pp.

Private Records

Black, Richard B., "Narrative of East Base, U. S. Antarctic Expedition, 1939-1941," 161 pp. Appendix, "Emergency Evacuations," typescript, 40 pp.

Cartographic Records

Butler, Raymond A., Four overlapping sheets without title, part of Marie Byrd Land in the vicinity of Ruppert Coast and Edsel Ford Ranges. Scale approximately 1 mile equals 1 inch. Unfinished manuscript drawing in ink and pencil. Area covered: 77°57′ S to 77°03′ S, 143°30′ W to 146°30′ W. Appendix VII (entry 22), item (28).

"Chart of Flight Operations. Marie Byrd Land." 41½″ x 27½″. Scale: 1:2,661,120. Azimuthal Equidistant Projection.

"Chart of Trail Operations. Marie Byrd Land." 42″ x 29″. Similar to the chart listed above, except that it shows sledging routes.

Dyer, J. Glenn, East Base. "Palmer Peninsula, Antarctica. Operations Chart." 41″ x 30″. Scale approximately 1:4,400,000. Mercator Projection. Shows isogonic lines, trail operations, flight lines, and new discoveries.

——, East Base. "Stonington Island." 30″ x 41″. Scale: 1:1,020. Contour interval 5 feet. A de-tailed map of the site of East Base.

Hilton, D. C., Map of "Antarctic Regions, East Base and Vicinity." 35½″ x 26½″. Scale: 1:486,-970. Mercator Projection. Includes data from sledge trips and airplane flights.

Ronne, Finn, "Antarctic Regions. Pacific Coast Area, East Base." 36″ x 56″. Scale: 1:729,132. Polyconic Projection. Planimetric map with flight lines and sledge routes.

Presidential Memoranda and Orders

Roosevelt, President Franklin D., Memorandum to Acting Secretary of State Sumner Welles, January 7, 1939, File No. 9-13-2, Administrative General, Records of the Division of Terri-tories and Island Possessions, Record Group 126, U. S. National Archives. President ap-proved planning that had been done by Departments of State, War and Navy. Made sug-gestions to include Department of Interior and for continual occupation of Antarctic bases.

——, Order of the President, November 25, 1939, to Admiral Richard E. Byrd. Published in *Preliminary Inventories*, No. 90, of the Records of the United States Antarctic Service, *supra*, pp. 15-18.

Record Group 24

Records of the Bureau of Naval Personnel: Sub-Group, Records of the Bureau of Naviga-tion (In 1942 the Bureau of Navigation was combined with the Bureau of Naval Personnel.)

Deck log of the U.S.S. *Bear*, September 11, 1939, to June 2, 1941.

II. Material not in the National Archives

Central Files of the National Academy of Sciences, Records of the Interim Advisory Committee of the U. S. Antarctic Service, National Academy of Sciences.

Report of Meeting of the Interim Advisory Committee, July 28, 1939.

Barrows, Albert, Executive Secretary of the National Academy of Sciences, letter, dated Sep-tember 25, 1939, to Dr. Isaiah Bowman, The Johns Hopkins University, Chairman of the Interim Advisory Committee.

——, A second letter, dated September 25, 1939, to Dr. Isaiah Bowman.

PLATE XV-A. The Southeastern-Eternity Range Survey Party, Joseph Healy, Glenn Dyer, and Lytton Musselman, at their camp on the Dyer Plateau (70° 16′S, 66° 59′W). Photograph by courtesy of Finn Ronne.

PLATE XV-B. Conference of leaders of "Operation Highjump"; l. to r., Captain Richard H. Cruzen, Captain Robert S. Quackenbush, Jr., Rear Admiral Richard E. Byrd, Captain Charles A. Bond, and Captain George J. Dufek. At the time of this picture, during the period of organization, Cruzen had not yet been promoted to Rear Admiral. U. S. Information Agency Photo No. 306-NT-549D-1 in the National Archives.

PLATE XVI-A. Icebreaker *Northwind* leading the ships of the Central Group through the pack ice of the Ross Sea. Navy Dept., Photo No. 26-G-31847(4) in the National Archives.

PLATE XVI-B. Icebreaker *Burton Island* pushing through the pack ice of the Ross Sea. Navy Dept., Photo No. 80-G-614520 in the National Archives.

22

THE U. S. NAVY ANTARCTIC DEVELOPMENTS PROJECT, "OPERATION HIGHJUMP," 1946–1947

SIGNIFICANCE OF THE EXPEDITION

The U. S. Navy Antarctic Developments Project, 1946-47, was by far the largest Antarctic expedition. In no expedition before or since have so many ships, aircraft, and men been involved. During the International Geophysical Year, 1957-58, when the United States established and manned seven bases in support of numerous and varied scientific projects, far fewer men took part.

Depending on one's viewpoint, the expedition presents various facets. It was a Navy testing and training exercise, but it made important contributions to our knowledge of Antarctica and to polar exploration techniques. Much of the coast of Antarctica was photographed for the first time, providing information about significant areas that had not been seen before. It maintained the United States presence in Antarctica, where bases had been established in the South Shetlands and on the Antarctic Peninsula by the United Kingdom in 1944 and 1945 to counter territorial claims of Argentina and Chile.

ORGANIZATION AND ACCOMPLISHMENTS

ESTABLISHMENT OF THE PROJECT

The Chief of Naval Operations, Fleet Admiral Chester W. Nimitz, established the U. S. Navy Antarctic Developments Project, as it was officially titled, on August 26, 1946, and charged the Commander-in-Chief, U. S. Atlantic Fleet, with operational and administrative control. Rear Admiral Richard E. Byrd was designated Officer-in-Charge of the project and given technical control during Antarctic operations. The project, which was identified by the code word "Operation Highjump," was to be carried out by Task Force 68 of the Atlantic Fleet then conducting "Operation Nanook" in the Arctic. Rear Admiral Richard H. Cruzen, commander of Task Force 68, was given responsibility for carrying out the project and tactical control of operations at all times.

August 26 was late in the season for the organization of such a project, but prior to the departure of the Task Force for the Arctic in early July Admiral Cruzen had been apprised of preliminary discussions concerning an Antarctic expedition. Consequently, he and his staff made tentative plans for the operation, and several members of the staff were later flown back to Washington to participate in the planning there. On October 15 operational and administrative instructions for the project were issued by Admiral Marc A. Mitscher, Commander-in-Chief, U. S. Atlantic Fleet, and the several ships to be assigned to Task Force 68 were designated.

Personnel and material had to be assembled hastily if the Task Force was to reach Antarctica in time to carry out its mission during the austral summer, and

later the activities of field parties were impeded by the inevitable mistakes in collecting and stowing equipment and supplies. There was little time for adapting
standard equipment for Antarctic conditions or for the procurement of equipment designed for polar conditions, which would have increased the efficiency
of the operation. Under the circumstances, standard naval equipment was more
thoroughly tested than it would have been if better preparations could have
been made. Although the personnel of "Operation Nanook" served as a nucleus
for staffing "Operation Highjump," the much greater size of the latter meant
that many of the posts had to be filled with men with no previous polar experience. Had more time been available, more of these posts might have been filled
by Antarctic veterans. As it was, the number of persons with polar experience
was increased. Such rapid progress was made in organizing the Task Force for
"Operation Highjump" that the ships were able to sail on December 2, 1946,
only seven weeks after the instructions had been issued.

Objectives and Accomplishments

Objectives. The objectives of the expedition were to:

(a) Train personnel and test equipment under Antarctic conditions;

(b) Consolidate and extend the basis for United States claims in the Antarctic,
if such should subsequently be made;

(c) Investigate problems in the selection of Antarctic base sites and in their
establishment, maintenance, and use;

(d) Develop techniques for establishment, maintenance, and use of air operational facilities on ice;

(e) Extend the knowledge of Antarctic hydrography, geography, geology, meteorology, and electomagnetic propagation;

(f) Supplement the 1946 Arctic "Operation Nanook."

Accomplishments. The expedition accomplished its objectives, in some cases
more and in others less fully than anticipated. More than 4700 naval and marine
personnel and 44 observers gained Antarctic experience, and the Navy obtained
valuable information on the performance of equipment. Icebreakers, used for
the first time on an Antarctic expedition, more than proved their worth and
gave evidence that larger, more powerful ones would do even better. A submarine, on the other hand, was unequal to surface operation in the pack ice and
had to be towed out. A helicopter was flown for the first time in Antarctica,[1] and
amphibious tractors made a successful six-day journey of 280 miles. The expedition sighted some 1,500,000 square miles of Antarctica, nearly half of it previously unexplored, and took some 15,000 aerial trimetrogon photographs. The program, however, did not include obtaining the ground control points for preparation of maps from these photographs.

For the first time, large aircraft equipped with combination wheel and ski
landing gear and launched from an aircraft carrier flew in to the continent and
landed at an air operational facility established on the ice shelf.

The expedition made important contributions to our knowledge of Antarctic
weather processes. It provided for the first time a network of simultaneous observations sufficient for twice-daily synoptic weather maps of the Antarctic. The

data collected primarily for forecasting flying weather also shed new light on the characteristics and movements of air masses and frontal systems. More than 10,-000 observations were taken in about 2½ months, all around the periphery of the continent but with the largest number in the Pacific area, where the weather appears to be most complex.

Expedition photographers took about 70,000 aerial reconnaissance photographs on 64 photographic flights, covering some 60 per cent (by longitude) of the coastline. About 25 per cent of this was reported as sighted for the first time and another 40 per cent as previously incorrectly charted. Mountain ranges reported as seen for the first time numbered at least 18, containing hundreds of peaks and several major mountains. Two ice-free areas on the Indian Ocean coast were photographed. An aircraft landed on an unfrozen lake in one of these areas and took water samples. The Ross Ice Shelf was studied intensively by air (Fig. 24).

When coupled with ground control obtained by the U. S. Navy's "Operation Windmill" (see Chapter 24), the aerial photography taken by "Operation Highjump" made possible the first accurate delineation of the coast of Wilkes Land. Photos were also later lent to other nations for the establishment of bases for the International Geophysical Year and for later operations.

The successful use of several pieces of military equipment for the purpose of exploration was an important contribution of the expedition. For example, the radar-equipped fire control director of the destroyer *Brownson* was successfully used as a range finder and to obtain elevation angles of peaks while doing offshore mapping. A magnetic airborne submarine detector was used an an airborne magnetometer to determine the nature of rocks over which the plane was flying. Barometric altimeters indicate the elevation of the plane above sea level, but radar altimeters indicate the elevation of the plane above the ground. By subtracting the latter from the former, flying personnel of "Operation Highjump" were able to obtain a more nearly accurate estimate of the elevation of terrain features than had formerly been the case. However, estimates of the elevation of mountain ranges, when compared to subsequent determinations, tended to be too high. Pilots on exploratory flights never are sure whether the weather will stay clear until they return to base, but radar operators in "Operation Highjump," once they became skilled in reading their scopes, were a tremendous assistance in bringing in a plane through overcast and fog.

COMPOSITION OF THE EXPEDITION

Ships. Thirteen ships were assigned to Task Force 68: seven from the Atlantic Fleet, five from the Pacific Fleet, and the icebreaker *Northwind,* which was loaned by the Coast Guard. The ships were distributed among four of the five Task Groups into which the Task Force was divided.[2] To Task Group 68.1 (TG 68.1), also known as the Central Group, were assigned the communications ship *Mount Olympus,* the supply ships *Yancey* and *Merrick,* the submarine *Sennet,* the Navy's icebreaker *Burton Island,* and the Coast Guard icebreaker *Northwind.* The *Mount Olympus,* flagship of the Task Force, was a specially designed command ship with positions for 50 radio operators. The radio beacon

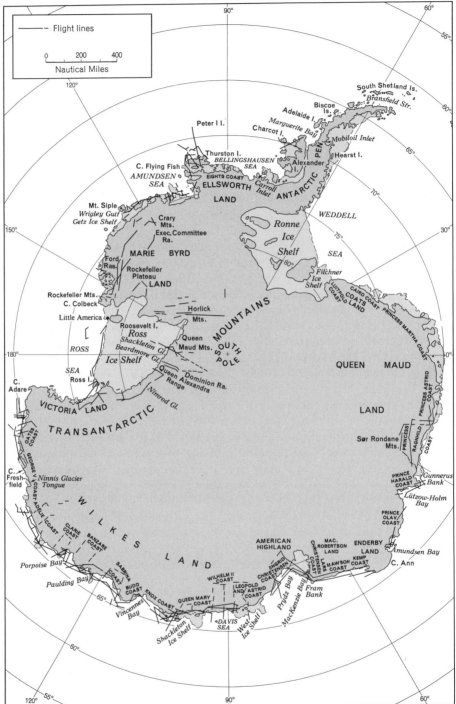

FIGURE 24. Map of Antarctica Showing Photographic Flight Lines of "Highjump" Aircraft.

of the *Mount Olympus* was to serve as a guide to aviators on exploratory flights from Little America.

The East and West Groups each consisted of a seaplane tender, a tanker, and a destroyer. Seaplanes would fly from the tenders on photographic flights over the coastal margins of the continent. The destroyers were included mainly for their speed, which would be very important in attempts to rescue the crew of a plane that had been forced down at sea. When a destroyer was separated some distance from the rest of the Task Group, it also served as an additional weather station. The Western Group (TG 68.2) consisted of the seaplane tender *Currituck*, the destroyer *Henderson*, and the tanker *Cacapon*. The Eastern Group (TG 68.3) was made up of the seaplane tender *Pine Island*, the destroyer *Brownson*, and the tanker *Canisteo*. The aircraft carrier *Philippine Sea* operated separately as the Carrier Group (TG 68.4).

Aircraft. Each of the seaplane tenders carried three Martin Mariner (PBMs) seaplanes, two of them operational and a third disassembled. These had been winterized and were equipped with trimetrogon cameras and special navigational gear. The aircraft carrier *Philippine Sea* carried six twin-engined Douglas R4D transport planes. These planes, known as DC-3s on commercial airlines, were equipped with skis with slots through which wheels projected about three inches. This innovation, which permitted the planes to take off from the carrier deck and land on a snow surface, proved highly successful. They were also equipped with JATO bottles (jet assist takeoff) which provided the extra boost necessary to get them in flight from the short runway of the carrier deck or from the compressed snow runway at Little America. The six R4Ds were flown from the *Philippine Sea* from a point outside the pack ice almost 700 miles to Little America, where they then became a part of and were operated by TG 68.5 or Base Group. The planes were equipped with trimetrogon cameras, a gremlin recorder, radar, deicing gear, a radar recording camera, radio altimeter, and special navigational gear. Supplementary gasoline tanks were also installed. Each of the seaplane tenders carried, in addition to the PBM Martin Mariner seaplanes, one smaller two-engine seaplane (SOC) and two helicopters (HO3S-1 and HOS-1) for scouting and possible rescue flights. Each icebreaker carried a single-engined amphibian plane (J2F6) and a helicopter for scouting. Utility aircraft assigned to the Base Group consisted of one helicopter, one JA-1 Noorduyn Norseman ski-plane, and two OY Grasshoppers. The helicopter carried by the *Philippine Sea* crashed before it could be delivered to Little America. The two Grasshoppers, one of which was never assembled, were transported from the aircraft carrier to the base by the *Burton Island*. The Norseman, the workhorse of the Base Group, was transported aboard the *Mount Olympus*.

Land Transport. Task Force 68 was equipped with a variety of vehicles, cargo carriers, and cargo handlers to be tested during "Operation Highjump." In addition to the transport, some of the equipment was used for the construction and maintenance of the airstrip at Little America. Among other pieces of equipment were eight Army ¾-ton amphibian cargo carriers (M29Cs), commonly known as Weasels, ten D-6 caterpillar tractors, Cletrac tractors, Jeeps, and LVTs (Landing Vehicle, Tracked).

Personnel. "Operation Highjump" was a large, complex project involving over 4700 naval and marine personnel. In addition, there were 16 military and 24 civilian scientists and observers and 11 reporters. The following list of personnel includes only the higher echelons of command and those military men of lower rank and civilians who particpated actively in the exploratory and scientific as distinct from the military activities of the expedition.

Asterisks preceding a name indicate the number of previous Antarctic expeditions in which the person participated.

***Rear Admiral Richard E. Byrd, U.S.N. Ret., Officer-in-Charge, Antarctic Development Project

*Rear Admiral Richard H. Cruzen, U.S.N., Commander, Task Force 68

Captain Robert S. Quackenbush, Jr., U.S.N., Aide and Chief of Staff

Captain H. R. Horney, U.S.N., Chief of Staff, Antarctic Development Project

Captain George F. Kosco, U.S.N., Aerology and Special Projects

Captain M. A. Norcross (SC), U.S.N., Logistics

Captain R. R. Moore, U.S.N., Captain U.S.S. *Mount Olympus*

Captain J. E. Cohn, U.S.N., Captain U.S.S. *Yancey*

Captain John J. Hourihan, U.S.N., Captain U.S.S. *Merrick*

Captain Charles W. Thomas, U.S.C.G., Captain U.S.C.G.C. *Northwind*

Commander Gerald L. Ketchum, U.S.N., Captain U.S.S. *Burton Island*

Commander Joseph B. Icenhower, U.S.N., Captain U.S.S. *Sennet*

Captain Charles A. Bond, U.S.N. Commander, Western Group

Captain John E. Clark, U.S.N., Captain U.S.S. *Currituck*

Captain R. A. Mitchell, U.S.N., Captain U.S.S. *Cacapon*

Commander C. F. Bailey, U.S.N., Captain U.S.S. *Henderson*

Lieutenant Commander David E. Bunger, U.S.N., Plane Commander and Pilot

Lieutenant Commander William J. Rogers, Jr., U.S.N., Plane Commander and Pilot

Lieutenant W. R. Kreitzer, U.S.N., Plane Commander and Pilot

Lieutenant Fred L. Reinbolt, U.S.N., Co-pilot and Navigator

Lieutenant Robert H. Gillock, U.S.N., Co-pilot and Navigator

Lieutenant James C. Jennings, U.S.N., Co-pilot and Navigator

Lieutenant James C. Stevenson, U.S.N., Co-pilot and Navigator

*Captain George J. Dufek, U.S.N., Commander, Eastern Group

Captain Henry Howard Caldwell, U.S.N., Captain U.S.S. *Pine Island*

Captain Edward K. Walker, U.S.N., Captain U.S.S. *Canisteo*

Commander H.M.S. Gimber, Captain U.S.S. *Brownson*

Lieutenant Commander John D. Howell, U.S.N., Plane Commander and Pilot

Lieutenant (jg) Ralph P. LeBlanc, U.S.N.R., Pilot and Plane Commander

Lieutenant (jg) William H. Kearns, Jr., U.S.N.R., Co-pilot

Lieutenant (jg) James L. Ball, U.S.N., Co-pilot

Lieutenant (jg) Robert G. Goff, U.S.N., Co-pilot

Captain Delbert S. Cornwell, U.S.N., Captain U.S.S. *Philippine Sea*

Commander Clifford M. Campbell, U.S.N., Commander, Base Group at Little America

Commander William M. Hawkes, Commander, R4D Unit

*Lieutenant Commander James C. McCoy, U.S.N., Pilot
Major Robert R. Weir, U.S.M.C., Pilot
Lieutenant George H. Anderson, U.S.N., Pilot
Captain Eugene C. McIntyre, U.S.M.C., Pilot
Lieutenant Robert J. McCarthy, U.S.M.C., Pilot
1st Lieutenant Pitman, U.S.M.C., Pilot
Lieutenant George W. Warden, Pilot
Lieutenant Conrad S. Shinn, Pilot
Lieutenant (jg) William K. Martin, U.S.N., Pilot
Lieutenant (jg) Erwin Spencer, U.S.N., Pilot
Lieutenant (jg) Harry W. Summers, U.S.N., Pilot
Commander R. M. Allison, U.S.N., Air Operations
*Lieutenant Commander Frederick G. Dustin, U.S.N.R.
Lieutenant Commander J. C. Heide, U.S.N.R., Hydrographic Officer
*Lieutenant Charles C. Shirley, U.S.N., Photographic Officer
**Captain Vernon D. Boyd, U.S.M.C., Transportation Officer
1st Lieutenant John H. Roscoe, U.S.M.C., Photogrammetric Officer
  Among the civilian and military scientists and observers were the following:
Lieutenant W. G. Metcalf, U.S.N.R., (Woods Hole, Oceanographer)
  (*Northwind*)
Lieutenant C. A. Schoene, C. and G.S. (Coast & Geodetic Survey)
  (*Mount Olympus*)
Captain C. H. Harrison, U.S.A., Army Observer, Meteorologist
  (*Mount Olympus*)
*Captain Murray A. Wiener, U.S.A., Army Observer, Air-Sea Rescue
  (*Mount Olympus*)
*Chief Warrant Officer A. J. L. Morency, U.S.A., Army Observer-Boat Mainte-
  nance (*Mount Olympus*)
***Dr. Paul A. Siple, Senior Representative, War Department (*Mount Olympus*)
Dr. H. H. Howe, Coast & Geodetic Survey (*Mount Olympus*)
Mr. B. C. Haynes, Weather Bureau (*Mount Olympus*)
Mr. J. R. Balsley, U. S. Geological Survey (*Mount Olympus*)
Dr. A. D. Howard, U. S. Geological Survey (*Mount Olympus*)
Mr. J. E. Perkins, Fish and Wildlife Service (*Mount Olympus*)
*Mr. Amory H. Waite, Signal Corps, U.S.A. (*Mount Olympus*)
Mr. R. M. Gilmore, Fish and Wildlife Service (*Canisteo*)
Mr. J. L. Hough, Woods Hole Observer (*Northwind*)

DETAILED RECORD OF OPERATIONS

Departure for the Antarctic

The flagship *Mount Olympus,* seaplane tender *Pine Island,* and destroyer *Brownson,* ships assigned to Task Force 68 from the Atlantic Fleet, and the Coast Guard icebreaker *Northwind* sailed from Norfolk, Virginia, on December 2, 1946. After passing through the Panama Canal they were joined by the tanker *Canisteo* and the submarine *Sennet* before sailing from Balboa on December

10. Elements of the Pacific Fleet assigned to the Task Force also sailed on December 2, the seaplane tender *Currituck* and destroyer *Henderson* from San Diego, the tanker *Cacapon* from San Pedro, and the supply ship *Yancey* from Port Hueneme. The supply ship *Merrick* followed three days later. All elements of the Eastern Group were, therefore, among the ships sailing from Balboa. On December 17 the *Currituck* and *Henderson* were detached and sailed for the vicinity of Peter I Island where they were to begin operations. The tanker *Canisteo* continued with the other ships toward the rendezvous of the Central Group at Scott Island.

Meanwhile the ships sailing from California ports, including all units of the Western Group, made a rendezvous at the Marquesas Islands from where the two supply ships proceeded to Scott Island to join the other elements of the Central Group. The Eastern Group reached the edge of the pack ice to the north of the Balleny Islands on December 24. On December 30 the Central Group met at Scott Island. Sonic sounding instruments on the ships made possible several new bathymetric profiles across the Pacific Ocean as they proceeded toward their respective rendezvous.

OPERATIONS OF THE CENTRAL GROUP

Following the rendezvous of the Central Group at Scott Island on December 30, 1946, the *Canisteo* was ordered to join the Eastern Group. While the ships of the Central Group remained in the vicinity of Scott Island, J. L. Hough and W. G. Metcalf of the Woods Hole Oceanographic Institution conducted soundings which revealed Scott Island to be one of two peaks, the other of which was submerged. Captain Charles W. Thomas made an ice reconnaissance in the *Northwind,* southward along the 180° meridian for about 100 miles through thin to moderately thick but broken pack ice. A helicopter was sent aloft to scout the pack for another 30 miles southward. Two well-defined leads were evident, and it was decided that the Central Group would proceed southward along this meridian along which previous expeditions had succeeded in finding a passage through the pack.

With Admiral Cruzen on board, the *Northwind* led the file of five ships into the pack. The ice, which at first gave little trouble, gradually became thicker and more closely packed. As the *Northwind* broke a passage through ice 10 feet thick, lines of weakness between the floes were responsible for the development of an irregular, zigzag lane of open water with jagged sides and sharp turns. This forced the ships to follow a twisting course, and as they negotiated sharp turns their thin-skinned hulls unavoidably struck projecting pieces of ice or large floes. Loose floes bobbed up and pressed against the sides of the ships. As a result, by the end of the second day all but the *Northwind* had been damaged. It was apparent that ice conditions were unusually difficult in 1946-47 and especially dangerous for ordinary steel-hull cargo vessels. Early on January 3 progress was extremely slow. Although the ships kept as close together as possible, loose floes frequently pressed in so tightly against one or another of them that the *Northwind* and those ships following were soon held fast. Each time the

Northwind would have to break the ships loose before the column could move again.

Ice also began drifting up over the hull and onto the deck of the *Sennet*, endangering the submarine and slowing the progress of the entire column. Therefore, it was necessary for the *Northwind* to tow the *Sennet* back through 65 miles of pack ice to open water in the vicinity of Scott Island. This operation, conducted in three stages, required the better part of three days, with the *Northwind* shuttling back and forth between the *Sennet* and the other three ships to free first one and then another from dangerous situations. In one instance the ships, although the pack ice pressed closely around them, succeeded in maneuvering barely enough to avoid two icebergs that were bearing down upon them. On January 5 the submarine was cast off in open water within sight of Scott Island, where she was ordered to carry out tests and serve as a weather station.

At 2:00 a. m., January 6, the *Northwind* rejoined the other ships and the column was soon heading southwestward through the pack ice. At 6:00 a. m. the column reached a pool of open water in about 70°11′ S, 178°23′ W where the three ships waited while the icebreaker, using a helicopter, carried on a reconnaissance of ice conditions to the south. Later that night the *Northwind* again led the ships southward, but heavy ice forced them to retreat to the open pool again the next morning, January 7. Three flights by the J2F Grumman amphibian plane and probing by the *Northwind*, with a helicopter assisting, revealed no passage southward. The Western Task Group had meanwhile been asked to halt its operations temporarily and move eastward toward Scott Island so as to be in a position to send out a Martin Mariner flying boat on a long-range reconnaissance mission over the Ross Sea pack ice. With the ice closing in on the three vessels of the Central Group, it was necessary for the *Northwind* to break them loose and move them to a new pool five miles south, on January 10. That same afternoon weather conditions finally permitted two Martin Mariners of the Western Task Group to take off, but by the time they were over the ships of the Central Group the weather was closing in, and they were ordered back to the *Currituck*. The ensuing bad weather, however, loosened the pack sufficiently so that on January 11 the *Northwind* was able to find a way open through which it led the column southward. As the column proceeded, ice conditions improved and finally, on January 14, the Central Task Group broke out into the open water of the Ross Sea. Soon the cliffed front of the Ross Ice Shelf was sighted. Discovery Inlet was briefly inspected as the ships skirted the edge of the ice shelf en route to the Bay of Whales, which was reached early on January 15.

The differential movement of the two parts of the Ross Ice Shelf, that part east of ice-drowned Roosevelt Island moving from the east against the great mass of the shelf to the west, with its northward movement, had almost obliterated the indentation in the front of the ice shelf known as the Bay of Whales. In 1947 the Central Task Group found the indentation to be only about two miles long and about 300 yards wide at its entrance. Beyond the entrance, the

Bay of Whales was filled with bay ice from six to ten feet thick.[3] Before the ships could unload the equipment and supplies, it was necessary for the *Northwind* to break out a harbor in this bay ice, a task which was completed in a little less than 72 hours.[4]

ESTABLISHMENT OF LITTLE AMERICA IV

Early on January 18 the *Yancey* was moored in the Bay of Whales and unloading began. Late on January 19 the *Merrick* was moored, and the *Mount Olympus* followed on January 22. Meanwhile, on January 16 and 17, landing parties led by Commander Clifford M. Campbell and Dr. Paul A. Siple visited Little America III of the U. S. Antarctic Service West Base, which was found in good condition. They selected a site for a temporary base camp (Little America IV) and laid out and marked with trail flags a route over which supplies could be hauled from the ships to the camp. The camp site was on the ice shelf, about 1½ miles southeast of the place where the ships were moored and 2½ miles north of Little America III. By the morning of January 17 the construction detail had laid a bridge across a chasm in the pressure ice at the head of the bay, over which the tractors pulling heavily loaded sleds would have to pass.

Unloading cargo began immediately. Antarctic veteran Captain Vernon D. Boyd soon had his tractors and heavy sleds hauling supplies and equipment to the base camp and airfield which the Seabees, under Commander C. O. Reinhardt, were hurriedly constructing. Original plans called for an airstrip 5000 feet long made of pierced planking, a development of World War II known as Marsten mat, for quickly constructing an airstrip over soft ground. The late arrival due to the difficult pack ice conditions left little time for the construction of this strip, and an experimental Marsten mat strip only 835 feet long was laid down. Three hard-surface snow runways, totaling 13,000 feet in length, served as a satisfactory substitute. Planes, however, were required to use skis instead of wheels, which would have permitted takeoffs with heavier loads. A Quonset hut was erected for aircraft maintenance and communication. Fifty-four pyramidal tents were set up on wooden floors in five widely spaced rows as living quarters for 300 men, and several other tents of various sizes were erected for a variety of purposes.

When, because of serious ice conditions, it was decided not to risk the *Mount Olympus, Merrick,* and *Yancey* by keeping them at the Bay of Whales after February 6, 1947, plans had to be altered still further. It had been hoped to use the radar and radio facilities of the *Mount Olympus* to assist tracking and landing the planes if the weather should close in on Little America while one of them was on a photographic mission. As a substitute, a Quonset hut was erected for communications over the buried buildings of Little America III, with which it was connected by a tunnel. The 1940 base was also supplied with food for 35 men for 14 months in the event that some personnel would have to winter over at Little America.

Since the base would be evacuated by the icebreaker *Burton Island,* the number of men remaining at Little America after February 6 was limited to the number that could be accommodated aboard that ship, and equipment that could not be returned aboard the supply ships would have to remain at Little America. Consequently, before the ships were completely unloaded, the tractors began shuttling back from the base with sleds loaded with equipment to be re-embarked, and part of the ships' crews were restowing cargo while others were unloading. During the three weeks that the ships were at the Bay of Whales, loading operations were interrupted three times and the ships forced to put to sea, on January 23 by an iceberg which entered the bay, on January 27 by a snow storm and 25-knot wind from the north, and on January 30 by a brief spell of bad weather following the arrival of the six R4D planes from the carrier *Philippine Sea.*

AIR OPERATIONS AT LITTLE AMERICA

Exploratory flights from Little America were carried out by six two-engine Douglas transport planes (R4Ds) transported to the Ross Sea by the aircraft carrier *Philippine Sea* which had sailed from Norfolk under the command of Captain Delbert S. Cornwell on January 2, 1947. Rear Admiral Richard E. Byrd, the plane crews, and their commander, Commander William M. Hawkes, were also aboard. Passing through the Panama Canal en route, the *Philippine Sea* reached the rendezvous in the vicinity of Scott Island on January 25. Here the tanker *Cacapon* of the Western Task Group, the destroyer *Brownson* of the Eastern Task Group, the submarine *Sennet,* and the *Northwind* met the carrier.

That same day, January 25, only a week after unloading had begun at the Bay of Whales, the air strip was practically ready to receive the planes which were prepared to take off from the carrier as soon as weather permitted. Meanwhile, a variety of cargo was transferred from the *Philippine Sea* to the other vessels, and the *Cacapon* refueled some of the ships.

On January 29 the *Philippine Sea* was lying to in a large embayment in the edge of the pack ice in about 68°50′ S, 174°40′ W, a place deemed suitable for launching the planes. The other ships were deployed in a manner to effect a rescue quickly in case of a forced landing at sea, the *Northwind* being stationed in the pack ice halfway to Little America. That evening weather conditions were favorable over the entire route of the projected flight to Little America, and preparations were made for takeoff, the first instance in which planes as large as the R4Ds had ever been launched from a carrier. Another innovation concerned the landing gear, unusually broad skis with slots through which the regular landing wheels protruded about three inches. Because of their wing spread the planes could use only that part of the flight deck forward of the superstructure. To compensate for the short runway, JATO (jet assist takeoff) bottles were mounted on the sides of the planes, and all unnecessary gear, including oxygen tanks, were removed. The lack of this oxygen supply subsequently proved a handicap on long photographic flights at high altitude, causing the planes' crews to experience hypoxia.

The first plane, with Commander William M. Hawkes as pilot and Admiral

Byrd as passenger, took off at 11:30 p. m. The tense moment of anxiety due to the novelty of the situation was immediately relieved when the plane rose easily into the air. Seventeen minutes later the second plane took off, and the two headed south for Little America on the radio beam transmitted by the *Mount Olympus*. At 5:28 a. m. the first plane landed on the snow strip at Little America, having flown the 700 miles against head winds in six hours. When word was received by the *Philippine Sea* that the first two planes had landed, the third plane took off at 8:00 a. m., January 30, followed in short order by the other three. Headwinds were again encountered, and the first plane landed at Little America at 1:30 p. m. About 200 miles from Little America the last plane developed trouble with its gyro compass and radio and was for a time lost. With the weather closing in, it landed at Little America at 2:06. A short time later the first blizzard that the expedition experienced at Little America set in. Later on January 30 the *Philippine Sea* began the return journey northward from the Antarctic waters, arriving at Balboa on February 18, and at Quonset Point, Rhode Island, February 28.

Following the arrival of the six Douglas transport planes, every effort was exerted to ready the base camp at Little America for the flight program before the ships departed. This included a number of local test and training flights with the big planes. When the ships sailed from the Bay of Whales on February 6 with Admiral Cruzen aboard, 197 officers, civilians, and enlisted men remained at Little America under the direction of Admiral Byrd to carry out the flight program and conduct scientific investigations. Among the latter was a study by Dr. Siple of the movement of the Ross Ice Shelf and its effect on the Bay of Whales. Siple calculated that the main body of the Ross Ice Shelf to the west of Roosevelt Island and the Bay of Whales was moving north at the rate of 4.4 feet a day while that part east of the Bay of Whales was moving west at the rate of 4.37 feet a day.[5] For this work and other flights about the base a JA-1 Noorduyn Norseman or a Stinson Sentinel (OY-1 Grasshopper) single-engine planes were used.

The best flying weather in Antarctica generally occurs from September to December. The few days on which planes can operate in February are separated by long stretches of bad weather, and 1947 was typical. After days of waiting, 10 long flights were made in rapid succession, beginning February 14. Two attempts earlier were unsuccessful: on the 9th, the two planes on a flight to the southeast had been turned back by bad weather after about 200 miles; on the 10th, a flight to the southwest was cut short by engine trouble, and a snow storm had set in by the time the two planes landed at the base. In these initial attempts and in all later flights, for reasons of safety, planes made all exploratory flights in pairs, and at least two R4Ds were always held at Little America for possible rescue missions should any of the other four be forced down.

February 14 dawned cold and clear, and shortly after midnight the aviation crews went into action. The first plane (V-1) to take off had Admiral Byrd as observer, Major Robert R. Weir as pilot, and Lieutenant (jg) Harry W. Summers as co-pilot. They flew south over the Ross Ice Shelf toward the Watson Escarpment, which had been seen from a distance by the Geological Party of the Second Byrd Antarctic Expedition in 1934. They ascended to the polar plateau via a broad hourglass-shaped glacier with a constricted mid-section which Admiral Byrd estimated to be approximately 60 miles east of the Scott Glacier.[6] Cloud banks up on the plateau forced a turn to the left and a southeastward course. The polar side of the Transantarctic Mountains could be seen to the left. In the distance, to the southeast, other mountains rose above the plateau surface. At this point rapidly falling oil pressure on one engine dictated a descent to lower elevation. When this lower level north of the Transantarctic Mountains was reached, oil pressure became normal, and the plane was headed eastward again along the north side of the mountains for about 70 miles before turning back to Little America.

The second plane (V-2), which was to have accompanied that of Admiral Byrd and Major Weir, was delayed in taking off by skis which had frozen to the snow; as a result, it flew a somewhat similar but solitary course. Lieutenant George H. Anderson and co-pilot Lieutenant (jg) William K. Martin, set a course to the south-southeast toward the Horlick Mountains, seen from a distance on a flight from Little America by the Second Byrd Antarctic Expedition in 1934. Anderson flew around the western end of what he thought to be the Horlick Mountains, a range about 9000 feet high. High peaks dead ahead forced him to turn left (southeast) and follow a low saddle between the Horlicks and this new range. The plane's altimeter indicated an elevation of 13,000 feet as they flew along the flank of this new range, but a steep mountain wall of reddish rock rose above them. The plane flew along this range for 180 miles to about 86°40' S, 96° W when the crew began experiencing hypoxia due to lack of oxygen at the high altitude. Consequently, Lieutenant Anderson deemed it prudent to return to Little America. The mountain range extended indefinitely toward the southeast. An especially high mass of rock rose in the distance to an estimated 15,000 feet.[7]

As the first two planes returned two others were ready to take to the air on photographic flights. One of these planes (V-3), piloted by Captain Eugene C. McIntyre, flew inland for 500 miles on a course about 50 miles east of that followed by Lieutenant Anderson, but low clouds over the snow-covered surface blotted out terrain features except for a few black crests near the turning point.[8] For this reason the photographs were of little value. The fourth plane (V-6), flown by Lieutenant Conrad S. Shinn, followed a course still farther to the east. It flew at an elevation of 14,500 feet for at least an hour before attaining the broad expanses of the polar plateau. On this flight, too, clouds obstructed visibility, but many mountains were seen.

Every flying opportunity must be used in Antarctica, and when the weather continued good as the second pair of planes returned, near midnight on February 14, the first two planes (V-1 and V-2) were ready to take off again, this time to the southwest. With Mount Wade as a landmark they headed for the foot of Shackleton Glacier, the eastern flank of which is dominated by that 14,000-foot peak. One plane flew up the east side of the glacier and the other up the west side. After reaching the 11,500-foot head of the glacier, they continued southwestward to about 87° S, 116°50' E, then turned and headed northeasterly toward lofty Mount Kirkpatrick on the west flank of Beardmore Glacier. They descended this mighty ribbon of ice, the route of Shackleton and Scott to the Polar plateau earlier in the century, one plane along each side of the glacier.

The clear weather and good visibility continued into the 15th, and Commander Hawkes made the most of it. Two planes (V-3 and V-5) were serviced and ready for a flight over Marie Byrd Land to the east. The crews were pretty well exhausted by this time, however, and Dr. Siple volunteered as navigator on one of the planes. Other veterans of the U. S. Antarctic Service Expedition of 1939-41 helped to round out the crew. James C. McCoy served as pilot and Lieutenant Charles C. Shirley as photographer. The other plane was piloted by Commander Hawkes. The plan was to explore the area about Mount Siple and the Getz Ice Shelf immediately west of it, but when they reached the Executive Committee Range, clouds blotted out Mount Siple to the north and barred the way to the east. When the planes reached a point about 76° S, 123° W, they returned to Little America on a course about 100 miles south of the outbound flight. This was the first time that the Executive Committee Range and towering Mount Sidley (13,000 ft.) had been seen close up. The trend of the range appeared to be more south-southeast than had previously been assumed. To the south of the range they saw other mountains, above which rose a tremendous peak, estimated by Dr. Siple to be 20,000 feet high.[9] However, there must have been some confusion of direction here, perhaps as the aircraft was making its turn or in the subsequent report, for there are no such mountains to the south of the Executive Committee Range that could have been seen from the plane at that point. Siple probably saw the 11,000-foot Crary Mountains which are approximately 110 statute miles or 100 nautical miles southeast of the reported turning point. Moreover, the Executive Committee Range trends very nearly N-S, or perhaps more accurately, N by E to S by W.

The weather continued good, and shortly after 11 p. m. on February 15 two planes (V-1 and V-6) took off for a flight to the South Pole. In the lead plane (V-1) were Lieutenant Commander McCoy, Lieutenant Anderson, and Admiral Byrd. The second plane was piloted by Major Weir with Captain McIntyre as co-pilot. Commander Campbell, commander of the base at Little America, was also aboard. A course was set across the Ross Ice Shelf toward Mount Wade and Shackleton Glacier, which the planes ascended to gain the polar plateau. At the head of the glacier a course was set for the South Pole along the 180th meridian, with Grosvenor Mountains to the left and Dominion Range to the right. The former had been seen from the east by Byrd on his flight to the Pole in 1929. At about the 88th parallel Byrd noted a hump in the surface of the plateau, a rise of about 1000 feet, which both Amundsen and Scott had reported from the ground. Although this snow-covered feature was imperceptible from the air it was indicated on the radar altimeters of the planes. This feature had also been noticed on the altimeters of the two planes that had just a few hours earlier flown up Shackleton Glacier to the vicinity of 87° S, 116°50' E on the polar plateau. On this basis, Byrd assumed that the buried ridge must be at least 200 miles long.[10] The heating systems on the planes had failed, causing the men to suffer from $-40°$ F cold as well as from lack of oxygen (hypoxia). At 5 a. m. February 16, calculations of navigator Lieutenant (jg) Robert P. Heekin showed the plane to be over the Pole, and Byrd dropped a cardboard box containing the flags of all the members of the United Nations. After circling the Pole, the course continued on a straight line, now north, along the 0° meridian for 90 miles to 88°30′ S before turning east to 45° E and then returning on an easterly course, by which they descended to the Ross Ice Shelf over the mountains between Shackleton and Beardmore Glaciers. Shortly before noon, February 16, the planes landed at Little America.

The remaining part of the flight program concerned the photographing of the mountains of Victoria Land along the west side of the Ross Sea and the Ross Ice Shelf. Hopes to extend the range of the planes into the unknown land beyond by establishing a gasoline cache at McMurdo Sound had to be abandoned when the *Northwind*, designated for this task, had to be diverted to lead the supply ships and the *Mount Olympus* back through the pack ice upon their early departure from the Bay of Whales. In the meantime the icebreaker *Burton Island*, which had departed from San Diego on January 17, had reached the northern edge of the Ross Sea pack ice on February 6, entered the pack, and assisted the *Northwind* in escorting the ships to open water. On February 13, having completed this task, the *Burton Island*, with Admiral Cruzen aboard, headed for McMurdo Sound where she remained from February 16 to 20, acting as a weather station for the flight program.

The aerial photography program for Victoria Land was begun on February 17, but the first two planes (V-6 and V-1), after heading southwest over the Ross Ice Shelf, were turned back by engine trouble before reaching the mountains. A third plane (V-3) turned back when it ran into overcast and unpromising weather. A fourth (V-2), flown by Commander Hawkes with Lieutenant (jg) Erwin Spencer as co-pilot, however, made one of the most successful flights of the entire program. Hawkes flew southwest toward the foot of Beardmore Glacier, but short of that goal headed westward across the Queen Alexandra Range. Clouds barring the way to the westward beyond the mountains, Hawkes turned north and flew along the west side of the mountains which overlook the Ross Ice Shelf and which form a segment of the Transantarctic Mountains. Near the beginning of this northward leg of the flight and flanked by 13,000-foot Mount Markham on the south, Hawkes discovered what Admiral Byrd considered to be the largest known glacier.[11] This is Nimrod Glacier. Lucy and Marsh Glaciers and several smaller glaciers merge with the upper part of Nimrod Glacier to form a great fan-shaped mass of flowing ice more than 35 statute miles across. Nimrod Glacier merges with the Ross Ice Shelf in Shackleton Inlet. South of the 78th parallel the course was changed to the right, across the Royal Society Range toward Mount Erebus on Ross Island. Hawkes flew as near this active volcano as he dared and then followed the edge of the Ross Ice Shelf to Little America. Many new cracks and embayments were noticed in the edge of the shelf between Ross Island and Discovery Inlet.

Bad weather prevented any more flying until February 20. Although the weather was cloudy at Little America, the meteorologists, on the basis of reports from the far-flung ships of the expedition, predicted that the weather would probably be clear over Victoria Land, and Hawkes, with Lieutenant Anderson as co-pilot, again headed westward. A second plane, flown by Lieutenant Martin with Herbert Salyer as co-pilot, followed an hour later. Hawkes entered Victoria Land over Cape Murray (79°35' S, 160°10' E), with Mount McClintock (10,530 ft.) standing out as a landmark a short distance south. Again, 50 miles inland, clouds barred the way to the west, and Hawkes turned north for about 100 miles along the 155° E meridian and then east to the head of Ferrar Glacier to the tie-in with the photography of his February 17 flight. Hawkes directed Martin by radio to fly up the east side of the mountains on a photographic run while he photographed the west side as far north as Terra Nova Bay. This gave full photographic coverage to the many "dry valleys" resulting from local deglaciation that were seen on the flight.[12] These areas bare of ice and snow also exhibited a gigantic polygonal pattern typical of the tundra of the Arctic, apparently the result of frost action.

While two planes of the Central Group were over Victoria Land, a third R4D, flown by Major Weir, with an airborne magnetometer, made a special flight to the east over the Alexandra Mountains and the Rockefeller Mountains of the Edward VII Peninsula. The magnetometer had been adapted for geological exploration from the antisubmarine magnetic airborne detector developed during World War II and was being tested in Antarctica by Dr. James R. Balsley of the U. S. Geological Survey. The results were considered successful and highly promising for future investigation of bedrock even though buried by glacial ice.

The Rockefeller Mountains were also visited by a tractor party from Little America which started out on February 12 to set up an emergency aircraft fuel cache and weather outpost about 300 miles southeast of the main base. The exact position was to be determined by existing surface conditions in the area. The journey was made in two amphibious landing vehicles, tracked LVTs, by a party of seven men consisting of Captain Vernon D. Boyd, leader and navigator, First Lieutenant R. B. Thompson, in charge of LVT operation and photography, Major Dan Crozier, medical officer and weather observer, Chief Warrant Officer A. J. L. Morency, Technical Sergeant J. L. Thomas, Technical Sergeant G. H. Bigelow, and T. W. McGovern, radio operator. Boyd and Morency were veterans of the U. S. Antarctic Service Expedition, 1939-41, and Boyd had also been a member of the party which established a seismic station on Mount Franklin in the Rockefeller Mountains in 1940. This earlier experience proved valuable, for in 1947 the magnetic compass on the leading LVT did not function properly, a situation to be expected in this high latitude, and overcast made the astrocompass useless part of the time. As a consequence, a great part of the outward journey was made by dead reckoning. The open hatches of the LVTs were roofed over to provide protection and living quarters for the men. Each LVT pulled a sled loaded with five tons, and the lead vehicle also trailed a smaller sled carrying emergency equipment for the party. Sledge meters were also attached to this trailer, which also had a shelter for the protection of the man placing the trail flags at quarter-mile intervals.

PLATE XVII. An R4D aircraft taking off at Little America IV. This plane of the Base Group of "Operation Highjump" is using JATO (Jet Assist Take Off) in taking off from the compacted snow runway. Navy Dept., Photo No. 80-G-614096 in the National Archives.

PLATE XVIII-A. Crew of the seaplane tender U. S. S. *Currituck* is recovering Baker-3 seaplane after the flight of February 13, 1947. (See p. 504.) Navy Dept., Photo No. 80-G-60977 in the National Archives.

PLATE XVIII-B. Seaplane tender U. S. S. *Pine Island* in the lee of a tabular iceberg in the Amundsen Sea, January 24, 1947. Note the difference in the amount of pack ice on the two sides of the iceberg. (See p. 510.) Navy Dept., Photo No. 80-G-611426 in the National Archives.

On February 16, while the party was camped in sight of the Rockefeller Mountains, they received a message to return to Little America because flight plans had been changed. They were given permission to cache their gasoline and supplies at the base of Washington Ridge. Completing this task, the entire party rode one of the vehicles to the summits of Washington Ridge and Mount Franklin to collect geological specimens. Early on February 18 the party set out for Little America, where they arrived about 4 p. m., February 19. A number of times in the journey the vehicles had successfully crossed crevasses as much as 10 feet wide.

The flights of February 20 proved to be the last successful ones by the Central Group. Two planes attempted a flight to the southeast on February 22 to tie together the photography from previous flights over the Horlick Mountains, but they were turned back short of their goal by bad weather.

The icebreaker *Burton Island* left McMurdo Sound on February 20, following the conclusion of the flights over Victoria Land, and at 5:30 a. m., February 22, arrived at the Bay of Whales. Admirals Byrd and Cruzen decided on a rapid evacuation. After the planes and all heavy equipment and supplies had been secured for future use, smaller equipment, supplies, expedition records and personal gear were put aboard. Late on February 23 the last group arrived from Little America, and the *Burton Island* sailed out of the Bay of Whales. The belt of pack ice was easily traversed in about 48 hours, and early on February 26 the *Burton Island* came beside the *Mount Olympus,* which had been cruising in the vicinity of Scott Island since February 13, at which time the *Northwind, Yancey,* and *Merrick* had sailed for New Zealand. Personnel were transferred to the *Mount Olympus* from the *Burton Island* and both vessels got under way for New Zealand, where they arrived early in March.

OPERATIONS OF THE WESTERN TASK GROUP

Following the rendezvous at the Marquesas Islands on December 12 the three ships of the Western Task Group proceeded south on tracks 50 miles apart to obtain parallel bathymetric profiles with their sonic sounding apparatus. The first iceberg was sighted on December 23, and early the next morning the ships reached the edge of the pack ice northeast of the Balleny Islands. The weather was calm and clear, and operations were begun at once.[13]

These initial operations in the vicinity of the Ballenys were to a considerable extent experimental, for no member of the Western Task Group had ever been in the Antarctic before and few had ever seen pack ice or an iceberg. The destroyer *Henderson* and the tanker *Cacapon* fanned out to serve as weather stations with orders to radio reports to the *Currituck* every three hours. The seaplane tender carried three Martin Mariner flying boats (PBMs), a smaller seaplane (SOC) and two helicopters. One of the flying boats had its wings detached and was never used. For operational purposes, the other two Martin Mariners were designated Baker-1 and Baker-3. The first plane was sent out to the northwest to scout the weather, and a helicopter was also sent aloft on a reconnaissance mission. The *Currituck* spent the next several days lying to, fogbound in an embayment in the pack ice.

On January 1, 1947, while the seaplane tender was lying to in about 64° 17' S, 161° 14' E, a mass of cold and dry polar air surged out from the continent, bringing clear weather. Lieutenant Commander Bunger and his crew took off in Baker-1 and flew over the Balleny Islands toward the continent. Meanwhile the *Currituck* steamed eastward to stay in the cold air mass. Bunger had flown almost halfway to the continent when clouds barred the way. On the return flight half of the Balleny Islands were clear and were photographed. The plane landed at 8:30 p. m., local time, after a flight of 4½ hours. The good weather continued, and the next day two planes were launched. They photographed part of the Balleny Islands and continued to the Oates Coast. The crews saw many mountains, some estimated to be 10,000 feet high, but the photographs were too much obscured by clouds to be useful.

After a day of unsatisfactory weather, two planes were again able to take off on January 4 on photographic missions. The Ballenys were clouded over, but the planes were able to operate along the coast of the continent, where the crews experienced difficulty with hypoxia at 13,000 feet in spite of oxygen equipment. On January 5 Lieutenant Commander Bunger flew Baker-3 with Captain Charles A. Bond, Task Group Commander, as observer. On completion of this eight-hour flight, shortly after midnight January 6 (local time), the Western Task Group had photographed the coastline from Smith Inlet on the Oates Coast westward to a short distance west of Cape Freshfield on the George V Coast. A belt of open water of varying width appeared between the pack ice and the coast, but it was extremely difficult to distinguish between land ice and sea ice. On January 6 Lieutenant William R. Kreitzer, with Captain John E. Clark of the *Currituck* as observer, flew Baker-1 inland over the Oates Coast to about 71° S along 160° E, returning north along 157° E.

The photographic missions of the Western Task Group were suspended on January 6 when Admiral Cruzen requested the *Currituck* to steam eastward to the Ross Sea, from whence it could launch one or two of the PBMs for long reconnaissance flights south over the pack ice to assist the Central Task Group in breaking through to the Bay of Whales. The *Henderson* and *Cacapon* remained north of the George V Coast to serve as weather stations. Stormy or overcast weather prevented these flights from being carried out until January 11, when two planes took off and flew south to the ships of the Central Group, only to be ordered back because of a low ceiling and icing of the wings. The next day the two planes were launched again and flew south on flight tracks 10 miles apart, continuing about 75 miles south of the Central Group to about 73° S in spite of a ceiling of from 400 to 500 feet. On January 13 Admiral Cruzen dismissed the *Currituck* to resume its photographic missions off the George V Coast.

When on January 16 the *Currituck* had reached its new operating area in about 64°54' S, 148°34' E, north of the Ninnis Glacier Tongue, fog, drizzle, and snow prevented any flying. The *Henderson* was stationed 300 miles to the westward, and the *Cacapon,* which normally would have been from 300 to 400 miles to the northwest, was ordered to proceed to Scott Island for a rendezvous with the carrier *Philippine Sea* to pick up mail and cargo, including survival gear for the PBMs, destined for the Western Task Group. For several days bad weather prevented the flying boats from being launched. On January 21 the *Henderson* reported the approach of a polar high and the attendant clear weather, and the *Currituck* steamed westward to meet it.

On January 22 the promised clear weather arrived, but it was of short duration. Both planes were in the air by 8:15 a. m., local time. Lieutenant Commander Bunger in Baker-1 photographed the coast from 136° E to 129°30' E. The continental slope upward from the coast was gradual and featureless, and the actual shoreline was difficult to determine. Lieutenant Commander William J. Rogers, Jr. flew Baker-3 south for an estimated 380 miles over the continent, through a great deal of clouds. While the planes were away, the *Cacapon,* en route to the Ross Sea from its position to the northwest, drew alongside to take on mail and fuel the *Currituck*. Before the planes could return, bad weather, including a heavy snowfall, set in. By 4:00 p. m., both planes were aboard.

There was still a considerable photographic gap to the eastward, and the *Currituck* steamed in that direction looking for a somewhat sheltered area in which to launch the planes when the high wind subsided. At 11:50 on January 23 the bottom began to shoal rapidly to 45 fathoms. A hand line was used to get bottom samples of mud and sand at 55 fathoms. As the *Currituck* steamed slowly eastward, on January 24 she passed a Japanese whale catcher, a floating factory, and a tanker. During the early operations off Oates Coast, while these vessels were to the westward, their weather reports had proven useful.

Instead of improving, the weather deteriorated and wind velocities increased, causing Captain Bond to reverse his course. He decided to seek better conditions to the west of 130° E, with the hope of completing the photography between 138° E and 151° E from the new location. During the night of January 25, the *Currituck* lay to in an ice embayment in about 65°09' S, 137°05' E, with a cluster of weathered bergs to the south, but by morning the high winds had broken up the pack, forcing the ship to continue probing to the westward on January 26. Conditions began to improve during the day, and by 6:00 p. m. Lieutenant Kreitzer was in the air with Baker-1 on a flight east as far as Commonwealth Bay. The photographs showed the drifting caused by the catabatic winds in this area, so aptly named the "Home of the Blizzard" by Sir Douglas Mawson in 1914, and now considered to be the windiest place in the Antarctic.

On the morning of January 27 two planes were launched. Lieutenant Commander Rogers piloted Baker-3 inland over the continent for 110 miles to a point where the ice surface reached 7500 feet. Turning westward for 60 miles, he then flew back to the coast west of Porpoise Bay which was obscured by clouds. Then he made a reconnaissance of the pack ice for 100 miles to the west before returning to the ship about 1:00 p. m. The pack, in which there were many grounded bergs, was 60 miles wide. Baker-1, with Lieutenant Commander Bunger at the controls, flew inland to about 68°18' S, 138°15' E, where the radar altimeter recorded an elevation of the ice cap of 8500 feet. Bunger returned to the coast at Commonwealth Bay (142°40' E), and finding ceiling and visibility unlimited, turned eastward to Mertz Glacier Tongue, which could be seen dimly on the radar screen before clouds barred the way.

At this point Captain Bond decided to continue the *Currituck* westward in the hope of finding better weather and less trouble with the swell from the north, which often prevented launching or hoisting the planes at times when other conditions were satisfactory. This decision meant that the photographic gap from Cook Ice Shelf to Commonwealth Bay could not be completed. By noon, January 28, the *Currituck*'s position was 64°58' S, 124°51' E. A bay in the pack ice was discovered a short distance to the westward, and from it the planes took off in late afternoon on photographic missions. The planes were tracked on the ship's radar as they flew along the coast, enabling the operators to plot in the coastline on their charts with a fair degree of accuracy. Lieutenant Commander Rogers in Baker-3 photographed the coast from 122° E to 130° E and in the process completed a rectangular course inland over the ice cap to 68°25' S, where it rose to 6500 feet. The coast was essentially featureless, marked mostly by an ice cliff. Lieutenant Kreitzer piloted Baker-1 on a photographic flight covering the coast from 112° E to 125° E. The major features discovered on this stretch of coast, which was originally charted by Wilkes from shipboard in 1840, were Paulding Bay and Totten Glacier. Shortly after midnight on January 29 both planes were back aboard after flights which had each lasted approximately five hours. For the rest of that day the *Currituck* lay to with winds too high and too much brash to permit additional launchings. On the afternoon of January 30, however, Baker-3 was launched and Bunger made a flight along the coast from 127° E to 115° E to fill in areas missed, due to camera failure, on the previous flights. Turning inland, he flew along the 115th meridian to 68° S, where the ice cap reached an elevation of 4500 feet. He flew east along this parallel to about 118° E and then returned to the ship. A warm front began moving in with a northwest wind and the weather became overcast, forcing the *Currituck* to lay to until February 1 in about 64°47' S, 119°52' E.

While in this position, on the morning of February 1 an encouraging southeast breeze sprang up, and Lieutenant Kreitzer took off in Baker-1 at 8:07 a. m. on a flight over the Budd Coast. At 9:35 he was forced to return when he lost a piece of engine cowling. This turned out to be fortunate, for shortly after he landed a bad swell set in and the weather became cloudy. The *Currituck* steamed westward until the next morning, hoping to avoid the swell.

Late on the afternoon of February 2 both planes flew again from a position north of Budd Coast. Bunger piloted Baker-3 eastward, but found most of the coast hidden in low-lying clouds. The radar altimeter, however, confirmed the existence of Reynolds Trough, discovered on a previous flight. Kreitzer in Baker-1, on the other hand, made one of the most significant discoveries of the entire expedition. He photographed the coast from 114° E westward to 105° E, confirming the dome-like shape of Budd Coast which is suggested by Wilkes' chart of 1840. Four large glaciers were discovered, but more significant was the discovery of an ice-free area of the Budd Coast on the east side of Vincennes Bay. These rocky islands and promontories, now called Windmill Islands as a result of their having been the site of a ground control survey by "Operation Windmill" in 1948, appeared to Kreitzer to be a good place to land, once the ship was able to get through the pack ice. A belt of open water lay between the coast and the pack. Kreitzer's appraisal was prophetic, for the Windmill Islands became the site of the United States' Wilkes Station during the International Geophysical Year, 1957-58.

After the planes were recovered on the evening of February 2, Captain Bond decided to reverse his course and steam eastward again in an effort to follow the outburst of polar air which had provided the good flying weather. The next morning, however, a warm front had caught up with and enveloped the *Currituck* in fog. Calling the *Henderson* in, Captain Bond now decided to steam northwest to clear the front and rendezvous with the destroyer approaching from the west. Refueling and provisioning the *Henderson* was completed just after midnight of February 5, and both vessels headed westward, meeting six Norwegian whale catchers and a floating factory.

Another polar air mass brought fine weather on February 7, and, as usual, the *Currituck* tried to follow it eastward. Although the weather was clear, strong winds or a heavy swell prevented the planes from being launched. On February 8 the *Cacapon* was met on its return from the Ross Sea. The *Currituck* was fueled and received cargo transshipped from the *Philippine Sea*. The tanker then refueled the *Henderson* and took up position as a weather station about 400 miles northwest of the *Currituck*. This function was now more important than ever because operations had moved so far westward as to make the Australian weather reports useless. Meanwhile the *Currituck* was riding out a 45-knot wind.

On February 10 the *Currituck* headed westward again and then south to skirt the edge of the pack, meeting the British factory ship *Balaena* and a flotilla of whale catchers. February 11 brought clear weather, a 12- to 20- knot west-southwest wind and a temperature of 24° F. By 10:00 a. m. both planes were airborne. Lieutenant Commander Bunger piloted Baker-1 south along the east side of Shackleton Ice Shelf, discovering an ice-free area of about 20 square miles in extent in about 66°18′ S, 100°45′ E. The rolling surface consisted of bare rock liberally strewn with boulders and morainic deposits left as the ice front melted back from the area. Pools of meltwater occupied depressions in this hummocky surface, the water being colored brown, red, or green by accumulations of algae. This ice-free area was originally given considerable publicity as Bunger's Oasis and is now officially named Bunger Hills. Some of the "lakes" are actually inlets of seawater partially dammed by glacial ice.

From this unusual area at the eastern end of the Knox Coast, Bunger flew westward to Gaussberg, the extinct volcano on Wilhelm II Coast, 66°48′ S, 89°12′ E, and beyond to the eastern edge of the West Ice Shelf. The southern part of Davis Sea was open, but the outer portion was blocked by pack ice. Lieutenant Commander Rogers, flying Baker-3, at first ran into low-lying clouds over the coast. Changing his course, he got his bearings over Denman Glacier and then flew inland 75 miles, where the ice cap reached an elevation of 6000 feet. Nunataks near the coast rose to elevations of 5000 feet, and some not on the chart were photographed. The photographs also helped to delineate the coast east of Shackleton Ice Shelf. By 6:48 p. m. both planes were back on board.

When the weather closed in again as the *Currituck* was steaming westward at 15 knots to a new point of operations, Captain Bond decided on a drastic change in the plan of operations. He proposed to move rapidly westward to the vicinity of Amundsen Bay on the west side of Enderby Land, flying only if weather permitted and covering only the coastal areas. From Amundsen Bay he would move eastward with the clear weather of polar highs. Thus with long-er spells of good weather he hoped to be able to make flights inland as well as fill in gaps in the coastal photography. He hoped thereby to gain time to make a landing to investigate the ice-free area discovered by Lieutenant Kreitzer on the east side of Vincennes Bay (Windmill Islands).

While steaming westward in accord with this new plan, with the destroyer and tanker in their usual role of weather outposts, the *Currituck* ran into good flying conditions north of Davis Sea on February 13. First Baker-3 took off at 8:45 a. m. on a weather reconnaissance flight to the northwest. Captain Bond flew with Lieutenant Kreitzer. A favorable radio report from Kreitzer sent Bung-er aloft in Baker-1 at 10:30. He flew south along 91° E to 69° S, where the ice cap reached an elevation of 8300 feet on the radar altimeter. Turning east, he flew to the 94th meridian and then north to the coast. He then flew east along the coast to fill in some gaps previously missed in the photography. When he reached the Bunger Hills, he set the plane down on one of the larger lakes. A crew member obtained a sample of the water, which when analyzed later was found to be sea water.

Meanwhile Baker-3 had returned from the weather reconnaissance and headed south along the 88th meridian when the coast to the westward was found clouded in. At 69° S the plane turned west over the ice cap, which here was 8000 feet above sea level. The 85th meridian was followed to the coast, which was still shrouded in fog and mist. Except for long SE-NW sastrugi, the inland area of the ice cap appeared featureless. Near the coast, crevasses marked the depressions, and swells in the surface formed as the ice flowed over the ir-regularities of the underlying bedrock. By 8:00 p. m. both planes had been hoisted aboard, and the *Currituck* was steaming westward at 15 knots. The me-teorologists forecast no flying for 36 hours. Off the West Ice Shelf a great many old, weathered icebergs enshrouded in fog caused the ship's speed to be cut to 5 to 10 knots.

The next flights were made on February 22, by which date the *Currituck* had steamed eastward almost a quarter of the way around the continent to the Princess Ragnhild Coast. High winds, foul weather, or a heavy swell in good weather had prevented any planes being launched en route westward. On this passage, seamen on the *Currituck* got their first view of the Antarctic continent off the Kemp Coast on February 17. It was the first land they had seen since mid-December. On February 18 the ship rounded Cape Ann, Enderby Land. On the 19th Admiral Cruzen radioed an order to continue mapping to the westward to the limit of safe operations, before returning eastward. The end of operations was to be determined by the weather. As a result, the *Currituck* headed farther west, proposing to find suitable conditions for launching the planes to the westward or in the lee of Gunnerus Bank, where it was hoped the swell would be less dangerous. This objective was reached late on February 21.

On the morning of February 22 the *Currituck* lay in about 67°42′ S, 34°15′ E. Winds were light and variable and scattered clouds dotted the sky. At 9:55 Lieutenant Kreitzer took off in Baker-1 on a flight to the westward. He discovered that the coast was fringed by a belt of shelf ice 30 to 45 miles wide and thus had been incorrectly plotted on charts. The land rose from the coast in a series of ice falls to the 10,000-foot Sør Rondane Mountains, which act as a dam for the glacial ice behind them. The ice pours down between the peaks in great glaciers. From his altimeter Kreitzer estimated that the mountains rose to an elevation of 13,000 feet. During the flight the coast was mapped from 34° E to 15° E. Baker-3, delayed by mechanical difficulties, took off shortly after noon with Rogers at the controls and flew southeastward along Prince Harald Coast along the west side of Lützow-Holm Bay. Rogers flew as far east as 50° E, but between 40° E and 50° E the coast could be seen only by means of radar. He had been able to photograph the south and west sides of Amundsen Bay but not the east side. Both planes were back aboard before 10:00 p. m.

The three vessels of the Western Task Group now got under way eastward, Captain Bond hoping the *Currituck* would be able to operate off the Kemp Coast by February 25. Off Enderby Land the *Currituck* ran into a snow storm and a 45-knot wind which coated the ship with frozen spray. By sunset on February 25 the ship was off the Kemp Coast. The weather cleared in the afternoon, but the northeast swell was too heavy. The next morning conditions were satisfactory, and Baker-3, with Rogers as pilot, took off at 7:50. He started west over Enderby Land in an attempt to tie in the photography of February 22 at Amundsen Bay. He was turned back shortly by clouds at about 56° E, and reversing his course eastward, he photographed the coast to 70° E, where clouds again barred the way. Radar operators had been able to follow the plane for 100 miles, making it possible to plot the position of the coast from the ship. While Rogers was in flight, the *Currituck* had steamed eastward, hoping to keep ahead of an approaching storm front, but as the plane was being hoisted at 4:10 p. m., the front caught up with the ship.

On February 27, however, the weather was fine again. Winds were easterly and southerly; the temperature ranged from 20° to 25° F and the sea was smooth. The ship had reached a position at the edge of the pack near Fram Bank, 67°18′ S, 70°00′ E. At 2:33 p. m. Bunger took off in Baker-1, followed 45 minutes later by Kreitzer in Baker-3. Bunger ran into thick weather along the eastern shore of the Mackenzie Bay and as a result could not distinguish the shoreline. Kreitzer flew well inland along the Lars Christensen Coast on the land side of the Amery Ice Shelf. His flight carried him to almost 70° S, 74° E, where the ice cap rose to 8000 feet. One new mountain range, presumably the Prince Charles Mountains, and several small peaks were reported south of Prydz Bay, but because the film magazine of the trimetrogon camera froze up, the features were plotted in by radar. About six hours after taking off, he was back at the ship.

The *Currituck* remained in the vicinity of Prydz Bay on February 28. The weather was clear but windy and the temperature was −6° F. The season was drawing to a close. On the last launching the boats used by the launching crews iced up shortly after hitting the water.

On March 1 the last flights were made. Baker-1 returned from two attempts because of a broken gas line, but Baker-3 succeeded in photographing the Ingrid Christensen Coast, including another ice-free area, the Vestfold Hills, that had been discovered by Klarius Mikkelsen in 1935.

With Baker-3 back on board, the *Currituck* headed northward on the evening of March 1. Captain Bond issued orders for the return voyage, and on March 3 all ships were in company. They proceeded separately to a rendezvous in Bass Strait from where they steamed in company to Sydney, Australia. While en route north, the *Currituck* rolled so violently in a severe storm on March 9 that the spare Martin Mariner flying boat broke loose and rolled overboard. Other minor damage was also sustained. The other two vessels, being on the edge of the storm, had no damage. On March 14, 1947, the three ships of the Western Task Group steamed into Sydney harbor.

OPERATIONS OF THE EASTERN TASK GROUP

The three ships of the Eastern Task Group, the seaplane tender *Pine Island,* the tanker *Canisteo,* and the destroyer *Brownson,* sailed from Balboa, Canal Zone, on December 10, 1946, in company with the command ship and flagship of the expedition *Mount Olympus,* the icebreaker *Northwind,* and the submarine *Sennet.* As in the case of the ships which sailed from California ports, they soon dispersed to stations on tracks 50 miles apart so as to obtain a series of bathymetric profiles with their sonic sounding instruments en route to the Antarctic. On December 17 in about 22°30′ S, 97°50′ W, the *Pine Island* and the *Brownson,* after refueling from the *Canisteo,* proceeded to the vicinity of Peter I Island, where they were to begin operations. The *Canisteo* continued with the ships of the Central Task Group to the vicinity of Scott Island and subsequently rejoined the Eastern Task Group.

The ships experienced unusually fine weather in the passage south. The first iceberg was sighted on December 24 in about 62°41′ S, 99°30′ W, much farther south than expected and an indication that 1946-47 was likely to be a difficult year for ice navigation. Later that day the *Brownson* was ordered to take a position 200 miles west of the *Pine Island* to serve as a weather station and emergency seadrome. At 5:00 a. m. (local time, December 25) the Antarctic Circle was crossed at 100°35′ W. Open pack ice was met 27 nautical miles farther south. Following an ice reconnaissance flight by one of the helicopters, the *Pine Island* was moved to an ice bay in the lee of a large iceberg a few miles farther west, where conditions were satisfactory for launching the flying boats. Aircraft carried by the *Pine Island* were similar to those on the *Currituck.* For operational purposes the Martin Mariner flying boats (PBMs) aboard the *Pine Island* were designated George-1, George-2, and George-3.

The first PBM was launched early on December 26, but an accident to the port wing tip float caused it to be hoisted on board again. The weather began to deteriorate and for several days continued unsatisfactory for flying. By noon, December 29, it had cleared sufficiently to permit the launching of George-1. Flight tests were completed, and with Lieutenant Commander John D. Howell as pilot and Captain George J. Dufek, Task Group Commander, as observer, the plane departed at 2:35 p. m. (local time) for the Antarctic continent on the first photographic and exploratory flight of the expedition. They reached the coast near Cape Flying Fish at the tip of Thurston Island and flew in over Peacock Sound and the Demas Ice Tongue, features discovered by Admiral Byrd in a flight from the U.S.S. *Bear* February 24, 1940, and sighted by Dufek on a second flight the next day.[14] As a result of the 1940 flights, the coastline was only roughly charted; a detailed delineation of the coast was impossible before the photography of 1947.

When a radio report of favorable weather over the continent was received from George-1, George-2 was launched and took off on a photographic flight at 6:35 p. m. with Lieutenant (jg) James L. Ball at the controls. Ball covered part of the area photographed by George-1, and additional territory to the east and south.

George-1 returned to the ship shortly after 11:00 p. m., and although there were signs that the weather was deteriorating slightly, it was decided to make another flight immediately. Consequently, George-1 remained on the water to be refueled and given a mechanical check. About 2:45 a. m. she took off with a new crew consisting of Lieutenant (jg) Ralph Paul LeBlanc, pilot, Lieutenant (jg) William H. Kearns, Jr., co-pilot, Ensign Maxwell Lopez, navigator, Wendell K. Hendersin, radio operator, Frederick W. Williams, engineer, Owen McCarty, photographer, William Warr, mechanic, and James Robbins, radio operator. Captain Henry Howard Caldwell of the *Pine Island* went along as an observer. Several of these men had had experience in the Arctic, and except for Williams, who was new, the crew had had considerable experience as a flying unit.[15]

While George-1 was en route south the weather began to deteriorate. After three hours of flight they were in sight of the continent, but by then the ceiling was down to 1000 to 500 feet with the sky completely overcast. Visibility was less than two miles. At 6:08 a. m. the *Pine Island* lost radio contact with the plane when it was in the plotted position of 71°22′ S, 99°30′ W. The plane had by then encountered a "white-out," that condition where light is so diffused between the overcast above and the snow below that there are no shadows and the horizon is obliterated. Under such conditions depth perception is almost impossible and one cannot judge distances. This is one of the greatest hazards which aviators face in the Antarctic, for without a horizon they cannot judge how high above the ground they are flying. (See Plate XXI-B.)

As George-1 reached the coast, conditions became extremely grave. Kearns, who had relieved LeBlanc, climbed from the 600- to the 1000-foot level. Due to icing, the plane was sluggish, and the altimeters registered inconsistently. Peering through snow squalls, the men thought they saw land rising up into the overcast ahead of them. Kearns decided to turn back and made a shallow left turn. Suddenly there was a crunching sound and a sharp jolt as the plane's hull scraped the surface and then bounded into the air. Immediately Kearns pulled more to the left and gave it full throttle, but in another instant the plane exploded. The plane was torn apart and all but LeBlanc were thrown clear of the burning wreckage of the forward part of the plane. Robbins, Warr, and Kearns quickly regained their senses; although Kearns had a broken arm, they succeeded in rescuing the semiconscious Le Blanc, who was still strapped in the burning cockpit. Captain Caldwell, who had been blown clear with the nose section, soon came to. McCarty lay unconscious with a large gash in his head. Hendersin and Lopez were killed, and Williams died two hours later. The survivors sought shelter in the tunnel section of the after fuselage, which had been blown clear of the burning wreckage. Here the men lay for a day and a half in a shock-induced stupor. Later the able-bodied searched the wreckage for emergency gear and food supplies, most of which, except for medical supplies, had been thrown clear. Two tents were rigged for living quarters, but the disabled LeBlanc and Kearns remained in the tunnel section. The men remained here for 13 days, hopeful, if not confident, of rescue. While the weather remained bad, they knew planes could not reach them. As the atmosphere cleared, their anxiety increased, although they knew that conditions would also have to be satisfactory at the ship before a flight could be made. During these days Captain Caldwell's composure and leadership was a strong factor in maintaining the men's morale.

Back at the *Pine Island* the anxiety at losing radio contact with George-1 was heightened when the plane became overdue and the persistent efforts of the radio operators failed to re-establish contact. At 5:41 a. m., December 30, shortly before contact had been lost with George-1, George-2 returned from its photographic mission and was hoisted aboard. The weather was closing in fast, and further flights were out of the question. A desperate impatience arose aboard ship as the weather continued bad for the next several days. Meanwhile the wings were assembled on George-3, which was made ready for flight. Signs of clearing resulted in two different attempts at flying, but in each case the weather closed in before takeoff. Finally at 5:00 p. m., January 5, George-3 was able to take off on a search flight, but the weather closed in to the south, forcing a return to the ship. George-3 was able to make a flight south again the next day, but again the weather closed in over the continent. On this flight, however, 100 additional miles of coastline were photographed. On each of the next three days, attempted flights had to be canceled.

On January 10 Captain Dufek decided to move the *Pine Island* westward to 67°00′ S, 104°00′ W in search of better weather, and the hoped-for improvement arrived the next day. At 6:41 a. m., January 11, Lieutenants (jg) James L. Ball and Robert G. Goff took off in George-2 on a flight in search of the missing plane. They passed over the wreckage without seeing it on the outward flight, but on the return noticed the smoke plume from a fire the men had lighted to attract their attention. Food and supplies were dropped for the survivors and a report of the rescue was radioed to the *Pine Island*. A message was also dropped to the men informing them that open water existed about 10 miles to the north, and when they signaled they could walk that far, the plane crew dropped flags marking the way. At that point, George-2 had to return to the ship because of its dwindling fuel supply.

Upon receipt of the message from George-2, Lieutenant Commander John D. Howell took off in George-3. By 1½ hours after George-2 had departed from Thurston Island on which the survivors were located about 10 miles from the coast in about 98°47′ W, George-3 had sighted the wreckage. Meanwhile the survivors, having placed LeBlanc on a sled, were slowly trudging through deep snow to the open water. Howell received permission to land, and he and Richard Conger set out to meet the men desperately struggling through waist-deep snow and across crevasses in traversing the slope down to the shore. Suffering extreme fatigue, the men continued to struggle against time, for they could see a heavy fog bank closing in from the north. With the aid of their rescuers on the last part of the trek, they finally reached the shore, having covered the 10 miles in about 12 hours. The fog had settled down over the plane, and it was another eight hours before the weather cleared sufficiently to permit it to take off for the *Pine Island*. At 10:44 a. m., on January 12, the plane landed beside the ship. Shortly thereafter the weather closed down, and for the next 10 days flying was impossible.

The original plan called for the Eastern Task Group to continue operations to the eastward, but Admiral Byrd, with Admiral Cruzen's consent, requested that the coast from Mount Siple to the Thurston Peninsula also be photographed. That coastline had only been seen from a distance, and as a consequence the coast as sketched in on the chart was not reliable. Meanwhile, the destroyer *Brownson* had been ordered to proceed to the Ross Sea to serve as a rescue station for any of the six R4Ds that might be forced down in flying from the carrier *Philippine Sea* to the Ross Sea. On January 17 the *Brownson* joined the *Pine Island* and both ships proceeded southwestward. The next day five of the survivors of the crash of George-1 (Captain Caldwell remained in command of the *Pine Island*) were transferred to the *Brownson* as that ship departed for the Ross Sea. Here the survivors were taken aboard the *Philippine Sea* for transfer to the United States.[16]

The weather cleared up slightly on the afternoon of January 19, and a helicopter flight was made with Captain Dufek as an observer to look for a suitable place in the edge of the pack ice to launch the planes. The ceiling closed down before the helicopter returned to the ship, resulting in severe icing on the rotor blades and making it necessary to crash land the craft beside the *Pine Island*. Personnel were rescued, but the helicopter was lost.

Following the ice reconnaissance flight, the *Pine Island* proceeded northwestward and then skirted the pack along the 67th parallel to 120° W. Heavy weather had opened the pack sufficiently to permit the ship to reach a position of 68°13′ S, 119°34′ W on January 22, its farthest south to that date. The next morning the ship moved to the lee of a large iceberg nearby, where the water was found to be fairly smooth and free of floating ice. On the evening of January 23 two planes took off for the south from 68°13' S, 119°31' W on a flight to the coast. George-3, commanded by Howell, photographed the coast westward to the Getz Ice Shelf and then flew northeast over Wrigley Gulf, passing Mount Siple on the northwest, on the return to the ship. George-2, commanded by Ball, photographed the coast eastward to about 110° W. After these two successful flights it was decided to move eastward again to avoid the swell and brash ice which were much worse in the Amundsen Sea than they had been north of Thurston Island.

The *Pine Island* moved eastward and by 8:20 p. m., January 25, reached a position of 68°40' S, 106°17' W. The heavy weather and snow squalls which had set in even before the planes had been recovered from the last flight on the morning of January 24 still held forth, and the *Pine Island* lay to in this new position waiting for conditions to improve. Early on the morning of January 26 the weather began clearing, and the two planes were launched for photographic flights to the south. When they returned early in the afternoon of January 26, they had closed the photographic gap between 105° W and Thurston Island. The coastline had now been photographed from 95°30' W to 127°30' W, but there were gaps in the photography. The belt of pack ice was so broad that the PBMs were unable to go far inland after reaching the coast without exceeding their range. On such an irregular coast this was a serious handicap to accurate delineation, especially with no ground control available.

The next point of operations was to be Peter I Island. The *Pine Island* met and refueled from the *Canisteo* on January 27 and then both ships proceeded northeastward, the tanker subsequently being positioned at 102° W at the edge of the pack ice. On January 30 the *Pine Island* was 85 miles north of Peter I Island at the edge of the pack ice. General ice conditions and two short reconnaissance helicopter flights indicated that Peter I Island was surrounded by pack and inaccessible at this time. The ship lay to in this position in a heavy fog until February 2 and then began working eastward toward Marguerite Bay. The edge of the pack ice and brash ice forced the *Pine Island* to the east-northeast until late on February 5 when it was possible for the ship to work to the south. She lay to at the edge of the pack ice to the northwest of Charcot Island in about 69°46' S, 79° W at 10:00 p. m. on February 6. Heavy overcast and intermittent snow squalls prevented flying operations until the morning of February 8, when the two planes were launched. One was able to get over Charcot Island, but the weather closed down so quickly that both planes were forced to return to the ship, having been airborne only about two hours.

The next morning the weather was again satisfactory for flying, and the two planes were launched. Ball flew George-2 as far east as Marguerite Bay while Howell and his crew in George-3 photographed part of Charcot Island and the entire west side of Alexander Island, reaching the edge of the continent at Ronne Entrance of George VI Sound. As the weather began to close in during the afternoon, the planes were called in, and snow fell as they were being hoisted aboard.

While the planes were in flight, the *Brownson*, which had returned from the Ross Sea, transferred cargo and mail to the *Pine Island*. Encouraged by reports of the plane crews, Captain Dufek decided to attempt a landing on the north shore of Charcot Island. For that purpose he transferred to the *Brownson*, which worked south through ice floes on February 10. At 9:35 Dufek, Commander Gimber of the *Brownson*, and five others set out in a motorboat to attempt a landing. Dodging between floes, they got to within 500 yards of the shoreline, when the shifting pack prevented further progress. After the party returned, the ship continued to reconnoiter without finding a place where a landing might be attempted. On the afternoon of the 11th the *Brownson* began working north-eastward toward Rothschild Island, and the *Pine Island* was ordered to proceed to Marguerite Bay. As the destroyer cruised along the shore of Rothschild Island and then along the northern shore of Alexander Island, the radar-equipped fire control range finder was used to obtain angles on peaks and headlands to plot in land features on the chart.

The *Pine Island* and the *Brownson* rendezvoused off the southwestern coast of Adelaide Island on February 13. While they were waiting for the weather to improve before entering Marguerite Bay they were ordered by Admiral Cruzen, on February 14, to rendezvous and proceed in company to the Weddell Sea. The *Canisteo* joined the group at 66° S, 70° W, and the three ships set a course to the northeast which took them through Bransfield Strait. Passing to the north of the South Orkney Islands, the Task Group separated, with each ship proceeding separately to an assigned station on the 66th parallel. Overcast weather and fog prevailed a great deal of the time while the ships steamed across the outer margin of the Weddell Sea. There was much heavy pack ice, and on its outer margin much brash and drift ice. Such conditions were not conducive to flying, and away from the edge of the pack the seas were too heavy to permit launching the planes. On February 27 the *Pine Island* crossed the intersection of the prime meridian and the Antarctic Circle. The weather over the ship began to clear on February 28 as the *Pine Island* neared the junction of the Princess Martha and Princess Astrid Coasts. Both planes were launched on March 1 and again on March 2, but in each instance heavy cloud banks over the continent turned them back at the coast. The weather had been unsatisfactory for days, and at this time of the year there was little hope for improvement. On March 3 Admiral Cruzen ordered the Task Group to cease operations and proceed to Brazil.

On March 4 the Eastern Task Group departed from the Antarctic on a great circle course for Rio de Janeiro, which was reached on March 18. After a six-day stay at Rio, the ships sailed for their home ports in the United States. Ships of the Western Group which had called at Sydney, Australia, and of the Central Group which had called at New Zealand ports also were directed to their several stations in the United States.

NOTES

1. A Kellett autogyro, a precursor of the helicopter in vertical flight, was used by the Second Byrd Antarctic Expedition, 1933-35, for high altitude temperature soundings at Little America. Ten flights were made from September 1 until it crashed on September 25, 1934.

2. The five groups were (TG 68.1) The Central Group; (TG 68.2) The Western Group; (TG 68.3) The Eastern Group; (TG 68.4) The Carrier Group; and (TG 68.5) The Base Group.

3. R. H. Cruzen, Report of Operation Highjump, U. S. Navy Antarctic Developments Project 1947, June 10, 1947, Annex I-a, p. 7. This report is the primary source upon which the account is based.

4. C. W. Thomas, "Narrative U.S.C.G.C. Northwind (WAG 282)," *in* Report of Operation Highjump, *op. cit.,* Annex I-i, p. 2.

5. Paul A. Siple, "Glaciological Study of Bay of Whales Area," *Army Observers' Report of Operation Highjump, Task Force 68, U. S. Navy,* Washington, 1947, p. 392.

6. Rear Adm. Richard E. Byrd, "Our Navy Explores Antarctica," *National Geographic Magazine,* vol. 92, No. 4, October, 1947, pp. 484-485. This was possibly the Leverett Glacier.

7. The plane probably flew between the Wisconsin Range (7500 ft.) and the Ohio Range (8000 ft.) to the northeast of it and both part of the Horlick Mountains. At the turning point of the flight they were probably viewing the Thiel Mountains (7500 ft.).

8. *Ibid.,* p. 490.

9. *Ibid.,* p. 491.

10. *Ibid.,* p. 467.

11. *Ibid.,* pp. 473-479. Some clarification is necessary here. Shackleton Inlet, in which Nimrod Glacier terminates, was discovered by Capt. Robert F. Scott, Dr. Edward A. Wilson, and Lt. Ernest H. Shackleton, December 28-31, 1902, as they reached the end of their sledge journey on the Ross Ice Shelf from Hut Point on Ross Island. They thereby set a record for man's "farthest south." Although he did not have a clear view up the inlet, Scott inferred from the manner in which the surface of the ice shelf was disturbed in front of the inlet that a great glacier fed into it. Scott named the inlet after Shackleton, but he only implied a name for the glacier and did not show it on his maps. See Capt. Robert F. Scott, *The Voyage of the Discovery* (London, 1907), vol. II, pp. 55-60, 308, 311. On November 26, 1908, Shackleton, then leader of his own expedition, viewed the inlet on his trek south to ascend Beardmore Glacier to the polar plateau. He was farther east than Scott was and did not describe or name a glacier feeding into the inlet. See E. H. Shackleton, *The Heart of the Antarctic* (London, 1909), vol. I, pp. 296-297. Scott made no mention of the inlet on his trek to the South Pole in 1911. Consequently, Hawkes was the first to actually see fully this great outlet glacial system. The Advisory Committee on Antarctic Names of the U. S. Board on Geographic Names subsequently named the main glacier Nimrod Glacier after Shackleton's ship on the 1907-09 expedition rather than for Shackleton. His name had already been applied to the great outlet glacier flowing down from the polar plateau through the western part of the Queen Maud Range. This glacier had been discovered by Siple and others on a flight from West Base of the U. S. Antarctic Service Expedition on February 29, 1940.

12. One of these deglaciated or "dry" valleys, Taylor Valley, which reaches down to New Harbor on the west side of McMurdo Sound, was discovered by Capt. Robert F. Scott in December 1903. See Capt. Robert F. Scott, *The Voyage of the "Discovery," op. cit.,* vol. 2, pp. 213-217. On Scott's second expedition it was explored in February 1911 by a four-man party led by Griffith Taylor. See Griffith Taylor, "The Western Journeys," *Scott's Last Expedition* (London, 1913), vol. 2, pp. 190-197; also "A Resume of the Physiography and Glacial Geology of Victoria Land, Antarctica," by Taylor, pp. 420-432 of the same volume. See also, Griffith Taylor *With Scott: The Silver Lining* (New York, 1916), pp. 130-149.

13. The account is principally based on Capt. Charles A. Bond's "Narrative of Western Task Group (T.G.68.2)," Report of Operation Highjump, *op. cit.,* Annex I-b.

14. Roger Hawthorne, "Exploratory Flights of Admiral Byrd (1940)," *Reports on Scientific Results of the United States Antarctic Service Expedition, 1939-1941, Proceedings of the American Philosophical Society,* No. 1, vol. 89, April, 1945, pp. 398c-398d. Other members of the crew on both flights were Ashley C. Snow and Earl B. Perce. At that time Thurston Island was thought to be a peninsula and was so named. Its true nature was determined by personnel on the U. S. S. *Glacier* and U. S. S. *Burton Island* in February 1960.

15. William H. Kearns, Jr., and Beverley Britton, *The Silent Continent* (New York, 1955), p. 186. Pages 184 to 203 contain a description of the crash of George-1 and the rescue of the survivors.

16. LeBlanc had been badly burned, and his feet had been frozen. Gangrene necessitated the amputation of both legs below the knee en route home aboard the *Philippine Sea.*

BIBLIOGRAPHY

PUBLISHED MATERIAL

Army Observers' Report of Operation Highjump, Task Force 68, U. S. Navy, War Department, Washington, 1947, viii and 398 pp., illus., maps.

Bailey, H. C., "Electronics in the Antarctic; U. S. Navy Antarctic Expedition," *Electronics,* vol. 20, 1947, pp. 82-88.

Bertrand, Kenneth J., "A Look At Operation Highjump Twenty Years Later," *Antarctic Journal of the United States,* vol. 2, No. 1, January-February 1967, pp. 5-12.

Byrd, Rear Adm. Richard E., "Our Navy Explores Antarctica," *National Geographic Magazine,* vol. 92, No. 4, October, 1947, pp. 429-522.

Dietz, Robert S., "Some Oceanographic Observations on Operation Highjump: Final Report," *U. S. N* [avy] *E* [lectronics] *L* [aboratory] Report No. 55, Washington, 1948, 97 pp., illus., maps, tables, diagrs.

——, "Deep Scattering Layer in the Pacific and Antarctic Oceans," *Journal of Marine Research,* vol. 7, No. 3, 1948, pp. 430-442.

Henry, Thomas R., *The White Continent, the Story of Antarctica* (New York, William Sloane Associates, 1950), xxii and 257 pp.

Kearns, William H., Jr., and Beverley Britton, *The Silent Continent* (New York, Harper & Bros., 1955), x and 237 pp., endpaper maps. Chapters 10 and 11 deal with "Operation Highjump."

Menster, William J., Chaplain, USNR, *Strong Men South* (Milwaukee, Bruce Publishing Co., 1949), vii and 206 pp. An account by the Chaplain with the Central Task Group.

Moody, Alton B., "Navigation in the Antarctic," *Navigation,* vol. 1, Nos. 7 and 8, 1947, pp. 157-164

Palmer, Wendell S., *The U. S. S. Currituck, Pictorial Log of Antarctic Cruise "Operation Highjump"* (Philadelphia, Dunlap, 1948), 44 pp.

Schoene, Charles A., "Operation Highjump," *Journal of the Coast and Geodetic Survey,* No. 2, April, 1949, pp. 75-81, maps.

Sullivan, Walter, *Quest for a Continent* (New York, McGraw-Hill, 1957), xiv and 372 pp., illus., maps. Chapters 15-19, inclusive, deal with "Operation Highjump."

Thomas, Charles W., *Ice Is Where You Find It* (Indianapolis, Bobbs-Merrill Co., 1951), xxvi and 378 pp. Chapters 33-39, inclusive, deal with "Operation Highjump."

MANUSCRIPT MATERIAL

Report of Operation Highjump, U. S. Navy Antarctic Developments Project, 1947. Three volumes mimeographed for official use. Originally classified as confidential; now declassified. The report consists of 24 parts (Annexes), some of which consist of several parts. Annex I, "Narratives," is comprised of the reports of the several commanding officers. The 17 narratives total 286 pages.

23

THE RONNE ANTARCTIC RESEARCH EXPEDITION, 1947-1948

SIGNIFICANCE AND ACCOMPLISHMENTS OF THE EXPEDITION

From the late 1930s to the present, nearly all Antarctic operations, not only of the United States but of foreign countries as well, have been carried on under government sponsorship. Expeditions have become so complex, involving co-ordinated sea, air, and land operations and highly sophisticated and very specialized scientific observations, and at the same time costs in general have increased so greatly, that Antarctic exploration in recent decades has been largely beyond the scope of private financing. Since 1939, the only privately organized expedition from the United States has been the Ronne Antarctic Research Expedition. Even this expedition received major assistance from government agencies through the loan of equipment, the detail of two personnel, and the granting of contracts for research to be carried on. Ronne's expedition was a small one, judged by modern standards, made up in large part of men with no previous polar experience, but making up for this by enthusiasm for the job to be done. As a result, a great amount of useful work was accomplished. The experience of this expedition indicates that even in this day of massive governmental enterprises there may still be a place for smaller private expeditions having limited objectives and receiving adequate governmental cooperation.

One of the most extensive programs up to that time of aerial photography coupled with concurrent establishments of ground control points for mapping purposes was carried on by the Ronne expedition. Ronne used the so-called leap-frog method of aerial operations whereby one plane carrying extra fuel supported and extended the range of the photographic plane. This novel and highly successful method was later used by planes of the Ellsworth Station during the International Geophysical Year, 1957-58.

Although exploring in part the same territory covered by the eastern element of the United States Antarctic Service Expedition of 1939-41, the Ronne expedition greatly extended the area explored by Americans in Palmer Land, the southern half of the Antarctic Peninsula, and adjacent areas.[1] It established more firmly the United States interests in this region. Partly as a result of the knowledge gained and the interest generated during this expedition, the U. S. base at Ellsworth Station was established in 1957 for IGY work.

The Ronne expedition explored one of the largest remaining gaps in the Antarctic coastline hitherto not seen by man. The eastern end of the front of the vast ice shelf at the head of the Weddell Sea had been seen by Dr. Wilhelm Filchner, leader of a German expedition, who attempted to erect a base on the ice shelf in January 1912. Not until one of Ronne's planes flew over it from the west, however, was the extent of its seaward edge known.[2]

A significant feature of the expedition was the high degree of cooperation in field work achieved between the Americans and a British party stationed nearby. As a result of this cooperation and the use of the aircraft of the Ronne expedition, the ground survey work of a joint British-American dog-team party traversing the east coast of the Antarctic Peninsula was considerably extended.

The Ronne expedition was the first on which women wintered on the Antarctic continent. On two occasions during the 1930s, women accompanied Norwegian expeditions, but Mrs. Finn Ronne and Mrs. Harry Darlington are believed to have been the first members of their sex to winter over.

ESTABLISHMENT OF THE PROJECT

Finn Ronne acquired an interest in Antarctica from his father, Martin Ronne, who was a member of Roald Amundsen's 1910-12 expedition to Antarctica and of the first Byrd Antarctic Expedition, 1928-30. The younger Ronne took part in the Second Byrd Antarctic Expedition and was second in command of the party at East Base during the United States Antarctic Service Expedition. During World War II, Ronne formulated plans for an expedition that would explore the southward extension of the Antarctic Peninsula and along the Weddell Sea coast, utilizing the former East Base on Stonington Island, Marguerite Bay. The East Base had been left intact and stocked with considerable supplies at the time the USAS was evacuated in 1941. Ronne's preparations began in earnest at the close of the war. By November 1946, sufficient support had been secured from private and governmental sources to assure the sailing of the expedition.

The expedition was sponsored by the American Antarctic Association, Inc., which was created for this purpose. The facilities of the American Geographical Society were made available to Ronne during the planning and preparation of the enterprise. The Bartol Research Foundation of the Franklin Institute sponsored the cosmic ray program. The Geological Society of America sponsored the geologist of the expedition. Other private educational and scientific institutions: Brown, Fordham, Columbia, and St. Louis universities, and the Carnegie Institution, aided the expedition by lending scientific instruments. The expedition had a contract with the North American Newspaper Alliance for continuous news coverage. Approximately $50,000 was secured from private sources, and individuals assisted in other ways.

A number of governmental agencies, including the Army, Navy, and Air Force, cooperated in making the expedition possible, especially by providing equipment. Scientific work was done through a contract with the Office of Naval Research of the United States Navy Department. An act of Congress authorized the provision of a suitable vessel for the expedition.[3] Individuals of other government agencies also provided advice and assistance.

OBJECTIVES AND ACCOMPLISHMENTS

It was Ronne's intention, as stated in a prospectus drawn up during the preparatory stage of the expedition,[4] to explore the area of the continent lying south of 73° S latitude and between 35° and 80° W longitude, with the following objectives in view:

(1) To determine the western coast line of the Weddell Sea and its connection, if any, with the Filchner Ice Shelf to the east;

(2) To determine the direction and extent of the Palmer Land mountain range;

(3) To carry out extensive mapping operations both from surface and air over the area and southward in the direction of the South Pole;

(4) To answer the following questions from the knowledge gained from operations as stated above:

  a. Does the Palmer Land mountain range continue in a southerly direction and join with the Queen Maud Mountains?

  b. Does the Palmer Land mountain range extend in a southwest direction and join the mountains located in Marie Byrd Land?

  c. Does the Weddell Sea join the Ross Sea, thus dividing the continent into two parts?

In addition to expanding our knowledge of the geography of Antarctica, Ronne planned to carry on a program of observations in the geophysical sciences.

In general, the Ronne expedition achieved its objectives. The true alignment and configuration of the southwestern coast of the Weddell Sea was determined, it being found to be some 30 miles west of its previously plotted position. Many coastal features, mountains, and glaciers were discovered and named. South of Mount Austin, the coast was discovered to trend toward the southwest, forming an escarpment flanked on the west by mountains. The front of the ice shelf at the head of the Weddell Sea was determined, and an indentation in the ice front — named Gould Bay — was discovered near its eastern extremity.

The expedition flights did not penetrate far enough inland to prove a connection between the Palmer Land mountains and the Queen Maud Mountains or the ranges of Marie Byrd Land, although from the trend of the mountains, Ronne surmised such a connection. Ronne concluded, on the basis of visual observations and altimeter readings from aircraft, that the continental surface inland from the ice shelf at the head of Weddell Sea ascends gradually to an elevation of about 5000 feet in the vicinity of Mount Hassage, and that the possibility of any connection between the Ross and Weddell Seas seemed to be eliminated.

Even before the Ronne expedition, however, the belief was widely held that Antarctica was one continent rather than two land masses separated by a strait between the Ross and the Weddell embayments. The findings of the Second Byrd Antarctic Expedition, the West Base Antarctic Service Expedition, and the Central Group of "Operation Highjump" had seemed to confirm this belief from the Ross Sea side, as the finding of Ronne further appeared to confirm it from the Weddell Sea side. The operations of the IGY and later geophysical traverses have led to revisions in previously held concepts of the nature of Antarctica, for the continental ice has now been found in some places to rest on a rock foundation that is at varying distances below sea level. The idea of a low-level connection of tectonic origin between the Ross Sea and the Weddell Sea has been considered by geographers and explorers since the beginning of the 20th century, and it was a primary matter for investigation in the proposed program of the German expedition led by Filchner (1911-12) and the second expedition of Sir Ernest Shackleton (1914-16). However, while the existence of such a trough may be surmised from the quite different structures of the block-faulted Transantarctic Mountains on one side and the folded metasedimentary rocks with various volcanic and intrusive rocks of the Antarctic Peninsula, Ellsworth Land, and Marie Byrd Land on the other side, there is nothing in the relief of the surface of the glacial ice cap to prove or even suggest its presence.

In carrying out the mapping program of the Ronne expedition, photographic flights covered both coasts of the Antarctic Peninsula from about 66° S southward to the main body of the continent, as well as Alexander, Charcot, and Adelaide Islands. Ground control for the aerial photography was secured at points where the planes landed and by a sledge party on a route paralleling the flight lines. An area of approximately half a million square miles (about half of this seen for the first time) was covered by 14,000 trimetrogon photographs.

In addition to its work in exploration and mapping, the expedition carried on a program of observation in several sciences and tested various types of clothing and equipment for the armed forces. The scientific work was reported in a series of technical publications of the Office of Naval Research and in articles in professional journals, as listed in the accompanying bibliography. Geological and glaciological investigations were undertaken in the Marguerite Bay area during the course of about 150 days spent on the trail for these purposes. The meteorological program consisted of the sending of synoptic observations to the U. S. Weather Bureau in Washington, from aboard ship during the voyages to and from Antarctica, from the Stonington Island Main Base for a period of almost a year, from the plateau weather station 25 miles east of the Main Base for three months, and from the Cape Keeler Advance Base on the Weddell Sea for 74 days. Included among these observations were data from numerous pilot balloon ascents at the three bases. The weather observing program was a necessary adjunct to the flight operations.

Two seismographs were set up on Stonington Island to measure earth movements. In addition to regular data secured from these instruments, a study was made of the relation of minor earth vibrations to weather changes. Hourly tidal readings were taken from a gauge installed at the Main Base. Magnetic observations were taken at the Main and Cape Keeler Bases and by one of the sledge parties. Studies were also made of cosmic rays, solar radiation, and atmospheric refraction.

COMPOSITION OF THE EXPEDITION

The expedition vessel was the former ATA-215, renamed *The Port of Beaumont, Texas,* a wooden-hulled oceangoing tug loaned by the Navy. She was a 1190-ton vessel 183 feet in length, powered by two 750-horsepower diesel electric motors. The vessel, commanded by the veteran Arctic and Antarctic explorer, Commander Isaac Schlossbach, USN (Retired), was manned by the members of the expedition — most of them without previous sailing experience. After arrival in the Antarctic, the *Beaumont* was purposely frozen in the ice near Stonington Island for the duration of the expedition, this being the only United States expedition to follow this procedure.[5]

Three aircraft were secured on a loan basis from the Office of Research and Development of the Army Air Force. The largest of these was a twin-engine Beechcraft C-45 in which the trimetrogon cameras were mounted for aerial photography. Second in size was a Noorduyn C-64 (Norseman), a single-engine cargo plane developed in Canada for cold-weather operations. The smallest was a Stinson L-5, a two-seater reconnaissance plane. All three planes were mounted with skis for taking off and landing on snow surfaces. The original Beechcraft secured for the expedition fell to the dock while being loaded on the vessel. It was so badly damaged that it had to be replaced by a second plane of the same type loaded aboard the *Beaumont* at Balboa, Canal Zone, en route to the Antarctic.

Two Weasels were obtained from the Army. For its major surface journeys, however, the Ronne expedition relied on dog sledges. Despite their innoculation against distemper, the original complement of 43 huskies was reduced by almost one half by an epidemic of what appeared to be distemper that broke out aboard ship while the expedition was bound for Antarctica.

The trimetrogon installation on the Beechcraft consisted of three K-17 cameras with a six-inch focal length, suitable for low and medium altitude aerial mapping. Another special piece of equipment was a Geiger counter provided by the Office of Naval Research. Among the other items loaned to the expedition by the armed services for testing purposes were radios, heaters, tents, and winter clothing.

Expedition personnel numbered 23. The members were:

Commander (later Captain) Finn Ronne, U.S.N.R., Leader
Commander Isaac Schlossbach, U.S.N. (Ret.), Second in Command and Captain of the *Port of Beaumont, Texas*
Dr. Robert L. Nichols, Geologist and Senior Scientist, Trail Man
Harris-Clichy Peterson, Physicist, in charge of meteorological, solar radiation, atmospheric refraction, and cosmic ray investigations
Andrew A. Thompson, Geophysicist, in charge of seismological, magnetic and tidal investigations
Mrs. Finn Ronne, Recorder
Captain James W. Lassiter, U.S.A.F., Chief Pilot
Lieutenant Charles J. Adams, U.S.A.F., Pilot
Harry Darlington, III, Pilot
Mrs. Harry Darlington
James B. Robertson, Aviation Mechanic
Charles Hassage, Ship's Chief Engineer, in charge of Main Base during Ronne's absence
William R. Latady, Photographer
C. O. Fiske, Climatologist
Walter Smith, Ship's Mate, Navigator, Trail Man

Nelson McClary, Ship's Mate

Sigmund Gutenko, Chief Commissary Steward, U.S.N., on furlough with the expedition

Lawrence Kelsey, Radio Operator

Robert H. T. Dodson, Assistant Geologist, Surveyor, Trail Man

Dr. Donald McLean, Medical Officer

Ernest A. Wood, Ship's Engineer

Arthur Owen, Boy Scout, Trail Man

Jorge di Giorgio Valdés (Chilean), Mess Cook

DETAILED RECORD OF OPERATIONS

DEPARTURE FOR ANTARCTICA

The Ronne expedition departed from Beaumont, Texas, on January 25, 1947. The ship transited the Panama Canal and, after taking aboard the substitute Beechcraft plane, sailed from Balboa on February 9. During the passage southward, the Beechcraft was fitted out with its trimetrogon cameras, radio altimeter, extra radio equipment, and two additional gas tanks to increase its cruising range. Such portions of the scientific program as could be carried on aboard ship were also started. These included meteorological and atmospheric refraction observations, measurements of ocean water temperature, and collection of plankton. Calls were made at Valparaiso and Punta Arenas, Chile. Stonington Island, which was to be the location of the Main Base, was reached on March 12.

Before anchoring the *Beaumont* in its final position for the winter freeze-in, an attempt was made to penetrate to the northern entrance to George VI Sound in order to land, if possible, a cache of supplies for the establishment of an advance operational base for field work. Following a reconnaissance flight in the small Stinson L-5 on March 19 by Darlington and Latady, the ship sailed south on March 23 through Marguerite Bay to the entrance to the sound. The front of the shelf ice in the sound had retreated some 35 miles since 1940, but the entrance to the sound was blocked by icebergs. No suitable place for a landing could be found, and the attempt to establish the advance base in this quarter had to be abandoned. The trip nevertheless resulted in the discovery of the Bugge Islands (69°12' S, 68°25' W) in southern Marguerite Bay. The *Beaumont* penetrated to 69°20' S, believed to be a new southing record for a ship in this area, before returning to Stonington Island. The ship was moored near the Main Base and became frozen in the bay ice during May (Fig. 25).

ESTABLISHMENT OF THE BASE

Upon arrival at Stonington Island, Ronne found that the buildings of the former Antarctic Service East Base had been left in considerable disorder, presumably by personnel from several foreign expeditions that had visited the site in the years since the departure of the previous U. S. expedition in 1941.[6] The buildings themselves, however, were in good condition, and the supplies of coal upon which the Ronne Expedition was to depend were practically untouched. A great amount of gasoline, however, had been used by visitors.[7] It was also

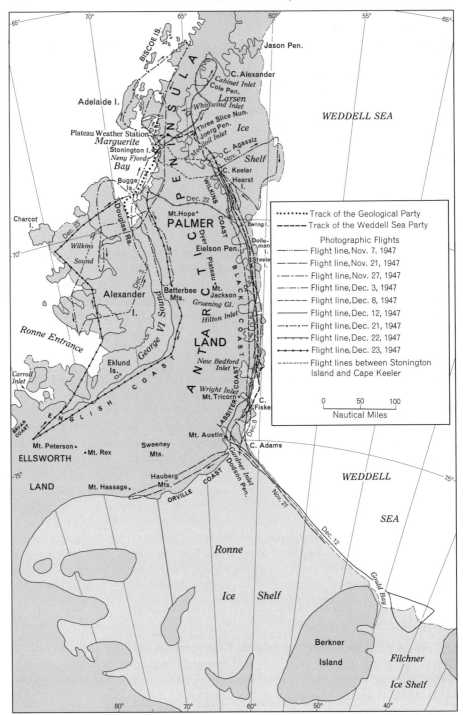

FIGURE 25. Field Operations of the Ronne Antarctic Research Expedition, 1947-1948.

found that the British Falkland Islands Dependencies Survey had established an 11-man base not far from the U.S. campsite, under the command of Major K. S. Pierce-Butler. An amicable personal relationship was readily established between the two groups.

The day after arrival at Stonington Island the personnel of the expedition were divided into two groups, one to clean up and recondition the camp and the other to unload the vessel. Bad weather interrupted operations for various lengths of time, and floating icebergs were also a concern when they came near the ship. The two larger planes were left on board to be unloaded after the bay ice could support their weight. To unload the small Stinson L-5 aircraft and other heavy equipment a barge was formed by lashing two boats together and building a platform over them. These operations continued into May, by which time most of the equipment except the two larger planes had been unloaded and the base camp fully established. At this stage the camp consisted of a large combination bunkhouse, galley, and mess hall, a science building, a machine shop, a small shack for living quarters, a blubber house, storage hut, and installations for tidal, seismic, and geomagnetic observations.

Finding a suitable sledging route south for operations to begin in the austral spring was a major concern. This had also been a problem in 1940 for the men at East Base of the U. S. Antarctic Service Expedition — a problem for which there is no satisfactory solution short of an airlift.[8] Traveling on sea ice may be feasible on the outward trek but not on the return trip, and getting over the peninsular upland and down on the Weddell Sea coast is difficult and hazardous. Ronne considered the use of Weasels as well as dog teams for surface travel. The L-5 plane was unloaded on March 15, and three days later was ready for a test flight which was made on March 18. This was followed on the next day by the reconnaissance flight to Marguerite Bay preparatory to the southward cruise of the *Beaumont,* previously mentioned. Subsequently the small plane was used for two more flights to the entrance to George VI Sound, and a flight on April 12 over Neny Fjord to the Traffic Circle on the peninsular upland. On April 22 Ronne and six others took a motor boat into Neny Fjord to look for a safe land route for the sledgers.

During the succeeding months of the Antarctic winter, preparations were continued for the operations of the ensuing field season. Supplies and equipment for use on the trail were made ready, and the scientific observations, started soon after arrival at base, were carried forward.[9] A fruitful cooperative arrangement was worked out between Ronne and Pierce-Butler whereby the Americans and the British would pool their resources for a sledge party to establish control points on the ground for aerial surveys. The Ronne expedition found itself short of huskies as a result of the distemper epidemic, whereas the British had a full complement of sledge dogs but only one small Auster aircraft at their disposal. It was accordingly agreed that the dog power of the British would be combined with the air power of the Americans in order to extend the range of the Weddell coast field party.

In July a meteorological station was established on the Antarctic Peninsula

522 AMERICANS IN ANTARCTICA, 1775-1948

upland east of the Main Base, to assist in forecasting weather for the air and ground operations. The station was set up by a sledge party consisting of Ronne, Latady, Owen, Adams, Peterson, and Dodson, of whom the latter two were to man the station. It took two days to reach the upland level, but on the night of July 16, their first on the upland, a storm commenced. On the eighth day it moderated sufficiently for Ronne and the other three members of the supporting party to leave for the Base Camp. The Base Camp lost radio contact with Peterson and Dodson and it was not until July 26 that the weather permitted a flight in the L-5 to resupply them, as planned. Two flights were made over the tent of the meteorological station without contacting the occupants.

A search by air and by a sledge party would have begun at dawn, but that night the mystery was cleared up when Dodson appeared at the Base Camp. During the snow storm that had continued at the upper level after the supporting party had left for Stonington Island a sleeping bag in the tent had got wet and the tent itself had begun to rip under the weight of the snow. Peterson and Dodson accordingly abandoned the camp and started to return to base. While they were making their way down the crevassed surface of the glacier Peterson suddenly disappeared from sight. He became lodged head downward in a crevasse, at a depth of about 110 feet. Ronne immediately organized and led the rescue party, including several of the British, to the place where the accident had occurred. Richard Butson, a British physician and the smallest in the party, was lowered into the crevasse to secure a line around Peterson, who was safely recovered without serious injury after 12 hours in the ice. In spite of this unfavorable beginning, the "plateau weather station" was re-established August 28 by a sledge party consisting of McClary, Robertson, Owen, and Dodson. After they had marked off a landing strip, the weather station was supplied by Adams in a flight with the L-5. The station operated until the end of the flying season by two men, with various changes in personnel.

In August the Norseman and Beechcraft were hoisted off the ship and let down onto the bay ice. Each was then towed by a Weasel to a point near the Main Base where the wings were attached and the planes made ready for flight. They were adapted for polar work by removing unnecessary equipment to save weight, by adding supplementary gasoline tanks, and by installing special instruments and equipment.[10] The Norseman, named *Nana* for the North American Newspaper Alliance, was test flown on September 14. The Beechcraft, which Ronne named the *Ed Sweeney,* was test flown on September 30.

The establishment of the Cape Keeler Advance Base on the eastern shore of the Antarctic Peninsula was also marked by an inauspicious beginning. The original plan had been to set up an advance base at or near the "elbow" or southeast corner of George VI Sound, for exploration on both sides of the Antarctic Peninsula and southward. Following the inability of the expedition to establish a cache of supplies for such a base with the *Beaumont* at the northern entrance of the Sound, from where it later could be moved south, a sledge party and a tractor party was organized to accomplish this in one of the Weasels. When these two parties were forced to return due to soft ice and slush on the surface of the

PLATE XIX-A. U. S. A. S. East Base in 1947. It was then the center of operations for the Ronne Antarctic Research Expedition. The camp of the Falkland Islands Dependencies Survey is in the middle ground. Photograph by courtesy of Finn Ronne.

PLATE XIX-B. Flight crew of the Ronne Antarctic Research Expedition; l. to r., William Latady, photographer, Capt. James Lassiter, pilot, and Capt. Finn Ronne, navigator and expedition leader. Photograph by courtesy of Finn Ronne.

PLATE XX. *Port of Beaumont.* The Ronne Antarctic Research Expedition ship is shown here near the close of the expedition, February 19, 1948, moored to fast bay ice. The larger Beechcraft airplane has already been put aboard. In the background are the United States base (l.), and the British base (r.). Photograph by courtesy of Finn Ronne.

Bay, it was decided to locate the Advance Base at Cape Keeler, 125 miles south-east of Main Base, and from there explore southward by air along the Weddell Sea. On September 15, 1947, the British Auster plane took off for Cape Keeler with the intention of marking a landing for the Norseman, which was to carry supplies for the base. The two planes became separated in flight and darkness and bad weather prevented them from making contact again at the point of ren-dezvous. The Norseman returned to base, but the British plane remained mis-sing for eight days. Lassiter and Adams made numerous search flights in the Norseman and the L-5 in attempting to find the Auster, success finally being achieved by Lassiter on the ninth day when he spotted the three downed Brit-ish flyers on the ice of Marguerite Bay slowly making their way on foot toward Stonington Island. After landing at Cape Keeler and not finding the Norseman, the British plane had attempted to return, had lost its way in the bad weather and crash-landed on the bay ice south of the Main Base. Finally, on September 29, the weather was clear enough for Lassiter, Smith, and Fiske to fly supplies in the Norseman to Cape Keeler. The Norseman was accompanied by the L-5, flown by Adams, who alighted first to stake out a landing for the larger plane.

Air Exploration

The Main and Advance bases having now been laid out, the stage was set for the long exploratory flights planned. The weather remained unsuitable for fly-ing throughout October, however, except for a few hours during which gasoline was lifted over the plateau to Cape Keeler. On November 7, 1947, the L-5 car-ried Ronne and Adams on a short exploratory flight to the eastern edge of the Larsen Ice Shelf from Cape Keeler. After reaching the iceberg-studded water of the Weddell Sea they turned south and followed the edge of the ice shelf to about 69°45′ S, near the southern end of Hearst Island. Islands reported east of Cape Keeler by previous expeditions and also supposedly seen by Ronne per-sonnel from Cape Keeler were not found in the Weddell Sea, but Ronne did discover the low dome of Ewing Island, covered by the ice shelf, about 25 miles southwest of his final turning point.[11] He attributed the reports of the non-ex-istent islands to cloud formations or mirages mistaken for land.

The first long southern flight from Cape Keeler occurred on November 21. This flight was made by the Norseman and the Beechcraft. The Norseman, with Adams as pilot and Schlossbach as co-pilot, carried five drums of gasoline as car-go. In the Beechcraft Lassiter was pilot, Latady photographer, and Ronne navi-gator. The two planes flew along the Weddell Sea coast as far as Mount Austin in 74°53′ S, 63°10′ W. The original plan to land at Mount Tricorn was changed when it was discovered that it was actually 55 miles north of where it was thought to be. They landed instead on the snow-covered surface of Gardner In-let beside Mount Austin and transferred part of the fuel from the Norseman to the Beechcraft. The Beechcraft then took off for a further southern flight while the Norseman remained at Mount Austin as a precautionary measure. The Beechcraft, with its trimetrogon cameras in operation, followed the mountain-ous escarpment of Palmer Land southwestward to about 77°30′ S, 72° W. Shortly after taking off, a low bulge in the western end of the ice shelf at the head of the Weddell Sea was thought to be an island, but subsequent examination of the photographs showed it may be a peninsula which Ronne named for Robert H. T. Dodson, his assistant geologist. The snow-covered surface, studded with scattered mountain peaks, rose steadily to the southwestward. Ronne named this upland the Joerg Plateau. When the plane had reached the limit of its range, Lassiter circled Mount Hassage while Latady dropped an American flag in the name of the United States.[12] The return course toward Mount Austin paralleled the outward route about 20 miles to the northwest. Within 30 miles of Mount Austin the plane was headed southeastward to fly along the front of the ice shelf. In about 77° S, 50° W the dwindling fuel supply necessitated a reversal of course and return to the Mount Austin stand-by base. The two planes then headed for Cape Keeler, the Beechcraft taking aerial photographs on the trip back. An emergency landing was effected at Steele Island because of ground fog. The following day, November 22, the planes flew back to Cape Keeler and then to the Main Base.

Five days after the southern flight, a photographic flight was made by Lassiter and Latady on the western side of the Antarctic Peninsula. The plane flew northward to Barilari Bay (65°55′ S, 64°43′ W), where ground fog forced Lassiter to turn and fly south along the axial line of the plateau upland of the Antarctic Peninsula. At the Wordie Ice Shelf they turned southwest and crossed the northern end of George VI Sound, cleared the Douglas Range, and crossed Alexander Island to within sight of Charcot Island. After a southward loop in Wilkins Sound, they returned to Stonington Island by flying along the northwestern margin and rounding the northern end of Alexander Island.

Another clear day on December 3 made possible a photographic flight, but after flying south along the east side of George VI Sound, Lassiter, Ronne, and Latady were turned back by clouds in the vicinity of the Batterbee Mountains. Returning to the northern end of the Sound, they flew west across Alexander Island toward Charcot Island, but again clouds barred the way. Turning southwest and then south, the plane reached the Ronne Entrance of George VI Sound, but clouds along the southern margin of Alexander Island once more forced a change in course. Lassiter then flew east and northeast to the northern limb of George VI Sound, which he followed back to the Main Base.

Ronne considered that exploration of the Weddell Sea coast was still incomplete, since the plane had been forced to return before reaching the eastern extremity of the ice shelf at the head of Weddell Sea, the Filchner Ice Shelf. Accordingly, when on December 8, 1947, the Cape Keeler Advance Base and Weddell Coast Sledge Party reported clear weather, the two larger planes again headed south along the Weddell coast. Three 55-gallon drums of gasoline were picked up at Cape Keeler by Adams in the Norseman. Two drums of the five they had hoped to carry had to be unloaded to enable Adams to take off from the sticky surface. This reduced the projected range of the photographic flight. At Wright Inlet (73°57′ S, 61°26′ W) the two planes landed, by prearrangement, beside the Weddell Coast Sledge Party organized jointly by agreement between Ronne and

Pierce-Butler. Gasoline was transferred to the Beechcraft which took off on a course due south. Ronne's plan to fly this course for three hours before turning northeast to fly to the edge of Filchner Ice Shelf near Moltke Nunataks had to be abandoned when, after an hour's flight, heavy overcast forced Lassiter to return to Wright Inlet. They landed and camped beside the sledge party close to Mount Tricorn. Although the sledge party was able to continue southward, bad flying weather kept the planes grounded for four days. On December 12 Ronne, Lassiter, and Latady again took off in the Beechcraft and flew south to the edge of the ice shelf and then southeastward along its seaward margin until further progress was stopped by heavy clouds ahead. Ronne felt the plane was then less than 80 nautical miles from the Moltke Nunataks, although they were not visible. Lassiter then flew southwest for some distance before doubling back for a return to base. An American flag was dropped at this point, as had been done at the most southerly point reached on the flight of November 21. Ronne named the area from the farthest west seen on November 21 to the farthest east seen on December 12, Edith Ronne Land, in honor of his wife and claimed it on behalf of the United States. An indentation discovered in the front of the ice shelf near the limit of the flight was named Gould Bay in honor of Laurence M. Gould, who was one of the sponsors of the expedition. Altimeter readings and crevassed ice indicated that the land rose to the south.[13] Subsequent investigations, during IGY and later, have confirmed Ronne's and Lassiter's impressions. However, in the vicinity of Gould Bay, where the plane made its southward loop to begin the return flight, the steep gradient in the surface is due to the presence of ice-drowned Berkner Island and not to the ice-covered continental land.[14] Geophysical investigations which have revealed Berkner Island have also shown that the ice shelf extends inland almost to the base of the Pensacola Mountains and to the base of the Heritage Range of the Ellsworth Mountains. The surface of the ice shelf rises perceptibly toward these mountains, and on the northwestern margin of the Ronne Ice Shelf the Orville Coast also has a steep gradient.

The return flight retraced the outward course along the Weddell coast, Adams in the Norseman flying on to Cape Keeler from Wright Inlet, while the photographic party in the Beechcraft landed at the foot of Gruening Glacier to refuel from drums of gasoline previously cached there. Since this was the last major flight on the east side of the Antarctic Peninsula, Adams evacuated the personnel at the Advance Base at Cape Keeler as he made the final leg of the return flight to Stonington Island.

In the latter part of December two flights were made north from the main base, one on December 21 over Adelaide Island and the west coast of the Antarctic Peninsula. On December 22 Lassiter and Latady flew south to the Wordie Ice Shelf and then crossed the peninsula to the north of Mount Hope, then known as Mount Wakefield. The east coast was followed northward to Cabinet Inlet, from whence the plane returned to base.[15] On this day the Advance Base at Cape Keeler was also dismantled and the equipment flown back to the Main Base.

On December 23 the last major photographic flight was undertaken. The route lay down the eastern and southern coast of George VI Sound to a landing point on the smooth, snow-covered surface in about 74° S, 79°35' W. Sun shots were taken for lines of position, and the plane took off again, heading northeast across Ronne Entrance and north across Alexander Island to Charcot Island, where a second landing was made. Ronne's party thus became the only men ever to set foot on Charcot Island. Sun shots were again taken for lines of position before the plane headed eastward across Alexander Island on the way to the Main Base. The weather was closing in fast, and Lassiter was forced to land on the ice in Neny Fjord, four miles from Stonington Island. Summoned by radio, a Weasel was driven out to tow the Beechcraft back to the base. On this long flight, Ronne discovered several new mountains and secured aerial photography along George VI Sound that could be matched with the ground control obtained by him and Carl Eklund during the U. S. Antarctic Service Expedition.

SURFACE EXPLORATION

Ronne had originally planned to send a sledging party and a Weasel, with air support, south along George VI Sound to establish an advance base at the angle in the sound where planes would refuel and a trail party would set out across the Antarctic Peninsula for a journey down the Weddell coast. This plan was abandoned when a sledging party of four men and three teams which had left Stonington Island on August 30 returned on September 8 after struggling for a week over slush-covered bay ice, inching over thin new ice or detouring around open leads. A reconnaissance flight by Adams in the Stinson L-5 had shown that conditions farther south were no better.[16]

Under the revised plan, two principal trail operations were conducted. One was for the purpose of geological investigations in the Marguerite Bay area; the other, for the securing of ground control along the east coast of the Antarctic Peninsula. Some geological work had been done by Nichols and Dodson in the vicinity of the Main Base as early as April, but the main effort did not begin until after the abortive start of the trail party to establish the base in George VI Sound. On September 28, Nichols and Dodson, accompanied on the first stage of the journey by two men from the British base, set off southward along the coast of Marguerite Bay. With their 13-dog team they struggled over difficult surfaces requiring much relaying of the loads. They visited small islands in the bay, crossed to the coast of Alexander Island, which they followed southward for some distance, and then returned to the Main Base by approximately the same route they had taken outward. On their outward journey they had cached food at several points for the return. They had also expected a resupply by air when they reached their southernmost point, but this failed to materialize because of bad flying weather and their inability to contact the base by radio. The Norseman contacted them on the return journey, however, and parachuted supplies. Later, Ronne landed in the Beechcraft and furnished them additional supplies. They reached the Main Base on December 26, having covered 450 miles in 90 days. Nichols later made other geological trips in the area surrounding Marguerite Bay, one of them lasting 29 days.

By agreement between Ronne and Pierce-Butler, the Weddell coast sledge trip was a joint undertaking. The party of four men and 23 dogs pulling three sledges departed from the Main Base on October 9, crossing the Antarctic Peninsula to Cape Keeler. After several changes of personnel, the party leaving Cape Keeler consisted of two British members: Pierce-Butler, leader, and Douglas Mason, surveyor; and two Americans: Owen, radio operator and dog driver, and Smith, surveyor. The Norseman laid caches of supplies for the Weddell coast party at Cape Keeler and points along the coast to the south. In turn, the party stood by for a time at Wright Inlet as emergency support for the second long southeastern flight, and its trail weather reports to the Main Base assisted flight operations. North of Wright Inlet, both on the outward and on the return journey, the party was known officially as the Joint British-American Weddell Coast Sledge Party, whereas south of the inlet it was designated the Ronne Weddell Coast Party.

The party progressed southward along the undulating ice surface at the foot of the mountainous coast. They were favored by generally good sledging surfaces and were not often confined to camp by prolonged blizzards. Crevasses and open leads in the ice gave them trouble, but since seals were usually found beside the leads, they also afforded fresh meat for the men and the dogs. The Ronne Weddell Coast Party reached the center of the Bowman Peninsula, overlooking Gardner Inlet and within sight of Mount Austin on December 13. Here the men made surveys and performed geological work. The combined party then returned rapidly northward, favored by good surfaces in the far southern part of their journey. Their record was 31 miles in 8½ hours, but they traveled 27, 25, and 23½ miles respectively on successive days.[17] Although the Advance Base had already been evacuated, they halted at Cape Keeler for a day to rest the dogs and make canvas shoes for the dogs whose paws were wearing thin. They were weathered in for a few days on the peninsular upland, but reached the Main Base on January 22, 1948, having covered 1180 miles in 105 days.

CLOSING THE EXPEDITION

In early January preliminary preparations were made for bringing the expedition to an end. Personnel of the Cape Keeler Advance Base had already been evacuated to the Main Base after the second long southern flight. During the first week of January the two larger planes were dismantled and loaded aboard the ship. By this time the bay ice had begun to deteriorate as a result of the summer thaw, making it unsuitable as a runway for these planes. It was also important that they be put aboard the ship while the bay ice could still support their weight. Later in the month the L-5 was also loaded on the ship when there were no longer any surfaces from which it could take off safely. Dwindling fuel supplies also made further air operations impossible.

Departure had originally been planned for the middle of March, in the belief that by that time the bay ice would have cleared sufficiently for the *Beaumont* to get out. Returning cold weather in February, however, made it appear that an early Antarctic autumn would overtake the summer thaw. The ship again became frozen in and as time passed the probability increased that she might remain ice-locked for another winter season. At this time U. S. Navy Task Force 39, consisting of the icebreakers *Burton Island* and *Edisto* were approaching the vicinity of Marguerite Bay after circumnavigating the Antarctic continent. As a result of an exchange of messages between Ronne and Commander Gerald Ketchum, USN, of the Task Force, it was agreed that the icebreakers would call at Stonington Island to break a passage for the *Beaumont* to open water. This operation was effectively accomplished on February 20, 1948.

Some last bits of geological and seismological work were done as the vessels left the area. The *Burton Island*'s helicopter landed Nichols and Dr. Earl T. Apfel, the task force geologist, on islands near Adelaide Island for some work, including the setting off of a charge of dynamite to test the seismographs which had been left in the custody of the British.

Because of steering gear trouble, it was necessary for the *Burton Island* to tow the *Beaumont* through the pack northward from Adelaide Island. When they emerged from the pack, repairs were made and the *Beaumont* was able to proceed under her own power. She parted company with the icebreakers on February 23, proceeded through a storm to Punta Arenas, and arrived in New York on April 15, 1948.

APPENDIX

AGREEMENT FOR BRITISH-AMERICAN WEDDELL COAST PARTY
[Verbatim copy of original agreement in Finn Ronne's personal files]

Leaving Stonington Island on approximately October 8, 1947, there will be a Joint British-American Weddell Coast Sledge Party consisting of four persons, two British members of the Falkland Island Dependencies Survey, K. S. Pierce-Butler and Douglas Mason; and two American members of the Ronne Antarctic Research Expedition, Nelson McClary and Arthur Owen. There will be three teams of nine dogs each, a total of twenty-seven dogs. The party will travel up the Northeast Glacier, across the Mile High Plateau to Cape Keeler, along the Weddell Coast, passing Cape Keeler, and Cape Knowles to Mt. Tricorn. Upon reaching Mt. Tricorn, the two American members of the R.A.R.E. will form the Ronne Weddell Coast Party and continue to sledge south from Mt. Tricorn along the Weddell Coast as far as rations and weather will permit and will then retrace their route to Mt. Tricorn. During this time, the two British members of the F.I.D.S. will occupy themselves in the general vicinity of Mt. Tricorn to await the return of the Ronne southern group and upon their return will together retrace their route to Stonington Island.

In order that the above outlined sledge trip will be brought to a successful conclusion in every respect, the two leaders of the British and American Bases, Major K. S. Pierce-Butler of F.I.D.S. and Commander Finn Ronne, U.S.N.R., of the R.A.R.E., have agreed to the following points:

1. That one of the nine dog British teams be loaned to the R.A.R.E. and is the full responsibility of the R.A.R.E. for the duration of the sledge journey.

2. That until the Joint Party arrives at Mt. Tricorn, and on its return journey to base from Mt. Tricorn, the decisions of Major K. S. Pierce-Butler, or his representative, shall be final.

3. That a cache of approximately 1900 pounds be flown to Cape Keeler in the R.A.R.E.'s Norseman plane.

4. That an additional cache of 1800 pounds be laid by the R.A.R.E.'s Norseman plane in the vicinity of Cape Knowles. The exact location of the cache to be determined by the weather and surface conditions of the terrain when the Joint British-American Weddell Coast Sledge Party approaches that vicinity while sledging on its way south.

5. That the R.A.R.E.'s Norseman plane will provide a cache of food, etc., in the vicinity of Mt. Tricorn for the J.B.-A.W.C.S.P. to wait for a Norseman plane flight to bring additional supplies. That this twenty days supply is in case of such a delay in waiting for the plane flight.

6. That an additional twenty days food ration will be supplied by the Norseman plane for the *Ronne Weddell Coast Sledge Party* to utilize on its way south of Mt. Tricorn and for the British party to utilize in the general vicinity of Mt. Tricorn.

7. That up until Mt. Tricorn the Joint British-American Sledge Party will be ready to do any emergency rescue within their power that they might be called upon to attempt in case of a downed aircraft.

8. That after reaching Mt. Tricorn, both the R.W.C.S.P. and the British Party in the vicinity of Mt. Tricorn will be ready to go to the emergency rescue of a downed plane and its personnel.

9. That upon the return to Mt. Tricorn of the *Ronne Weddell Coast Party,* the two groups will again form the Joint British-American Weddell Coast Party and return to Stonington Island via their outward route using the caches they set down on the outward journey.

10. It is, of course, understood, that in the event of any unforeseen emergency to the sledge party, the three planes of the R.A.R.E. will be utilized in an attempt to reach the sledge party.

11. The sledge party will at all times keep radio communication with both home bases (F.I.D.S. and R.A.R.E.) and give constant weather reports which will govern the airplane flights over the Weddell Coast.

12. That the scientific and geographical investigations done by the Joint British-American Weddell Coast Party will be the common property of both the F.I.D.S. and the R.A.R.E. for use in whatever way either group sees fit and when published by either group will give credit as having been obtained by the Joint British-American Weddell Coast Party.

13. That the scientific and geographical investigations done by the *Ronne Weddell Coast Party* south from Mt. Tricorn on the Weddell Coast will be made available to the F.I.D.S. for their use prior to American publication. If any of these results are published by the F.I.D.S. prior to American publication by the R.A.R.E., due credit will be given to the Ronne Weddell Coast Party.

14. That the scientific and geographical investigations done by the British group in the vicinity of Mt. Tricorn will be governed in the same manner as point No. 13.

15. That the naming of the geographical features along the Weddell Coast from Darlington Island to Mt. Tricorn shall be done by the F.I.D.S.

16. That the naming of the geographical features from Mt. Tricorn and including the inlet where Mt. Tricorn is located and south along the Weddell Coast shall be done by the R.A.R.E.

17. That the above agreements are subject to change upon the occurrence of any unforeseen events but with the understanding that the agreements entered into were done freely and willingly by both leaders and that this same cooperative spirit toward getting the maximum job done will prevail should any changes in the above plans and agreements be deemed necessary.

Signed: Cmdr. Finn Ronne, USNR
            Leader, R.A.R.E.

Signed: Major K. S. Pierce-Butler
            Leader of F.I.D.S.

NOTES

1. For a history and explanation of the application of geographic names to the peninsula see Chap. 4, note 2. Adjacent areas include Alexander Island (first known as Alexander I Land and later as Alexander I Island), and the eastern part of Ellsworth Land.

2. The indeterminate area of ice shelf adjacent to Luitpold Coast of Coats Land was shown for decades on the maps as Filchner Ice Shelf. Ronne named the major portion which he had discovered the Lassiter Ice Shelf, but this name was not generally accepted. Instead, there was a tendency to apply Filchner's name to the entire extent of the front of the shelf, and the U. S. Board on Geographic Names approved the application of Filchner's name from the Bowman Peninsula of Palmer Land to Luitpold Coast. The two applications are reflected in *The Geographical Names of Antarctica*, U. S. Board on Geographical Names, Washington, D. C., Special Publication 86, 1947, p. 164, and *Geographic Names of Antarctica*, U. S. Board on Geographic Names, Gazetteer No. 14, Washington, D. C. 1956, p. 126. As a result of extensive exploration by air and on the surface, including geophysical work, during the IGY and subsequently by United States, British, and Argentine expedition personnel, the vast extent of the ice shelf has become known although its inland margins are still indefinite. Berkner Island, an ice-drowned island of some 30,000 square miles or more, separates the smaller eastern portion of the ice shelf from the main portion. For this reason the U. S. Board on Geographic Names in 1968 decided to approve Filchner Ice Shelf for the smaller eastern part and Ronne Ice Shelf for the major portion. This includes most of what Ronne named Edith Ronne Land.

3. Act of July 24, 1946; 60 Stat. 655.

4. Finn Ronne, *Antarctic Conquest* (New York, 1949), pp. 19-20.

5. Although a properly constructed vessel should be safe from internal ice pressure, permitting a ship to be frozen in in bay ice presents some hazards. It is possible that the ice may break up in the spring before the ship is ready for sea, or it may fail to break up at all, holding the ship prisoner for a second season. If the site has been well chosen, however, there should be little danger from floating icebergs, drifting pack ice, ocean swells, or lateral pressure exerted on the bay ice by glacial ice. The situation is quite different from being beset in drifting pack ice where the ship is subjected to tremendous ice pressure. In 1902 the *Gauss* of Drygalski's German expedition was accidentally frozen in off the Wilhelm II Coast and freed the following summer without damage. Scott permitted the *Discovery* to be frozen in at McMurdo Sound in 1902; it was freed in 1904. William S. Bruce permitted his *Scotia* to be frozen in for the winter of 1903 at Laurie Island, and Dr. Charcot did the same with his *Français* at Booth Island in the Palmer Archipelago in 1904 and with the *Pourquoi Pas?* at Petermann Island in 1909.

6. Ronne, *Antarctic Conquest, op. cit.*, pp. 52-57. This had not come as a surprise, for the British Embassy in Washington had informed the Department of State of the condition of the base in December 1946. The Falkland Islands Dependencies Survey had a base on Stonington Island, and Ronne was convinced that the British Government was trying to discourage him from using the island as his base of operations. *Ibid.*, pp. 28-34.

7. Personal communication from Captain Finn Ronne.

8. Many developments in the use of aircraft have occurred since 1955 and the preparations for IGY, but even today suitable runways for winged aircraft are a problem in Marguerite Bay and the whole Antarctic Peninsula region. For most of the summer season, sea ice cannot be relied on or is entirely lacking for taking off and landing. The small areas and steep slopes of bordering land ice limits the size and the carrying capacity of aircraft. Helicopters, with their vertical take off and landing capability, are the most suitable. This is particularly true of the turbo-powered HU-1B Iroquois, now being used by U. S. Support Forces at McMurdo, which can operate at altitudes up to 16,000 feet and which have sufficient range and load-carrying capacity.

9. Ronne, *Antarctic Conquest, op. cit.*, pp. 82-86.

10. *Ibid.*, pp. 142-144, 172-173.

11. *Ibid.*, pp. 192-193.

12. *Ibid.*, p. 204. Subsequent work has confirmed Dodson Peninsula but not Joerg Plateau.

13. *Ibid.*, pp. 225-227.

14. C. R. Bentley and others, "Physical Characteristics of the Antarctic Ice Sheet," *Antarctic Map Folio Series*, Folio 2, American Geographical Society (New York, 1964), Plate 2; "The Land Beneath the Ice," in *Antarctica*, edited by Trevor Hatherton (London, 1965), pp. 67-68, Fig. 80, p. 270.

15. This part of the east coast was just then being traversed by a Falklands Islands De-

pendencies Survey sledging party on a journey from Hope Bay at the northern tip of the Antarctic Peninsula to Stonington Island.

16. Ronne, *Antarctic Conquest, op. cit.*, pp. 146-149.

17. *Ibid.*, p. 248.

BIBLIOGRAPHY

PUBLISHED MATERIAL

Hassage, Charles, *Ships Engineering Plant "M/V Port of Beaumont Texas," During the Antarctic Winter*, Ronne Antarctic Research Expedition, Technical Report No. 8, Office of Naval Research, Washington, November, 1948, 9 pp.

Latady, William R., "A Year on the Antarctic Continent," *Appalachia*, vol. 27, No. 3, June, 1949, pp. 273-281.

——, "A Year on the Antarctic Continent," *Harvard Mountaineering*, No. 9, June, 1949, pp. 25-37, map.

——, "Antarctic Interlude," *The American Alpine Journal*, vol. 7, No. 3, September, 1949, pp. 233-247, illus.

——, "Report on the Aerial Photography of the Ronne Research Expedition," *Photogrammetric Engineering*, vol. 14, No. 2, June, 1948, pp. 205-222, map.

McIlvaine, Jane, and Jennie Darlington, *My Antarctic Honeymoon: A Year at the Bottom of the World* (Garden City, N. Y., Doubleday, 1956), 284 pp., illus.

Nichols, Robert L., *Bedrock Geology of Marguerite Bay Area, Palmer Peninsula, Antarctica*, Ronne Antarctic Research Expedition, Technical Report No. 13, Office of Naval Research, Washington, November, 1955, 60 pp.

——, "Elevated Beaches of Marguerite Bay, Antarctica," *Bulletin, Geological Society of America*, vol. 58, No. 12, Part 2, 1947, p. 1213. (Abstract of a paper at the G. S. A. meeting, Ottawa, December 29-31, 1947.)

——, "Geology of Stonington Island Area," *Bulletin, Geological Society of America*, Vol. 58, No. 12, Part 2, 1947, p. 1213. (Abstract of a paper read at the G. S. A. meeting, Ottawa, December 29-31, 1947.)

——, *Geomorphology of Marguerite Bay, Palmer Peninsula, Antarctica*, Ronne Antarctic Research Expedition, Technical Report No. 12, Office of Naval Research, Washington, August, 1953, 151 pp.

——, *Preliminary Report on the Geology of the Marguerite Bay Area, Antarctica*, Ronne Antarctic Research Expedition, Technical Report No. 6, Office of Naval Research, Washington, n. d., 5 pp.

Peterson, Harris-Clichy, *Antarctic Weather Statistics*, Ronne Antarctic Research Expedition, Technical Report No. 1, Office of Naval Research, Washington, September, 1948, 42 pp.

——, *Atmospheric Refraction Project*, Ronne Antarctic Research Expedition, Technical Report No. 2, Office of Naval Research, Washington, October, 1948, 4 pp.

——, *Guide for Stonington Island Aviation Meteorology*, Ronne Antarctic Research Expedition, Technical Report No. 5, Office of Naval Research, Washington, October, 1948, 25 pp.

——, *Results of the Solar Radiation Project of the Ronne Antarctic Expedition*, Ronne Antarctic Research Expedition, Technical Report No. 3, Office of Naval Research, Washington, October, 1948, 17 pp.

——, *Weather Observing Program*, Ronne Antarctic Research Expedition, Technical Report No. 4, Office of Naval Research, Washington, November, 1948, 39 pp.

Ronne, Edith, "Woman in the Antarctic, or the Human Side of a Scientific Expedition," *Appalachia*, vol. 28, No. 1, June, 1950, pp. 1-15.

Ronne, Finn, *Antarctic Conquest: The Story of the Ronne Expedition, 1946-1948* (New York, G. P. Putnam's Sons, 1949), xx and 299 pp., illus., maps, end papers. The official narrative of the expedition.

——, "Antarctic Mapping and Aerial Photography," *The Scientific Monthly*, vol. 71, No. 5, November, 1950, pp. 287-293.

——, "Antarctica — One Continent," *Explorers Journal*, vol. 26, Nos. 3 and 4, pp. 1-16, 45.

——, "Ronne Antarctic Research Expedition, 1946-1948," *Photogrammetric Engineering*, vol. 14, No. 2, June 1948, pp. 197-205.

——, "Ronne Antarctic Research Expedition, 1946-1948," *Geographical Review*, vol. 38, No. 3, July, 1948, pp. 355-391.

——, "Ronne Antarctic Research Expedition, 1946-1948," *Annual Report, Smithsonian Institution,* 1949, pp. 369-394, 8 plates.

Thompson, Andrew A., *Antarctic Seismological Bulletin,* Ronne Antarctic Research Expedition, Technical Report No. 9, Office of Naval Research, Washington, January, 1950, 33 pp.

——, *Establishment of Antarctic Seismological Station,* Ronne Antarctic Research Expedition, Technical Report No. 10, Office of Naval Research, Washington, January, 1950, 33 pp.

——, *Microseisms and Weather on Palmer Land Peninsula, Antarctica,* Ronne Antarctic Research Expedition, Technical Report No. 11, Office of Naval Research, Washington, April, 1950, 87 pp.

——, *Tidal Work on Marguerite Bay, Antarctica,* Ronne Antarctic Research Expedition, Technical Report No. 7, Office of Naval Research, Washington, November, 1948, 35 pp.

Walton, E. W. Kevin, *Two Years in the Antarctic,* (New York, Philosophical Library, 1955), 194 pp., illus.

24

THE U. S. NAVY SECOND ANTARCTIC DEVELOPMENTS PROJECT, "OPERATION WINDMILL," 1947-1948

ORGANIZATION AND ACCOMPLISHMENTS

SIGNIFICANCE OF THE EXPEDITION

The coast of Wilkes Land has been explored by three U. S. Navy expeditions, each of which contributed substantially to the accurate coastal delineation of this portion of Antarctica. The first was the United States Exploring Expedition of 1838-42 led by Wilkes, which explored this coast in 1840. The second was "Operation Highjump" of 1946-47, and the third was the Second Antarctic Developments Project of 1947-48. This third expedition, most often referred to unofficially as "Operation Windmill"[1] and carried out by Task Force 39, also operated in the Ross Sea and off the coast of West Antarctica, but its most significant work was done on the coast of Wilkes Land and on the Queen Mary Coast of East Antarctica. Here it secured geodetic ground control to match portions of the aerial photography taken the previous season by "Operation Highjump," thus contributing to the production of the first set of medium-scale maps of this region. Conditions discovered by the expedition also influenced decisions regarding the location of stations for the International Geophysical Year, 1957-58. At a time when other nations had embarked on a program of permanent bases in the Antarctic, the U. S. Navy Second Developments Project was a vehicle for continuing the United States "presence" there.

ESTABLISHMENT OF THE PROJECT

The Second Antarctic Developments Project was established by the Chief of Naval Operations in a directive dated August 1, 1947. The Commander-in-Chief, U. S. Pacific Fleet, was charged with operational control, whereas technical control was retained by the Chief of Naval Operations. Task Force 39 was established on September 15, 1947, to carry out the project. Preliminary planning began at once by a small staff in Washington carried over from "Operation Highjump." Commander Gerald L. Ketchum, USN, commander of the icebreaker *Burton Island* during "Operation Highjump," was designated Commander of Task Force 39. He took over actual control of planning on October 1, 1947, upon his arrival in Washington, only five weeks before the departure of the expedition. It is significant that in his report at the conclusion of the expedition Commander Ketchum included among his recommendations for consideration in planning future expeditions that directives "should be issued sufficiently in advance to allow the Task Force Commander, the Chief Staff Officer, the Operations Officer, and the Supply Officer to arrive at the planning center at least three months prior to the date of departure of units for the operating area."[2]

The short time available for planning and procurement resulted in some projects being deleted and others modified to fit available equipment when new or special equipment could not be or was not delivered on time. Because of limited appropriations and limited space for equipment and personnel, representatives of the press and foreign observers were explicitly excluded from the expedition, and the Chief of Staff of the U. S. Army was limited to a maximum of eight observers, including the Army Air Force. The Air Force was not then a separate branch of the armed services.

OBJECTIVES AND ACCOMPLISHMENTS

Briefly, the objectives as stated by the Chief of Naval Operations in establishing the project were to supplement those of "Operation Highjump" in training personnel, testing equipment, and reaffirming American interests in the region. The testing included investigating the condition of installations and equipment left at Little America. Also as a follow-up on "Highjump," the expedition was to extend "detailed exploration of Antarctic coastal areas, particularly those inshore of the pack ice eastward from the Ross Sea and in the vicinity of the Bunger ('Warm Water') Lakes."[3] The expedition was also instructed to investigate conditions of electromagnetic propagation and to collect geographic, hydrographic, oceanographic, geologic, and meteorologic information in the areas visited.

The extensive aerial photography of "Operation Highjump" was of little value without ground control, and while it was generally understood among "old Antarctic hands" that the chief purpose of the Second Antarctic Developments Project was to get ground control for "Highjump" photography, this was not specifically mentioned in the list of purposes. Under "tentative concept of operations," however, the directive stated that the Task Force vessels were to penetrate the pack ice, getting close inshore, "for the purpose of conducting short-range exploration and producing coastal ground tie-ins for past air photography."[4] The importance of this objective was obvious in the selection of personnel and equipment for the expedition.

The Task Force, in carrying out these directives, operated in the pack ice bordering Antarctica for 69 days. The ships navigated in Antarctic waters that were for the most part unsounded and inadequately charted for approximately half of the circumference of Antarctica. The expedition was the first to transit the ice pack to the continent in the vicinity of the Knox Coast[5] and also successfully exited through the pack northeast of the Bay of Whales. The survey parties established 17 geodetic positions, 10 of which were of fair to good reliability. All of the positions are listed at the end of this chapter. Limited triangulation nets were laid out around the positions, whenever practicable. Some aerial photography was also taken. Oceanographic observations included the taking of seawater temperatures every four hours and the taking of seawater samples twice daily, except when the ships were at anchor or operating in heavy ice. Bottom sampling was done in the Antarctic whenever possible. Fathometers provided continuous soundings. Ice positions and types were plotted on the track charts, and studies were made of the physical characteristics of snow to determine the effects of such characteristics on snow construction techniques. Field work in geology and biology was carried on and a program of meteorological observations undertaken. The expedition also afforded an opportunity for photo interpreters, underwater demolition teams, and other Navy specialists to gain valuable experience.[6]

COMPOSITION OF THE EXPEDITION

Task Force 39 consisted of two icebreakers, the U.S.S. *Burton Island* (flagship) and the U.S.S. *Edisto*. The former carried one HO3S-1 Sikorsky helicopter and one HTL-1 Bell helicopter; the latter carried one HO3S-1 helicopter and one J2F-6 Grumman amphibian airplane. The two ships penetrated without difficulty heavy broken pack ice such as was encountered at most places that they visited around the fringe of the continent, but they were unable to penetrate the fields of heavy unbroken ice of the Amundsen Sea in the vicinity of Mount Siple.

The helicopters proved indispensable in landing shore parties to establish control points or do other exploratory work, and for ice reconnaissance while the ships were in the pack. The Grumman amphibian, a small, single-engine plane, was used for air photography and ice reconnaissance. All three helicopters sustained damage in the course of operations. The two Sikorsky helicopters were equipped with floats, the frames of which were broken in landings. The Bell crashed and was wrecked during a "white-out" at Bunger Hills.[7]

Provision of surface transportation was the responsibility of a U.S. Marine transportation unit equipped with four Weasels (vehicle M29C). Each Weasel pulled a one-ton sled, and at least two of them were provided with radios at all times. These vehicles were used where possible to transport ground parties to operating stations. Main reliance was placed on the helicopters, however, since they could work more rapidly and could reach sites not accessible to the Weasels. Most of the time the Weasels were kept in reserve for emergency purposes.

The expedition consisted of a total of 500 men headed by Commander Gerald L. Ketchum, Commander of Task Force 39. Commander Edwin A. McDonald was captain of the *Burton Island* and Commander Edward C. Folger, Jr., commanded the *Edisto*. Lieutenant Commander C. L. Browning was chief staff officer. Among the 14 members of the staff was Captain Vernon D. Boyd, USMC, transportation officer, who had been a member of the Second Byrd Antarctic Expedition, the U. S. Antarctic Service Expedition, and "Operation Highjump." Three military officers and ten civilians accompanied the expedition as observers and scientists from various branches of the armed services and civilian government agencies. One of the observers was Mr. John H. Roscoe of the Navy's Photo Interpretation Center, who had served as photogrammetrist on "Operation Highjump."

DETAILED RECORD OF OPERATIONS

The *Edisto*, after loading special equipment and stores at Boston, sailed on November 1, 1947, for Norfolk, where the observers and scientists embarked.

The vessel sailed from Norfolk on November 6 for a rendezvous with the *Burton Island* at Tutuila, American Samoa. She arrived at Colon, Panama, and transited the Panama Canal on November 12. After taking on stores at the U. S. Navy Submarine Base at Balboa, the *Edisto* sailed on November 15. November 21 was spent sounding for Germaine Bank, reportedly in the vicinity of 5° 10′ N, 107°35′ W, but the minimum sounding was 1980 fathoms in an area of 540 square miles.[8] On December 2 the *Edisto* arrived at Tutuila.

The *Burton Island* sailed from San Pedro, California, for Tutuila on November 20. En route a sounding profile was made on December 1 over a 144-square mile area in search of a reef reported by the *Wairuna* in the vicinity of 5°28′ S, 162°01′ W. No evidence of a shoal was found, the average depth being 2700 fathoms. On December 3 the ship arrived at Tutuila. This day and the next were devoted to conferences on division of duties and on cooperation between the two ships by the personnel concerned. Survey points 1, 2, and 3 near Shackleton Ice Shelf were assigned to the *Edisto,* points 4, 5, and 6 to the *Burton Island.* Each ship was prepared to operate independently regarding geodesy, communications, photography, meteorology, and both air and surface transport, necessary to the main task of obtaining ground control. The biological investigations were assigned to the *Edisto,* the geology to the *Burton Island.* Leaders of the various groups of specialists concerned with ground control were assigned to the *Burton Island,* their deputies to the *Edisto.* This division of personnel and equipment made it possible for the ships to operate independently or cooperatively while widely separated or in close proximity.[9] Meanwhile the crews were shifting supplies and equipment from one icebreaker to the other to fit the assigned tasks.

Both ships left the harbor at Pago Pago on December 5, and a course was set for Scott Island, the ships maintaining parallel courses 20 miles apart to provide for two bathymetric profiles. The first iceberg was sighted on December 14 at 60°46′ S, 177°29′ W, and on the following day light pack ice was encountered. The pack ice got heavier and icebergs more numerous. On December 16 the attempt to reach Scott Island was abandoned 40 miles north of the island, due to impenetrable pack ice, and course was reversed. The ships emerged from the pack on December 18, and the northern limits of the pack ice were followed and charted westward en route to the proposed control points near the Shackleton Ice Shelf. The British whaler *Southern Harvest* and her catchers were sighted and Christmas greetings were exchanged on December 24 (Fig. 26).

On December 25 the Task Force headed southward, breaking through the pack ice into Davis Sea. A helicopter was sent out on a reconnaissance flight to scout for leads in the pack ice. The ships moved in file and alternated in the lead position to equalize the fuel consumption. On the next day two helicopters were sent aloft, and open water was found 12 miles to the south. Open water was reached a few minutes after midnight on December 27. Two hours later Drygalski Island was picked up on radar, bearing 120°, 11 miles distant. At 3:00 a. m. the ships parted company to proceed to their assigned points. The *Burton Island* nosed into the ice south of Drygalski Island, heading for point 4 at the

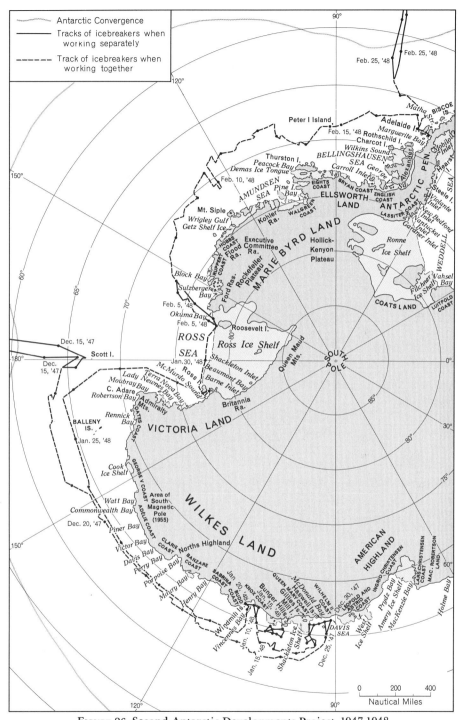

FIGURE 26. Second Antarctic Developments Project, 1947-1948.

Haswell Islands. The *Edisto* also went into the pack about 40 miles to the west. (See the Appendix for the listing of ground control points.)

The *Edisto* was first to land a party. Helicopter flights were made to scout the pack ice and to seek the location of point 2, the point then nearest the ship. By midnight three flights had been made to transport the field party and equipment to point 2, and by 4:00 a. m., December 28, camp had been completed on a narrow piece of shelf ice at the foot of a piedmont glacier, 25 miles west of Haswell Island. The party consisted of Mr. Glenn R. Krause of the Hydrographic Office; M. G. Snyder, QM1, USN; Corporal D. L. Green USMC; Lieutenant E. W. Midgeley (MC) USA; and Mr. T. E. Jones, photo interpreter.

The *Edisto* worked between icebergs and through the pack ice to within 35 miles of point 1 before being stopped. Point 1 was located on bay ice between two highly crevassed glaciers, 12 miles east of Gaussberg. By noon on December 28 three trips had been made by helicopter to land a party consisting of Mr. E. L. Merritt of the Hydrographic Office; R. Snedeker QM1, USN; Sergeant L. Peterson, USMC; Major E. R. Ardery, USA; and R. R. Conger CPHOM, USN. Both parties were hindered by cloudy weather and blizzards, and for 60 hours the party at point 1 was out of radio contact with the ship. Consecutive hours of sunshine were necessary for hourly sets of sun sights for the astro fix, but cloudy spells, if the weather was otherwise suitable, were used for laying out a base line, for completing triangulation, and for magnetic observations. Continued clear weather on January 1 permitted both parties to complete their work, which included eight hourly sets of sun sights at point 1 and nine at point 2. Krause was able to tie Gaussberg, a mountain about 50 miles to the west, into his triangulation.[10]

After the *Edisto* and the *Burton Island* had parted early on December 27 the latter headed south toward the Haswell Islands, the site previously selected for point 4. Part of the day was spent laying to in poor visibility, with the pack ice too thick to be practicable for the ship to break it. Finally, at midnight, visibility improved and a helicopter was sent aloft to look for leads. Course was then reversed to northeasterly to enter the reported leads. At 5:00 a. m. on December 28 the *Burton Island* was again stopped by impenetrable ice 17 miles north of the Haswell Islands. From here two Weasels were sent out in charge of Captain Boyd to transport the hydrographic party to point 1. The party consisted of Mr. R. C. Holl, of the Hydrographic Office, Dr. Earl T. Apfel of the U. S. Geological Survey and Syracuse University, Mr. John H. Roscoe of the Navy Photographic Center, Ensign R. O. Werlein, and J. J. O'Connor, PHOM 1. After camp was made on Haswell Island, the largest of the group, Holl conducted a reconnaissance of the island and an astronomic station was set up in the lee of some rocks on the northwest corner of the island. On December 29 triangulation points were established and sun shots were obtained. That evening Apfel and O'Connor were evacuated by helicopter. The next day further sun shots were made with the rising sun and, to complete the triangulation, a base line was established on the fast ice beyond the island and tied with the astronomic station and two northern peaks. The remaining personnel were evacuated on

December 31, using two Weasels. One of the Weasels broke down on the way to the *Burton Island,* and the party was forced to travel the remainder of the distance without it. Later in the day another party from the ship recovered the disabled Weasel. An interesting postscript to the detailed survey of the Haswell Islands and the expedition's experience in reaching them was the selection of Haswell Island by the Soviet Union as the site for its base, Mirnyy, for the IGY. Since then Mirnyy has continued to be a major Russian establishment in Antarctica.

As soon as the shore party and its equipment were recovered from Haswell Island the *Burton Island* moved eastward over against the western edge of Shackleton Ice Shelf. Although the ship was within $4\frac{1}{2}$ miles of the assigned position of point 5, it could not be located on a helicopter reconnaissance, and it was decided to proceed to the Gillies Islands, site of point 6. As they approached the ice shelf the water shoaled and the anchor was dropped in 48 fathoms early on January 1, 1948. Near where the ship anchored what at first looked like a small iceberg turned out, in better visibility, to be a great rock 1500 yards west of the edge of the ice shelf. Later that morning the Sikorsky helicopter located Gillies Islands, three granite rocks protruding above the Shackleton Ice Shelf, and a second trip began ferrying a survey party up to them. As the helicopter landed, it was disabled when the framework of the landing float was bent. Fortunately, no one was hurt. The smaller Bell helicopter was down for repairs, and the *Edisto* was summoned to assist.

When Commander Folger received word of the mishap at Gillies Islands, the party from point 1 and all but two men from point 2 had been returned to the *Edisto.* He dispatched Lieutenant Lloyd W. Tracy, USN, in the helicopter to the *Burton Island* and then set the *Edisto* on course to join the flagship. Anxiety was felt aboard ship when it was discovered that there had been a misunderstanding and that the *Burton Island* was not 40 but 80 miles away, a distance that would strain the flight range of the craft and put it out of radio range midway in the flight. However, Commander McDonald began homing operations, and Lieutenant Tracy landed safely on the *Burton Island.* Flight personnel ferried to the downed helicopter by Tracy repaired it sufficiently to be able to fly it safely back to the *Burton Island.* In the meantime the *Edisto* had reached the *Burton Island* and had been dispatched to complete the work at point 3. Later Tracy was released to return to the *Edisto* and immediately began ferrying the survey party to point 3, including the two men left at point 2. When he returned to the ship at 11:39 p. m., January 2 Lieutenant Tracy had made 12 flights, for an elapsed flight time of 16 hours and 15 minutes in a period of 36 hours, a magnificent performance.

Fortunately the good weather of January 1 continued through January 2, not only aiding in the recovery of the damaged helicopter but speeding the survey work as well. Immediately after the accident, Lieutenant (jg) R. G. Thomas and R. S. Taylor, CQM, USN, began to set up instruments on the highest of the three rocks that compose the Gillies Islands to take sun sights. Their survey work was completed by the time the damaged craft was ready to be flown back, and they returned with it to the ship. They had been absent only for 27 hours. Meanwhile, the rock which had been discovered when the ship came to anchor was also investigated. This rock, then called Burton Island Rock but later officially named Bigelow Rock for Sergeant George H. Bigelow, USMC, a tractor driver on both "Operation Windmill" and "Operation Highjump," is ten feet above water and covered with six feet of snow and ice. Between January 1 and 3 it was visited at various times. Holl and Werlein made an astro fix (point 7), and Apfel carried out geological work with the aid of Lieutenant (jg) Lewis O. Smith and part of his underwater demolition crew.

The good weather of January 1 and 2 was also used to advantage by the shore parties from the *Edisto*. Two photographic flights were made with the J2F amphibian plane, tying in points 1, 2, 3, and 4. Both Merritt and Krause were in the survey party at point 3, and work began immediately after landing at 7:00 p. m., January 2. They were soon joined by Snedeker, Snyder, Ardery, and Peterson. By the time camp was set up at 2:00 a. m., January 3, all observations had been completed. By 3:00 p. m. that day all remaining work was finished in spite of light snow. Krause and Merritt had spent 20 hours on station. They were then snowbound in camp for 48 hours before they could be returned to the *Edisto* late on January 5.

On the morning of January 6 the Task Force was reunited north of Bigelow Rock and the two ships proceeded in column to round Shackleton Ice Shelf en route to the Bunger Hills. The pack was heavy and compact, but with the aid of aerial reconnaissance they managed to break through to the open sea in somewhat more than 24 hours. The ships sailed eastward along the edge of the pack until early on January 8 when they headed south into the pack again in about 102° E.

Breaking a way through the pack ice toward the Bunger Hills proved to be extremely difficult, and a great deal of time and fuel were expended in the effort, thereby affecting the latter part of the program. However, the Task Force was specifically instructed to investigate this ice-free area, discovered in the previous year by "Operation Highjump."[11] Much speculation about the character of this region and the reason for its existence had resulted from Lieutenant Commander David E. Bunger's landing his seaplane there on an open water pool in February 1947. Consequently, Commander Ketchum persisted in his objective. First the ships proceeded in column and then worked independently some miles apart. Using air reconnaissance, they continued to probe the few and indefinite leads with little success. Late on January 10, three days after entering the pack ice, they were still 90 miles from the proposed site for the control point. That night a strong west wind cleared out much of the medium-thick ice. The *Edisto* continued probing and on January 12 finally entered a pool of open water northwest of Mill Island, within 40 miles of point 10 (later designated point 5). To reach this polynya the ship broke 28 miles of ice, which Commander Folger considered "some of the worst slugging type of ice breaking we've ever encountered — with Arctic or Antarctic."[12]

It was decided to stage the landing at Bunger Hills from the *Edisto*, since

PLATE XXI-A. The glaciated surface of the Bunger Hills. This was as the area appeared in 1948 when visited by the members of "Operation Windmill." Navy Dept., Photo No. 80-G-619947 in the National Archives.

PLATE XXI-B. A "white-out." Note the complete lack of a horizon. These are personnel of "Operation Windmill' in a weasel (see p. 507). Navy Dept., Photo No. 80-G-621931 in the National Archives.

PLATE XXII. "Operation Windmill" helicopter and icebreaker U. S. S. *Burton Island* at the Windmill Islands. Navy Dept., Photo No. 80-G-619762 in the National Archives.

by this time the *Burton Island* was in another open water pool, 54 miles to the east-northeast. The *Edisto* was moored to the edge of the solid old sea ice near the southeastern shore of Mill Island. The J2F amphibian plane was used to ferry personnel and equipment between the two ships and for aerial photography. It was also used to conduct the two helicopters from the *Burton Island* to the *Edisto* because the 54 miles between the two ships strained their flying range and exceeded the range of their radios. To assist the helicopters in ferrying personnel and equipment from the *Edisto* to the Bunger Hills two Weasels set up a camp and a gasoline cache as a relay station midway between the ship and the land. So rapidly did operations proceed that by the end of the day on January 12 Merritt and Krause were on the ground at Bunger Hills. In the early staging operations the small Bell helicopter crashed in a "white-out" seven miles from the ship, fortunately without serious injury to personnel. First one of the other helicopters and then the J2F were temporarily lost, but found their way back to the *Edisto* with very little fuel remaining. Soon all survey parties and observers from both ships were at work. They had reasonably good weather, especially on January 14. They completed their mission that day, and the parties were evacuated the next morning just before a blizzard struck. Three subsidiary control points were established in addition to main point 5.

Observations at Bunger Hills showed the ice-free area to consist of very complex metamorphic rocks, schists, gneisses, and quartzites intruded by dikes and sills of granite and basalt, part of the basement complex of the continental shield of East Antarctica. Much of the area is strewn with bouldery morainic drift left by the receding glaciers which have intensely scoured and grooved the bedrock. The Bunger Hills were thought to be ice-free because major ice drainage from the interior is diverted around the area, and the local climate is too arid to support local glacial centers. Low precipitation and high heat absorption of the bare rock in summer prevent snow accumulation from season to season. Several small depressions in the morainic material were found to be filled with highly saline water. The large water bodies occupy valleys crossing the Bunger Hills area and extending below sea level. Glacial tongues extend across one or both ends of such hollows, cutting them off from the sea. Sea ice may cover these large water bodies even in summer, and numerous icebergs were found in them.[13]

In 1957 the Soviet Union established its IGY base Oazis in the Bunger Hills. It was later transferred to Poland, and in 1959 it was closed.

On January 16 the ships met and personnel and equipment were moved back aboard the *Burton Island*. Time and fuel were running short, but strong winds the previous day had opened the pack considerably. Therefore, Commander Ketchum decided to try for two more control points before leaving the coast of Wilkes Land. As subsequent events have shown, this was a fortunate decision. The ships headed southeastward toward point 11 on the west side of Vincennes Bay and point 13 on the east side. This bay, 65 miles wide, was discovered by Lieutenant Charles Wilkes in the *Vincennes* in 1840.[14] Because of poor visibility the ships lay to part of the time on January 17, but on the next day the

Edisto headed for point 11 and the *Burton Island* for point 13. The former is on a small rocky island 500 yards from the ice-bound shore of Knox Coast. By noon, January 19, the landing party was back aboard the *Edisto,* its mission completed in somewhat more than 24 hours.

The *Burton Island* broke into open water off the Budd Coast and came to anchor in 45 fathoms within 800 yards of point 13, which is on one of a group of small rocky islands subsequently named Windmill Islands. For the first time Task Force personnel could go ashore by boat, and sometime during the 40 hours that the *Burton Island* lay at anchor everyone took advantage of the opportunity. Everyone literally had a field day, for unlike the Bunger Hills, there is life on the Windmill Islands. Whales were seen from the ship, some seals were on a bit of fast sea ice, and there were several Adélie penguin rookeries. Skuas and snow petrels were seen flying about. Some moss and lichens were found, and some algae was growing in meltwater ponds. The tidal range was found to be two feet.

The islands appeared to be continuations of peninsulas extending westward from the mainland, which was ice covered. Slopes are steep with sharp differences in local relief. Dr. Apfel discovered that the rock is mostly a massive dark gray granite which had been intruded into pre-existing metamorphosed sedimentary rocks. These latter have been greatly altered by intrusive dikes and sills. They apparently represent the basement complex of the shield of East Antarctica. The underwater demolition team quarried rock for samples and to determine the depth of weathering. From the latter it was assumed that some of the islands have been exposed for a long time. All have been severely glaciated, and boulders, including erratics, are scattered over the surface.

Survey work was going on apace. On the afternoon of January 19 the *Edisto* anchored beside the flagship, and three men were sent to assist the *Burton Island* parties in completing the main control point and three subsidiary points. A photographic flight, tying in points 11 and 13 was made with the J2F.[15]

The full description of the Windmill Islands in the report of the Task Force Commander must have influenced the decision of the U. S. Committee for the IGY to select them as the site for Wilkes Station. In 1959 this station was transferred to Australia, which has continued to operate it. The visit of Task Force 39 must have occurred during a brief spell of calm weather, for it did not experience the high wind velocities which have proven to be a characteristic feature of the locality.

On January 20 the Task Force left Vincennes Bay and course was set eastward along latitude 64° S, keeping clear of the pack, en route to the Ross Sea. North of the Balleny Islands on January 25 they met the Japanese whaler *Hashedate Maru* accompanied by two merchant vessels and several catchers. Three international observers aboard the whaler paid a visit to the *Burton Island,* and some of the Task Force officers visited the whaler.[16]

On January 26 the ships turned southward into the Ross Sea. They found mostly open water with only light pack ice in some places. Less than 24 hours on January 29 were spent in McMurdo Sound. Several members went ashore at different localities, either by helicopter or by Greenland cruiser. In this historic area, the location of the base camps for four British expeditions earlier in the century, there was little to do but sight-see. Shackleton's base at Cape Royds and Scott's bases at Cape Evans and Hut Point were visited.[17] Ensign Charles W. Mallory carried on studies of the physical characteristics of the snow in an area that since 1956 has been in the center of the Williams Air Facility serving the American base at McMurdo Sound.[18] The ships got underway again the same evening for Little America.

Arriving at the Bay of Whales, then only about 100 yards wide, the ships moored against the bay ice and parties went ashore on January 31. There was not much of a scientific nature that could be done here that would not have duplicated work of four previous American expeditions. However, the Weasels were hoisted out and for the better part of five days Captain Boyd, USMC, an old Antarctic hand, and Ensign Mallory directed studies of the effect of Antarctic frost and snow on structures and equipment left at former American bases, Little America III (1940) and IV (1947).[19] Several good sets of sun shots were obtained, and air and ground photography taken. The *Burton Island* evacuated the shore parties on February 5.

The day previous Commander Ketchum transferred to the *Edisto,* and that ship departed toward Cape Colbeck to scout for a route through the pack ice toward the northeast. All previous attempts to leave the Ross Sea by this route had been blocked by impenetrable ice. Air reconnaissance showed dense pack ice extending north and east of the cape, and the *Edisto* was forced to work north and northwestward before a northeasterly course could be followed. Late on February 6 the *Burton Island* joined the *Edisto* as the latter lay to, waiting for improved visibility in which to launch the J2F amphibian. Later they continued on a northeasterly course. About 265 miles north of Mount Siple a course was set for that huge landmark, but 24 hours later, on February 10, the course was reversed. They were still 80 miles from Mount Siple, and air reconnaissance showed nothing but impenetrable pack to the south.

Returning to the outer limit of the pack ice, the Task Force proceeded eastward looking for leads that would allow them to penetrate toward Mount Siple or Thurston Island. The latter was then thought to be a peninsula of the mainland. After penetrating the pack for about 100 miles, course was again reversed, due to impenetrable ice. The ships then moved eastward again, searching for a favorable lead toward Thurston Island. On February 14 this attempt was abandoned and course was set for Peter I Island (68°47′ S, 90°35′ W). The two ships anchored on the west side of the island, and a party from the *Burton Island* went ashore to collect geological samples. On February 16 a course was laid for Marguerite Bay to assist the Ronne Antarctic Research Expedition if it was frozen in.

Arriving at Stonington Island in Marguerite Bay the *Burton Island* and the *Edisto* moored near the frozen-in *Port of Beaumont.* The next day, February 20, the *Burton Island* broke the ice about the *Beaumont* and towed Ronne's ship out. Late in the day all three ships were moored near some small rocky islets on the south side of Adelaide Island. Dr. Apfel went ashore on a geological reconnaissance, and Lieutenant Smith's underwater demolition unit planted a charge of 7750 pounds of TNT as part of a seismological test monitored by Dr. Robert L. Nichols of the Ronne Expedition at Stonington Island. After the explosion on February 21 Dr. Nichols was picked up by the *Burton Island,* and the three vessels sailed north. Meanwhile, the *John Biscoe* of the British Falkland Islands Dependencies Survey arrived just in time to take advantage of the path broken through the pack ice by the Task Force. She discharged supplies and personnel for the British base on Stonington Island, embarked members who were leaving, and quickly followed the American vessels out. Without the aid of the icebreakers it is probable that the British base would not have been supplied nor the Ronne expedition have been able to leave. For three hours on February 23 the *Beaumont* was towed through the pack while her steering mechanism was being repaired. The next day the ships separated and the Task Force set a course for Callao, where it arrived March 12, 1948. After five days of shore leave the *Edisto* sailed for Norfolk where Commander Ketchum disembarked on March 28. The *Burton Island* arrived at San Pedro on April 1.

Events are milestones in the continuum of human progress in which each Antarctic expedition takes its place. Since the IGY, Antarctic research has centered around the continuously manned base, but this concept, begun with the U. S. Antarctic Service Expedition of 1939-41, was aborted by World War II. The Ronne Antarctic Research Expedition and the U. S. Navy's Task Force 39 left Antarctica simultaneously. Task Force 39 was one more manifestation of the increasing role of government in Antarctic scientific investigation, and four of the sites it surveyed subsequently became the locations of IGY bases. The Ronne expedition was the last of a long line of privately sponsored expeditions from many countries, going back to the latter part of the 19th century. Most of them were sponsored by and some of them were initiated by geographic and other scientific societies. Although 1948 was not so much the end of an era as a time of mutation or interchange in Antarctic exploration, it is a convenient point to end this account of American activity. Subsequent effort was centered around the IGY. It and the programs which have followed on a comparable level are another story.

APPENDIX
U. S. Navy Second Antarctic Developments Project, 1947-48
Ground Control Points Established

The numbers of the points are those originally assigned before the work was started. Since several of the planned points were canceled, the points actually established are not in consecutive order.

No.	Area	Corrected Position
1.	E of Posadowsky Bay	66°47′20.0″ S 89°49′13.0″ E
2.	1 mi. SW of Krause Point	66°34′26.0″ S 91°13′38.9″ E

3.	10 mi. W of Haswell Is.	66°31'24.0" S 91°48'29.0" E
4.	Haswell I.	66°31'06.0" S 93°16'05.6" E
5.	Bunger Hills on Thomas I.	66°07'24.5" S 100°56'36.2" E
	Subsidiary to Pt. 5:	
	Baker	66°08'36.2" S 100°53'02.2" E
	Fox	66°08'49.7" S 100°56'38.3" E
	West Base	66°06'56.4" S 100°54'01.9" E
6.	Gillies Is.	66°32'09.9" S 96°24'17.5" E
7.	Bigelow Rock	66°09'20.5" S 95°25'53.0" E
11.	Merritt I. off Knox Coast	66°28'24.0" S 107°11'12.3" E
13.	Windmill Is. on Holl I.	66°25'26.5" S 110°26'15.0" E
	Subsidiary to Pt. 13:	
	South Base	66°25'44.2" S 110°27'03.8" E
	North Base	66°25'05.3" S 110°26'05.9" E
	Mike 2	66°24'48.5" S 110°28'10.0" E
14.	Little America	78°27'48.0" S 163°54'28.0" W
20.	Marguerite Bay	68°06'26.0" S 68°55'32.0" W

NOTES

1. No code name was given to the expedition. "Operation Windmill" was coined by the press in reference to the Task Force's use of helicopters. The official name is often misspelled by dropping the "s" on Developments, which occurred in part of the official report.

2. Commander, Task Force Thirty-Nine, United States Pacific Fleet, "Report of Operations, Second Antarctic Development Project (1947-1948)," item 8a.

3. *Ibid.*, Enclosure A, p. ix, item 2d. This ice-free area was subsequently officially named the Bunger Hills.

4. *Ibid.*, Enclosure A, pp. ix-x, items 4d and 4e.

5. A broad belt of pack ice had prevented several 20th century expeditions from reaching land in the stretch of coast of Wilkes Land from the Adélie Coast to the Queen Mary Coast. With modern, powerful icebreakers this expedition succeeded in breaking through the pack to the Knox Coast and the Windmill Islands off the Budd Coast. In 1840 Wilkes, apparently

under favorable ice conditions and a short spell of good weather, approached very close to the shore of the Knox Coast on the west side of Vincennes Bay.

6. A by-product of this expedition and "Operation Highjump" was a manual with photo interpreter's keys, *Regional Photo Interpretation Series, Antarctica*, Air Force Manual 200-30 (Washington, 1953), the work of John H. Roscoe.

7. "Report of Operations . . .," *op. cit.*, ii-iii; Annex XII, pp. 1-5. Comdr. Ketchum questioned the value of the J2F-6 amphibian for this type of expedition. He said, "It cannot be flown while the ship is in ice and has such a limited range that normally it cannot reach any desired objective from outside the ice pack." He also recommended, in the future, helicopters with a greater pay load and range.

8. *Ibid.*, Annex IC, p. 2. Annex IB is a narrative log or journal for the *Burton Island* and IC for the *Edisto*. They are the principal sources for the account of ship operations.

9. Lewis O. Smith, Captain USN (Ret.), " 'Operation Windmill,' the Second Antarctic Developments Project.," *Antarctic Journal of the United States*, vol. 3, No. 2, March-April, 1968, p. 25. See also "Report of Operations. . . ." *op. cit.*, Annex II, p. 2.

10. "Report of Operations . . .," *op. cit.* Annexes I and VI are the principal sources for the surveying on the continent and the efforts to obtain ground control. Annex VI contains a section on "Geodetic Control," followed by "the computed field positions" of a series of points located for use in mapping from aerial photographs. The positions were determined by means of observations with a Wild T-2 one-second theodolite. Two chronometers were used to keep time. The computed positions as listed in Annex VI were later corrected in the Hydrographic Office. Not all of the positions obtained were usable for mapping purposes. The sites of the astro fixes were marked on the surface so as to be visible in aerial photographs taken from 10,000 feet by the J2F Grumman amphibian plane.

11. See Chap. 22, pp. 503 and 504. The area was first called Bunger's Oasis.

12. Comdr. Edward C. Folger, Jr., *Ibid.*, Annex IC, p. 17. For this accomplishment Folger gave credit to the ship-handling ability of Executive Officer, Lt. Comdr. H. W. Mabus.

13. *Ibid.*, Annex IA, pp. 9-14.

14. See Chap. 10, pp. 181-182.

15. The U. S. Navy Hydrographic Office in 1956 issued a detailed 2-sheet topographic map based on this survey and "Highjump" photography. See *Windmill Islands*, Sheet 1, Chart No. H. O. 16520-1 and Sheet 2, Chart No. H. O. 16520-2, 1:12,000. The various islands and rocks were named for Task Force personnel with approval of the U. S. Board on Geographic Names.

16. Smith, *op. cit.*, p. 31.

17. *Ibid.*, pp. 31-32.

18. *"Ibid.* and "Report of Operations . . .," *op. cit.*, Annex XI, pp. 1-2 and 20.

19. *Ibid.*, Annex VIII, pp. 7-9, Annex XI, pp. 7-14B. See also Smith, *op. cit.*, pp. 32-34. They were assisted in this work by the underwater demolition crew.

BIBLIOGRAPHY
PUBLISHED MATERIAL

Frazier, Comdr. Paul W. (USN), *Antarctic Assault* (New York, Dodd, Mead & Co., 1958), xiv and 237 pp., illus., end-paper maps.
Holl, R. C., "1947-1948 U. S. Navy Antarctic Expedition," *Photogrammetric Engineering*, vol. 15, No. 1, January, 1949, pp. 12-15.
McDonald, Edwin, "Southern Cruise of Two Navy Icebreakers," *United States Naval Institute Proceedings*, vol. 74, No. 550, 1948, pp. 1490-1503.
Nutt, Comdr. David C. (USNR), "Second (1948) U. S. Navy Antarctic Development Project," *Arctic*, vol. 1, No. 2, Autumn 1948, pp. 88-92.
Smith, Capt. Lewis O. (USN Ret.), " 'Operation Windmill,' The Second Antarctic Developments Project," *Antarctic Journal of the United States*, vol. 3, No. 2, March-April, 1968, pp. 23-36.
Sullivan, Walter, *Quest for a Continent* (New York, McGraw-Hill, 1957), xiv and 372 pp., illus. (Chap. 20 pertains to "Operation Windmill.")

MANUSCRIPT MATERIAL

[Comdr. Gerald L. Ketchum] Commander, Task Force Thirty-Nine, United States Pacific Fleet, "Report of Operations, Second Antarctic Development Project (1947-1948)." One volume including 15 annexes, independently paged. Limited number of copies mimeographed for official use only.

INDEX

Page numbers in boldface refer to maps, and roman numerals refer to plates. Names in italics are those of ships, except where otherwise indicated. Geographic names are limited to those of features which are described or discussed in the text.